HARRY LASS and PETER GOTTLIEB
Jet Propulsion Laboratory-
California Institute of Technology

PROBABILITY AND STATISTICS

ADDISON-WESLEY PUBLISHING COMPANY
Reading, Massachusetts · Menlo Park, California · London · Don Mills, Ontario

PREFACE

This text provides a thorough treatment of probability theory and statistics, starting with elementary concepts and leading the reader through many problems to a thorough understanding of all the important special topics. To make the book reasonably self-contained we have included in Appendix A a comprehensive discussion of such mathematical topics as difference equations, determinants, matrices, Jacobians, the Dirac impulse function, and Lagrange multipliers.

For the past six years the material in this text has been used for a six semester-hour course in probability and statistics in a program for engineering students. We feel that it will also be useful to most students of applied probability and statistics.

Needless to say there are many books available in the areas of probability theory and statistics. The present text has the following features, among others, which should make it uniquely valuable.

Firstly, the text provides a unified treatment of probability theory and statistics using a consistent notation. The statistical topics are presented as practical applications which follow readily from probability theory. Furthermore, the theory is presented in such a manner as to provide an understanding and flexibility which should enable the reader to modify and analogize the statistical techniques beyond the few particular cases which we were able to present within the limitations of this volume. Although many special techniques and procedures proliferate the field of statistics, we feel that the text provides a thorough discussion of the fundamentals on which most of these techniques are based (relying strongly on the extensive discussion of probability theory). At the end of each chapter we also provide a bibliography with sufficient discussion to guide the reader to the appropriate specialized treatments.

Secondly, the student of probability theory should find that the statistical applications serve to reinforce his understanding of the theory, while the student of statistics will find that the sophistication acquired from a better understanding of probability theory is well worth the effort spent. The important topics are covered with extensive explanations and, in many cases, from several points of view. Such a coverage makes the book useful in a self-teaching situation, while in the conventional classroom situation it enables the instructor to emphasize selected topics, leaving the student to study other areas on his own.

Each of the topics is illustrated by several examples and many more problems are left to the reader. Some of these problems extend the general discussions to important and interesting special applications. Many of the more than 700 problems are original and are designed to strengthen the student's intuitive understanding of the various concepts introduced in the text.

The first chapter covers some elementary aspects of set theory and Boolean algebra. We have found, in general, that the student has little difficulty in mastering the essential features of this chapter.

Chapter 2 provides an extremely comprehensive elementary discussion of combinatorial analysis. Prior to pursuing the essentials of this chapter we have found it useful to discuss elementary difference equations since many combinatorial problems are most easily solved by means of difference equation techniques. There is little doubt that a firm foundation in combinatorial analysis is a basic tool for an understanding of probability theory and its application. The extra time devoted to this much neglected study will greatly extend the reader's mathematical maturity.

Chapter 3 deals with discrete probability theory and makes ample use of the concepts of combinatorial analysis. It is a long chapter involving Laplace's definition of discrete probability theory, a brief axiomatic approach to the subject, conditional probability and Bayes' formula, independent events and various distributions, random variables, joint distributions, statistically independent events, distribution functions, mean and variance, along with higher moments including a discussion of correlation, generating functions, and their applications to recurrent events.

An elementary knowledge of the calculus is required for the study of continuous probability theory found in Chapter 4. The specific topics of continuous probability theory are largely equivalent to the discrete probability topics discussed in Chapter 3. A novelty in the discussion of the n-dimensional normal distribution is the use of matrix algebra including quadratic forms (extensively summarized in Appendix A). The central limit theorem is discussed with numerous examples. A brief discussion on geometrical probabilities is also given.

Chapter 5, on sampling theory, shows the application of probability techniques for predicting the behavior of important random variables which arise in situations dealing with sample data. Of particular practical importance is the discussion of the distribution of the random variables known as the sample mean and sample variance. The discussions of Chebyshev's inequality and the weak and strong laws of large numbers are also important for understanding the theoretical foundations of statistics.

Chapter 6, on point estimation, provides an exposition of maximum likelihood, Bayes, and least squares estimators, with a discussion of their relation to each other. The use of matrix algebra permits an elegant, but simple, derivation of the solution to the usually obscure problem of multi-dimensional linear regression.

In actual sampling situations one is interested in the accuracy of these estimators. Chapter 7 is devoted to the estimation of this accuracy through the notion of confidence intervals. Students usually find this material very simple; however, we have devoted an entire chapter to it since the fundamental probability theoretic basis is quite distinct from, and not as natural as, that found in most of the other topics discussed in this text.

Chapter 8, on order statistics, describes properties of estimators constructed by considering the rank, or order, of individual elements of a sample, such as the sample median which stands in the middle of a sample listed according to element size. Probability theory is applied extensively to show that order statistics are frequently more efficient than the unordered estimators. This chapter provides a thorough foundation for the advanced texts on this increasingly important topic.

The last chapter, on hypothesis testing, describes some of the most frequently used statistical tests, such as the Student t test and chi-square test. We also apply probability theory to develop some interesting and useful tests which are not usually found in elementary or general texts.

ACKNOWLEDGMENTS

The authors wish to thank Dr. Victor Elconin, president of West Coast University, for his constant encouragement and helpful suggestions, and their colleague Dr. Elgie McGrath for his help in proofreading the manuscript. Our thanks too, to the literary executor of the late Sir Ronald A. Fisher, F.R.S., to Dr. Frank Yates, F.R.S., and to Oliver and Boyd, Edinburgh, for permission to reprint Table 3 from their book *Statistical Tables for Biological, Agricultural, and Medical Research*. We are also grateful for the many long hours spent by Mrs. Ingeborg Briggs in typing and editing the manuscript and preparing the art.

Pasadena, California   H.L.
February 1970   P.G.

CONTENTS

vii

CHAPTER 1

SET THEORY AND BOOLEAN ALGEBRA

1.1 BASIC DEFINITIONS OF SET THEORY

In elementary mathematics one considers the collection, or set, of all positive integers, the set of rational numbers, the set of real numbers, the set of points interior to a given circle, etc. One may also consider the collection (class, set) of all millionaires, the set of all females, the set of all oranges, the set of all abstract thoughts, etc.

If R is the collection of all rational numbers, then the property of being a rational number determines the elements of R, and, conversely, if x is an element of R, then x possesses the property of being a rational number. This simple notion enables us to define a set.

Set. A collection of objects is called a *set*. We can specify a set by either naming, explicitly, the objects which belong to it, or by giving one or more properties which unambiguously specify the objects which belong to the set.

Upper-case letters such as A, B, C, etc., will be used to denote various sets. For example, let A be the set of positive integers which are less than 5. The elements of A are the integers 1, 2, 3, 4. Note that A itself is not a positive integer: A is a collection of four elements. If x is a member of A, we write $x \in A$, with the symbol "$\in$" meaning "is a member of." Thus $2 \in A$, whereas $6 \notin A$ (the integer 6 is not a member of A, or the integer 6 does not belong to the set A).

The set A above contains a finite number of distinct elements, so we say that A is a finite set, whereas the set of rational numbers, R, contains an infinite number of elements.

Order. The *order* of a finite set is the number of distinct elements which belong to the set.

Let B be the set of all positive integers less than 5 whose squares are greater than 20. Thus if $x \in B$, then $1 \leq x < 5$ and $x^2 > 20$. These statements are contradictory. There is no integer x satisfying these inequalities. Thus the set B contains no elements. This leads to the following definition.

Null set. The set with no elements is called the *null set*.

This set is of zero order. It will be represented by the letter ϕ.

We will see that the role of the null set (vacuous set) in set theory is analogous to the role of the number zero in ordinary arithmetic. In logic the null set is equivalent to a contradiction.

Let us return again to the set A consisting of those positive integers which are less than 5. Let B be the set of positive integers whose squares are less than 25. It should be clear that the sets A and B are equivalent although the prescriptions for determining whether or not an element belongs to A or B have been worded differently.

Equality of sets. [Two sets A and B are said to be equal or identical if every member of A belongs to B, and conversely.]

Thus $x \in A$ implies that $x \in B$, and $x \in B$ implies that $x \in A$. In terms of the two-way implication sign "$\Leftrightarrow$," we write

$$A = B \Leftrightarrow (x \in A \Leftrightarrow x \in B). \tag{1}$$

If D represents the odd positive integers less than 5, then D contains the integers 1, 3. Note that every element of D belongs to the set A whose elements are the integers 1, 2, 3, 4. We say that D is a subset of A.

Subset. [A set all of whose elements belong to another set is called a *subset* of that other set.]

In particular, any set is a subset of itself, and the null set, by definition, is a subset of every set.

Sample space. [The set of all elements considered in a particular problem or experiment is called the *universal set* or the *sample space*.]

The only property these elements of the sample under consideration may have in common is that they are considered in connection with a given problem or experiment.

Example 1. Consider an experiment in which we toss a single, six-faced die, for which we observe the number of the topmost face. The sample space, S, consists of the six possible outcomes, namely the face numbers 1 through 6. The order of the set S is six.

Let A be the set of elements defined by the property that its elements are face numbers less than 5. The elements of A are the face numbers 1, 2, 3, 4, and the order of A is 4. Let B be the even face numbers less than 5, so that B contains the face numbers 2, 4. Note that B is a subset of A. Let C be the elements of A whose face numbers are greater than four. Since there are no such elements, it follows that C is the null set, $C = \phi$.

PROBLEM

Consider a green and red die. Let x denote the outcome of the green die and let y denote the outcome of the red die. Now let S be the sample space consisting of all pairs (x, y). Show that S is of order 36 by enumerating all 36 elements of S. Let A be a subset of S such that if $x + y = 4$ or if $x + y = 7$, then $(x, y) \in A$. Show that A is of order 9. Let B be the set of elements such that $x + y \leq 4$ or $x + y = 7$. Is A a subset of B? Let C be the set of elements $\{(x, y)\}$ such that $x + y = 4$ and $x - y = 3$. Why is C the null set?

1.2 RELATIONS BETWEEN SETS

Set inclusion. According to a previous definition, we say that B is a subset of A if every element of B belongs to A. In mathematical shorthand we indicate this relationship by using "$\subset$" as the symbol for inclusion. The statement "B is a subset of A" or "B is included in A," is written $B \subset A$. This is equivalent to "A includes B," written $A \supset B$. Thus the statements

$$B \subset A, \qquad A \supset B \tag{1}$$

are equivalent. It is a simple matter to deduce the following relations involving the inclusion sign:

$$A \subset A, \tag{2}$$

which states that any set is a subset of itself.

$$\text{If} \quad A \subset B \quad \text{and} \quad B \subset C, \quad \text{then} \quad A \subset C, \tag{3}$$

which states that set inclusion is transitive. Formally we write

$$A \subset B, \; B \subset C \Rightarrow A \subset C. \tag{4}$$

If we accept the statements that "Joe Smith is a man" and "All men are mortal," then Eq. (4) yields the statement "Joe Smith is mortal," by letting A represent the single element "John Smith," B the set of all men, and C the set of all mortals. Finally, if S is the sample space of a particular problem and if A is a subset of S, then

$$\phi \subset A \subset S, \tag{5}$$

with ϕ the null set.

Now in arithmetic, if x and y are real numbers, then $x > y$, or $y > x$, or $y = x$. This result does not apply, in general, for set inclusion. Thus, if A is the set of all millionaires and B is the set of all females, we cannot conclude that $A \supset B$, or that $B \supset A$, or that $A = B$, if we assume that there is at least one male millionaire and one female who is not a millionaire.

Set equality. It follows from our previous definition of equality of two sets that $A = B$ implies $A \subset B$ and $B \subset A$. Conversely, it should be apparent that if $A \subset B$ and if $B \subset A$, then $A = B$. This rule will prove useful in showing the equality of two sets.

The reader should deduce the following simple relations:

$$A = A,\tag{6}$$

which states that any set is equal to itself;

$$A = B \Leftrightarrow B = A,\tag{7}$$

which states that set equality is symmetric; and

$$A = B, \ B = C \Rightarrow A = C,\tag{8}$$

which states that set equality is transitive.

Example 1. From Example 1 in Section 1.1, it follows that $B \subset A$. If we define D as the set of elements of S which are less than 5 and multiples of 2, then D consists of the face numbers 2 and 4. Obviously $B = D$. The statements defining B and D differ in that in one case we speak of even numbers and in the other case we speak of multiples of 2. These statements are logically equivalent, so we expect the two sets to be equal (one and the same set).

PROBLEM

In the problem of Section 1.1, involving the 36 element sample space S, let F be the set of (x, y) such that $x + y \leq 5$ and let G be the set of (x, y) such that $xy \leq 6$. Show that $F \subset G$, and show that there is at least one element in G which is not in F.

1.3 SET OPERATIONS — VENN DIAGRAMS

Set addition. [The *sum* $A + B$ (or *union* $A \cup B$) of two sets A, B is defined as the set containing all the elements of A and all the elements of B.]

Thus, if x is a member of $A + B$ ($x \in A + B$), then $x \in A$, or $x \in B$, or x belongs to both A and B. Hence the statement

$$C \equiv A + B = A \cup B\tag{1}$$

means that every member of C belongs to either A or B, or possibly to both A and B, and conversely.

If A is the set of all millionaires and B is the set of all females, then $C = A + B$ is the set of humans who are either millionaires or females or possibly both (millionaire females).

John Venn introduced a simple geometric device, now called *Venn diagrams,* to illustrate the union of two or more sets. In a Venn diagram, sets are represented by closed curves (contours) or areas enclosed by such curves. The elements of a set are represented by points (not usually shown explicitly) within the curve or curves representing the set. It is convenient at times to distinguish different sets by means of various kinds of shading. Actual proofs involving relationships between sets must be obtained by deductive reasoning. However, Venn diagrams are useful tools in analyzing certain results.

In Fig. 1 the sample space S is represented by the enclosing rectangle, while the sets A and B are represented by circles. The total shaded region represents the union of A and B.

The following laws are immediate consequences of the definition of the union of two or more sets, with S denoting the sample space.

Idempotent law of addition

$$A + A = A. \tag{2}$$

Commutative law of addition

$$A + B = B + A. \tag{3}$$

Associative law of addition

$$A + (B + C) = (A + B) + C \equiv A + B + C. \tag{4}$$

Absorption law of addition

$$\text{If} \quad A \subset B, \quad \text{then} \quad A + B = B. \tag{5}$$

In particular, since $\phi \subset A \subset S$, it follows that

$$\phi + A = A + \phi = A,$$
$$A + S = S + A = S. \tag{6}$$

We let the reader deduce that if $A \subset C$, $B \subset D$, then $A + B \subset C + D$.

Example 1. Let S consist of the fifteen positive integers 1 through 15. Let A be a subset of S whose elements are multiples of 3, and let B be a subset of S whose elements are multiples of 5. Thus A consists of the elements 3, 6, 9, 12, 15, and B consists of the elements 5, 10, 15. The elements of $C \equiv A + B$ are the integers 3, 5, 6, 9, 10, 12, 15. Note that 15 is the only element belonging to both A and B.

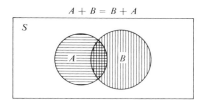

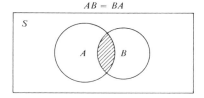

| Figure 1.1 | Figure 1.2 |

Set multiplication. The *product AB* (or *intersection $A \cap B$*) of two sets A and B is the set of elements which simultaneously belong to both A and B.

Thus, if $x \in A$ and $x \in B$, then $x \in AB$, and conversely. The Venn diagram of Fig. 2 illustrates the intersection of the two sets A and B. The shaded region yields the set of elements which belong to $C = AB$.

In Example 1 the set AB consists of a single element (15). If D is the set of all millionaires and E is the set of all females, then $DE = D \cap E$ is the set of all female millionaires.

The following laws are readily affirmed for any subsets of a sample space S.

Idempotent law of multiplication
$$AA = A. \tag{7}$$

Commutative law of multiplication
$$AB = BA. \tag{8}$$

Associative law of multiplication
$$A(BC) = (AB)C \equiv ABC. \tag{9}$$

Absorption law of multiplication
$$A \subset B \Rightarrow AB = A. \tag{10}$$

It is also immediately evident that
$$AS = A, \qquad A\phi = \phi, \tag{11}$$

since $\phi \subset A \subset S$. We note from $A + \phi = A$, $A\phi = \phi$ that the null set is analogous to the element zero of arithmetic. The sample space S behaves like the unit element, 1, with respect to multiplication.

Let us consider now two different sample spaces, S_1 and S_2. For example, let A be the event that a head occurs on the toss of a coin, and let A' be the event that a tail occurs, with $S_1 = A + A'$. Let S_2 be the sample space involving the six outcomes which occur when a die is cast. Let B be the event that a 6 is cast. The intersection of A and B is not defined, since A and B are elements (or sets) from two different sample spaces. From the point of view of logic we can define the logical product AB to mean that both A and B occur; in other words, that a head occurs and that a 6 is cast. Thus the logical product represents a "both this and that" statement. The statement $A + B$ (logical sum) means that a head occurs or a 6 is cast, or that both events occur. All the laws of set theory still apply even though Venn diagrams are not available.

Returning to the intersection of two sets we note that since every element of AB is an element of A it follows that $AB \subset A$. Also $AB \subset B$. These results still apply to the logical product, since if both A and B have occurred, one is certain that A has occurred ($AB \subset A$), and that B has occurred ($AB \subset B$), or simply $AB \Rightarrow A$, $AB \Rightarrow B$.

The reader is to deduce the following results for the case of intersections and for the case of the logical product:

$$\left. \begin{array}{l} A \subset C \\ B \subset D \end{array} \right\} \Rightarrow AB \subset CD,$$

$$\left. \begin{array}{l} A \subset C \\ B \subset D \end{array} \right\} \Rightarrow A + B \subset C + D. \tag{12}$$

Furthermore, he is to show that $AB \subset A(B + C)$, $AC \subset A(B + C)$, so that
$$AB + AC \subset A(B + C).$$

In order to prove the *distributive law*,
$$A(B + C) = AB + AC, \tag{13}$$

we need only show that $A(B + C) \subset AB + AC$ from the result above. Now let $x \in A(B + C)$ so that $x \in A$ and $x \in (B + C)$. If $x \in B$, then $x \in AB$, and if $x \in C$, then $x \in AC$. In any case, $x \in AB + AC$, so that

$$A(B + C) \subset AB + AC. \quad \text{Q.E.D.}$$

The reader is asked to illustrate the distributive law by means of a Venn diagram. By noting that $AB + AC \subset A$ we find that a simple consequence of the distributive law is

$$(A + B)(A + C) = A + BC. \tag{14}$$

Finally, if $AB = \phi$, we say that A and B are disjoint sets.

Set negation. [The complement A' (or negative, $\sim A$) of a set A which is a subset of a sample space S is the set of all elements of S which are not in A.]

Alternative expressions for "not-A" are $\bar{A}$ and $C(A)$.

The shaded region of Fig. 3 shows the set of elements belonging to A', the complement of A.

Various examples come to mind. If S is the set of real numbers and A is the set of rationals, then A' is the set of irrational numbers. If S is the set of all humans and A is the set of all males (human), then A' is the set of all human females.

The following are trivial consequences of the definition of set negation.

$$(A')' = A$$
$$A + A' = S$$
$$AA' = \phi$$
$$\phi' = S \tag{15}$$
$$S' = \phi$$
$$A = B \Leftrightarrow A' = B'$$

It should be clear that the statement AA' is a contradiction ($AA' = \phi$), and the expression $A + A' = S$ is a tautology.

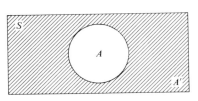

Figure 1.3

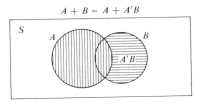

$A + B = A + A'B$

Figure 1.4

The reader is asked to deduce that if A and B are disjoint sets of S, $AB = \phi$, then $A \subset B'$ and $B \subset A'$. Conversely, if $A \subset B'$, then $AB \subset B'B = \phi$, so that $AB = \phi$, and A and B are disjoint sets.

It is often convenient to express the union of two sets as the union of two disjoint sets. If an element belongs to $A + B$ but does not belong to A, it must be a member of B and of A', and hence of $A'B$.

Thus,

$$A + B \equiv A + A'B. \tag{16}$$

Furthermore, A and $A'B$ are disjoint sets since $A(A'B) = (AA')B = \phi B = \phi$. The Venn diagram of Fig. 4 illustrates the expression (16).

A Venn diagram immediately yields the result that if $A \supset B$, then $B' \supset A'$. The inductive proof is as follows: If $x \notin A$, then $x \notin B$, since every element of B belongs to A. Hence $x \in A'$ implies $x \in B'$, which yields $B' \supset A'$.

De Morgan's laws

$$(A + B)' = A'B', \tag{17}$$

$$(AB)' = A' + B'. \tag{18}$$

To derive (17), we note that $A + B \supset A$, $A + B \supset B$, so that

$$A' \supset (A + B)', \quad B' \supset (A + B)',$$

and hence

$$A'B' \supset (A + B)'.$$

Next we show that $(A + B)' \supset A'B'$. Let $x \in A'B'$, which means that $x \notin A$ and $x \notin B$, so that

$$x \notin (A + B) \quad \text{or} \quad x \in (A + B)' \quad \text{Q.E.D.}$$

We see that Eq. (18) is an immediate consequence of (17) by replacing A by A', B by B' in (17), which yields $(A' + B')' = AB$. A simple negation yields $(AB)' = A' + B'$.

The two laws of De Morgan are duals of each other. The following two examples will illustrate the general role of dualization which can be summarized as follows: The complement of any set-theoretic algebraic expression can be obtained by replacing each set in the original expression by its complement and replacing all products by sums and all sums by products.

Example 2. Let us simplify the expression $(A + B + C)'$. From Eqs. (17) and (18),

$$(A + B + C)' = [A + (B + C)]' = A'(B + C)' = A'B'C'.$$

Example 3.

$$(AB' + BC' + CA')' = (AB')' \, [BC' + CA']'$$
$$= (AB')' \, (BC')' \, (CA')'$$
$$= (A' + B) \, (B' + C) \, (C' + A)$$
$$= (A'B' + A'C + BC) \, (C' + A)$$
$$= A'B'C' + ABC.$$

PROBLEMS

1. Let the sample space S consist of the integers $1, 2, \ldots, 10$ (representing the faces of a 10-faced die). Let A be the set of all even elements of S; B the set of all elements of A less than 5; C the set of all elements of S less than 5; D the set of all elements of S less than 7.

   a) Which of the following statements are true?

       i) $B \subset C$,   ii) $A \subset B$,   iii) $C \subset A$,   iv) $AB \subset C$.

   b) List the elements of each of the sets.

       i) $A + B$,   ii) $A + D$,   iii) AD,   iv) $C + D$,   v) CD.

   c) List the elements of each of the sets.

       i) AB',   ii) AD',   iii) ACD',   iv) $A + D'$.

2. Simplify the following expressions.

   a) $(A + B)(A' + B')$ b) $(A + B)(A + B')$ c) $(A + B)(A' + C)(B' + C)$

3. State whether the following statements are true or false. Illustrate the true statements with Venn diagrams.

   a) $(A + B)BC = BC$ b) $AB(B + C) = ABC$

   c) $AB + BC \supset ABC$ d) $(A + B)B' = A$

   e) $A + B \supset AB + BC + CA$ f) $AB'C \subset A$

   g) $A + B = AB' + A'B + AB$ h) $AB' + A' = A' + B'$

4. If A and B are subsets of a sample space S, then $A - B$ is defined as all elements in A which do not belong to B, so that $A - B = AB'$. Show that

   a) $A + B + C = A + (B - AB) + (C - ABC)$

   b) $(A + B)'C = C - (A + B)C$

5. Show that $(A + B)(B + C)(C + A) = AB + BC + CA$.

6. If A and B are sets, then $C = AB' + A'B$ is a set containing those elements which are in A but not in B and those elements which are in B but not in A. Thus if $x \in C$, then x belongs to A or to B, but not to both, since $(AB')(A'B) = \phi$. If A and B are possible outcomes of an experiment or set of experiments, then $(AB' + A'B)$ represents the event that one of the outcomes A or B will occur, but not both. If A and B are statements, the expression $AB' + A'B = I$ means that either A is a true statement or B is a true statement, but not both A and B are true statements, with I the "universally" true statement.

   What sets involving unions and intersections describe the following situations?

   a) both A and B but not C b) all of A, B, C

   c) at least one of A, B, C d) at least two of A, B, C

   e) at most one of A, B, C f) exactly one of A, B, C

   g) none of A, B, C h) exactly two of A, B, C

   i) not more than two of A, B, C

7. Prove the following theorems.

   a) $A = B$ if and only if $AB + A'B' = S$.

   b) $A = B$ if and only if $AB' + A'B = \phi$.

   c) $AB = S$ if and only if $A = B = S$.

   d) $A \subset B$ if and only if $A' + B = S$.

8. Show that the following are true.

   a) $[(A + B)(AB)']' = A'B' + AB$
   b) $(A + B)(A' + B)(A + B') = AB$
   c) $(A' + B)' + AB = A$
   d) $A \supset B' \Leftrightarrow A + B = S$
   e) $A \subset B' \Leftrightarrow AB = \phi$

9. Simplify the following expressions.

   a) $[(A + B + C)' + AB'C' + BC']'$
   b) $(A' + B')(A + B')'$
   c) $(AB')' + (A'B)'$

10. If $AX = B$, show that $A'B = \phi$ and that $X \subset B + A'$.

11. For the logical sum show that if A implies B, then $A' + B = I$, with I the "universal" true statement.

12. Smith, Jones, and Robinson are the engineer, fireman, and brakeman on a train, not necessarily in that order. On the train are three passengers with the same three surnames, to be identified in the following statements by "Mr." before their names.

    Mr. Robinson lives in Los Angeles.

    The brakeman lives in Omaha.

    Mr. Jones long ago forgot all the algebra he learned in high school.

    The passenger whose name is the same as the brakeman's lives in Chicago.

    The brakeman and one of the passengers, a distinguished mathematician, attend the same church.

    Smith beat the fireman at billiards.

    Who is the engineer?

    Let S, J, R be Smith, Jones, and Robinson, respectively. Let S_1, J_1, R_1 be Messrs. Smith, Jones, and Robinson, respectively. Denote by L, O, C, all residents of Los Angeles, Omaha, and Chicago, respectively, and let M be the mathematician and P the passenger whose name is the same as the brakeman's.

    From the statements above, show that $R_1 \subset L$, $B \subset O$, $M = S_1 + R_1$, $P \subset C$, $M \subset O$, $S = B + E$. Then deduce that $PR_1 = \phi$ so that $P = S_1 + J_1$, and deduce that $M = S_1 + J_1 = S_1 + R_1$. Hence show that Mr. Smith is the mathematician and that the passenger is Mr. Jones, so that Jones is the brakeman. From $S = B + E$, show that Smith is the engineer.

13. If the baby is crying, then the barn is burning. If the baby is not crying, then the wife is cunning. Moreover, one of the following statements is true.

    a) If the baby is not crying, then the barn is burning.
    b) If the wife is cunning, then the barn is burning.

    Show that the barn is burning (see Problem 11).

14. Some emotional problems are incurable. All emotional problems are deviations from the norm. If some deviations from the norm are incurable, then to be spurned

is not a deviation from the norm. To have true love and yet be spurned is an emotional problem. Is it possible to have true love and yet be spurned? [*Hint:* Set up an appropriate Venn diagram.]

BIBLIOGRAPHY

1. S. A. ADELFIO, Jr., and C. F. NOLAN, *Principles and Applications of Boolean Algebra*, Hayden Book Company, New York, 1964. Elementary exposition of Boolean algebra with many examples of applications.

2. F. HOHN, *Applied Boolean Algebra*, Macmillan Company, New York, 1966. Provides many illustrations of the use of Boolean algebra, with particular emphasis on the logical design of electrical networks.

CHAPTER 2

COMBINATORIAL ANALYSIS

2.1 INTRODUCTION

Combinatorial analysis—sometimes called *sophisticated counting*—is the study of methods for determining the order (number of elements) of sets formed in various ways from given finite sets. Various examples come to mind immediately. One may be interested in the number of five-card poker hands which can be dealt from a deck of 52 cards, or in the number of bridge hands which may be dealt in a game of bridge. If a coin is tossed five times, one may be interested in the total number of sequences of heads and tails. In information theory one may wish to determine the number of sequences composed of dots and dashes which can be transmitted in time T, if dots and dashes require one and two seconds, respectively, for their transmission rates. In number theory one may require a knowledge of the number of ways an integer can be written as the sum of k nonnegative integers. The physicist may wish to determine the number of ways in which n indistinguishable particles may be assigned energy levels $E_1, E_2, \ldots, E_k$.

Further examples will arise, subsequently, and the solutions to these problems will depend on a few elementary principles discussed below.

2.2 FIRST FUNDAMENTAL PRINCIPLE

Let us consider the following problem. A building has four entrances, labeled E_1, E_2, E_3, E_4 and three exits labeled X_1, X_2, X_3. Furthermore we assume that the entrances and exits are independent in the sense that one may use any one of the three exits no matter which entrance was used. We are interested in determining the number of ways one may pass through (i.e., both enter and leave) the building. The answer is at once apparent since for every entrance there are three exits; hence there are $4 \cdot 3 = 12$ ways of performing the acts A (entrance) and B (exit) in succession, with A represented by the set of all entrances, and B represented by the set of all exits.

We exhibit below the 12 methods for both entering and exiting.

$$
\begin{array}{lll}
(E_1, X_1) & (E_1, X_2) & (E_1, X_3) \\
(E_2, X_1) & (E_2, X_2) & (E_2, X_3) \\
(E_3, X_1) & (E_3, X_2) & (E_3, X_3) \\
(E_4, X_1) & (E_4, X_2) & (E_4, X_3)
\end{array}
$$

In simple notation, the 12 pairs may be represented by the set of pairs (i, j), $i = 1$, 2, 3, 4, and $j = 1, 2, 3$, so that $(3, 2)$ represents (E_3, X_2), etc. It is also important to recognize that in the example above the acts or events A and B were assumed to be independent. If, for example, one were restricted to always use X_1 if the entrance is E_1, with no restrictions otherwise, then the total number of ways of performing both acts is

$$1 \cdot 1 + 3 \cdot 3 = 10.$$

Without further ado we state the following *first fundamental principle.* If there are m ways in which an event A can occur, and n ways in which an independent event B can occur, then there are mn ways in which the events A and B can occur in succession.

One of many alternative statements of this principle is that if there are m different outcomes of one test or experiment, and n of another (the second experiment may be of an entirely different sort from the first), then there are mn joint outcomes of the two experiments performed successively, provided there are no connections or restrictions between the results of the experiments.

If the distinct outcomes of the experiment A are designated by $a_1, a_2, \ldots, a_m$, and those of experiment B by $b_1, b_2, b_3, \ldots, b_n$, then the mn joint outcomes (a_i, b_j), $i = 1, 2, \ldots, m$, $j = 1, 2, \ldots, n$, may be tabulated as shown in Table 1.

Table 1

A \ B	b_1	b_2	$\ldots$	b_n		
a_1	a_1, b_1	a_1, b_2	$\ldots$	a_1, b_n	$\to n$ terms	
a_2	a_2, b_1	a_2, b_2	$\ldots$	a_2, b_n	$\to n$ terms	m terms
.	.	.	.	.		
.	.	.	.	.		mn terms
.	.	.	.	.		
a_m	a_m, b_1	a_m, b_2	$\ldots$	a_m, b_n	$\to n$ terms	

By mathematical induction one can extend the principle above to include the general case of k independent events $A_1, A_2, \ldots, A_k$ with m_r ways in which the event A_r, $r = 1, 2, \ldots, k$, can occur, yielding $(m_1 m_2 \ldots m_k)$ ways in which the events can occur jointly (i.e., successively).

We emphasize that the principle enunciated above is associated with the joint occurrence of independent events. If A and B are mutually exclusive events, i.e., if the occurrence of A prevents the occurrence of B, and conversely, then the number of ways in which either A or B can occur, written $N(A \cup B)$, is

$$N(A \cup B) = N(A) + N(B).$$

The statement that A and B are mutually exclusive is equivalent to the statement in set theory that A and B are disjoint sets, $AB = \phi$.

It is a simple matter to show that, in general,

$$N(A \cup B) = N(A) + N(B) - N(AB),   \tag{1}$$

since in counting the ways in which either A or B occurs we have counted $N(AB)$ twice, once in $N(A)$ and once in $N(B)$; see Fig. 1.

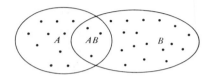

Figure 2.1

From $A \cup B \cup C \equiv A + (B + C)$ we have

$$N(A \cup B \cup C) = N(A) + N(B + C) - N[A(B + C)]$$

$$= N(A) + N(B) + N(C) - N(BC) - N(AB + AC)$$

$$= N(A) + N(B) + N(C)$$
$$- N(AB) - N(AC) - N(BC) + N(ABC)   \tag{2}$$

by applying Eq. (1) twice. The reader should deduce this result from a Venn diagram.

Example 1. Let us consider a die with six faces. If A is the event of casting a die, then A consists of six possible outcomes, namely the numbers 1, 2, 3, 4, 5, 6, which may occur on the top face of the die. If B represents the outcomes of a second die, the number of ways of casting a pair of independent dice is $6 \cdot 6 = 36$ from our fundamental principle. We list the 36 possible outcomes,

(1, 1)	(1, 2)	(1, 3)	(1, 4)	(1, 5)	(1, 6)
(2, 1)	(2, 2)	(2, 3)	(2, 4)	(2, 5)	(2, 6)
(3, 1)	(3, 2)	(3, 3)	(3, 4)	(3, 5)	(3, 6)
(4, 1)	(4, 2)	(4, 3)	(4, 4)	(4, 5)	(4, 6)
(5, 1)	(5, 2)	(5, 3)	(5, 4)	(5, 5)	(5, 6)
(6, 1)	(6, 2)	(6, 3)	(6, 4)	(6, 5)	(6, 6)

where the subset of pairs lying between two successive diagonal lines yields the same sum (points) when the elements of the pair are added together.

From the matrix above we can denumerate quickly the number of ways in which the points 2, 3, 4, . . . , 12 occur:

Sum	2	3	4	5	6	7	8	9	10	11	12
Number of ways	1	2	3	4	5	6	5	4	3	2	1

However, if 10 dice are tossed, it would be difficult to enumerate the number of ways in which the total points would equal 38. In Section 2.5, Problem 6, we will determine a method for calculating this number.

Example 2. A coin is flipped three times. Determine the number of possible outcomes.

Solution. Determining the number of possible outcomes is essentially a problem in enumerating the number of triples consisting of heads (H) and tails (T). First we enumerate the possible outcomes by means of the "tree" shown in Fig. 2. This yields the eight outcomes

$$HHH, \quad HHT, \quad HTH, \quad HTT, \quad THH, \quad THT, \quad TTH, \quad TTT.$$

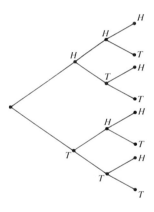

Figure 2.2

The fact that we have eight possible outcomes can be deduced immediately. There are two choices (H or T) for the first outcome, two independent choices for the second outcome, and two independent choices for the third outcome. Hence there are $2 \cdot 2 \cdot 2 = 2^3 = 8$ possible outcomes.

Example 3. In how many ways can we order the integers 1, 2, 3?

Solution. First we list all possible arrangements:

$$123, \quad 132, \quad 213, \quad 231, \quad 312, \quad 321.$$

The six sequences above are the permutations of the integers 1, 2, 3. We can determine the total number of permutations as follows. There are three positions to fill, _ _ _ . For the first position we have three choices (1, 2, or 3). Having chosen one of these integers for the first position, we find that there always remain two integers available to fill the second position. Hence there are always two choices for the second position. For our third position there will always be just one choice, the single element that remains. Hence there are $3 \cdot 2 \cdot 1 = 3! = 6$ ways of permuting the integers 1, 2, 3, or any three integers which are different from one another, say (1, 2, 4), etc.

A knowledge of difference equations is required for the following examples.

Example 4. Consider n ordered transmissions of zeros and ones. Any sequence consisting of n elements will be called an n-sequence. Now there are 2^n sequences consisting of zeros and ones, since there are two choices for each of the n positions. We wish to determine the number of sequences for which two consecutive ones occur for the first time on the $(n - 1)$st and nth transmission. For example, if $n = 8$, then 1 0 1 0 0 0 1 1 is such a sequence. For $n = 2$ there is only one such sequence, namely 1 1, and for $n = 3$ there is only one such sequence, namely 0 1 1. The sequence 1 1 1 is not permissible since two consecutive ones have occurred before the third trial.

Solution. Let $f(n)$ be the number of sequences in which we are interested. These sequences will either begin with a zero or with a one. If a sequence begins with a zero, then the only way we can obtain a successful n-sequence is to obtain a successful $(n - 1)$ sequence. In other words, we must now obtain two consecutive ones on the $(n - 1)$st and $(n - 2)$nd transmissions after the zero has been transmitted. Schematically, we have

$$0 \; [\_ \_ \_ \_ \cdots \underline{1} \; \underline{1}].$$
$$(n - 1) \text{ transmissions}$$

If the sequence starts with a one, the next element must be a zero for $n > 2$, otherwise the sequence would terminate at $n = 2$, and subsequently we must be successful in $(n - 2)$ transmissions. Schematically, we have

$$1 \; 0 \; [\_ \_ \_ \_ \cdots \underline{1} \; \underline{1}].$$
$$(n - 2) \text{ transmissions}$$

Since these cases are mutually exclusive, and exhaustive, it follows that

$$f(n) = f(n - 1) + f(n - 2), \qquad n \geq 3 \tag{3}$$

with $f(1) = 0$, $f(2) = 1$, $f(3) = 1$. The solution is

$$f(n) = \frac{\sqrt{5}}{5}\left[\left(\frac{1 + \sqrt{5}}{2}\right)^{n-1} - \left(\frac{1 - \sqrt{5}}{2}\right)^{n-1}\right].$$

Example 5. Refer to Example 4 above. We wish to determine the number of n-sequences such that two consecutive ones occur anywhere in the sequence.

Solution Let $g(n)$ represent the number of such sequences. Schematically we have

Case 1:
$$\underline{0} \; [\_ \_ \cdots \_ \_]$$
$$(n - 1) \text{ transmissions}$$

Case 2: $\underline{1}\ \underline{0}\ [\_\_ \cdots \_\_]$
(n − 2) transmissions

Case 3: $\underline{1}\ \underline{1}\ [\_\_ \cdots \_\_]$
(n − 2) transmissions

In case 1 we must be successful in $(n - 1)$ transmissions, yielding $g(n - 1)$ such sequences. In case 2 we must be successful in $(n - 2)$ transmissions, yielding $g(n - 2)$ such sequences. In case 3 we are successful after two transmissions so that the remaining $(n - 2)$ transmissions can be fulfilled by any combination of zeros and ones yielding 2^{n-2} such sequences. Since the three cases are mutually exclusive, and exhaustive (they cover every contingency), it follows that

$$g(n) = g(n - 1) + g(n - 2) + 2^{n-2}, \qquad n \geq 2, \tag{4}$$

with $g(0) = g(1) = 0$, $g(2) = 1$.
The solution is

$$g(n) = 2^n - \left(\frac{15 + 7\sqrt{5}}{10}\right)\left(\frac{1 + \sqrt{5}}{2}\right)^{n-2} - \left(\frac{15 - 7\sqrt{5}}{10}\right)\left(\frac{1 - \sqrt{5}}{2}\right)^{n-2}.$$

Example 6. Suppose that the transmission time for a dot is one second and that for both a dash and asterisk two seconds. Determine the number of different messages which can be transmitted in time T, T an integer.

Solution. Let $N(T)$ be the required number of different messages of duration T. Three different types of messages can occur, depending on the symbol which is transmitted initially. Schematically we have

Case 1: · [(T − 1) seconds remain]

Case 2: * [(T − 2) seconds remain]

Case 3: − [(T − 2) seconds remain]

Show that
$$N(T) = N(T - 1) + N(T - 2) + N(T - 2)$$
$$= N(T - 1) + 2N(T - 2), \qquad T \geq 3, \tag{5}$$

with $N(1) = 1$, $N(2) = 3$. Equation (5) holds for $T \geq 1$ if we assign $N(0) = 1$, $N(-1) = 0$. The solution of Eq. (5) is

$$N(T) = \tfrac{1}{3}[2^{T+1} - (-1)^{T+1}].$$

PROBLEMS

1. Three dice are cast. How many possible outcomes can occur?

2. Five coins are tossed. How many possible outcomes can occur?

3. In how many ways can the integers 1, 2, 3, 4 be permuted?

4. In how many ways can eight horses finish a race if there are no ties?

5. In how many ways can six people be seated in a row of six seats, one person per seat?

6. In how many ways can four women and four men be seated in a row with no two men and no two women seated next to each other?

7. The integers 1 through 9 are used to construct five-digit numbers all of whose digits are different. How many such numbers exist?

8. In how many ways can ten different traffic tickets be assigned to the seven days of the week?

9. How many three-digit numbers can be formed from the nine numbers $1, 2, \ldots, 9$ if no digit can be used more than twice in the construction of the three-digit numbers?

10. We are to pick two different integers from the integers 1, 2, 3, 4, 5, 6, and then we order these two integers. How many such ordered pairs exist?

11. How many n-sequences consisting of zeros and ones are such that a one follows a zero for the first time on the $(n-1)$st and nth transmission?

12. Referring to Problem 11, set up a difference equation for the number of sequences for which three consecutive ones occur for the first time on the $(n-2)$nd, $(n-1)$st, and nth transmissions.

13. A dot requires one second and a dash requires two seconds of transmission time. Determine the number of messages which can be transmitted in time T.

14. An urn contains the integers $1, 2, \ldots, n$, or, n balls labeled $1, \ldots, n$. The balls are withdrawn one at a time without replacements until k balls are withdrawn, yielding a k-sequence. For example, if $n = 9$ and $k = 4$, and the draw produces the numbers 8, 2, 4, 3 in that order, we obtain the sequence 8243. How many k-sequences can arise?

15. Refer to Problem 14. If a replacement occurs after each withdrawal, how many k-sequences can arise? Is $n^k > n!/(n-k)!$ for $k > 1$?

16. Refer to Problem 15 (replacements). How many sequences will be such that M is the largest number in the sequence?

17. Any integer can be written as $N = p_1{}^{\alpha_1} p_2{}^{\alpha_2} \cdots p_k{}^{\alpha_k}$, with the p_i primes, α_i positive integers. Show that the number of integer divisors of N is $(\alpha_1 + 1)(\alpha_2 + 1) \cdots (\alpha_k + 1)$. For example, if $N = 28 = 2^2 \cdot 7^1$, there are $(2 + 1)(1 + 1) = 6$ divisors of 28, namely the integers 1, 2, 4, 7, 14, 28.

18. Referring to Problem 17, show that the sum of the divisors of N is

$$\frac{(1 - p_1{}^{\alpha_1+1})(1 - p_2{}^{\alpha_2+1}) \cdots (1 - p_k{}^{\alpha_k+1})}{(1 - p_1)(1 - p_2) \cdots (1 - p_k)}.$$

19. A circle is composed of p sectors, with p a prime number. If N different colors are available for coloring the sectors, show that there are $(N^p - N)/p$ different ways of coloring the circle if at least two sectors have different colors. This is a theorem of Fermat which states that if p is a prime number, then $N^p - N$ is divisible by p for any integer N.

2.3 PERMUTATIONS

Consider four different (distinguishable) objects, say A_1, A_2, A_3, A_4. We need deal only with the integers 1, 2, 3, 4 if we wish to determine the total number of ways in which these four objects can be ordered. By brute force we list all permutations using all four objects.

1234	2134	3124	4123
1243	2143	3142	4132
1324	2314	3214	4213
1342	2341	3241	4231
1423	2413	3412	4312
1432	2431	3421	4321

It follows from the fundamental principle of Section 2.2 that there are 24 such permutations since there are four choices for the first element, followed by three choices for the second element, followed by two choices for the third element, with only one choice for the fourth element. Hence there are $4 \cdot 3 \cdot 2 \cdot 1 = 4! = 24$ ways of permuting four different elements four at a time, using all elements in every 4-sequence.

If P_n^n represents the number of ways of permuting n different objects (ordering n objects), the objects taken n at a time, then

$$P_n^n = n! = 1 \cdot 2 \cdot 3 \cdots n. \tag{1}$$

If we write

$$P_n^n = F(n),$$

we can set up a difference equation involving $F(n)$ and $F(n-1)$. For every choice of the first element (there are n such choices), we have $F(n-1)$ further permutations of the remaining $(n-1)$ elements. Thus

$$F(n) = nF(n-1). \tag{2}$$

Since $F(1) = 1$, it follows that $F(2) = 2 \cdot 1 = 2!$, $F(3) = 3F(2) = 3 \cdot 2! = 3!$, and by mathematical induction, $F(n) = n!$. An alternative point of view is to consider $P_n^n = n!$ as the number of different ways one can withdraw n different objects from an urn by withdrawing one at a time without replacements. The total number of ordered sequences is simply P_n^n.

At times we may be interested in the number of permutations of n objects taken k at a time, written P_k^n. Thus P_k^n represents the number of k-sequences, each element of the sequence being different from any other element, the elements chosen from a group of n different objects. For the case $n = 5$, $k = 2$, we list all permutations of five different objects taken two at a time,

12			
13	23	34	
14	24	35	45
15	25		

$$
\begin{array}{llll}
21 & & & \\
31 & 32 & & \\
41 & 42 & 43 & \\
51 & 52 & 53 & 54
\end{array}
$$

obtaining 20 such sequences. Half the permutations are such that the second element is greater than the first element, and conversely. The answer, 20, is obtained simply by noting that there are five choices for the first element, and no matter what this choice, there are four choices for the second element. Thus

$$P_2^5 = 5 \cdot 4 = 20.$$

For the general case, show that if P_k^n represents the number of permutations of n different objects taken k at a time, then

$$
\begin{aligned}
P_k^n &= n(n-1)(n-2)\cdots[n-(k-1)] \\
&= \frac{n(n-1)(n-2)\cdots(n-k+1)(n-k)(n-k-1)\cdots 1}{(n-k)(n-k-1)\cdots 1} \\
&= \frac{n!}{(n-k)!}
\end{aligned}
\tag{3}
$$

Alternatively we may consider P_k^n as the number of ordered sequences that exist if k objects are withdrawn one at a time without replacements from an urn containing n different elements.

Since $P_n^n = n!$, it follows that, Eq. (3) requires $0! = 1$, a useful convention! Formally, Eq. (3) yields

$$P_0^n = \frac{n!}{n!} = 1.$$

Also $P_{n+1}^n = 0$ since one cannot permute n different objects $(n+1)$ at a time, all $(n+1)$ objects being different. Formally, Eq. (3) yields

$$P_{n+1}^n = \frac{n!}{(-1)!} = 0,$$

so, of necessity, we define $(-1)! = \infty$, with a similar result for the factorial of any negative integer.

A difference equation involving P_k^n and P_{k+1}^n can be obtained by noting that for every k-sequence (there are P_k^n such sequences) there are $(n-k)$ further choices for the $(k+1)$-position, so that

$$P_{k+1}^n = P_k^n(n-k), \qquad 1 \le k+1 \le n. \tag{4}$$

Since $P_1^n = n$, we have

$$P_2^n = n(n-1), \qquad P_3^n = P_2^n(n-2) = n(n-1)(n-2),$$

and, by mathematical induction, we can show that

$$P_k^n = \frac{n!}{(n-k)!}, \qquad 0 \le k \le n.$$

Example 1. Consider the 7! permutations of the seven integers $1, \ldots, 7$, using all seven integers. We consider now certain subsets of this group of permutations. How many of these sequences are such that:

1) *the even integers occur before the odd integers?*

Solution. The first three elements of the sequence must consist of the even integers which can be permuted in 3! ways. The last four positions must be occupied by the odd integers which can be permuted in 4! ways. Since these events are independent, there are $N = (3!)\,(4!) = 144$ such sequences.

2) *the odd and even integers alternate?*

Solution. The odd positions must be occupied by the odd integers, yielding 4! permutations, and the remaining positions are occupied by the even integers, yielding 3! permutations. Again there are $(4!)\,(3!) = 144$ such sequences.

3) *the integer 1 is immediately followed by the integer 2?*

Solution. We think of the element $(1, 2)$ as a single element so that there are six different elements to be permuted six at a time, yielding $N = P_6^6 = 6! = 720$ such sequences.

4) *the integer 1 occurs in the sequence before the integer 2?*

Solution. The answer is $\frac{1}{2} P_7^7 = \frac{1}{2}(5040) = 2520$, since for every sequence in which the 1 precedes the 2 there is a corresponding sequence for which the 2 precedes the 1 (interchange 1 and 2).

5) *the integers 1 and 2 occur before the integers 3 and 4?*

Solution. There are $4! = 24$ permutations of the four integers 1, 2, 3, 4, and of these four are such that 1 and 2 occur before 3 and 4. Please show this. Hence $\frac{1}{6}$ of the total number of permutations satisfies our requirements, yielding the answer $\frac{1}{6}(7!) = 840$.

6) *the integer 1 occurs before the integer 2, which in turn occurs before the integer 3?*

Solution. Of the $3! = 6$ permutations of the integers 1, 2, 3, only one of these is successful, so, again, the solution is $\frac{1}{6}(7!) = 840$. One such sequence is 1524736, whereas 2514736 fails to meet our requirements since the 2 occurs before the 1.

7) *the sum of the first two digits in the 7-sequence is less than 8?*

Solution. If 1 is in the first position, there are five choices for the second position; if 2 is in the first position, there are four choices for the second position, etc. Furthermore, there are 5! permutations of the remaining elements, no matter which elements occupy the first two positions. Thus, our solution is
$$N = (5 + 4 + 3 + 3 + 2 + 1)5! = 18(120) = 2160.$$

8) *the product of the last two integers is less than 8.*
$$N = (14)\,(5!) = 1680.$$

PROBLEMS

1. In Example 1, solve cases 1 through 8 for 9! permutations of the integers $1, \ldots, 9$.
2. Consider the $P_3^7 = 210$ permutations of the seven integers $1, \ldots, 7$, taken three at a time. How many of these permutations are such that
   a) they contain the integer 1?
   b) they contain two specified integers?
   c) neither 1 nor 2 is in the sequence?
   d) the integers in the sequence increase in order?
   e) an odd integer is followed by two even integers?
3. Given N_1 flags of one color, N_2 flags of another color, $\ldots$, N_k flags of a final color, $N = N_1 + N_2 + \ldots + N_k$, show that the number of distinct permutations of the N flags is

$$\frac{N!}{(N_1)! \, (N_2)! \ldots (N_k)!}.$$

4. How many sequences consisting of four 0's and four 1's
   a) begin with a 0?
   b) begin with a 0 and end in a 1?
   c) are such that two 0's occur before three 1's?
5. How many of the $n!$ permutations of the integers $1, 2, 3, \ldots, n$ are such that k specified integers are between the integers 1 and n?

2.4 COMBINATIONS

Suppose that one desires to hire three people from among five applicants. It is apparent that the order in which the three people are hired is immaterial. It is in this sense that a set of three different objects without regard to their order is called a combination.

Let us label the five people by P_1, P_2, P_3, P_4, P_5. We ask the following question: In how many ways can we hire three people from among the five applicants? Let us look at one such choice, say (P_1, P_2, P_3). Now we can order or permute the elements P_1, P_2, P_3 in $3! = 6$ ways. At the risk of being repetitious, we list these six permutations using only the subscripts of the P's. Thus we obtain

$$123, \ 132, \ 213, \ 231, \ 312, \ 321.$$

Although every order listed above is a different permutation of the integers 1, 2, 3, we note that all contain the same combination of elements, namely the elements (1, 2, 3). Note that any combination of three different elements yields 3! permutations. Hence the number of permutations of five elements taken three at a time, P_3^5, is the product of the number of combinations of five elements taken three at a time, say C_3^5, and the number of permutations of three elements taken three at a time. Hence $P_3^5 = C_3^5 \, (3!)$ so that

$$C_3^5 = \frac{P_3^5}{3!} = \frac{5!}{2! \, 3!} = 10.$$

We list these ten combinations:

$$(1, 2, 3) \quad (1, 2, 4) \quad (1, 2, 5) \quad (1, 3, 4) \quad (1, 3, 5)$$
$$(1, 4, 5) \quad (2, 3, 4) \quad (2, 3, 5) \quad (2, 4, 5) \quad (3, 4, 5)$$

In general, if $C_k^n \equiv \binom{n}{k}$ represents the number of combinations of n different objects taken k at a time, then

$$P_k^n = \binom{n}{k}k!, \tag{1}$$

since every combination yields $k!$ permutations. Thus

$$C_k^n \equiv \binom{n}{k} = \frac{P_k^n}{k!} = \frac{n!}{k!(n-k)!} = \binom{n}{n-k} = C_{n-k}^n. \tag{2}$$

This is a most important result in combinatorial analysis and discrete probability theory.

From Eq. (2) we note that $\binom{n}{0} = n!/0!n! = 1$, which we interpret to mean that the number of ways of choosing no objects from n is simply one, namely, do not pick any objects. The reason for $\binom{n}{k} = \binom{n}{n-k}$ is obvious. Each group or combination of k objects also yields another group of $(n - k)$ objects, those left over.

Example 1. Ten strangers shake hands with one another. How many handshakes occurred?

Solution. There are

$$\binom{10}{2} = \frac{10!}{2!\,8!} = \frac{10 \cdot 9}{2} = 45$$

different pairs of people, since this is the number of ways of picking two people from among 10 different people. Each pair produces one handshake, so that 45 handshakes occurred.

Example 2. How many different five-card poker hands can be dealt from a deck of 52 different cards?

Solution. Since the final holding of five cards is independent of the order of receiving the five cards, the answer is that $\binom{52}{5} = 2{,}598{,}960$ different five-card poker hands can be dealt.

Example 3. A full house in poker consists of three cards of one denomination and a pair of another kind. Enumerate the total number of full houses in five-card draw.

Solution. Let us look at the number of full houses consisting of three sevens and a pair of queens. Since there are four sevens in the deck, there are $\binom{4}{3} = 4$ ways of choosing the three sevens. There are $\binom{4}{2} = 6$ ways of choosing the two queens. Hence there are $4 \cdot 6 = 24$ full houses consisting of three sevens and a pair of queens. The same result occurs for any full house of a specified type. Now there are 13 choices for the denomination yielding three of a kind, followed by 12 choices for the denomination yielding a pair. Consequently there are $24 \cdot 13 \cdot 12 = 3744$ different full houses.

Example 4. Compute the number of different hands consisting of two pairs in five-card draw.

Solution. There are $\binom{13}{2} = 78$ ways of choosing the two denominations, each yielding a pair. Note that a pair of sevens and a pair of nines is equivalent to a pair of nines and a pair of sevens. This is why we deal with combinations in choosing the two denominations. Now each pair can be chosen in $\binom{4}{2} = 6$ ways. Finally, the fifth card can be chosen from any one of 44 cards. Hence

$$N = \binom{13}{2} \binom{4}{2} \binom{4}{2} 44 = 123{,}552.$$

Example 5. How many five-sequences, composed of heads and tails, will have exactly two heads and three tails?

Solution. We will solve this problem by two methods. First let us look at the five vacant positions, $\_\ \_\ \_\ \_\ \_$. We need only choose two of these five positions to place the heads; the remaining three positions must be occupied by the tails. For example, if we choose the second and fourth positions for the occupancy of the heads, we obtain the sequence T H T H T. Now, choosing the fourth and second positions for the occupancy of the heads yields the same result. This is why we are interested only in the number of combinations of five objects taken two at a time; i.e., the number of ways of choosing two objects from among five different objects. Thus our answer is $\binom{5}{2} = 10$. We list the ten sequences composed of two heads and three tails.

H H T T T	H T H T T
H T T H T	H T T T H
T H H T T	T H T H T
T H T T H	T T H H T
T T H T H	T T T H H

Let us look at this problem from another point of view. We designate the two heads by H_1, H_2 and the three tails by T_1, T_2, T_3. Now, all the objects are different, so that there exist 5! sequences composed of $(H_1, H_2, T_1, T_2, T_3)$. If the heads are indistinguishable, we can interchange the two heads and obtain the same sequence. Hence the number of sequences is reduced by a factor of $1/2! = 1/2$. Similarly, there are $3! = 6$ ways of permuting the three tails, all yielding the same sequence. Hence the total number of different sequences composed of two heads and three tails must be

$$\frac{5!}{2!\,3!} = \binom{5}{2} = \binom{5}{3} = 10.$$

To be explicit about this second method, consider 12 sequences that yield but one sequence when the subscripts are removed:

$$H_1 \, H_2 \, T_1 \, T_2 \, T_3 \qquad H_2 \, H_1 \, T_1 \, T_2 \, T_3$$
$$H_1 \, H_2 \, T_1 \, T_3 \, T_2 \qquad H_2 \, H_1 \, T_1 \, T_3 \, T_2$$
$$H_1 \, H_2 \, T_2 \, T_1 \, T_3 \qquad H_2 \, H_1 \, T_2 \, T_1 \, T_3$$
$$H_1 \, H_2 \, T_2 \, T_3 \, T_1 \qquad H_2 \, H_1 \, T_2 \, T_3 \, T_1$$
$$H_1 \, H_2 \, T_3 \, T_1 \, T_2 \qquad H_2 \, H_1 \, T_3 \, T_1 \, T_2$$
$$H_1 \, H_2 \, T_3 \, T_2 \, T_1 \qquad H_2 \, H_1 \, T_3 \, T_2 \, T_1.$$

Example 6. A drawer contains six red socks and five blue socks. How many wearable pairs of socks exist?

Solution. There are $\binom{6}{2} = 15$ pairs of red socks and $\binom{5}{2} = 10$ pairs of blue socks. Hence there are $15 + 10 = 25$ wearable pairs of socks. A mixed pair of socks is not considered wearable.

Example 7. An urn contains three white and four red balls. If two balls are withdrawn without replacements (one at a time or both at the same time), how many combinations can arise?

Solution. Actually only three different events can occur. We will obtain either two white balls, or two red balls, or a white and a red ball. However, in dealing with probability problems, it is convenient to consider the three white balls as being distinguishable, say as W_1, W_2, W_3, and the four red balls as being distinguishable, say R_1, R_2, R_3, R_4. Now the number of ways of choosing two objects from among seven different objects is $\binom{7}{2} = 21$. We list these 21 combinations (the order in which the balls are withdrawn is immaterial).

$$(W_1, W_2) \qquad (W_1, W_3) \qquad (W_2, W_3)$$
$$(R_1, R_2) \qquad (R_1, R_3) \qquad (R_1, R_4)$$
$$(R_2, R_3) \qquad (R_2, R_4) \qquad (R_3, R_4)$$

$$(W_1, R_1) \qquad (W_1, R_2) \qquad (W_1, R_3) \qquad (W_1, R_4)$$
$$(W_2, R_1) \qquad (W_2, R_2) \qquad (W_2, R_3) \qquad (W_2, R_4)$$
$$(W_3, R_1) \qquad (W_3, R_2) \qquad (W_3, R_3) \qquad (W_3, R_4)$$

There are $\binom{3}{2} = 3$ ways of obtaining two white balls, $\binom{4}{2} = 6$ ways of obtaining two red balls, and $\binom{3}{1}\binom{4}{1} = 12$ ways of obtaining both a red ball and a white ball, or $3 + 6 + 12 = 21$ different combinations. If we were to consider all 21 events as equally likely to occur, we would assign a probability of $12/21 = 4/7$ of obtaining both a red ball and a white ball, since there are 12 successful ways out of a possible 21 equally likely events. If we remove the subscripts, it should be clear that obtaining a red and a white ball is more likely to occur than obtaining two white balls.

Example 8. *The binomial expansion.* Consider

$$(x + y)^4 = (x + y)(x + y)(x + y)(x + y)$$
$$= x^4 + 4x^3y + 6x^2y^2 + 4xy^3 + y^4 \tag{3}$$

by direct multiplications. Let us obtain this result by use of combinatorial analysis. The product of the four factors of Eq. (3) yields products of the x's and y's of the following types: x^4, x^3y, x^2y^2, xy^3, y^4. From each factor we must choose an x or a y, and there are four factors. There is only one way of obtaining x^4 by choosing x from each of the four factors. There are $\binom{4}{3}$ ways of obtaining terms of the type x^3y, by choosing any three of the four factors to be an x, the remaining factor yielding a y. Similarly, there are $\binom{4}{2}$ terms of the type x^2y^2, $\binom{4}{1}$ terms of the type xy^3, $\binom{4}{0} = 1$ term of the type $y^4 = x^0y^4$. Hence

$$(x + y)^4 = \binom{4}{4}x^4 + \binom{4}{3}x^3y + \binom{4}{2}x^2y^2 + \binom{4}{1}xy^3 + \binom{4}{0}y^4,$$

yielding the above result.

By combinatorial analysis, one can show that

$$(x + y)^n = \sum_{k=0}^{n} \binom{n}{k}x^k y^{n-k} \tag{4}$$

for any positive integer n. Equation (4) is Newton's binomial expansion, and for this reason, $\binom{n}{k}$ are called the *binomial coefficients*. Many results involving these binomial coefficients can be obtained from Eq. (4).

The Taylor series expansion of $(x + 1)^m$ is

$$(x + 1)^m = 1 + mx + \frac{m(m - 1)}{2!}x^2$$
$$+ \frac{m(m - 1)(m - 2)}{3!}x^3 + \cdots$$
$$+ \frac{m(m - 1)(m - 2) \cdots (m - k + 1)}{k!}x^k + \cdots$$

for any number m, not necessarily an integer. Thus

$$(x + 1)^m = \sum_{k=0}^{\infty} \binom{m}{k}x^k, \qquad |x| < 1,$$

with the binomial coefficient $\binom{m}{k}$ defined as

$$\binom{m}{k} = \frac{m(m - 1)(m - 2) \cdots (m - k + 1)}{k!}.$$

Given m as an integer, deduce that $\binom{m}{k} \equiv C_k^m$.

Example 9. Setting $x = y = 1$ in Eq. (4) yields

$$2^n = \sum_{k=0}^{n} \binom{n}{k}.$$

For example, $n = 3$ yields

$$2^3 = 8 = \binom{3}{0} + \binom{3}{1} + \binom{3}{2} + \binom{3}{3}$$
$$= 1 + 3 + 3 + 1 = 8.$$

Derive this result from a combinatorial analysis.

Solution. We recall that 2^n is the total number of n-sequences composed of zeros and ones. Now, any specific sequence will contain k zeros and $(n - k)$ ones, with $k = 0, 1, 2, \cdots, n$. The number of sequences containing k zeros is $\binom{n}{k}$, since we can choose any k of the n available positions to place the zeros, the remaining positions being filled by ones. Since these cases are mutually exclusive,

$$2^n = \sum_{k=0}^{n} \binom{n}{k}.$$

Example 10. Differentiating Eq. (4) with respect to x yields

$$n(x + y)^{n-1} = \sum_{k=1}^{n} k\binom{n}{k}x^{k-1} y^{n-k}.$$

Setting $x = y = 1$ yields

$$n2^{n-1} = \sum_{k=1}^{n} k\binom{n}{k}.$$

Derive this result by a combinatorial analysis.

Solution. Consider n-sequences of the type such that an asterisk occurs exactly once, the remaining positions being filled by zeros and ones. There are $n \cdot 2^{n-1}$ sequences, since there are n choices for the position of the single asterisk, the remaining $(n - 1)$ positions being filled by zeros and ones in 2^{n-1} ways. For $k = 1$, $2, \ldots, n$, we can choose any $(n - k)$ positions for the zeros in $\binom{n}{n-k} = \binom{n}{k}$ ways, followed by k choices for the position of the asterisk, the remaining positions being filled by ones. Hence

$$n2^{n-1} = \sum_{k=1}^{n} k\binom{n}{k}.$$

Example 11. *Pascal's triangle.* The binomial coefficients may be listed as shown below.

Pascal's Triangle

Many interesting properties of the binomial coefficients can be obtained by examining Pascal's triangle. For example, note that

$$\binom{n+1}{k} = \binom{n}{k} + \binom{n}{k-1}. \tag{5}$$

It is not difficult to verify Eq. (5) by noting that

$$\binom{n}{k} + \binom{n}{k-1} = \frac{n!}{k!(n-k)!} + \frac{n!}{(k-1)!(n-k+1)!}$$

$$= \frac{n!}{k!(n-k+1)!}\,[(n-k+1)+k]$$

$$= \frac{(n+1)!}{k!(n+1-k)!}$$

$$= \binom{n+1}{k}.$$

Let us derive Eq. (5) by a combinatorial analysis. Consider $(n+1)$ different elements and segregate one of them, say object $(n+1)$, from the others (see Fig. 3).

Case I   Case II

Figure 2.3

Now, we can choose k objects from the $(n+1)$ objects in two mutually exclusive ways. Either choose all k objects from the n objects in $\binom{n}{k}$ ways, case I of Fig. 3, or choose $(k-1)$ objects from the n objects and adjoin to this set the $(n+1)$st element in $\binom{n}{k-1}$ ways, case II of Fig. 3. From this analysis, it follows that Eq. (5) holds. By a similar argument, deduce that

$$\binom{n+m}{k} = \binom{n}{k}\binom{m}{0} + \binom{n}{k-1}\binom{m}{1} + \binom{n}{k-2}\binom{m}{2} + \cdots + \binom{n}{0}\binom{m}{k}$$

$$= \sum_{r=0}^{k} \binom{n}{k-r}\binom{m}{r}. \tag{6}$$

The special case $k = m = n$ yields

$$\binom{2n}{n} = \sum_{r=0}^{n} \binom{n}{n-r}\binom{n}{r} = \sum_{r=0}^{n} \binom{n}{r}^2, \tag{7}$$

which may also be obtained by expanding

$$(x + y)^{2n} = (x + y)^n(x + y)^n.$$

Example 12. Consider the grid in Fig. 4, consisting of m horizontal blocks or paths and n vertical blocks or paths. Determine the number of paths from A to B if one is forced to move only to the right and only up, but not necessarily in that order.

Solution. Every path under the above stipulation requires that one traverse a total of $(m + n)$ blocks:

$$\overline{1}\ \overline{2}\ \overline{3}\ \overline{4}\quad \cdots\quad \overline{(m + n - 1)}\ \overline{(m + n)}.$$

Now, choose any m of the $(m + n)$ blocks, or any m of the $(m + n)$ positions above, and designate these positions by the letter H (i.e., horizontal motions). The remaining positions will be designated by a V (i.e., vertical motions). Thus, for $m = 3$ and $n = 4$, the sequence $HVVHVHV$ yields the path shown in Fig. 5.

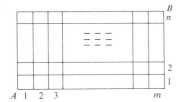

Figure 2.4

Figure 2.5

Conversely, any path yields a sequence composed of m H's and n V's. Hence, the number of paths is

$$N = \binom{m + n}{n} = \binom{m + n}{m} = \frac{(m + n)!}{n!\,m!}. \tag{8}$$

Example 13. *Einstein-Bose statistics.* The solution for the problem of Example 12 enables one to solve the following problem. Determine the number of ways a positive integer can be written as the sum of k nonnegative integers, or, equivalently, determine the number of ways n indistinguishable particles may be assigned k different energy levels. For example, if $n = 8$ and $k = 4$, we have

$$8 = 0 + 0 + 0 + 8 = 0 + 0 + 8 + 0 = 2 + 3 + 1 + 2, \ldots$$

Consider $0 + 0 + 0 + 8$ different from $0 + 0 + 8 + 0$ in the same sense that eight particles with energy level E_4 are different from eight particles with energy level E_3, $E_3 \neq E_4$.

For this special example, consider the grid in Fig. 6. The special path from A to B shows two vertical paths above $x = 1$, one vertical path above $x = 2$, three vertical paths above $x = 3$, and two vertical paths above $x = 4$. Since there are eight vertical paths, we have $8 = 2 + 1 + 3 + 2$, yielding one way in which 8 can be written as the sum of four nonnegative integers. It should be clear that there is a one-to-one correspondence between every path from A to B and every way of expressing 8 as the sum of four nonnegative integers. Since there are 3 horizontal paths, one less than k, and 11 total paths to be traversed, the result of Example 12 yields $\binom{11}{3}$ ways in which 8 can be written as the sum of four nonnegative integers.

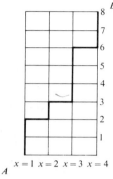

Figure 2.6

Deduce that a positive integer, n, can be written as the sum of k nonnegative integers in

$$f_k(n) = \binom{n + k - 1}{k - 1} = \frac{(n + k - 1)!}{n!(k - 1)!} \tag{9}$$

distinguishable ways in the sense discussed above.

When the distinguishable ways of partitioning n indistinguishable particles among k energy levels are assumed to occur equally likely, one speaks of *Einstein-Bose statistics*.

On the other hand, if the particles are distinguishable and can assume any one of k energy levels, then there are k^n possible sequences or outcomes for the energies assigned to n ordered particles. If all these events are assumed to occur equally likely, the physicist speaks of *Maxwell-Boltzmann statistics*. In *Fermi-Dirac statistics*, one assumes that no two particles can be in the same energy state. Thus the number of possible outcomes is $\binom{k}{n}$, with $k \geq n$.

There exists an elegant method involving the occupancy of k cells or urns by n indistinguishable balls which enables one to verify Eq. (9). For the example above with $n = 8$ and $k = 4$, consider four urns and eight zeros to be placed in these four urns. For the case $8 = 2 + 1 + 3 + 2$, we obtain

$$\frac{|\ 00\ |\ 0\ |\ 000\ |\ 00\ |}{2\ +\ 1\ +\ 3\ +\ 2}\ .$$

Now remove the base of the urns, obtaining the sequence

$$1]00101000100[1.$$

Note that this sequence contains eight zeros; it begins and ends with a one, and it has $4 - 1 = 3$ further ones. Removing the exterior ones involves sequences composed of eight zeros and three ones. There are $\binom{11}{3}$ sequences, and each sequence yields an arrangement for placing eight zeros in four cells. For example, the sequence 10000100100 corresponds to

$$1] \quad 1\ 0000\ 1\ 00\ 1\ 00\ [1$$

$$\begin{array}{c|c|c|c} & 0000 & 00 & 00 \\ \hline 0 & 4 & 2 & 2 \end{array}$$

so that

$$10000100100 \leftrightarrow 8 = 0 + 4 + 2 + 2.$$

It is a simple matter to show that Eq. (9) results from this type of consideration. The formula of Eq. (9) is useful also in considering the following problem.

Consider all four-digit numbers using the integers 1, 2, 3, . . . , 9, yielding the numbers 1111, 1112, . . . , 9999. Any two numbers containing the same quadruplet of integers will be considered to be equivalent ($1335 \sim 5133$) in the sense that obtaining an ace (1), two threes, and a five is equivalent to obtaining a five, an ace, and two threes. By brute force, we can calculate the total number of different four-digit numbers. There are $\binom{9}{1}$ different numbers with all four integers the same. There are $2\binom{9}{2}$ four-digit numbers with three of the integers the same, $\binom{9}{2}$ numbers having two pairs of different integers, $3\binom{9}{3}$ numbers having just one pair, and $\binom{9}{4}$ numbers for which the integers are all different. As defined above, the total number of different four-digit numbers is

$$N = \binom{9}{1} + 2\binom{9}{2} + \binom{9}{2} + 3\binom{9}{3} + \binom{9}{4} = 495.$$

Placing four balls in nine urns labeled 1, 2, . . . , 9 yields a set of four integers. For example, if one ball is placed in urn 1, two balls in urn 3, and one ball in urn 5, we obtain the set of integers (1, 3, 3, 5). Hence, the number of ways of placing four indistinguishable balls in nine urns must yield N above, so that

$$N = \binom{4 + 9 - 1}{9 - 1} = \binom{12}{8} = \binom{12}{4} = 495.$$

To determine the number of distinguishable ways of placing n indistinguishable objects into k different urns with at least one object in each urn, we need only place one object in each urn, leaving $(n - k)$ objects to be placed arbitrarily in the k urns, which can be performed in $\binom{n-k+k-1}{k-1} = \binom{n-1}{k-1}$ ways. Thus, $\binom{n-1}{k-1}$ also represents the number of ways an integer n can be written as a sum of k positive integers. For $n = 5$ and $k = 3$ we list the $\binom{4}{2} = 6$ representations.

$$5 = 1 + 1 + 3$$
$$= 1 + 3 + 1$$
$$= 3 + 1 + 1$$
$$= 2 + 2 + 1$$
$$= 2 + 1 + 2$$
$$= 1 + 2 + 2$$

Example 14. *Sequences with an even number of runs.* Consider the sequence

$$0\ 0\quad 1\ 0\quad 1\ 1\ 1\quad 0\ 0\quad 1\ 1\ 1\ 1.$$

The sequence consists of six runs of zeros and ones. Now, suppose all sequences are composed of m zeros and n ones. How many of these sequences will consist of an even number of runs, say $2k$? Since runs of zeros and ones must alternate, a sequence with an even number of runs must begin with a run of zeros and end in a run of ones, or begin with a run of ones and end in a run of zeros.

Solution. Consider $2k$ cells labeled $1, 1', 2, 2', 3, 3', \ldots, k, k'$. The number of ways of placing m zeros in cells $1, 2, \ldots, k$, with at least one zero in each cell, is $\binom{m-1}{k-1}$, and the number of ways of placing n ones in cells $1', 2', \ldots, k'$, with at least a one in each cell, is $\binom{n-1}{k-1}$. This yields $\binom{m-1}{k-1}\binom{n-1}{k-1}$ different runs.

A similar remark applies to runs beginning with ones, so that

$$N_{2k} = 2\binom{m-1}{k-1}\binom{n-1}{k-1} \tag{10}$$

represents the number of different sequences composed of m zeros and n ones, yielding exactly $2k$ runs.

The *multinomial coefficients* are obtained from the following considerations. The number of distinct ways of placing N different balls in k urns with N_1 balls to be placed in urn 1, N_2 to be placed in urn 2, $\ldots$, N_k balls to be placed in urn k, $N = \sum_{i=1}^{k} N_i$, can be determined as follows.

There are $\binom{N}{N_1}$ ways of choosing the N_1 balls that are placed in urn 1. From the remaining $N - N_1$ balls, there are $\binom{N-N_1}{N_2}$ ways of choosing N_2 balls to be placed in urn 2. Then, there are $\binom{N-N_1-N_2}{N_3}$ ways of choosing the N_3 balls to be placed in urn 3. Continuing, we find that

$$M = \binom{N}{N_1}\binom{N-N_1}{N_2}\binom{N-N_1-N_2}{N_3} \cdots 1$$

$$= \frac{N!}{(N_1)!\,(N-N_1)!}\frac{(N-N_1)!}{(N_2)!\,(N-N_1-N_2)!}\frac{(N-N_1-N_2)!}{(N_3)!\,(N-N_1-N_2-N_3)!} \cdots$$

$$= \frac{N!}{N_1!\,N_2!\cdots N_k!}, \qquad \sum_{i=1}^{k} N_i = N. \tag{11}$$

We let the reader deduce that Eq. (11) yields the number of different sequences composed of N_1 indistinguishable objects of one type, N_2 indistinguishable objects of a second type, and so forth, with

$$N = \sum_{i=1}^{k} N_i.$$

The elements

$$\frac{N!}{N_1! \, N_2! \ldots N_k!}, \qquad \sum_{i=1}^{k} N_i = N$$

are called the multinomial coefficients. They arise in a natural manner by considering the expansion of the multinomial, $(x_1 + x_2 + \cdots + x_k)^N$. By a combinatorial analysis the reader can deduce that

$$(x_1 + x_2 + \cdots + x_k)^N \equiv (x_1 + x_2 + \cdots + x_k)(x_1 + x_2 + \cdots + x_k)$$
$$\cdots (x_1 + x_2 + \cdots + x_k)$$

$$= \sum \frac{N!}{N_1! \, N_2! \cdots N_k!} \, x_1^{N_1} x_2^{N_2} \cdots x_k^{N_k}, \tag{12}$$

where the summation extends over all $N_1, N_2, \ldots, N_k$ such that

$$\sum_{i=1}^{k} N_i = N.$$

From Eq. (9), there are $\binom{N+k-1}{k-1}$ different terms in the expansion of Eq. (12). By setting $x_1 = x_2 = \cdots x_k = 1$, it also follows that k^N is the sum of the multinomial coefficients.

We conclude this section with a generalization of the result of Eq. (2), in Section 2.2. Consider k sets $A_1, A_2, \ldots, A_k$ containing $N(A_1), N(A_2), \ldots, N(A_k)$ distinct elements. The number of distinct elements in the union of these sets is

$$N\left(\bigcup_{i=1}^{k} A_i\right) = \Sigma N(A_i) - \Sigma N(A_i A_j) + \Sigma N(A_i A_j A_k)$$
$$- \Sigma N(A_i A_j A_k A_l) + \cdots + (-1)^{k-1} N(A_1 A_2 \cdots A_k), \tag{13}$$

where in each sum on the right the indices range over all possible combinations of distinct values. For example, in the third term, the indices range over all distinct combinations of three integers from the set $(1, 2, 3, \ldots, n)$.

To verify the result of Eq. (13), let P be any element that belongs to exactly m of the sets $A_1, A_2, \ldots, A_k$. Thus P is counted m times in

$$\sum_{i=1}^{k} N(A_i),$$

$\binom{m}{2}$ times in $\Sigma N(A_i A_j)$, and so on, so that the number of occurrences of the element P in Eq. (13) is

$$\binom{m}{1} - \binom{m}{2} + \binom{m}{3} - \binom{m}{4} + \cdots \equiv \binom{m}{0} = 1$$

from Eq. (4) by setting $x = -1$ and $y = 1$. Hence, the series of Eq. (13) counts every element just once.

PROBLEMS

1. Find the number of sequences consisting of
   a) four heads and three tails,
   b) either four heads and three tails or five heads and two tails.

2. An urn contains four white and six black balls. In how many ways can one obtain two white and three black balls from this urn?

3. An urn contains four white, five red, and six black balls. In how many ways can one obtain two white, three red, and two black balls?

4. How many sequences can one form from two zeros, four ones, and three twos, using all nine elements?

5. Show that
$$\binom{2n-2}{n-1} = \frac{n}{2(2n-1)} \binom{2n}{n}.$$

6. Show that
$$n(n+1) 2^{n-2} = \sum_{k=1}^{n} k^2 \binom{n}{k}.$$

7. Show that
$$\binom{2n-2}{n-1} = \frac{n}{2n-1} \binom{2n-1}{n}.$$

8. By a combinatorial analysis, show that

$$n(n-1) 2^{n-2} = \sum_{k=1}^{n} k(k-1) \binom{n}{k}.$$

9. Show that
$$\sum_{k=0}^{n} (-1)^k \binom{n}{k} = 0.$$

10. Consider a set of $2n$ boys and $2n$ girls. In how many ways can the $4n$ children be split into equal groups ($2n$ in each group) so that each group contains the same number of boys and girls?

11. In how many ways can n indistinguishable objects be placed in k urns, each urn containing at least two objects, $n \geq 2k$?

12. Consider all sequences consisting of n ones and m zeros. How many such sequences are such that no two consecutive zeros occur, $n \geq m - 1$? [*Hint:* consider the sequence $\sqrt{1} \sqrt{1} \sqrt{1} \cdots \sqrt{1}\sqrt{}$ with, at most, one zero in a check-marked position.]

13. Referring to Problem 12, how many such sequences exist for which the kth one is preceded by l zeros?

14. In the grid of Example 12, how many rectangles can one obtain?

15. In Example 14, show that the number of sequences having $2k + 1$ runs is

$$N_{2k+1} = \binom{n-1}{k}\binom{m-1}{k-1} + \binom{m-1}{k}\binom{n-1}{k-1}.$$

16. The number of ways of obtaining n as the sum of six integers is $\binom{n+5}{5}$. In terms of throwing a die n times, what does this number represent?

17. Let $f_k(n)$ represent the number of ways that the integer n can be written as a sum of k nonnegative integers. Show that

$$f_k(n) = \sum_{m=0}^{n} f_{k-1}(n-m)$$

$$= f_{k-1}(n) + \sum_{m=1}^{n} f_{k-1}(n-m).$$

Then, deduce that $f_k(n) = f_{k-1}(n) + f_k(n-1)$. From $f_1(n) = 1$ for $n = 1, 2, \ldots$, show that $f_2(n) - f_2(n-1) = 1$, $n = 2, 3, \ldots$. Then, show that $f_2(n) = n + 1$, since $f_2(1) = f_1(1) + f_2(0) = 1 + 1$ or 2.

18. N points on the circumference of a circle are mutually joined by straight lines. If no three or more lines intersect interior to the circle, show that $\binom{N}{4}$ represents the number of intersection points interior to the circle.

19. Consider a function of k variables. Assuming differentiability, how many nth partial derivatives exist?

20. If m and k are integers show that $\binom{-m}{k} = (-1)^k C_k^{m+k-1}$.

21. *Card matching problem.* How many of the $n!$ permutations of the integers $1, 2, \ldots, n$ are such that at least one of the integers corresponds to its position in the sequence? For example, $2\,4\,3\,1$ is such a sequence, since integer 3 is in the third position. [*Hint:* let A_i be the event that the integer i is in the ith position, with $i = 1, 2, \ldots, n$.] We are interested in

$$N\left(\bigcup_{i=1}^{n} A_i\right).$$

Use Eq. (13) to show that

$$f(n) = n!\left[1 - \frac{1}{2!} + \frac{1}{3!} - \frac{1}{4!} + \cdots + \frac{(-1)^{n-1}}{n!}\right].$$

22. In Problem 21, let $g(n) = n! - f(n)$. Show that $g(n) = (n-1)[g(n-1) + g(n-2)]$ after properly interpreting $g(n)$.

23. The number of $(n + m)$-sequences containing n heads and m tails is $\binom{m+n}{m}$. Consider a sequence of n heads, and consider $(n + 1)$ boxes between the heads as shown below.

$$\sqcup H \sqcup H \sqcup H \sqcup \ldots \sqcup H \sqcup$$

In how many ways can m tails be placed in these boxes (Einstein-Bose statistics)? Why did you expect this answer? Is this an alternative proof regarding Einstein-Bose statistics?

24. Referring to Problem 18, how many sectors are formed by t new line which intersects no other line in the interior co sector. If the new line intersects another line in the interic sectors are formed—one for the new line and one for the in

25. Referring to Problem 18, show that the number of triangular may partly overlap) is

$$\binom{n}{3} + 4\binom{n}{4} + 5\binom{n}{5} + \binom{n}{6}.$$

Hint: Show that the number of triangles determined by thre is $\binom{n}{3}$, etc.

26. Referring to the two preceding problems, find the number of

2.5 FURTHER CONSIDERATIONS

Example 1. *The ballot problem.* An urn contains n ones (A's l (B's ballots). The ballots are withdrawn one at a time withou possible number of sequences composed of ones and zeros number of sequences such that the number of ones (A's ballots) number of zeros (B's ballots) at every stage of the draw, $n > m$

Solution. Compute the number of sequences that fail to meet These failures can be segregated into two mutually exclusive gro fails if the sequence begins with a zero or if the sequence begii subsequently a tie ensues.

The number of sequences that begin with a zero is $\binom{n+m-1}{n}$, s: $(n + m - 1)$-sequence is composed of n ones and $m - 1$ zerc any sequence that begins with a one but for which a tie event example, consider the sequence $1110100100|xxx\ldots$, with a tie tenth ballot. Now, for each such sequence there is a corresp $0001011011|xxx\ldots$, obtained by interchanging the zero and (tie, the remaining elements left invariant. Conversely, every seque a zero must eventually lead to a tie, since there are more ones tha

Interchanging the ones and zeros through the tie shows the (spondence between sequences of the two types discussed above. of successful sequences is

$$N = \binom{n+m}{n} - 2\binom{n+m-1}{n} = \frac{(n+m)!}{n!\,m!} - \frac{2(n+m-1)!}{n!\,(m-1)!}$$

$$= \frac{(n+m-1)!}{n!\,(m-1)!}\left[\frac{n+m}{m} - 2\right] = \frac{(n-m)(n+m-}{n!\,m!}$$

$$= \frac{n-m}{n+m}\frac{(n+m)!}{n!\,m!} = \frac{n-m}{n+m}\binom{n+m}{n}.$$

Example 2. *Gambler's ruin problem.* A person has b units. If a l gains one unit, and if a tail occurs he loses one unit. Determine

ad tails such that the person (gambler) will be ruined (broke)

sent the number of heads and y the number of tails for the above event. Then $x + y = 2n + b$, $y - x = b$, so that

$$x = n, \qquad y = n + b.$$

d in sequences composed of n heads and $n + b$ tails. There er. Consider the following sequence composed of n heads

$$HTT - - - - \mid HT.$$

Such a sequence is not permissible, since the gambler would be ruined on a $\cdot$ $(b - 2r - 2)$. The only valid sequences are those which, when viewed from right to left, contain more tails than heads at every stage. This problem was solved in Sect. 1. Let $r = y$ and $m = x$ in Eq. (1), which yields the solution

$$N = \frac{y - x}{y + x}\binom{y + x}{y} = \frac{b}{b + 2n}\binom{b + 2n}{n}. \tag{2}$$

Example 3. For $|x| < 1$, we know from elementary arithmetic that $1/(1 - x) = 1 + x - x^2 + \cdots + x^r + \cdots$. Consider

$$\frac{1}{(1 - x)^k} = (1 - x + x^2 + \cdots)(1 + x + x^2 + \cdots)\cdots(1 + x + x^2 + \cdots).$$

All integral powers of x will occur when the k factors are multiplied. Consider the coefficient of x^n. Any k factors

$$x^{\alpha_1} x^{\alpha_2} \cdots x^{\alpha_k} = x^{\left(\sum_{i=1}^{k} \alpha_i\right)}$$

will yield x^n provided $n = \alpha_1 + \alpha_2 + \cdots + \alpha_k$ with α_i a nonnegative integer, $i = 1, 2, \ldots, k$. Recall that $x^0 \equiv 1$. In Example 13 in Sect. 2.7, the number of ways the integer n could be written as the sum of k nonnegative integers was shown to be $\binom{n+k-1}{k-1}$. Now, the coefficient of x^n is just this number, so that

$$\frac{1}{(1 - x)^k} = (1 - x)^{-k} = \sum_{n=0}^{\infty} \binom{n+k-1}{k-1} x^n, \qquad |x| < 1, \tag{3}$$

for any integer k. We may deduce this result by differentiating

$$(1 - x)^{-1} = \sum_{n=0}^{\infty} x^n, \qquad k - 1 \text{ times.}$$

This method yields an alternative derivation of Eq. (9) in Sect. 2.4.

Example 4. Determine the number of ways an integer n can be written as the sum of k integers, each of which is less than or equal to a fixed integer m.

Solution. Consider

$$(1 + x + x^2 + \cdots + x^m)^k \equiv (1 + x + x^2 + \cdots + x^m) \cdots (1 - x + x^2 + \cdot + x^m),$$

and note that the coefficient of x^n is simply the number of term for which

$$x^n = x^{\alpha_1} x^{\alpha_2} \cdots x^{\alpha_k},$$

with $n = \alpha_1 + \alpha_2 + \cdots + \alpha_k$ and $0 \le \alpha_i \le m$, with $i = 1, 2, \ldots, k$.

Now,

$$1 + x + x^2 + \cdots + x^m = \frac{1 - x^{m+1}}{1 - x},$$

so that

$$(1 + x + x^2 + \cdots + x^m)^k = (1 - x)^{-k}(1 - x^{m+1})^k. \tag{4}$$

From the binomial expansion, we have

$$(1 - x^{m+1})^k = \sum_{s=0}^{\infty} \binom{k}{s}(-1)^s x^{(m+1)s},$$

and from Eq. (3), we find that

$$(1 + x + x^2 + \cdots + x^m)^k = \sum_{r=0}^{\infty} \binom{r+k-1}{k-1} x^r \sum_{s=0}^{k} \binom{k}{s}(-1)^s x^{(m+1)s}.$$

The coefficient of x^n is obtained by setting $r + (m + 1)s = n$, or $r = n - (m + 1)s$. Hence,

$$N = \sum_{s=0}^{k} (-1)^s \binom{n - (m+1)s + k - 1}{k - 1} \binom{k}{s} \tag{5}$$

is the number of ways a positive integer n can be written as the sum of k integers, which may take on the values $0, 1, 2, \ldots, m$.

For example, for $n = 8$, $k = 3$, and $m = 4$, we have

$$N = \sum_{s=0}^{3} (-1)^s \binom{10 - 5s}{2} \binom{3}{s}$$

$$= \binom{10}{2}\binom{3}{0} - \binom{5}{2}\binom{3}{1} = 45 - 30 = 15.$$

Note that the integer 8 can be written six ways as the sum of the integers (1, 3, 4), three ways as the sum of the integers (2, 2, 4), three ways as the sum of the integers (3, 3, 2), and three ways as the sum of the integers (0, 4, 4), totaling 15 ways.

PROBLEMS

1. Deduce that

$$\binom{a+b+c}{r} = \sum_{n=0}^{r} \sum_{m=0}^{r} \binom{a}{r-m-n}\binom{b}{n}\binom{c}{m}.$$

2. Why is it obvious that

$$\binom{n+m}{k} > \binom{n}{k} + \binom{m}{k}, \qquad k > 1?$$

3. Refer to the ballot problem with $n = m$. How many sequences are there such that the number of ones always exceeds the number of zeros until the last draw?

4. In how many ways can n different balls be placed in m urns such that urn 1 contains exactly k balls?

5. An urn contains the integers $1, 2, \ldots, n$. If m integers are withdrawn at random yielding $\binom{n}{m}$ combinations, how many of these combinations will contain the integers $1, 2, \ldots, k$?

6. Consider $(x + x^2 + \cdots + x^m)^k = x^k (1 + x + x^2 + \cdots + x^{m-1})^k$. Show that the numbers of ways a positive integer n can be written as the sum of k integers, each of which is greater than, or equal to, one and less than, or equal to, m, is

$$N = \sum_{s=0}^{k} (-1)^s \binom{n-ms-1}{k-1} \binom{k}{s}.$$

Apply this result to the toss of five dice, and determine the number of ways the total points are 15.

7. Poker can be played by tossing five dice. The possible outcomes are as follows:

a) one pair;   example: (3, 3) (1) (2) (6)
b) two pairs;   example: (3, 3) (5, 5) (1)
c) three of a kind;   example: (4, 4, 4) (2) (5)
d) full house;   example: (2, 2, 2) (6, 6)
e) four of a kind;   example: (6, 6, 6, 6) (2)
f) five of a kind;   example: (4, 4, 4, 4, 4)
g) bust;   example: (1) (2) (3) (5) (6)
h) straight;   example: (2) (3) (4) (5) (6)

Show that the numbers of different outcomes for a) through h) are, respectively, 60, 60, 60, 30, 30, 6, 4, 2. Explain why the total number of different outcomes is $\binom{10}{5}$ or 252.

8. Derive the result of Problem 6 above by means of Eq. (5). [*Hint:* replace n by $n - k$, m by $m - 1$.]

9. Show that the number of ways a positive integer n can be written as the sum of k integers, which may take on the integral values $a, a + 1, a + 2, \ldots, m$ is

$$N = \sum_{s=0}^{k} (-1)^s \binom{n-ka-(m-a+1)\,s+k-1}{k-1} \binom{k}{s}.$$

For $n = 12$, $k = 4$, $a = 2$, and $m = 4$, show that $N = 19$, and enumerate the 19 cases.

10. Refer to the ballot problem. If a tie is allowed, show that the number of successful sequences is

$$N = \frac{n + 1 - m}{n + 1 + m} \binom{n+1+m}{n+1}.$$

11. Referring to Example 4 above, the number of ways an integer n can be written as the sum of k nonnegative integers, each of which is less than or equal to m, can be determined as follows: Let A_i be the event that $0 \le \alpha_i \le m$, with $n = \sum_{i=1}^{k} \alpha_i$. Show that

$$N(A_1 A_2 \cdots A_k) = \binom{n+k-1}{k-1} - N\left(\bigcup_{i=1}^{k} A_i'\right).$$

Next show that $N(A_1') = \binom{n-(m+1)+k-1}{k-1}$, $N(A_1' A_2) = \binom{n-2(m+1)+k-1}{k-1}$, etc.
From the inclusion–exclusion formula involving $N(\bigcup_{i=1}^{k} A_i')$, derive Eq. (5) above.

BIBLIOGRAPHY

1. FELLER, W. *An Introduction to Probability Theory and Its Applications*, 3rd ed., Vol. I, John Wiley & Sons, New York, 1968. Describes the basic principles from a slightly more abstract point of view, and includes a number of additional identities involving binomial coefficients.

2. PARZEN, E. *Modern Probability Theory and Its Applications*, John Wiley & Sons, New York, 1960. Provides a condensed discussion of the basic principles.

3. RIORDAN, J. *An Introduction to Combinatorial Analyses*, John Wiley & Sons, New York, 1958. A brief summary of the basic principles, followed by a great number of extensions and applications, many quite interesting and many quite difficult.

4. USPENSKI, J. V. *Introduction to Mathematical Probability*, McGraw-Hill Book Company, New York, 1937. A classic description of the basic principles and applications.

CHAPTER 3

DISCRETE PROBABILITY THEORY

3.1 INTRODUCTION

The mathematical development of probability theory is an invention of man that enables him to make definitive statements about chance events. In other words, probability theory provides a quantitative method of evaluating the effects of random phenomena. Everyone who has played cards, tossed dice, flipped coins, wagered on athletic events, or driven on a freeway realizes that chance plays an important role in his everyday experiences. There is good evidence that a chance mutation changed the ancestors of man into carnivorous killers.

Classical physics deals with more or less certain or necessary events, whereas the theory of probability embraces those events in which the final outcome is uncertain. Thus one may say with impunity that the sun will rise tomorrow, that objects near the earth will be attracted by the earth, that water will boil if heated to a sufficiently high temperature, that a current will exist in a wire if portions of the wire are at different potentials. The physical laws invented by man that embrace these physical facts seem to hold very well, and one would be quite surprised if they were violated.

In contradistinction to these necessary events are those events for which the outcome is not certain before the event occurs. If a coin is tossed one cannot be certain whether heads or tails will occur. Before embarking on a trip, one cannot be certain that no accident will befall the traveler. One cannot be certain as to the state of the weather three days hence.

Now, suppose we ask for the probability that a head appears if a coin is tossed. If we have a great deal of patience, we can toss the coin a large number of times. If after n tosses we note that a head has appeared r_n times, we can form the ratio r_n/n, the ratio of successes to total trials. One might define

$$p = \lim_{n \to \infty} \frac{r_n}{n} \tag{1}$$

as the probability of a head occurring on the toss of this coin. Unfortunately, we cannot actually determine this limit precisely, because r_n is not a determinate function of n.

Let us turn for the moment to the science of physics. Newton's second law of motion concerns the motion of a particle or point mass. Although such ideal mass points (i.e., those having no spatial extension whatsoever) do not exist in nature, the physicist calculates the motions of extended bodies under the assumption that they are dense collections of mass points, and such calculations have proved remarkably accurate. The mathematician working in probability theory encounters a similar phenomenon. No die is perfect, but man has the ability to make abstractions. For example, he visualizes a perfect die and postulates that all six faces of the die are "equally likely" to appear. Thus, a true coin, by definition, is one for which the occurrence of "heads" or "tails" is equally likely.

The chance that one has an accident in driving a vehicle is governed by a large number of factors such as the conditions of the roads and the driver, not to mention the other drivers, lighting conditions, speeds, or the behavior of the driver under stress. In order to assign a specific number as the probability of having an accident, one is forced to the frequency interpretation, namely, the actual counting of the accidents that occur under various combinations of road conditions, driver status, and distance traveled. This is the approach taken by statisticians working for insurance companies. Moreover, the frequency of occurrence of deaths due to some disease may change abruptly because of the discovery of a new vaccine. We might add that poll takers encounter even more difficulty in determining the probability that a candidate will win an election, since they are reduced to dealing with relatively small samples.

The mathematical theory of probability began in the 17th century when Antoine Gombaud, Chevalier de Mere, proposed some simple problems involving games of chance (dice, to be specific) to the celebrated French writer, philosopher, and mathematician, Blaise Pascal. Correspondence between Pascal and the equally famous mathematician, Fermat, led to the formulation of probability theory.

A vast number of mathematicians have since contributed to the theory of probability. The Russian school of mathematicians has broadened this field extensively. Such fields as statistical mechanics, quantum theory, noise and communication theory, information theory, theory of games, and statistics are dependent on the results of probability theory. This is a theory of statistical regularities among random phenomena, a theory of *orderly disorder*.

3.2 LAPLACE'S DEFINITION OF MATHEMATICAL PROBABILITY

Let us consider the casting of a die. There are six possible outcomes. According to Jacob Bernoulli, one would consider the six outcomes as equally probable if, after taking into consideration all the relevant evidence, no one of the six events ought to have any preference over any other of the possible outcomes. This idea leads to the so-called classical definition of probability (Laplace's extension of Bernoulli's earlier work). Note that the six outcomes are mutually exclusive in pairs in the sense that if a 2 occurs, then a 5 cannot occur, and conversely. If A represents the event that a 2 occurs, whereas B represents the event that a 5 occurs, then the statement that A and B are mutually exclusive events is equivalent to the statement that A and B are disjoint sets,* namely, that $A \cap B = AB = \phi$.

Laplace's definition of mathematical probability. Let S be an event with n possible outcomes that are mutually exclusive and whose occurrences are equally likely. If m of these cases are favorable to an event A, then the probability of A occurring, written $p(A)$, is $p(A) = m/n$.

We consider now a great variety of problems to which Laplace's definition can be applied.

Example 1. A card is chosen at random from a deck of bridge cards. Find the probability that an ace is extracted.

Solution. There are 52 possible outcomes, four of which are favorable cases. Hence,

$$p = \tfrac{4}{52} = \tfrac{1}{13}.$$

Note that the top card of the deck (assuming randomness in the shuffle) also has a probability, $p = \tfrac{1}{13}$, of being an ace.

Example 2. A card is chosen at random from a deck of cards and put aside without noting its denomination. What is the probability that a card withdrawn from the remaining 51 cards is an ace?

Solution. The intelligent gambler knows intuitively that the answer is $p = \tfrac{1}{13}$, since if he places the second card face down next to the first card, he realizes that the second card is just as likely to be an ace as the first card. Good stud poker players use this fact when they survey their opponents' cards, not knowing what the hole cards are. Let us obtain $p = \tfrac{1}{13}$ by combinatorial analysis. There are $4 \cdot 3 = 12$ ways for the first and second cards to be aces (four choices for the first ace, and three choices for the second ace), and there are $48 \cdot 4 = 192$ ways for the first card not to be an ace and the second card an ace.† Hence, there are $12 + 192 = 204$ favorable cases for the event that the second card is an ace. Now, there are $(52)(51)$ possible outcomes (52 choices for the first card followed by 51 choices for the second card). Hence,

$$p = \frac{4 \cdot 51}{52 \cdot 51} = \frac{1}{13}.$$

Example 3. In Example 2, find the probability that both cards are aces.

Solution. There are $\binom{52}{2}$ ways of obtaining two cards from the deck of 52 cards; the order in which we obtain these two cards is immaterial. Since there are four aces, there are $\binom{4}{2}$ favorable cases. Hence,

$$p = \frac{\binom{4}{2}}{\binom{52}{2}} = \frac{4}{52} \cdot \frac{3}{51} = \frac{1}{221}.$$

---

* For the set-theoretic interpretation of events, see Chapter 1.

† See the first fundamental principle in Chapter 2.

If we order the occurrence of the two cards, we obtain the same result, since there are $4 \cdot 3$ ordered pairs of aces and $52 \cdot 51$ ordered outcomes.

Example 4. Find the probability of obtaining a full house in five-card draw.

Solution. There are $\binom{52}{5}$ possible outcomes of which 3744 are favorable, see Example 3 in Sect. 2.4. Hence,

$$p = \frac{3744}{\binom{52}{5}} = 0.00144 \ldots$$

Example 5. An urn contains three red and six white balls. If a ball is chosen at random what is the probability that it is red?

Solution. It is obvious that $p = \frac{3}{9} = \frac{1}{3}$. It will be convenient to label the red balls R_1, R_2, R_3, and the white balls $W_1, W_2, W_3, W_4, W_5, W_6$, for a discussion of the next two examples.

Example 6. For the urn of Example 5 suppose that a ball is chosen at random and put aside without noting its color. If a second ball is then withdrawn, what is the probability that it is red?

Solution. Since the second ball cannot be distinguished from the first ball before we look at either of them, the answer must be $p = \frac{1}{3}$. Note that there are $9 \cdot 8 = 72$ possible outcomes (nine choices for the first ball followed by eight choices for the second ball). The favorable cases are either a red ball followed by a red ball, yielding $3 \cdot 2 = 6$ favorable cases, or a white ball followed by a red ball, yielding $6 \cdot 3 = 18$ favorable cases. Hence

$$p = \frac{(6 + 18)}{72} = \frac{1}{3}.$$

Roughly speaking, this is what occurs. One third of the time the first ball is red and two thirds of the time the first ball is white, so that on the average there remains $3 - \frac{1}{3} = \frac{8}{3}$ red balls and $6 - \frac{2}{3} = \frac{16}{3}$ white balls, and

$$p = \frac{\frac{8}{3}}{(\frac{8}{3} + \frac{16}{3})} = \frac{1}{3}.$$

In other words, the balance of red and white balls remains invariant if a ball is withdrawn without noting its color. Of course, if we knew the color of the first ball the probability that the second ball is red is not $\frac{1}{3}$. For example, the probability that the second ball will be red is $p = \frac{2}{8} = \frac{1}{4}$ if the first ball is red, and $p = \frac{3}{8}$ if the first ball is white.

Example 7. From the urn of Example 5, three balls are chosen at random. Find the probability that one of them is red and that the remaining two are white.

Solution. There are $\binom{9}{3} = 84$ equally likely events. To obtain the favorable number of cases, we note that there are $\binom{3}{1} = 3$ different ways of obtaining a red ball and

$\binom{6}{2} = 15$ ways of choosing two white balls from the six white balls. Hence, there are $3 \cdot 15 = 45$ ways of obtaining one red and two white balls, so that

$$p = \tfrac{45}{84} = \tfrac{15}{28}.$$

Example 8. A fair coin is flipped five times. Find the probability that exactly two heads occur.

Solution. We are dealing with a 5-sequence of heads and tails, yielding $2^5 = 32$ possible outcomes. There are $\binom{5}{2}$ such sequences yielding exactly two heads. Thus

$$p = \frac{\binom{5}{2}}{2^5} = \frac{5}{16}.$$

Show that if a fair coin is flipped n times, then

$$p_k = \frac{\binom{n}{k}}{2^n}$$

is the probability that exactly k heads occur, and that

$$\sum_{k=0}^{n} p_k = 1.$$

Example 9. An urn contains n white balls, labeled $W_1, W_2, \ldots, W_n$, and m red balls, $R_1, R_2, \ldots, R_m$. If $(\alpha + \beta)$ balls are withdrawn at random, find the probability that α are white and β are red.

Solution. From combinatorial analysis there are $\binom{n+m}{\alpha+\beta}$ possible outcomes of which $\binom{n}{\alpha}\binom{m}{\beta}$ are favorable events. Hence

$$p = \frac{\binom{n}{\alpha}\binom{m}{\beta}}{\binom{n+m}{\alpha+\beta}}.$$

The reader may answer the following questions. Would the answer be different if the $\alpha + \beta$ balls were withdrawn one at a time without replacements? One at a time with replacements?

Example 10. Referring to the urn of Example 9, balls are withdrawn one at a time without replacements until only balls of one color remain. Find the probability that this color is white.

Solution. It is apparent that this color will be white if we exhausted the balls in the urn and the last ball withdrawn is white. But the probability that the last ball be white should be the same as the probability that the first ball is white, namely

$$p = \frac{n}{(m + n)}.$$

Why? In any case we note that the number of favorable cases for the last ball to be white is $\binom{n+m-1}{n-1}$, so that

$$p = \frac{\binom{n+m-1}{n-1}}{\binom{n+m}{n}} = \frac{n}{m+n}.$$

Example 11. Each of n balls, labeled $B_1, B_2, \ldots, B_n$, is placed at random in one of N urns, labeled $U_1, U_2, \ldots, U_N$. Find the probability that urn U_1 will contain exactly k balls.

Solution. The total number of events is $N^n = N \cdot N \cdots N$, since there are N choices for the urn occupied by ball 1, and so on. To determine the number of favorable cases we note that there are $\binom{n}{k}$ ways to choose k of the n balls to be placed in U_1. The remaining $n - k$ balls can be placed in the other $(N - 1)$ urns in $(N - 1)^{n-k}$ ways. Hence

$$p = \frac{\binom{n}{k}(N-1)^{n-k}}{N^n}.$$

Example 12. A pair of dice are cast until a 4 or 7 appears (total points of the dice). Find the probability that a 4 will occur before a 7.

Solution. This problem does not appear to be solvable from Laplace's definition of probability. However, let us note that the points 2, 3, 5, 6, 8, 9, 10, 11, 12 are irrelevant, so that on the toss of a pair of dice there are three favorable cases for the occurrence of a 4 and six unfavorable cases for the occurrence of a 7. Thus our problem is analogous to the problem of Example 5, and $p = \frac{1}{3}$. We can also look at the problem from the following point of view. Let A be the event of casting a 4 and B the event of not casting a 4 or a 7. It is easily seen that

$$p(A) = \tfrac{3}{36} = \tfrac{1}{12}, \qquad p(B) = \tfrac{36-9}{36} = \tfrac{3}{4}.$$

A 4 will occur before a 7 if the following mutually exclusive events occur, namely A, or BA, or BBA, or $BBBA$, etc., with BA the event of not casting a 4 or 7 on the first try followed by casting a 4 on the second try, etc. Subsequently we will show that the probability of casting a 4 before a 7 is

$$P = p(A) + p(BA) + p(BBA) + - -$$

$$= p(A) + p(B)p(A) + [p(B)]^2 p(A) + - - -$$

$$= \frac{1}{12}\left[1 + \left(\frac{3}{4}\right) + \left(\frac{3}{4}\right)^2 + - - \right] = \frac{1}{12}\frac{1}{1-\frac{3}{4}} = \frac{1}{3},$$

assuming independent events.

Example 13. A die is tossed n times. Find the probability that a 5 or 6 occurs at least once.

Solution. There are 6^n possible outcomes and the number of unfavorable cases is 4^n. Thus

$$p_n = \frac{6^n - 4^n}{6^n} = 1 - (\tfrac{2}{3})^n,$$

with $p_1 = \tfrac{1}{3}$, $p_2 = \tfrac{5}{9}$, so that the odds are slightly in favor of obtaining at least a 5 or 6 in two tosses of a die as against neither a 5 nor a 6 appearing.

Example 14. An urn contains n ones and m zeros. The elements are withdrawn one at a time yielding an $(n + m)$ sequence. Find the probability that no two consecutive zeros are withdrawn, $n \geq m - 1$.

Solution. There are $(n + 1)$ positions between the n ones as shown here: $x1x1x1x$ ... $x1x$. If m of the checked positions are replaced by zeros we will have the number of favorable cases for which no two consecutive zeros will occur. This can be accomplished in $\binom{n+1}{m}$ ways, so that

$$p = \frac{\binom{n+1}{m}}{\binom{n+m}{m}},$$

since there are $\binom{n+m}{m}$ total events.

Example 15. In the ballot problem of Example 1, Section 2.5, what is the probability that the number of ones always exceeds the number of zeros if the balls are withdrawn as in the example above?

Solution. From previous results we have $\frac{n-m}{n+m}\binom{n+m}{n}$ favorable events, so that

$$p = \frac{n - m}{n + m} \frac{\binom{n+m}{n}}{\binom{n+m}{n}} = \frac{n - m}{n + m}.$$

We note that

$$1 - p = 1 - \frac{n - m}{n + m} = 2\frac{m}{n + m},$$

which is exactly twice the probability that the first number removed is a zero.

Example 16. *Gambler's Ruin problem.* A gambler has b units and plays a fair game against an adversary with an infinite amount of capital. If one unit is exchanged per game, find the probability that the gambler will be ruined (zero capital) for the first time after $b + 2n$ games.

Solution. In Example 2, Section 2.5, it was shown that the number of favorable sequences of games (unfavorable for the gambler) is

$$N = \frac{b}{b + 2n}\binom{b + 2n}{n}.$$

The total number of sequences or outcomes is 2^{b+2n} since there are two possible outcomes in each of the $b + 2n$ games. Hence

$$p = \frac{b}{b + 2n} \binom{b + 2n}{n} \frac{1}{2^{b + 2n}}.$$

Example 17. Find the probability of obtaining a given sum, n, in k tosses of a die.

Solution. Each toss of the die contributes either 1, 2, 3, 4, 5, or 6 to the sum of points. Hence the number of favorable events is the number of ways the integer n can be written as the sum of k integers, each integer lying between 1 and 6. The solution is given in Problem 6, Section 2.5, so that

$$p = \frac{1}{6^k} \sum_{s=0}^{k} (-1)^s \binom{n - 6s - 1}{k - 1} \binom{k}{s},$$

since there are 6^k possible outcomes.

The probability of obtaining a total of 12 points in three tosses of a die (or the single toss of three dice) is

$$p = \frac{1}{6^3} \sum_{s=0}^{3} (-1)^s \binom{12 - 6s - 1}{2} \binom{3}{s}$$

$$= \frac{1}{6^3} \left[\binom{11}{2} - \binom{5}{2}\binom{3}{1} \right] = \frac{25}{216}.$$

Example 18. *Lottery.* An urn contains N balls numbered $1, 2, \ldots, N$. Find the probability that exactly k of M specified numbers will be among a sample of n balls withdrawn from the urn.

Solution. Figure 1 shows how to compute the number of favorable cases. The reader should deduce that

$$p = \frac{\binom{N-M}{n-k} \binom{M}{k}}{\binom{N}{n}}.$$

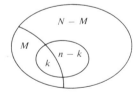

Figure 3.1

PROBLEMS

1. An urn contains seven red balls and five white balls. If five balls are withdrawn at random (no replacements) what is the probability that exactly three are red and two are white? What is the probability of this event if five balls are withdrawn one at a time with replacements?

2. A fair coin is tossed seven times. What is the probability that exactly three heads occur?

3. The event A is the occurrence of a 4, 5, or 6 on the toss of a die. If a die is cast six times, what is the probability that the event A will occur exactly twice?

4. Urn I contains two white and three red balls. Urn II contains three white and two red balls. A ball is chosen at random from both urns. What is the probability that the two balls have different colors?

5. Urn I contains m white and n red balls. Urn II contains k white and k red balls. A ball is withdrawn from each urn. What is the probability that the colors match?

6. Eight balls are distributed at random among 15 urns numbered 1–15. What is the probability that urn 1 contains exactly three balls?

7. A and B are two men among n who are placed at random in a row. What is the probability that there will be exactly r specified men between A and B?

8. Assuming that boys and girls are equally likely to occur, independent of the sex of prior children in a family, find the probability that in a family of six children (a) all the children are of the same sex, (b) the four oldest will be boys and the two youngest girls, (c) exactly half of the children will be boys.

9. In a bridge game (13 cards dealt at random to each of four players), it is known that North has no ace. What is the probability that his partner, South, has exactly two aces?

10. North and South have 10 trumps. What is the probability that all three remaining trumps are in the same hand (East or West has no trumps)?

11. A and B match pennies as follows. Each flips two coins. A wins if he flips the same number of heads as B, otherwise B wins. What is the probability that A wins? Under the same set of rules, what is the probability that A wins if each flips n coins?

12. In a six-card draw (no replacements), what is the probability of obtaining exactly three aces?

13. Urn I contains nine balls numbered 1–9, and urn II contains seven balls numbered 1–7. One ball is removed from each urn. What is the probability that their sum exceeds 12; that their product exceeds 8?

14. For the urns of Problem 13, what is the probability that the ball drawn from urn I has a greater value than the ball drawn from urn II?

15. A drawer contains five red socks and seven blue socks. What is the probability that two socks chosen at random will be of the same color?

16. A closet contains three identical pairs of brown shoes and five identical pairs of black shoes. What is the probability that two shoes withdrawn at random will form a wearable pair?

17. A bag contains seven balls numbered 1–7. The balls are withdrawn one at a time without replacements. Find the probability that:
   a) The odd-numbered balls are withdrawn first.
   b) The odd- and even-numbered balls alternate.
   c) The first withdrawn ball is even numbered and the last is odd numbered.

    d) The sum of the first two digits withdrawn is less than eight.

    e) The first digit withdrawn is greater than the fifth digit withdrawn.

    f) The first three digits withdrawn increase in order.

    g) The digit 4 immediately follows the digit 7.

18. Three balls are distributed at random among five urns. What is the probability that no urn contains more than one ball?

19. Three urns I, II, III, contain balls numbered (1, 2), (1, 2, 3), (1, 2, 3, 4), respectively. One ball is removed at random from each urn. Find the probability that the number withdrawn from urn I is less than the number withdrawn from urn II, and that this second number is less than the number withdrawn from urn III.

20. Three players (A, B, C) flip fair coins and play the following game. The player whose coin does not match the other two coins (odd coin) wins one unit from each of the other two players. Otherwise no money is exchanged. What is the probability that after six games A is ahead by four units?

21. Each of three urns contains six balls numbered 1–6. One ball is withdrawn at random from each of the three urns. Find the probability that 4 is the largest number withdrawn.

22. Four dice are cast. Find the probability that the total points add up to 12.

23. A fair coin is tossed $2n$ times. Find the probability that the number of heads and tails are equal for the first time after the $(2n)$th toss.

24. An urn contains a white and b black balls. The balls are withdrawn at random one at a time without replacements. Find the probability that the kth ball withdrawn is white.

25. An urn contains the n integers 1–n. If m integers are withdrawn at random (no replacements), what is the probability that the largest number withdrawn is the integer k, $m \leq k \leq n$?

26. An urn contains M red balls and N black balls. Samples are drawn from the urn $(m + n)$ times with replacements. Show that the probability of obtaining exactly m red balls and n black balls is

$$P = \binom{m+n}{m} p^m (1 - p)^n, \qquad p = \frac{M}{M+N}.$$

Hint: Imagine that the red and black balls have different labels. Show that there are $(M + N)^{m+n}$ different sequences of which $\binom{m+n}{m} M^m N^n$ are favorable.

27. Returning to Problem 26 and sampling without replacements, show that the probability of obtaining m red and n black balls is

$$P_1 = \frac{\binom{M}{m}\binom{N}{n}}{\binom{M+N}{m+n}} = \binom{m+n}{m} \frac{M!\, N!\, (M + N - m - n)!}{(M + N)!\, (M - m)!\, (N - n)!}.$$

For the case $M \gg 1$, $N \gg 1$, $m \gg 1$, $n \gg 1$, $m \ll M$, $n \ll N$, and Stirling's approximation, $\ln M! \approx M \ln M$, etc., show that $P_1 \approx P$. Hence for this case, sampling without replacements is essentially the same as sampling with replacements. Is this result intuitively obvious?

3.3 AN AXIOMATIC APPROACH TO DISCRETE PROBABILITY THEORY

Let us consider n distinct elements labeled $A_1, A_2, \ldots, A_n$. We wish to determine the number of subsets which can be formed from these elements. The number of subsets consisting of just one element is $\binom{n}{1} = n$, namely the elements $(A_1), (A_2), \ldots,$ (A_n). The number of subsets containing exactly two elements is $\binom{n}{2}$, namely the number of ways of choosing two elements from n elements, yielding the subsets $(A_1, A_2), (A_1, A_3), \ldots, (A_1, A_n), (A_2, A_3), \ldots, (A_{n-1}, A_n)$, with $(A_1, A_2) \equiv (A_2, A_1)$. Furthermore, if we consider the A_i, $i = 1, 2, \ldots, n$, as events in a probability space, then by (A_1, A_2) we mean that either A_1 or A_2 has occurred, so we write $(A_1, A_2) \equiv A_1 \cup A_2$, etc. The number of subsets containing three elements is $\binom{n}{3}$, etc. The full set, E, is the complete set $(A_1, A_2, \ldots, A_n) \equiv \cup_{i=1}^{n} A_i$. To these subsets we adjoin the null set, ϕ. Thus the total number of subsets is

$$\binom{n}{0} + \binom{n}{1} + \binom{n}{2} + \cdots + \binom{n}{n} = 2^n, \tag{1}$$

a simple enough answer.

With these subsets we may perform unions, intersections, and complements relative to E. Thus the complement of (A_3, A_4) is the subset $(A_1, A_2, A_5, \ldots, A_n)$. The intersection of (A_1) with (A_1, A_2) is $A_1 \cdot (A_1 + A_2) = (A_1)$, since $A_1 A_2 = \phi$. The union of (A_1, A_2) with (A_1, A_3, A_4) is the set (A_1, A_2, A_3, A_4), and so on.

Example 1. Consider the toss of a coin for which heads (H) and tails (T) are the two elementary events. There are $2^2 = 4$ subsets in all, namely

$$\boldsymbol{G}: \quad H, T, E = H \cup T, \quad \phi = H \cap T.$$

No new sets can be formed by considering further unions, intersections, and complements relative to E. Thus the complement of heads is $H' = T$, with $T' = H$, $E' = \phi$, $\phi' = E$, $H \cup E = E$, etc.

The set $\boldsymbol{G}$ of sets, is said to be *closed*, and we call $\boldsymbol{G}$ a field of sets. A field of probability is defined as follows: Let E be any collection of elements $x, y, z, \ldots,$ which are called elementary events, and let $\boldsymbol{G}$ be a collection of subsets of E. The following axioms or postulates are assumed to hold.

   I: $\boldsymbol{G}$ contains E and the null set.

   II: $\boldsymbol{G}$ is a field of sets.

   III: To each set A in $\boldsymbol{G}$ there corresponds a real nonnegative number, written $p(A)$, with $0 \le p(A) \le 1$. We call the number, $p(A)$, the probability that an element of A will occur, or simply, the probability that A will occur.

   IV: $p(E) = 1$, that is, one of the elements of E is sure to occur.

   V: If A and B are subsets of $\boldsymbol{G}$ such that $AB = \phi$ (in set theory $AB = \phi$ signifies that A and B are disjoint sets; in logic and in probability theory, if $AB = \phi$ we say that A and B are mutually exclusive events, for, if A occurs, B cannot occur, and conversely), then

$$p(A \cup B) = p(A + B) \equiv p(A) + p(B). \tag{2}$$

The single toss of a coin discussed above is a simple example of a field of probability. For a fair coin we define $p(H) = p(T) = \frac{1}{2}$, so that $p(E) = p(H \cup T) = p(H) + p(T) = 1$, and a head or tail is sure to occur.

From $E = \phi + E$, $\phi E = \phi$, it follows from Eq. (2) that $p(E) = p(\phi) + p(E)$, so that $p(\phi) = 0$.

Since we have exhibited a realistic example which yields a field of probability, the postulates above must be self consistent. The elementary possible outcomes of an experiment are often called the points of the sample space. Thus for the toss of a coin one has two sample points, namely heads and tails. If a coin is flipped five times there are $2^5 = 32$ sample points, the 32 sequences composed of heads and tails.

Returning to Eq. (2), the reader may better understand this postulate from the following Venn diagram (Fig. 2).

Imagine that one throws a dart at the region E, and that the dart is certain to fall in E, $p(E) = 1$. In Fig. 2 we note that $AB = \phi$, and A and B are mutually exclusive events. It should be apparent that the probability that the dart falls in either A or B, say $p(A + B)$, is simply $p(A) + p(B)$.

Events such as tossing a coin, spinning a roulette wheel, casting a die, picking a ball from an urn, etc., yield finite probability fields, since there are only a finite number of elementary events which may occur. If the number of elementary events is finite or countably infinite, we say that the probability field is discrete.

Example 2. The elementary events for the toss of a single die are the occurrences (1), (2), (3), (4), (5), (6). For a true die we define

$$p(1) = p(2) = p(3) = p(4) = p(5) = p(6) = \tfrac{1}{6}.$$

If A is the event $(3, 5) \equiv (3 \cup 5)$, then from postulate V we have

$$p[(3, 5)] = p[(3 \cup 5)] = p(3) + p(5) = \tfrac{1}{3},$$

since (3) and (5) are mutually exclusive events. If B is the event that an even number occurs on the face of the die, then

$$p(B) = p[(2 \cup 4 \cup 6)] = p(2) + p[(4 \cup 6)]$$
$$= p(2) + p(4) + p(6) = \tfrac{1}{2},$$

since (2) and $(4 \cup 6)$ are mutually exclusive events, as are (4) and (6).

The reader should deduce that if $A_1, A_2, \ldots, A_k$ are mutually exclusive in pairs, then for a field of probability,

$$p(A_1 + A_2 + \cdots + A_k) = p(A_1) + p(A_2) + \cdots + p(A_k). \tag{3}$$

It also follows from $A + A' = E$, $AA' = \phi$, and postulates IV, V, that $p(E) = 1 = p(A) + p(A')$, so that

$$p(A') = 1 - p(A). \tag{4}$$

Thus the probability that A does not occur, $p(A')$, is one minus the probability that A occurs, an expected result.

Another useful result is a consequence of our postulates. Let A and B be two events in a field of probability. From set theory it follows that $A + B = A + A'B$, with $A(A'B) = \phi$. Thus we have expressed $A + B$ as the union of two disjoint sets, so that

$$p(A + B) = p(A) + p(A'B).$$

Now

$$B = B(A + A') = BA + BA',$$

with

$$(BA)(BA') = \phi.$$

Hence, $p(B) = p(BA) + p(BA')$. Combining this result with the result above yields

$$p(A + B) = p(A) + p(B) - p(AB). \tag{5}$$

The Venn diagram of Fig. 3 illustrates the result of Eq. (5). The probability that the dart falls in the region $A \cup B$ is less than $p(A) + p(B)$ since we have counted $p(AB)$ twice, once in computing $p(A)$ and once in computing $p(B)$. Hence we must subtract $p(AB)$ from $p(A) + p(B)$ to obtain $p(A + B)$.

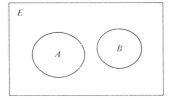

Figure 3.2

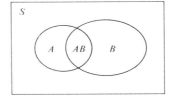

Figure 3.3

To extend the result of Eq. (5) to three sets is simple, since

$$p(A + B + C) = p(A) + p(B + C) - p[A(B + C)]$$
$$= p(A) + p(B) + p(C) - p(BC) - [p(AB) + p(AC) - p(ABAC)]$$
$$= p(A) + p(B) + p(C) - p(AB) - p(BC) - p(CA) + p(ABC). \tag{6}$$

By finite mathematical induction we may deduce that

$$p\left(\bigcup_{i=1}^{k} A_i\right) = \sum_{i=1}^{k} p(A_i) - \sum_{i>j\geq 1} p(A_i A_j)$$
$$+ \sum_{i>j>l\geq 1} p(A_i A_j A_l) + \cdots$$
$$+ (-1)^{k-1} p(A_1 A_2 \ldots A_k). \tag{7}$$

Compare this result with that of Eq. (13), Section 2.4.

Example 3. Consider two events A, B of a probability field such that $p(A) = \frac{1}{2}$, $p(B) = \frac{1}{3}$, and $p(A + B) = \frac{3}{4}$. Determine $p(AB)$, $p(AB')$, $p(A'B')$.

Solution. From Eq. (5) it follows that $p(AB) = \frac{1}{2} + \frac{1}{3} - \frac{3}{4} = \frac{1}{12}$, so that the probability that both A and B occur together is $\frac{1}{12}$. To find $p(AB')$ we note that $A = AB + AB'$, so that $p(A) = p(AB) + p(AB')$, since $(AB)(AB') = \phi$. Thus $p(AB') = \frac{1}{2} - \frac{1}{12} = \frac{5}{12}$. To determine $p(A'B')$ we note that $A'B' = (A + B)'$, so that $p(A'B') = 1 - p(A + B) = 1 - \frac{3}{4} = \frac{1}{4}$.

Example 4. Each of n urns contains three balls numbered 1, 2, 3. A ball is chosen at random from each urn, yielding a group of integers. Find the probability that this group contains each of the integers 1, 2, 3 at least once.

Solution. Let A_k be the event that the integer k is not in the group, $k = 1, 2, 3$, so that

$$p(A_1) = p(A_2) = p(A_3) = (\tfrac{2}{3})^n,$$

since the group will not contain the integer 1, for example, if, and only if, the integers 2 and 3 are chosen from each urn, yielding 2^n sequences from a total of 3^n possible outcomes. We may deduce that

$$p(A_1 A_2) = p(A_2 A_3) = p(A_3 A_1) = 1/3^n$$

and

$$p(A_1 A_2 A_3) = 0,$$

since one of the integers must be found in the group.

Now we are interested in

$$
\begin{aligned}
p_n &= p(A_1' A_2' A_3') = p[(A_1 + A_2 + A_3)'] \\
&= 1 - p(A_1 + A_2 + A_3) \\
&= 1 - [p(A_1) + p(A_2) + p(A_3) - p(A_1 A_2) - p(A_2 A_3) - p(A_3 A_1) \\
&\quad + p(A_1 A_2 A_3)] \\
&= 1 - 3(\tfrac{2}{3})^n + 3(\tfrac{1}{3})^n,
\end{aligned}
$$

which is the required solution.

We note that

$$p_1 = p_2 = 0,$$
$$p_3 = \tfrac{2}{9},$$
$$p_4 = \tfrac{12}{27},$$
$$p_5 = \tfrac{50}{81} > \tfrac{1}{2}.$$

If the letters C, I, G were distributed equally among cigarette packs, one letter to each pack, and one purchased five packs, the probability would be $\frac{50}{81}$ that the word "CIG" could be formed from the letters obtained.

PROBLEMS

1. Given that A and B are elements of a probability field, show that $p(A) \leq p(B)$ if A is a subset of B.

2. A fair coin is tossed until a head occurs. Let A_n be the event that a head occurs for the first time on the nth toss, and determine $p_n = p(A_n)$. Show that

$$\sum_{n=1}^{\infty} p_n = 1 .$$

3. A, B, C are 3 subsets of a probability field, with the following values.

$$p(A) = p(B) = \tfrac{1}{4}$$
$$p(C) = \tfrac{1}{8}$$
$$p(A + B) = \tfrac{3}{8}$$
$$p(A + C) = \tfrac{5}{16}$$
$$p(B + C) = \tfrac{5}{16}$$
$$p(A + B + C) = \tfrac{13}{32}$$

Show the following to be true.

$$p(AB) = \tfrac{1}{8}$$
$$p(BC) = \tfrac{1}{16}$$
$$p(AC) = \tfrac{1}{16}$$
$$p(ABC) = \tfrac{1}{32}$$

4. Derive Eq. (3) by mathematical induction.

5. Derive Eq. (7) by mathematical induction.

6. Generalize Example 4 to the case for which each of the n urns contains m integers numbered 1–m, and show that

$$1 - p = \binom{m}{1} \frac{(m-1)^n}{m^n} - \binom{m}{2} \frac{(m-2)^n}{m^n} + \binom{m}{3} \frac{(m-3)^n}{m^n} - + \cdots$$

7. Let A, B, C be 3 events of a probability space. The expression $AB'C'$ is the event that A occurs and that B and C do not occur. Find expressions for the events that of A, B, C:

a) Only A and B occur.
b) All three events occur.
c) At least one event occurs.
d) At least two events occur.
e) Exactly one of the events occurs.
f) None of the events occur.

8. A_1, A_2, A_3, A_4 are mutually exclusive events in a probability field, with $p(A_i) = \tfrac{1}{8}$, $i = 1, 2, 3, 4$. Let $A = A_1 + A_2 + A_3$, $B = A_3 + A_4$. Show that

$$p(A + B) = \tfrac{1}{2}, \qquad p(AB) = \tfrac{1}{8}, \qquad p(A'B) = \tfrac{1}{8}, \qquad p(A' + B) = \tfrac{3}{4} .$$

9. Matching problem.   Balls numbered $1, 2, \ldots, n$ are placed in n urns numbered $1, 2, \ldots, n$, at random, one ball to each urn.   Show that the probability of having at least one match (number of ball corresponds to number of urn) is

$$p_n = 1 - \frac{1}{2!} + \frac{1}{3!} - \frac{1}{4!} + \cdots + (-1)^{n-1} \frac{1}{n!}.$$

From

$$e^x = \sum_0^\infty \frac{x^n}{n!}$$

show that

$$\lim_{n \to \infty} p_n = \frac{e-1}{e}.$$

3.4 CONDITIONAL PROBABILITY, BAYES' FORMULA

Let us assume that one throws a dart at a board, and that the dart is certain to fall at one of 12 equally likely points (see Fig. 4).

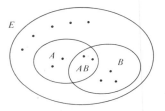

Figure 3.4

If A and B are the events shown in Fig. 4, then

$$p(A) = \tfrac{4}{12} = \tfrac{1}{3},$$
$$p(B) = \tfrac{5}{12},$$
$$p(AB) = \tfrac{2}{12} = \tfrac{1}{6}.$$

Now suppose that you are in another room and you are told that the event B has occurred, so you know that the dart has settled among one of five points comprising the event B.   One may now ask you what is the probability that the event A has occurred.   From Laplace's point of view you may reason as follows: As far as you are concerned there are five equally likely outcomes, since you know that the event B has occurred.   Of these five possible outcomes, only two are favorable for the event A (see Fig. 4).   Hence you might define $p(A|B) = \tfrac{2}{5}$ as the conditional or *a posteriori* probability that the event A occurs under the hypothesis that the event B has occurred.   Note that

$$p(A \mid B) = \frac{\tfrac{2}{12}}{\tfrac{5}{12}} = \frac{p(AB)}{p(B)}.$$

It is not strange that Bayes defined

$$p(A \mid B) = \frac{p(AB)}{p(B)}, \qquad p(B) \neq 0, \tag{1}$$

as the conditional probability for the occurrence of A given that B has occurred. Henceforth we will accept Eq. (1) as the definition of conditional probability.

It follows from Eq. (1) that

$$p(AB) = p(B)\, p(A \mid B) = p(A)\, p(B \mid A) \tag{2}$$

by interchanging the roles of A and B. Stated in simple terms, Bayes' formula or theorem states that the probability that both A and B occur is the probability that B occurs times the conditional probability that A occurs given that B has occurred, with a similar result obtained by interchanging the roles of A and B.

Example 1. A group of 100 girls contains 30 blondes and 70 brunettes. Twenty-five of the blondes are blue-eyed and the rest are brown-eyed, whereas 55 of the brunettes are brown-eyed and the rest are blue-eyed. A girl is chosen at random and it is determined that she is blue-eyed. Find the conditional probability that she is a blonde.

Solution. Let A be the event of being a blonde, and B the event of being blue-eyed. Now $p(B) = \frac{40}{100} = \frac{2}{5}$ since there are 40 blue-eyed females. Also $p(AB) = \frac{25}{100} = \frac{1}{4}$ since there are 25 blue-eyed blondes. We are interested in

$$p(A \mid B) = \frac{p(AB)}{p(B)} = \frac{\frac{1}{4}}{\frac{2}{5}} = \frac{5}{8}.$$

Example 2. Urn I contains three red and five white balls and urn II contains two red and five white balls. A ball is chosen at random from urn I and transferred to urn II (its color is not noted). Now a ball is chosen at random from urn II; find the probability that the ball is red.

Solution. Let A be the event that a red ball is chosen from urn I and A' be the event that a white ball is chosen from urn I. If B is the event that a red ball is obtained from urn II, then $B = B(A + A') = BA + BA'$, so that $p(B) = p(AB) + p(A'B)$. From Bayes' formula it follows that

$$p(B) = p(A)p(B|A) + p(A')p(B|A'). \tag{3}$$

Equation (3) is fairly obvious. The event B can occur only if A occurs followed by B given that A has occurred, or if A' occurs followed by B given that A' has occurred. Now

$$p(A) = \tfrac{3}{8}, \qquad p(A') = \tfrac{5}{8}.$$

To determine $p(B|A)$ is a simple matter, for if A has occurred, urn II will now contain three red balls and five white balls, so that $p(B|A) = \tfrac{3}{8}$. Similarly, $p(B|A') = \tfrac{2}{8} = \tfrac{1}{4}$. Hence

$$p(B) = \tfrac{3}{8} \cdot \tfrac{3}{8} + \tfrac{5}{8} \cdot \tfrac{2}{8} = \tfrac{19}{64}.$$

From a simple point of view one can obtain this answer by the following analysis. On the average, $\frac{3}{8}$ of a red ball and $\frac{5}{8}$ of a white ball are transferred to urn II. Hence, on the average, urn II will contain $2 + \frac{3}{8} = \frac{19}{8}$ red balls and $5 + \frac{5}{8} = \frac{45}{8}$ white balls. Hence

$$p(B) = \frac{\frac{19}{8}}{\frac{19}{8} + \frac{45}{8}} = \frac{19}{64}.$$

Equation (3) is a special case of the following result. Let the full space E be comprised of k events, $A_1, A_2, \ldots, A_k$, which are assumed to be mutually exclusive in pairs. For any event B we have

$$B = BE = B(A_1 + A_2 + \cdots + A_k)$$
$$= BA_1 + BA_2 + \cdots + BA_k.$$

Since

$$(BA_i) \cap (BA_j) = BA_iA_j = \phi \qquad \text{for} \qquad i \neq j,$$

it follows from the addition formula that

$$p(B) = p(BA_1) + p(BA_2) + \cdots + p(BA_k)$$
$$= p(A_1)p(B|A_1) + p(A_2)p(B|A_2) + \cdots + p(A_k)p(B|A_k) \tag{4}$$

by applying Bayes' formula to $p(BA_1)$, etc.

Furthermore, we have

$$p(A_j|B) = \frac{p(A_jB)}{p(B)} = \frac{p(A_j)p(B|A_j)}{p(B)} = \frac{p(A_j)p(B|A_j)}{\sum\limits_{i=1}^{k} p(A_i)p(B|A_i)}, \tag{5}$$

provided

$$p(B) = \sum\limits_{i=1}^{k} p(A_i)p(B|A_i) \neq 0.$$

Equation (5) is a useful extension of Bayes' formula.

Example 3. Urn I contains two red and eight black balls and urn II contains one red and nine black balls. An urn is chosen at random $(p(I) = p(II) = \frac{1}{2})$, and a ball chosen at random from this urn turns out to be red. Find the conditional probability that the ball came from urn I, $p(I|R)$. We call $p(I|R)$ the *a posteriori* probability that urn I was chosen, given that a red ball appeared on the draw. Its meaning and interpretation is made more clear below.

Solution. From Eq. (5) it follows that

$$p(I|R) = \frac{p(I)p(R|I)}{p(I)p(R|I) + p(II)p(R|II)}.$$

From

$$p(I) = p(II) = \frac{1}{2}, \qquad p(R|I) = \frac{2}{10}, \qquad p(R|II) = \frac{1}{10},$$

we have

$$p(I|R) = \frac{\frac{1}{2} \cdot \frac{2}{10}}{\frac{1}{2} \cdot \frac{2}{10} + \frac{1}{2} \cdot \frac{1}{10}} = \frac{2}{3}.$$

To understand this result, suppose we perform $20n$ experiments, n very large. On the average each urn will be chosen $10n$ times. For urn I on the average, $2n$ red balls will be chosen and $8n$ black balls. For urn II on the average, n red balls will be chosen and $9n$ black balls. Thus

$$20n \rightarrow \begin{array}{l} 10n \text{ urn I} \left[\begin{array}{l} \rightarrow 2n \text{ red} \\ \rightarrow 8n \text{ black} \end{array} \right. \\ \\ 10n \text{ urn II} \left[\begin{array}{l} \rightarrow \; n \text{ red} \\ \rightarrow 9n \text{ black} \end{array} \right. \end{array}$$

In the problem above we were told that a red ball occurred. Hence the $8n$ and $9n$ occurrences of black balls need not concern us. We see that urn I yields $2n$ red balls whereas urn II yields n red balls, so that

$$p(I|R) = \frac{2n}{2n + n} = \frac{2}{3}.$$

Example 4. Three urns, I, II, III, contain, respectively, two red and three black balls; one red and four black balls; three red and one black ball. An urn is chosen at random

$$p(I) = p(II) = p(III) = \tfrac{1}{3}$$

and a ball drawn at random from this urn turns out to be red. Find the conditional probability that the red ball came from urn I.

Solution. Applying Eq. (5) yields

$$p(I|R) = \frac{p(I)p(R|I)}{p(I)p(R|I) + p(II)p(R|II) + p(III)p(R|III)}$$

$$= \frac{\frac{2}{5}}{\frac{2}{5} + \frac{1}{5} + \frac{3}{4}} = \tfrac{8}{27}.$$

Example 5. *Crap game.* The game of craps is played as follows. A pair of dice is cast and the player wins immediately if a seven or eleven occurs (total points). He loses if a 2, 3, or 12 occurs on the first cast (craps). If his first point is k, $k = 4, 5, 6, 8, 9, 10$, he continues to cast, and only his point k and 7 are considered; all other numbers which occur are disregarded. The caster wins if he duplicates his point, k, before a 7 occurs, otherwise he loses. Find the probability that the player wins.

Solution. The probability of winning on the first toss is

$$p(7, 11) = p(7) + p(11) = \tfrac{1}{6} + \tfrac{1}{18} = \tfrac{2}{9}.$$

A win also occurs ($k = 4$) if a 4 occurs on the first cast followed by a 4 before a 7 on subsequent casts. The probability of casting a 4 is $\frac{1}{12}$, and we have previously seen that the probability of casting a 4 before a 7 is $\frac{1}{3}$ (see Example 12). Thus the probability of winning by casting a 4 and then a 4 before a 7 is

$$\tfrac{1}{12}\cdot\tfrac{1}{3} = \tfrac{1}{36}.$$

A similar reasoning for the points 5, 6, 8, 9, 10, yields

$$p = \tfrac{2}{9} + 2(\tfrac{1}{36} + \tfrac{2}{45} + \tfrac{25}{396})$$

$$= \tfrac{244}{495} = 0.49292\ldots$$

In a friendly game one should always bet against the caster. Make certain, however, that the dice hit a wall, for otherwise an expert roller can control the dice to some extent. At gambling tables you do not win if you bet against the caster and he rolls a 12 on the first cast.

Example 6. Urns numbered 2, 3, 4, ..., n, ..., each contain one white and two red balls, whereas urn 1 contains one white and one red ball. A ball is chosen at random from urn 1 and placed in urn 2, then a ball is chosen at random from this urn and placed in urn 3, and the process is repeated. At no stage in the game is the color of the ball noted. Determine the probability, p_n, that the nth urn yields a white ball.

Solution. The nth urn will yield a white ball in two mutually exclusive ways. Either a white ball is transferred from the $(n - 1)$st urn with probability, p_{n-1}, and then a white ball is picked from the nth urn with probability $\frac{2}{4} = \frac{1}{2}$, or a red ball is transferred from the $(n - 1)$st urn with probability, $1 - p_{n-1}$, and then a white ball is picked from the nth urn with probability $\frac{1}{4}$. From Bayes' formula it follows that

$$p_n = \tfrac{1}{2} p_{n-1} + \tfrac{1}{4}(1 - p_{n-1}), \qquad n \geq 2,$$

$$= \tfrac{1}{4} p_{n-1} + \tfrac{1}{4}. \tag{6}$$

Since $p_1 = \frac{1}{2}$, it follows that Eq. (6) holds for $n = 1$ if we define $p_0 = 1$. The solution of Eq. (6) is

$$p_n = A(\tfrac{1}{4})^n + \tfrac{1}{3},$$

and from $p_1 = \frac{1}{2}$, or from $p_0 = 1$, we obtain $A = \frac{2}{3}$, so that

$$p_n = (\tfrac{2}{3})(\tfrac{1}{4})^n + \tfrac{1}{3}.$$

Note that

$$\lim_{n\to\infty} p_n = \tfrac{1}{3},$$

an expected result, for after a great number of transfers the initial condition, $p_1 = \frac{1}{2}$, becomes immaterial. We may also note that if urn 1 initially contained one white and two red balls, then $p_1 = \frac{1}{3}$, $A \equiv 0$, and $p_n = \frac{1}{3}$ for all n, so that the balance of balls in each urn remains invariant.

Example 7. Three drawers or urns, I, II, III, contain, respectively, two gold pieces, a gold and silver piece, and two silver pieces. A drawer is chosen at random, and a piece chosen at random from this drawer turns out to be gold. Find the probability that the other piece in the drawer is gold.

Solution. If the first piece is gold it should be apparent that either urn I or urn II was chosen, leaving either a gold piece (urn I) or a silver piece (urn II). Do not be misled into assuming that these events are equally likely. It should be clear that if urn I were chosen one would always obtain a gold piece, whereas if urn II were chosen there is a 50% probability that the first piece would be gold. Cogent reasoning should lead to $p(I|G) = \frac{2}{3}$.

From Bayes' formula we have

$$p(I|G) = \frac{p(I)p(G|I)}{p(I)p(G|I) + p(II)p(G|II) + p(III)p(G|III)}$$

$$= \frac{\frac{1}{3} \cdot 1}{\frac{1}{3} \cdot 1 + \frac{1}{3} \cdot \frac{1}{2} + \frac{1}{3} \cdot 0} = \frac{2}{3}.$$

PROBLEMS

1. Referring to Eq. (5), show that

$$\sum_{j=1}^{k} p(A_j \mid B) = 1.$$

Why is this a necessary result?

2. Show that

$$p[(A + B) \mid C] = p(A \mid C) + p(B \mid C) - p(AB \mid C).$$

3. Show that

$$p(ABC) = p(A \mid BC)\, p(B \mid C)\, p(C).$$

Extend this result to $p(A_1 A_2 \cdots A_n)$.

4. Urns I, II, III, contain, respectively, two red and three black balls, three red and one black ball, two red and two black balls. An urn is chosen at random, and a ball chosen at random from this urn turns out to be red. Find the probability that the ball came from urn II.

5. Boys and girls occur with equal probability in all families. It is known that a certain family with three children has at least one boy. Find the probability that all three children are boys.

6. Urn I contains three white and five red balls. Urn II contains four white and six red balls. An urn is chosen at random and three balls chosen at random from this urn (no replacements) yields two white balls and one red. Find the probability that they came from urn I.

7. Referring to Problem 6, the two white balls and one red ball were obtained from the unknown urn one at a time with replacements. Find the probability that they came from urn I.

8. Urn I contains two red and three black balls. Urn II contains three red and two black balls. A ball is chosen at random from urn I (its color is not noted) and transferred to urn II. If a ball now chosen at random from urn II turns out to be red, find the probability that a red ball was transferred.

9. What is the conditional probability of casting a 7 with a pair of dice if the total number of points has been noted to be odd?

10. Consider the 52 cards of a bridge deck. A card is withdrawn at random from the deck and it turns out to be a red card. The card is laid aside. Now 13 cards are withdrawn from the remaining 51 cards and you are told that they are of the same color. Find the probability (conditional) that this color is black.

11. A man tosses three fair coins. Find the conditional probability that at least two heads occur, given that he has tossed at least one head.

12. Consider two events A and B such that $p(A) = \frac{1}{4}$, $p(B|A) = \frac{1}{2}$, $p(A|B) = \frac{1}{4}$. Which of the following statements are true?

a) A and B are mutually exclusive events.
b) $p(A'|B') = \frac{3}{4}$.
c) $p(A|B) + p(A|B') = 1$.

13. Urns numbered $1, 2, 3, \ldots, n, \ldots$, each contain one red ball and two white balls. A ball is chosen at random from urn 1 and transferred to urn 2 if it is white, and replaced if it is red. Then a ball is chosen at random from urn 2 and the process is repeated (the ball is transferred to the next urn if it is white and not transferred if it is red). Let p_n be the probability that a white ball be withdrawn from the nth urn. Show that

$$p_n - \tfrac{1}{12} p_{n-1} = \tfrac{2}{3}$$

and that

$$p_n = \tfrac{8}{11} [1 - (\tfrac{1}{12})^n].$$

14. Urns I, II, III, IV, contain, respectively, four gold pieces; three gold and one silver piece; two gold and two silver pieces; one gold and three silver pieces. An urn is chosen at random and an object drawn from this urn turns out to be a gold piece. If the gold piece is returned to this urn, find the probability that a further random draw from this urn will yield a gold piece.

15. A and B each have two units. A fair coin is tossed repeatedly. When a head occurs, B pays A one unit; when a tail occurs A pays B one unit. Let p_n be the probability that B is ruined within $n \geq 2$ games. Show that

$$p_n = \tfrac{1}{4} + \tfrac{1}{2} p_{n-2}$$

and that

$$p_{2n} = p_{2n+1} = \tfrac{1}{2} (1 - \tfrac{1}{2n}) \qquad \text{for} \qquad n \geq 1.$$

3.5 INDEPENDENT EVENTS

A and B are said to be independent events if $p(A|B) = p(A)$ and $p(B|A) = p(B)$, so that the occurrence of the event B yields no additional information about the conditional probability of the occurrence of the event A, and conversely. From Bayes' formula it follows that

$$p(AB) = p(A)p(B|A) = p(B)p(A|B) = p(A)p(B), \qquad (1)$$

provided A and B are independent events. Conversely, if $p(AB) = p(A)p(B)$ it follows that $p(B) = p(B|A)$ for $p(A) \neq 0$ and $p(A) = p(A|B)$ for $p(B) \neq 0$. We accept $p(AB) = p(A)p(B)$ as the condition which specifies that A and B are independent events.

For example, if A is the occurrence of a head, $p(A) = \frac{1}{2}$; and if B is the occurrence of a 6 on the cast of a die, $p(B) = \frac{1}{6}$. Then the assumption that A and B are independent events yields $p(AB) = \frac{1}{12}$. The sample space of flipping a coin and casting a die is composed of the following 12 events.

$$\begin{array}{cccccc}
(H, 1) & (H, 2) & (H, 3) & (H, 4) & (H, 5) & (H, 6) \\
(T, 1) & (T, 2) & (T, 3) & (T, 4) & (T, 5) & (T, 6)
\end{array}$$

Assigning $p = \frac{1}{12}$ to each of these sample points assumes, in effect, that flipping a coin and casting a die are independent events.

One feels, intuitively, that if A and B are independent events, then A and B' are independent events. To show this we note that $A = A(B + B') = AB + AB'$, so that $p(A) = p(AB) + p(AB')$, since $AB \cdot AB' = \phi$. From $p(AB) = p(A)p(B)$ we obtain

$$p(AB') = p(A)\,[1 - p(B)] = p(A)p(B') \text{ Q.E.D.}$$

We can deduce that A' and B' are independent events if A and B are independent events.

Example 1. Consider two fair coins and assume that the two coins yield independent events. Let A be the event that a head occurs on the first coin, B the event that a head occurs on the second coin, and C the event that a head and tail occur on the two coins in any order. We note that

$$p(A) = p(B) = p(C) = \tfrac{1}{2},$$
$$p(AB) = p(A)p(B) = \tfrac{1}{4},$$
$$p(AC) = p(A)p(C|A) = \tfrac{1}{2} \cdot \tfrac{1}{2} = \tfrac{1}{4}$$
$$= p(A)p(C) = \tfrac{1}{2} \cdot \tfrac{1}{2},$$

so that A and C are independent events. Similarly, one easily shows that B and C are independent events, so that A, B, C are mutually independent in pairs. However, these events are not mutually independent, since $ABC = \phi$, and

$$p(ABC) = p(\phi) = 0 \neq p(A)p(B)p(C) = \tfrac{1}{8}.$$

Example 2. *Bernoulli trials.* A sequence of independent trials for which the probability of success on each trial remains a fixed constant p is called a sequence of Bernoulli trials.

Bernoulli trials occur for the repeated toss of a coin, calling the occurrence of a head a success. The repeated production of an item may involve Bernoulli trials. If the item is acceptable under certain standards, a success occurs. If the item is unacceptable, a failure occurs. Baseball games do not involve Bernoulli trials since the outcome of any game depends quite heavily on the pitchers involved, as well as other human factors.

Now let us consider n Bernoulli trials, n fixed, and determine the probability, f_k, that exactly k successes occur, $0 \le k \le n$. There are $\binom{n}{k}$ mutually exclusive sequences of events for which exactly k successes occur. The probability of occurrence of any one of these sequences is $p^k q^{n-k}$, $p + q = 1$. Hence

$$f_k = \binom{n}{k} p^k q^{n-k}, \qquad k = 0, 1, 2, \ldots, n, \tag{2}$$

represents the probability that exactly k successes will occur in a sequence of n Bernoulli trials.

We note that

$$\sum_{k=0}^{n} f_k = \sum_{k=0}^{n} \binom{n}{k} p^k q^{n-k} = (p + q)^n = 1.$$

This result must hold, since in n Bernoulli trials we must either have no successes, or exactly one success, or exactly two successes, etc.

It is of interest to determine the value of k which makes f_k a maximum. From

$$\frac{f_k}{f_{k-1}} = \frac{p}{q} \frac{\binom{n}{k}}{\binom{n}{k-1}} = \frac{p}{q} \frac{n - k + 1}{k} \tag{3}$$

we obtain $f_k \ge f_{k-1}$, provided

$$\frac{p(n - k + 1)}{qk} \ge 1 \qquad \text{or} \qquad k \le p(n + 1).$$

Thus the sequence $f_0, f_1, f_2, \ldots, f_n$ is monotonic increasing until $k > p(n + 1)$. If $p(n + 1)$ is an integer, then $f_{k-1} = f_k$, and there are two values $k - 1, k$ for which a maximum occurs. For $p = \frac{1}{2}$, $n = 19$, we have $p(n + 1) = 10$, so that $f_9 = f_{10}$ yield the maximum value. For $p = \frac{1}{2}$, $n = 20$, we have $p(n + 1) = \frac{21}{2}$ so that f_{10} is the maximum. For $p = \frac{1}{3}$, $n = 60$, we have $p(n + 1) = \frac{61}{3}$, so that f_{20} is the maximum.

Continuing with this example, let X be a random variable denoting the number of successes in n Bernoulli trials, so that

$$\Pr(X = k) = f_k = \binom{n}{k} p^k q^{n-k}, \qquad k = 0, 1, 2, \ldots, n,$$

$$\sum_{k=0}^{n} f_k = 1. \tag{4}$$

Henceforth we will say that a random variable, X, is of the class $B(p, n)$ if X represents the number of successes in n Bernoulli trials, with p the probability of success on any trial. The random variable X associated with the set $\{f_k\}$ defined by Eq. (4) is referred to as the binomial random variable, and the individual f_k are the components of the frequency function, written ff. A random variable X which has an ff of the form given by Eq. (4) is said to have a binomial distribution.

Example 3. *The Pascal or geometric distribution.* Again we consider a sequence of Bernoulli trials. Let Y be a random variable designating the number of trials until the first success occurs. Thus

$$f_k = \Pr(Y = k) = q^{k-1}p, \qquad k = 1, 2, 3, \ldots, \tag{5}$$

since we must have $(k - 1)$ failures followed by a success.

The random variable Y, with its associated frequency function given by Eq. (5), is said to be Pascal or geometric distributed. It is a simple matter to note that

$$\sum_{k=1}^{\infty} f_k = p \sum_{k=1}^{\infty} q^{k-1} = \frac{p}{1 - q} = 1,$$

so that if $p \neq 0$ a first success must eventually occur.

Example 4. *The generalized Pascal distribution or the negative binomial distribution.* We consider a sequence of Bernoulli trials and let Z be a random variable designating the number of trials until the mth success occurs, m a fixed nonnegative integer. We are interested in $f_k = \Pr(Z = k)$. In order for the mth success to have occurred on the kth trial there must be $(m - 1)$ successes in the first $(k - 1)$ trials, and $(k - 1) - (m - 1) = k - m$ failures. There are $\binom{k-1}{m-1}$ sequences for which $(m - 1)$ successes will occur in $(k - 1)$ trials, so that

$$f_k = \Pr(Z = k) = \binom{k-1}{m-1} p^m q^{k-m}, \qquad k \geq m, \tag{6}$$

since a success must occur on the last trial.

Furthermore,

$$\sum_{k=m}^{\infty} f_k = \sum_{k=m}^{\infty} \binom{k-1}{m-1} p^m q^{k-m}$$

$$= p^m \sum_{r=0}^{\infty} \binom{r+m-1}{m-1} q^r = p^m (1 - q)^{-m} = 1,$$

see Eq. (3), Section 2.5. The frequency function, f_k, defined by Eq. (6), yields the generalized Pascal distribution associated with the random variable Z.

Example 5. *The hypergeometric distribution.* Consider an urn (or a population) containing N different elements, M of which belongs to a class A. Given that n elements are withdrawn at random from the urn without replacements, find the probability that exactly k of the n elements belong to class A.

Solution. From Fig. 5 we note that there are $\binom{M}{k}$ ways of choosing k elements from the M elements composing the set A, followed by $\binom{N-M}{n-k}$ independent ways of choosing the remaining $(n-k)$ elements from the set A'. The total number of possible withdrawals is $\binom{N}{n}$. Thus

$$f_k = \frac{\binom{M}{k}\binom{N-M}{n-k}}{\binom{N}{n}}, \qquad k = 0, 1, 2, \ldots \tag{7}$$

Let the reader show, using Eq. (6), Section 2.4 that $\sum_{k=0}^{n} f_k = 1$.

There are three parameters (N, M, n) associated with the hypergeometric ff given by Eq. (7).

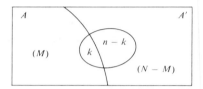

Figure 3.5

Example 6. *The multinomial distribution.* In the binomial distribution there were only two possible outcomes at each trial. Now suppose that each trial may lead to r possible outcomes or events, say $E_1, E_2, E_3, \ldots, E_r$, with

$$p_i = p(E_i), \qquad i = 1, 2, \ldots, r, \qquad \sum_{i=1}^{r} p_i = 1.$$

If n trials ensue, what is the probability that exactly k_1 yield the event E_1, k_2 yield the event $E_2, \ldots, k_r$ yield the event E_r, with

$$n = \sum_{i=1}^{r} k_i.$$

We assume independent trials.

Solution. In Section 2.4 (see Eq. 11) we have shown that the number of ways the above event can occur is $n!/k_1! \cdots k_r!$, each event occurring with probability $p_1^{k_1} p_2^{k_2} \ldots p_r^{k_r}$, since we have assumed independent trials. Thus

$$f(k_1, k_2, \ldots, k_r) = \frac{n!}{k_1! \, k_2! \cdots k_r!} \, p_1^{k_1} p_2^{k_2} \ldots p_r^{k_r}, \tag{8}$$

with

$$\sum_{i=1} k_i = n.$$

From Eq. (12), Section 2.4 it follows that

$$\sum_{\Sigma k_i = n} f(k_1, k_2, \ldots, k_r) = (p_1 + p_2 + \cdots + p_r)^n = 1^n = 1.$$

The summation extends over all $k_1, k_2, \ldots, k_n$ such that

$$\sum_{i=1}^{r} k_i = n.$$

Example 7. *The Poisson distribution.* Let us assume that the probability that a success occurs in the time interval $(t, t + dt)$, $dt \ll 1$, is $dp = \lambda dt$, except for infinitesimals of higher order, with λ a constant. Furthermore, we assume that this probability of a success in the time interval $(t, t + dt)$ is independent of past successes. This model is fairly appropriate for the case of telephone calls, autos passing a fixed point, certain elementary birth processes, etc. We are interested in determining the probability that in time t exactly k successes occur, say $f_k(t)$, $k = 0, 1, 2, \ldots$, with $f_0(0) = 1$, and $f_k(0) = 0$ for $k > 0$, since at the start, $(t = 0)$, no success has occurred, as seen from

$$\lim_{dt \to 0} dp = \lim_{dt \to 0} \lambda dt = 0.$$

Solution. In order to have k successes in time $t + dt$ we must either have k successes in time t followed by no success in time dt (with probability $1 - \lambda dt$), or $(k - 1)$ successes in time t followed by a single success in time dt. We need not be concerned with having two or more successes in time dt, for the probability of such an occurrence is an infinitesimal of higher order in dt. Thus

$$f_k(t + dt) = f_k(t)[1 - \lambda dt] + f_{k-1}(t)\lambda dt, \tag{9}$$

except for infinitesimals of higher order.

It follows that

$$\frac{f_k(t + dt) - f_k(t)}{dt} = -\lambda f_k(t) + \lambda f_{k-1}(t),$$

and (letting $dt \to 0$) we obtain the differential-difference equation

$$\frac{df_k(t)}{dt} + \lambda f_k(t) = \lambda f_{k-1}(t), \qquad k = 0, 1, 2, \ldots, \tag{10}$$

with

$$f_{-1}(t) = 0 \qquad \text{for all } t,$$
$$\left.\begin{array}{l} f_0(0) = 1 \\ f_k(0) = 0 \end{array}\right\} \quad \text{for} \quad k > 0.$$

To solve this equation for $f_k(t)$ we make use of the generating function

$$F(s, t) = \sum_{k=0}^{\infty} f_k(t)s^k \tag{11}$$

discussed in Section 3.9. Since

$$\sum_{k=0}^{\infty} f_k = 1,$$

of necessity the power series converges for $0 \le s \le 1$.

Let us multiply Eq. (10) by s^k and sum over $k = 0, 1, 2, \ldots$, obtaining

$$\sum_{k=0}^{\infty} \frac{df_k(t)}{dt} s^k + \lambda \sum_{k=0}^{\infty} f_k(t)s^k = \lambda s \sum_{k=0}^{\infty} f_{k-1}(t)s^{k-1}. \tag{12}$$

From Eq. (11) we obtain, formally,

$$\frac{\partial F}{\partial t} = \sum_{k=0}^{\infty} \frac{df_k(t)}{dt} s^k,$$

so that Eq. (12) becomes

$$\frac{\partial F}{\partial t} + \lambda F = \lambda s F,$$

$$\frac{1}{F} \frac{\partial F}{\partial t} = \lambda(s - 1). \tag{13}$$

A simple integration yields $\ln F(s, t) = \lambda(s - 1)t + K$. At $t = 0$ we have

$$F(s, 0) = \sum_{k=0}^{\infty} f_k(0)s^k = f_0(0) = 1,$$

so that $K \equiv 0$. Thus

$$F(s, t) = e^{-\lambda t}e^{\lambda st} = e^{-\lambda t} \sum_{k=0}^{\infty} \frac{(\lambda t)^k s^k}{k!}. \tag{14}$$

Comparing Eqs. (11) and (14) yields

$$f_k(t) = e^{-\lambda t} \frac{(\lambda t)^k}{k!}, \qquad k = 0, 1, 2, \ldots \tag{15}$$

We leave it as a simple exercise for the reader to show that $f_k(t)$ satisfies Eq. (10). For $t = 1$ (unit time) we obtain the Poisson distribution whose ff (frequency function) is given by

$$f_k = e^{-\lambda} \frac{\lambda^k}{k!}, \qquad k = 0, 1, 2, \ldots, \tag{16}$$

with

$$\sum_{k=0}^{\infty} f_k = e^{-\lambda} \sum_{k=0}^{\infty} \frac{\lambda^k}{k!} = e^{-\lambda}e^{\lambda} = 1.$$

Example 8. A tells the truth with probability p_1 and B tells the truth with probability p_2, independently. A makes a statement and B says that A lied. Find the probability that A told the truth.

Solution. Let α represent the event that A has told the truth and let β represent the event that B has told the truth. Now only $\alpha\beta'$ or $\alpha'\beta$ can have occurred, since if

A told the truth then *B* lied, and conversely. If we let $\gamma = \alpha\beta' + \alpha'\beta$, then we are interested in $p(\alpha|\gamma)$. From Bayes' formula we have

$$P = p(\alpha|\gamma) = \frac{p(\alpha\gamma)}{p(\gamma)} = \frac{p(\alpha\beta')}{p(\alpha\beta' + \alpha'\beta)}$$

$$= \frac{p(\alpha)p(\beta')}{p(\alpha\beta') + p(\alpha'\beta)}$$

$$= \frac{p(\alpha)p(\beta')}{p(\alpha)p(\beta') + p(\alpha')p(\beta)}$$

$$= \frac{p_1(1 - p_2)}{p_1(1 - p_2) + p_2(1 - p_1)},$$

since $p(\alpha\beta') = p(\alpha)p(\beta')$, etc., (assumption of independence).

The example above is a very simplified version of a problem posed by A. S. Eddington: Four people, *A*, *B*, *C*, *D*, tell the truth with probability $\frac{1}{3}$ each, independently. *D* makes a statement and *A* affirms that *B* denied that *C* declared that *D* was lying. What is the conditional probability that *D* told the truth? Different solutions have been obtained by not taking Eddington's statement literally. Thus some students assume that *A*, *B*, *C*, and *D* all made statements. This need not be so, since if *A* lied we are not sure whether or not *B* and *C* made any statements whatsoever. The reader may find it of interest to obtain Eddington's answer of $P = \frac{25}{71}$, and the answer $\frac{13}{41}$ if one assumes that all four individuals did make statements.

Example 9. *A* and *B* play a fair game, exchanging one unit per game. *A* starts with two units and *B* with one unit. Under the assumption of independence (Bernoulli trials) find the probability that *A* ruins *B* within *n* games.

Solution. Let f_n be the probability that *A* ruins *B* within *n* games. Obviously $f_1 = \frac{1}{2}$. For $n \geq 2$, *A* may ruin *B* within *n* games if he either wins the first game or loses the first game and wins the second (he cannot lose the first two games and be a winner), and now must ruin *B* within the remaining $(n - 2)$ games. Note that in this latter case *A* again has two units and *B* has one unit. Thus

$$f_n = \tfrac{1}{2} + \tfrac{1}{4}f_{n-2}, \qquad n \geq 1, \tag{17}$$

provided we define $f_{-1} = f_0 = 0$. The solution of Eq. (17) is

$$f_n = \tfrac{2}{3} + A(\tfrac{1}{2})^n + B(-\tfrac{1}{2})^n,$$

so that

$$f_n = \tfrac{2}{3} - (\tfrac{1}{2})^{n+1} - \tfrac{1}{6}(-\tfrac{1}{2})^n.$$

Note that $\lim_{n\to\infty} f_n = \tfrac{2}{3}$, an expected result.

Example 10. In a sequence of Bernoulli trials, zeros and ones are transmitted with equal probability. Find the probability, f_n, that two successive zeros occur for the first time on the $(n - 1)$st and nth transmission.

Solution. If the initial transmission is a one, we are reduced to being successful in the remaining $(n - 1)$ transmissions, with probability f_{n-1}. If the initial transmission is a zero, then for $n > 2$ we must next transmit a one (otherwise the game would be over) and subsequently be successful in the remaining $(n - 2)$ transmissions. Hence

$$f_n = \tfrac{1}{2}f_{n-1} + \tfrac{1}{4}f_{n-2}, \qquad n > 2,$$

with $f_1 = 0, f_2 = \tfrac{1}{4}, f_3 = \tfrac{1}{8}$. The solution is

$$f_n = \frac{5 - \sqrt{5}}{10}\left(\frac{1 + \sqrt{5}}{4}\right)^n + \frac{5 + \sqrt{5}}{10}\left(\frac{1 - \sqrt{5}}{4}\right)^n.$$

Example 11. *Gambler's Ruin problem.* Let A start with a-units, B with b-units. They play a fair game exchanging one unit per game. They continue to play until one or the other is ruined. Assuming independent games, determine the probability that A ruins B.

Solution. Suppose that at any stage of the game A has k units left (B, of course, has $a + b - k$ units left). Let f_k be the probability that A will subsequently ruin B. After the next game A will have $(k + 1)$ units with probability $\tfrac{1}{2}$ or A will have $(k - 1)$ units with probability $\tfrac{1}{2}$. Thus

$$f_k = \tfrac{1}{2}f_{k+1} + \tfrac{1}{2}f_{k-1}, \qquad 1 \le k \le a + b - 1. \tag{18}$$

It is apparent that $f_0 = 0, f_{a+b} = 1$. The solution of Eq. (18) is

$$f_k = A + Bk,$$

so that

$$f_k = \frac{k}{a + b} \quad \text{and} \quad f_a = \frac{a}{a + b},$$

the required solution.

PROBLEMS

1. In 10 Bernoulli trials, $p = \tfrac{1}{4}$; find the probability of having at least two successes.

2. For $B(\tfrac{1}{3}, 6)$ find the probability of obtaining either two or four successes.

3. A fair coin is tossed (Bernoulli trials) repeatedly. Find the probability that two consecutive heads occur before two tails (not necessarily consecutive).

4. A fair coin is tossed four times. Let A be the event that a head occurs on the first toss, and let B be the event that two heads and two tails occur on the four independent tosses. Show that A and B are independent events.

5. The probability of success on any trial is $\tfrac{1}{2}$ if the previous trial yielded a success, and is $\tfrac{1}{4}$ if the previous trial yielded a failure. Given that a success occurred on the first trial, find the probability that the nth trial will yield a success.

6. A and B alternate shots in a duel. The probability of A hitting B is p_1 and the probability of B hitting A is p_2. If A fires first, what is the probability that A wins the duel, assuming Bernoulli trials?

7. Three men, A, B, C alternate firing at a target in that order. The probabilities that A, B, C strike the target are p_1, p_2, p_3, respectively. Assuming Bernoulli trials, find the probability that A will hit the target first, and the probability that B will hit the target first.

8. A has $(n + 1)$ coins and B has n coins. The coins are tossed at random to a floor. Find the probability that A will have more heads showing than B, and the probability that both will have the same number of heads showing.

9. In a sequence of Bernoulli trials, $p = \frac{1}{2}$. Find the probability that a success is followed by a failure for the first time on the $(n - 1)$st and nth trials.

10. A, B, C tell the truth independently with probabilities $\frac{1}{3}$, $\frac{1}{4}$, $\frac{1}{5}$, respectively. C makes a statement and B says that C has lied, whereas A says that C has told the truth. Find the probability that C made a true statement.

11. By means of difference equations, find the probability of having an odd number of successes for n Bernoulli trials, $B(p, n)$.

12. An infinite sequence of urns is such that the odd numbered urns contain one white and two red balls whereas the even numbered urns contain one red and two white balls. A ball is chosen at random from urn 1 and placed in urn 2. Then a ball is chosen at random from urn 2 and placed in urn 3, etc. Find the probability that the ball picked from urn $-2n$ is white. [*Hint:* find two relationships between f_{2n-2}, f_{2n-1}, f_{2n}, and eliminate f_{2n-1}.]

13. Referring to the Gambler's Ruin problem of Example 11, let p be the probability that A wins a unit from B, and $q = 1 - p$ the probability that B wins a unit from A, with $p \neq q$. Show that the probability that A ruins B is

$$P = \frac{1 - \left(\dfrac{q}{p}\right)^a}{1 - \left(\dfrac{q}{p}\right)^{a+b}}.$$

Is this problem equivalent to that of A playing against an adversary with an infinite amount of capital such that A quits when he is ruined or when he has won b units?

14. A gambler with an initial capital n plays against an infinitely rich adversary and wins two units or loses one unit with probabilities p and q, respectively, $p + q = 1$. Show that the probability that the gambler becomes ruined is

$$q_n = \left[-\frac{1}{2} + \sqrt{\frac{1}{4} + \frac{q}{p}} \right]^n \quad \text{for} \quad q < 2p,$$

$$= 1 \quad \text{for} \quad q \geq 2p.$$

15. Let A start with a units and B with b units. The probability of A winning a unit is p, of A losing a unit is q, and of a tie (draw) occurring is r, $p + q + r = 1$. Find the probability that A ruins B (see Problem 13).

16. At any stage of a process one has a choice of playing either of two games. For game I the probability of winning one unit is p_1, of winning two units is p_2, and of the process terminating with no win or loss is p_0. A similar result applies to game II with respective probabilities p_1', p_2', p_0'. Whenever at least one unit is won the process continues. Let F_k be the probability of gaining exactly k units, using an optimal strategy, before the process terminates. If one begins with game I, the probability of winning exactly k units is $p_1 F_{k-1} + p_2 F_{k-2}$, with a similar result if one begins with game II. Show that

$$F_k = \max (p_1 F_{k-1} + p_2 F_{k-2}, \; p_1' F_{k-1} + p_2' F_{k-2}),$$

with $F_0 = \max (p_0, p_0')$. What is F_0 if we wish to win at least k units? Does the above formula for F_k still apply?

17. Consider a sequence of Bernoulli trials with $p \geq q$. Let P be the probability that eventually more successes than failures will occur. Show that $P = p + qP^2$, and that $P = 1$.

3.6 RANDOM VARIABLES · JOINT DISTRIBUTIONS · STATISTICALLY INDEPENDENT EVENTS · DISTRIBUTION FUNCTIONS

Before we introduce the definition of a random variable let us consider a few simple examples. On the toss of a fair coin there are two possible outcomes, H and T, the sample elements of our space of probabilities. Let us assume that one unit is gained if a head occurs and one unit is lost if a tail occurs, so that we have the correspondence

$$H \leftrightarrow +1,$$

$$T \leftrightarrow -1.$$

We can consider now the real-valued random variable X such that

$$f_1 = \Pr(X = 1) = p(H) = \tfrac{1}{2},$$

$$f_{-1} = \Pr(X = -1) = p(T) = \tfrac{1}{2}.$$

Now suppose that a fair coin is tossed three times, and consider

$$S = X_1 + X_2 + X_3,$$

with $X_i = \pm 1$ occurring with equal probability, $i = 1, 2, 3$. Then S is also a random variable designating the net gain after three tosses of the coin. The possible outcomes of S are $S = -3$ with probability $\tfrac{1}{8}$, $S = -1$ with probability $\tfrac{3}{8}$, $S = +1$ with probability $\tfrac{3}{8}$, and $S = +3$ with probability $\tfrac{1}{8}$. In this example the sample event (T, T, T) has been mapped into $S = -3$, the three sample events (T, T, H), (T, H, T) (H, T, T), have been mapped into $S = -1$, the three sample events (H, H, T), (H, T, H), (T, H, H) have been mapped into $S = +1$, and the sample event (H, H, H) has been mapped into $S = +3$.

As another example consider the event wherein each of three people, A, B, C, tosses a fair coin. If all three coins yield the same result (all heads or all tails) no money is exchanged. In all other cases the person with the odd coin receives one unit from each of the other two opponents. From A's point of view the following situation prevails:

$$(H, T, T) \rightarrow +2 \qquad (H, T, H) \rightarrow -1$$
$$(T, H, H) \rightarrow +2 \qquad (T, H, T) \rightarrow -1$$
$$(H, H, H) \rightarrow 0 \qquad (H, H, T) \rightarrow -1$$
$$(T, T, T) \rightarrow 0 \qquad (T, T, H) \rightarrow -1$$

Thus A would define a random variable X which takes on the values $X = -1$, 0, 2 with probabilities $p(X = -1) = \frac{1}{2}$, $p(X = 0) = \frac{1}{4}$, $p(X = 2) = \frac{1}{4}$.

Other examples come quickly to mind. The number of successes in a sequence of n Bernoulli trials is a random variable. The number of aces dealt to an individual in a poker game is a random variable, as is the number of telephone calls per unit time in a Poisson process; etc.

In simple terms a discrete random variable, X, takes on a finite or at most a countably infinite set of values $x_1, x_2, \ldots, x_n, \ldots$, with corresponding probabilities $f_1, f_2, \ldots, f_n, \ldots$, such that

$$f_n = \Pr(X = x_n), \qquad n = 1, 2, 3, \ldots \tag{1}$$

The function f_n defined over the x_n's is often called the frequency function, ff, associated with the random variable X, or simply the probability distribution of X. Clearly

$$f_n \geq 0 \qquad n = 1, 2, 3, \ldots,$$
$$\sum_{n=1}^{\infty} f_n = 1. \tag{2}$$

In essence, a random or stochastic variable is a real-valued function defined on a sample space.

Example 1. A fair coin is tossed six times. Let X designate the number of times that heads occur in the six tosses. The following table exhibits the values of the random variable X and the associated probabilities.

X	0	1	2	3	4	5	6
$f(X)$	$\dfrac{1}{2^6}$	$\dfrac{6}{2^6}$	$\dfrac{15}{2^6}$	$\dfrac{20}{2^6}$	$\dfrac{15}{2^6}$	$\dfrac{6}{2^6}$	$\dfrac{1}{2^6}$

Example 2. Two dice are tossed. Let X represent the total points scored; let Y represent the product of the points on each die; let $Z = 1$ if a 7 or 11 occurs, $Z = 0$ otherwise. Thus X, Y, and Z are three random variables defined over the same sample space much as x, $\sin x$, e^x are three different functions defined over the reals.

The values of X, Y, and Z with their associated probabilities are shown below.

X	2	3	4	5	6	7	8	9	10	11	12
$f(X)$	$\frac{1}{36}$	$\frac{2}{36}$	$\frac{3}{36}$	$\frac{4}{36}$	$\frac{5}{36}$	$\frac{6}{36}$	$\frac{5}{36}$	$\frac{4}{36}$	$\frac{3}{36}$	$\frac{2}{36}$	$\frac{1}{36}$

Y	1	2	3	4	5	6	8	9	10	12	15	16	18	20	24	25	30	36	
$f(Y)$	1	2	2	3	2	4	2	1	2	4	2	1	2	2	2	1	2	1	$\times \frac{1}{36}$

Z	1	0
$f(Z)$	$\frac{8}{36}$	$\frac{28}{36}$

Example 3. Consider an urn containing four balls numbered 1, 2, 3, 4. A ball is chosen at random and is not replaced. Let X be the random variable which takes on the value of the number withdrawn, so that $f_i = \Pr(X = i) = \frac{1}{4}$, for $i = 1, 2, 3, 4$. A second ball is now obtained at random from the three remaining balls. Let Y be the random variable which takes on the value of the number withdrawn at this second venture. Our experiment provides 12 equally likely events, namely

$$(1, 2) \quad (1,3) \quad (1, 4) \quad (2, 1) \quad (2, 3) \quad (2, 4)$$
$$, \quad (3, 1) \quad (3, 2) \quad (3, 4) \quad (4, 1) \quad (4, 2) \quad (4, 3),$$

with (i, j) meaning that ball i was followed by ball j.

Now X and Y take on the values 1, 2, 3, 4. It makes sense to ask for the joint probability

$$f_{ij} = \Pr(X = i, Y = j), \qquad i, j = 1, 2, 3, 4, \tag{3}$$

which may best be exhibited in the matrix Table (1) below.

Table 1

f_{ij}	$Y = 1$	$Y = 2$	$Y = 3$	$Y = 4$	$g_i = P(X = i)$
$X = 1$	0	$\frac{1}{12}$	$\frac{1}{12}$	$\frac{1}{12}$	$\frac{1}{4}$
$X = 2$	$\frac{1}{12}$	0	$\frac{1}{12}$	$\frac{1}{12}$	$\frac{1}{4}$
$X = 3$	$\frac{1}{12}$	$\frac{1}{12}$	0	$\frac{1}{12}$	$\frac{1}{4}$
$X = 4$	$\frac{1}{12}$	$\frac{1}{12}$	$\frac{1}{12}$	0	$\frac{1}{4}$
$h_j = P(Y = j)$	$\frac{1}{4}$	$\frac{1}{4}$	$\frac{1}{4}$	$\frac{1}{4}$	

Note that f_{ij} is the element in the ith row and jth column. On the margins are the individual frequency functions g_i, h_j for X and Y.

In general, consider two random variables X and Y which take on the values $x_1, x_2, \ldots, x_n, \ldots$, and $y_1, y_2, \ldots, y_n, \ldots$, respectively. The event (set of outcomes) for which $X = x_i$ and $Y = y_j$ occur jointly yields a joint probability distribution, or joint frequency function, f_{ij}, such that

$$f_{ij} = \Pr(X = x_i, Y = y_j), \qquad i, j = 1, 2, \ldots \tag{4}$$

Of necessity,

$$f_{ij} \geq 0, \qquad \Sigma_j \Sigma_i f_{ij} = 1, \tag{5}$$

where the summation occurs over all i, j, and $f_{ij} \geq 0$ for all i, j. It should be clear that $X = x_i$ can occur in the following mutually exclusive ways:

$$(x_i, y_1), (x_i, y_2), \ldots, (x_i, y_j), \ldots,$$

so that

$$g_i = \Pr(X = x_i) = \Sigma_j f_{ij}, \qquad i = 1, 2, \ldots \tag{6}$$

Similarly,

$$h_j = \Pr(Y = y_j) = \Sigma_i f_{ij}, \qquad j = 1, 2, \ldots \tag{7}$$

The functions g_i, h_j are called the marginal frequency functions of X and Y, respectively, although the word "marginal" is redundant (see Table 1).

It is a simple matter to extend the notion of joint distributions to systems of more than two random variables. Of interest, also, are the conditional frequency functions which arise from Bayes' formula. Thus

$$k_{i|j} = \Pr(X = x_i | Y = y_j) = \frac{f_{ij}}{h_j}, \qquad h_j \neq 0, i = 1, 2, \ldots,$$

$$\tag{8}$$

$$l_{j|i} = \Pr(Y = y_j | X = x_i) = \frac{f_{ij}}{g_i}, \qquad g_i \neq 0, j = 1, 2, \ldots$$

represent, respectively, the conditional frequency function of X given $Y = y_j$, and the conditional frequency function of Y given $X = x_i$. We note immediately that

$$\Sigma_i k_{i|j} = \frac{1}{h_j} \Sigma_i f_{ij} = \frac{h_j}{h_j} = 1,$$

$$\tag{9}$$

$$\Sigma_j l_{j|i} = \frac{1}{g_i} \Sigma_j f_{ij} = \frac{g_i}{g_i} = 1.$$

These results must hold, since if we are given that $Y = y_j$ has occurred, of necessity one of the values of X must occur, and conversely. Now let us suppose that

$$\Pr(X = x_i | Y = y_j) = \Pr(X = x_i)$$

for all i, j, so that the occurrence of $Y = y_j$ does not affect the occurrence of $X = x_j$. Thus $k_{i|j} = g_i$, and Eq. (8) yields

$$f_{ij} = g_i h_j, \qquad i, j = 1, 2, \ldots \tag{10}$$

We say that X and Y are statistically independent random variables if condition (10) holds, i.e., if $k_i|_j = g_i$ and $l_j|_i = h_j$ for all i, j. If $f_{ij} \neq g_i h_j$ for at least one pair of values of i, j, we say that X and Y are statistically dependent.

Show that if F is the matrix $\{f_{ij}\}$, G the column vector $\{g_i\}$, and H the row vector $\{h_j\}$, then $F = GH$ is a necessary and sufficient condition that X and Y be statistically independent.

Example 4. Referring to Example 3 we note that $f_{11} = 0 \neq g_1 h_1 = \frac{1}{4} \cdot \frac{1}{4}$. Hence X and Y are statistically dependent. This is immediately evident since the occurrence of $X = 1$ denies the occurrence of $Y = 1$. We may also note that

$$\Pr(Y = 2 | X = 1) = \tfrac{1}{3} \neq \Pr(Y = 2) = \tfrac{1}{4}.$$

Now compute in matrix form $k_i|_j$, $l_j|_i$ for this example, and verify Eq. (9).

We conclude this section with a brief discussion of the cumulative distribution function (not to be confused with the frequency function). The real-valued function, defined by

$$F(x) = \Pr(X \leq x), \qquad -\infty < x < \infty,$$

$$= \sum_{x_i \leq x} f_i, \tag{11}$$

is called the cumulative distribution function associated with the discrete random variable X. Three simple properties of $F(x)$ are apparent immediately:

$$F(x) \geq F(y) \qquad \text{if} \qquad x \geq y,$$

$$F(-\infty) = 0, \tag{12}$$

$$F(\infty) = 1.$$

A simple example illustrates how one constructs $F(x)$. Let X be a random variable such that

$$p(X = -1) = \tfrac{1}{2}, \qquad p(X = 0) = \tfrac{1}{4}, \qquad p(X = 2) = \tfrac{1}{4},$$

so that

$$f_{-1} = \tfrac{1}{2}, \qquad f_0 = \tfrac{1}{4}, \qquad f_2 = \tfrac{1}{4},$$

with

$$f_{-1} + f_0 + f_2 = 1.$$

Since the random variable X takes on no value of $x < -1$, it follows that $F(x) = 0$ for $x < -1$. Furthermore,

$$F(-1) = \Pr(X \leq -1) = \tfrac{1}{2}.$$

Now consider

$$F(-\tfrac{1}{2}) = \Pr(X \leq -\tfrac{1}{2})$$

$$= \Pr(X = -1) = \tfrac{1}{2},$$

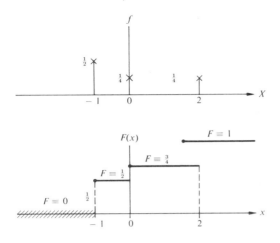

Figure 3.6

since $X = -1$ is the only value X takes on with nonzero probability which is less than $-\frac{1}{2}$. We see that $F(x) = \frac{1}{2}$ for $-1 \le x < 0$. Next we note that

$$F(0) = \Pr(X \le 0) = \Pr(X = -1) + \Pr(X = 0) = \frac{1}{2} + \frac{1}{4} = \frac{3}{4},$$

and that

$$F(x) \equiv \frac{3}{4} \qquad \text{for} \qquad 0 \le x < 2.$$

For $x \ge 2$ it is apparent that $F(x) \equiv 1$.

Now we graph both f_i and $F(x)$, Fig. 6, and note that $F(x)$ is discontinuous at three points, $x = -1, 0, 2$; these are precisely the values that X assumes with nonzero probabilities. Furthermore, the jump in the discontinuity of $F(x)$ at these three points is exactly the value of the frequency function at these points.

The preceding statements apply to all distribution functions associated with discrete random variables.

PROBLEMS

1. The joint ff of X and Y is shown below.

X \ Y	1	2	3
1	$\frac{1}{6}$	$\frac{1}{6}$	0
2	0	0	$\frac{1}{3}$
3	0	$\frac{1}{3}$	0

Find the marginal ff's of X and Y. Are X and Y statistically independent?

2. The number of cars, X, a dealer sells is a random variable with a ff given by

$$f_k = \Pr(X = k) = \begin{cases} A\,k, & k = 1, 2, 3, 4, 5 \\ A(10 - k), & k = 6, 7, 8, 9 \end{cases}$$
$$= 0, \qquad \text{otherwise.}$$

Show that $A = \frac{1}{25}$ and determine the probability of the following.

a) Exactly seven cars will be sold.
b) At most seven cars will be sold.
c) At least seven cars will be sold.
d) An even number of cars will be sold.

Sketch the distribution function associated with X.

3. An urn contains four balls numbered 1, 2, 3, 4. Let X be the number obtained from a random draw. If $X = k$ has been obtained, then Y is obtained at random from the numbers which are greater than or equal to k, $k = 1, 2, 3, 4$. Find the joint ff of X and Y, and the marginal ff's of X and Y.

4. A man has n keys, one of which opens a door. The keys are tried at random without replacements (if a key does not fit it is put aside). Show that $f_k = 1/n, k = 1, 2, \ldots, n$, is the probability that the kth try will open the door. If replacements occur, show that

$$f_k = \left(1 - \frac{1}{n}\right)^{k-1} \frac{1}{n}, \qquad k = 1, 2, 3, \ldots,$$

is the probability that the kth try will open the door. Is this the Pascal ff ?

5. An urn contains the three integers 1, 2, 3. An integer is obtained at random and replaced, and a second integer is obtained at random. Let X be the minimum of the two numbers withdrawn, and let Y be the maximum of the two numbers withdrawn. Set up a matrix for the joint ff of X and Y, and find the marginal ff's of X and Y.

6. Two fair dice are tossed. Let X be the point on the first die, Y the point on the second die, and let Z be the maximum of these two points, $Z = \max(X, Y)$. Set up a matrix for the joint ff of X and Z. Find the ff of Z and sketch its distribution function.

7. Balls numbered $1, 2, \ldots, n$ are placed at random into n cells numbered $1, 2, \ldots, n$, one ball to each cell. Let $X = 1$ if ball 1 falls into cell 1, $X = 0$ otherwise, and let $Y = 1$ if ball 2 falls into cell 2, $Y = 0$ otherwise. Find the joint ff of X and Y.

8. Let X and Y be independent binomial random variables of type $B(p, n)$, $B(p, m)$ respectively. Let $Z = X + Y$, and show that $Z = k$ for the mutually exclusive cases

$$(X = 0,\ Y = k),\ (X = 1,\ Y = k - 1),\ \ldots,\ (X = i,\ Y = k - i),\ \ldots,\ (X = k,\ Y = 0).$$

Show that

$$h_k = \Pr(Z = k) = \binom{m+n}{k} p^k q^{(m+n)-k},$$

so that Z is of the type $B(p, m + n)$.

9. Let X and Y be independent Poisson random variables with parameters λ_1, λ_2. Show that $Z = X + Y$ is also Poisson with parameter $\lambda_1 + \lambda_2$.

3.7 MEAN, OR EXPECTATION, OF A RANDOM VARIABLE

Consider four men whose heights are 70 in., 72 in., 72 in. and 76 in. The reader has no quarrel with defining the mean or average height as

$$\mu = \frac{70+72+72+76}{4}$$

$$= \tfrac{1}{4}(70) + \tfrac{1}{2}(72) + \tfrac{1}{4}(76) = 72.5 \text{ in.}$$

Let us note that we can obtain μ as follows: Consider an urn containing the four numbers above. Let X be a random variable whose values are the possible numbers which can be withdrawn from the urn, so that

$$p(X = 70) = \tfrac{1}{4}, \qquad p(X = 72) = \tfrac{1}{2}, \qquad p(X = 76) = \tfrac{1}{4}.$$

Thus we define the mean value of X by

$$\mu = E(X) = 70p(X = 70) + 72p(X = 72) + 76p(X = 76)$$

$$= 70(\tfrac{1}{4}) + 72(\tfrac{1}{2}) + 76(\tfrac{1}{4}) = 72.5 \text{ in.}$$

We note that we can consider $X = 72$ as occurring once with probability $\tfrac{1}{2}$, or twice, each occurrence having an associated probability $\tfrac{1}{4}$.

The example above suggests the following definition. Let X be a discrete random variable which takes on the values $x_1, x_2, \ldots, x_n, \ldots$, with corresponding probabilities $f_1, f_2, \ldots, f_n, \ldots$ The *mean* or *expected* value of X is defined by

$$\mu = E(X) = \sum_i x_i f_i, \tag{1}$$

provided the series converges absolutely, i.e., $\sum_i |x_i| f_i < \infty$. If $\sum_i |x_i| f_i = \infty$ we say that X has no finite expectation.

The reason we desire $\sum_i |x_i| f_i < \infty$ is to guarantee that the series $\sum_i x_i f_i$ converges to the same limit independent of the order of summation of the terms of this series. The expectation $E(X)$ is also called the mean value of X, and in quantum mechanics it is often written as $\langle X \rangle$ or $\bar{X}$.

The above definition of the mean has a direct analogue in analytic mechanics. If the point masses $M_1, M_2, \ldots, M_n$ are located on the x-axis at the corresponding points $x_1, x_2, \ldots, x_n$, then the center of mass is defined by

$$\bar{x} = \frac{1}{M} \sum_1^n M_i x_i = \sum_1^n \left(\frac{M_i}{M}\right) x_i = \sum_1^n f_i x_i, \tag{2}$$

with

$$f_i = \frac{M_i}{M} \quad \text{and} \quad M = \sum_1^n M_i.$$

If X and Y are joint random variables with a joint ff given by f_{ij}, we can consider the new random variable $Z = X + Y$, which takes on the values $x_i + y_j$ for $i, j = 1, 2, \ldots$. Now, for simplicity, let us assume that X and Y take the integral values 0, 1, 2, 3, ..., n, ..., with respective frequency functions g_n, h_n, so that

$$E(X) = \sum_0^\infty ng_n, \qquad E(Y) = \sum_0^\infty nh_n.$$

Furthermore we assume $E(X)$ and $E(Y)$ exist. To determine the ff associated with Z let us note that

$$k_n \equiv \Pr(Z = n) = f_{0n} + f_{1, n-1} + \cdots + f_{n0}, \tag{3}$$

since $Z = n$ only occurs for the mutually exclusive cases

$$(X = 0, \ Y = n), \ (X = 1, \ Y = n - 1), \ldots, (X = n, \ Y = 0).$$

Hence

$$E(Z) = \sum_0^\infty nk_n = \sum_{\substack{0 \le n \\ 0 \le i \le n}} nf_{i, n-i}. \tag{4}$$

The index of summation n is now replaced by the new index of summation j, defined by $n = i + j$. Equation (4) becomes

$$E(Z) = \sum_{i,j} (i + j)f_{ij}. \tag{5}$$

Since the double series converges absolutely, the order of summation is immaterial. Hence

$$E(Z) = \sum_i \sum_j if_{ij} + \sum_j \sum_i jf_{ij}$$
$$= \sum_i ig_i + \sum_j jh_j = E(X) + E(Y). \tag{6}$$

This result can be obtained without the restriction of X, Y to integral values. By mathematical induction we can then prove the following:

Theorem. If $X_1, X_2, \ldots, X_n$ are random variables with finite expectations, then the expected value of their sum is the sum of their expectations:

$$E(X_1 + X_2 + \cdots + X_n) = E(X_1) + E(X_2) + \cdots + E(X_n), \tag{7}$$

that is,

$$E\left(\sum_{i=1}^n X_i\right) = \sum_{i=1}^n E(X_i).$$

Example 1. Let X be of the class $B(p, n)$, so that

$$E(X) = \sum_{k=0}^n kf_k = \sum_{k=0}^n k\binom{n}{k}p^kq^{n-k} = np, \tag{8}$$

a result obtained by differentiating

$$(x + q)^n = \sum\binom{n}{k}x^kq^{n-k}$$

with respect to x, then setting $x = p$ and multiplying by p. Almost anyone would agree with this answer, for if $p = \frac{1}{4}$ one would expect an average of 250 successes in 1000 trials.

Let us derive this result by two other methods. Let $X_i = 1$ if a success occurs on the ith trial, otherwise $X_i = 0$. Then $E(X_i) = 0 \cdot q + 1 \cdot p = p$. Now let

$$S = X_1 + X_2 + \cdots + X_n,$$

with S a random variable designating the number of successes in n trials. It follows that

$$E(S) = \sum_{i=1}^{n} E(X_i) = np.$$

Another derivation is as follows. Let μ_n represent the expected number of successes in n Bernoulli trials. Now the mean number of successes for the first $(n - 1)$ trials is μ_{n-1}, and the mean number of successes on the last trial is $0 \cdot q + 1 \cdot p = p$. Hence $\mu_n = \mu_{n-1} + p$. Since $\mu_0 = 0$, we have

$$\mu_1 = p, \quad \mu_2 = 2p, \quad \mu_3 = 3p, \ldots, \mu_n = np.$$

Example 2. The mean number of successes for the Poisson distribution is

$$\mu = \sum_{0}^{\infty} nf_n = e^{-\lambda} \sum_{0}^{\infty} \frac{n\lambda^n}{n!}$$

$$= \lambda e^{-\lambda} \sum_{1}^{\infty} \frac{\lambda^{n-1}}{(n-1)!} = \lambda e^{-\lambda} e^{\lambda} = \lambda. \tag{9}$$

The parameter λ is the mean number of successes per unit time for a Poisson process.

Example 3. For the Pascal distribution we have

$$\mu = \sum_{0}^{\infty} nf_n = \sum_{0}^{\infty} npq^{n-1} = p \sum_{1}^{\infty} nq^{n-1} = \frac{1}{p}, \tag{10}$$

since

$$\sum_{0}^{\infty} x^n = \frac{1}{1-x},$$

whence

$$\frac{d}{dx} \sum_{0}^{\infty} x^n = \sum_{1}^{\infty} nx^{n-1} = (1-x)^{-2}.$$

The result is not surprising, for if $p = \frac{1}{5}$, (one chance in five for a success) we expect that one success on the average will occur in five games, or that on the average it will require five games for a success to occur.

Let us derive this result by another method. Let μ be the mean number of trials for a first success. The probability of a success on the first trial is p, and probability of a failure is q, so that $1 + \mu$ trials will be necessary, on the average, for the occurrence of the first success. Recall that one game has been played if a failure occurs. Hence $\mu = p \cdot 1 + q(\mu + 1)$, so that $\mu = 1/p$.

Example 4. In the Gambler's Ruin problem of Example 11, Section 3.5, we found that the probability that A ruins B was $P = a/(a + b)$. The solution depended on the use of difference equations. Let us derive this result by another method. Let P be the probability that A ruins B, and let Q be the probability that B ruins A. Let X represent A's capital when the game ends. Then (provided the game ends)

$$E(X) = P(a + b) + Q \cdot 0 = P(a + b).$$

However, $E(X) = a$, since A began with a units and plays a fair game, neither winning nor losing on the average, for each game played. Hence $P(a + b) = a$, and $P = a/(a + b)$.

Example 5. The result of Example 3 enables us to solve the following problem. Let an urn contain n different elements. Let us suppose that the elements are picked at random one at a time with replacements. Find the mean number of trials to obtain r different elements.

Solution. Let μ_r be this mean. Now, once $(r - 1)$ different elements have been obtained, the probability of obtaining a new element (success) is

$$p = \frac{n - (r - 1)}{n},$$

so that the mean waiting time for the rth success is

$$\frac{1}{p} = \frac{n}{n - r + 1}.$$

Thus

$$\mu_r = \mu_{r-1} + \frac{n}{n - r + 1}, \tag{11}$$

with $\mu_0 = 0$, $\mu_1 = 1$. Thus

$$\mu_r = \sum_{k=1}^{r} (\mu_k - \mu_{k-1}) = n \sum_{k=1}^{r} \frac{1}{n - k + 1}$$

$$= n \left[\frac{1}{n} + \frac{1}{n - 1} + \frac{1}{n - 2} + \cdots + \frac{1}{n - r + 1} \right] \tag{12}$$

for $r \geq 1$.

Example 6. An urn contains a white balls and b black balls. N balls are withdrawn without replacements; find the expected number of white balls withdrawn.

Solution. Let $X_i = 1$ if the ith ball withdrawn is white, $X_i = 0$ otherwise. We have previously noted that

$$p(X_i = 1) = \frac{a}{a+b}, \qquad p(X_i = 0) = \frac{b}{a+b},$$

so that

$$E(X_i) = \frac{a}{a+b}.$$

Now let

$$S = \sum_{i=1}^{N} X_i, \qquad \text{so that} \qquad E(S) = \frac{Na}{a+b}.$$

This is exactly the same result one would obtain if replacements occurred!

Example 7. *Random walk problem.* Starting at the origin, unit steps are taken to the right with probability p and to the left with probability $q = 1 - p$. Assuming independent trials, find the mean distance from the origin after n moves.

Solution. Let $X_i = +1$ if a move to the right occurs on the ith move, $X_i = -1$ if a move to the left occurs. Then

$$S = \sum_{i=1}^{n} X_i$$

represents the random distance from the origin after n moves. Since

$$E(X_i) = p \cdot 1 + q(-1) = p - q$$

for all i, it follows that

$$E(S) = n(p - q),$$

the required solution. For $p = q = \frac{1}{2}$ we have $E(S) = 0$.

Example 8. Find the mean number of Bernoulli trials needed to obtain two consecutive successes.

Solution. Either two consecutive successes occur on the first two trials, or a success is followed by a failure and eventually two consecutive successes occur, or a failure occurs initially and eventually two consecutive successes occur. Hence

$$\mu = 2p^2 + pq(\mu + 2) + q(\mu + 1),$$

yielding

$$\mu = \frac{p+1}{p^2}.$$

Example 9. For the Gambler's Ruin problem ($p = q = \frac{1}{2}$) show that the mean number of games played before A or B is ruined is ab.

Solution. Suppose that at some stage of the game A has k units, $1 \le k < a + b$, and let μ_k be the average number of games played until A or B is ruined. Note that $\mu_0 = 0$, $\mu_{a+b} = 0$. Show that

$$\mu_k = \tfrac{1}{2}(\mu_{k+1} + 1) + \tfrac{1}{2}(\mu_{k-1} + 1),$$

$$\mu_{k+1} - 2\mu_k + \mu_{k-1} = -2. \tag{13}$$

The solution is $\mu_k = (a + b)k - k^2$, yielding $\mu_a = ab$, the required solution.

At first glance this is an amazing result. If A starts with one unit and B starts with 100 units, it is difficult to conceive that on the average 100 games are required before A or B is ruined, since half the time A will be ruined on the first game. What actually happens in the other cases is that once A has obtained a few units it becomes exceedingly difficult for a ruin to take place.

Example 10. *Mean number of runs.* Let zeros and ones be transmitted with probabilities p and $q = 1 - p$, respectively. Find the mean number of runs (see Example 14, Section 2.4) for a transmission of n symbols.

Solution. Let the transmitted messages be denoted by $(X_1 X_2 \ldots X_i \ldots X_n)$, with $X_i = 0, 1$, for $i = 1, 2, \ldots, n$, so that $\Pr(X_i = 0) = p$, $\Pr(X_i = 1) = q$. We note that the sequence always begins with a run. If $X_2 \ne X_1$ a new run occurs, and if $X_2 = X_1$ no new run has been recorded. If $X_3 \ne X_2$ a new run occurs, and if $X_3 = X_2$ no new run has been recorded, and so on. For example, the sequence $0\,1\,1\,1\,0\,1\,0\,0\,1\,1$ has six runs, since $X_2 \ne X_1, X_5 \ne X_4, X_6 \ne X_5, X_7 \ne X_6, X_9 \ne X_8$, yielding $1 + 5 = 6$ runs. It is convenient to set

$$Z = 1 + f(X_1, X_2) + f(X_2, X_3) + \cdots + f(X_{n-1}, X_n), \tag{14}$$

with

$$f(X_i, X_{i+1}) = 0 \quad \text{if} \quad X_i = X_{i+1},$$

$$f(X_i, X_{i+1}) = 1 \quad \text{if} \quad X_i \ne X_{i+1}.$$

Hence Z is the number of runs for any particular sequence of zeros and ones, and Z is a random variable since the X_i are random variables. Note that

$$E[f(X_1, X_2)] = 1 \Pr(X_1 \ne X_2) + 0 \Pr(X_1 = X_2)$$

$$= 1(pq + qp) = 2pq,$$

since the sequences 01 and 10 occur with probabilities pq and qp, respectively. Thus

$$E(Z) = 1 + E[f(X_1, X_2)] + \cdots + E[f(X_{n-1}, X_n)]$$

$$= 1 + 2(n - 1)pq \tag{15}$$

For $p = q = \tfrac{1}{2}$, $n = 3$, we have $E(Z) = 2$. The eight different sequences and their corresponding runs are listed below

Sequences	Runs
000	— 1
001	— 2
010	— 3
100	— 2
110	— 2
101	— 3
011	— 2
111	— 1
	16

There are 16 runs for the eight sequences, yielding an average of two runs per sequence.

In concluding this section we discuss the product of two discrete random variables. Let X and Y be a joint pair of discrete random variables with a joint ff given by f_{ij}. Let $Z = XY$. Then it can be shown (let the reader show this!) that

$$E(Z) = \sum_j \sum_i x_i y_j f_{ij}, \tag{16}$$

provided the double series converges absolutely. Now if X and Y are statistically independent, then $f_{ij} = g_i h_j$, so that

$$E(Z) = \sum_j \sum_i x_i y_j g_i h_j$$
$$= \sum_i x_i g_i \sum_j y_j h_j = E(X)E(Y). \tag{17}$$

Thus we have the important result that if X and Y are statistically independent, then

$$E(XY) = E(X)E(Y). \tag{18}$$

A simple example shows that the converse is not true. Let X be a random variable assuming the values -1, 0, $+1$ with equal probability. If $X = \pm 1$, choose Y from the numbers -1, 1 with equal probability, and if $X = 0$, choose $Y = 0$. Now show that X and Y are not statistically independent. However, $E(X) = 0$, $E(Y) = 0$, $E(XY) = 0$, so that $E(XY) = E(X)E(Y)$. Thus if Eq. (18) holds, we cannot conclude that X and Y are statistically independent.

PROBLEMS

1. For Problem 4 of Section 3.6 (the key problem) show that in the first case (no replacements) the mean number of trials to open the door is $(n + 1)/2$, and that in the second case the mean number of trials is n.

2. For Problem 2 of Section 3.6 find the mean number of cars sold.

3. If X is a random variable such that $f_k = \text{Pr}(X = k) = (6/\pi^2)(1/k^2)$, $k = 1, 2, 3, \ldots$, so that

$$\sum_{k=1}^{\infty} f_k = 1,$$

does $E(X)$ exist?

4. A fair die is cast n times. Show that the expected value for the sum of the points is $7n/2$.

5. An urn contains n tickets numbered $1-n$. Given that m tickets are withdrawn (no replacements), what is the expected value for the sum of the tickets? Use the fact that

$$\sum_{k=1}^{n} k = \frac{n(n + 1)}{2}.$$

6. For n trials let P_k be the probability of success on the kth trial, $k = 1, 2, \ldots, n$. Show that the mean number of successes in the n trials is $E_n = P_1 + P_2 + \cdots + P_n$. If

$$\sum_{k=1}^{n} P_k^2 = rn, \qquad 0 < r < 1,$$

what values of the P_k, $k = 1, 2, \ldots, n$, make E_n a maximum?

7. An urn contains tickets numbered $1-n$. Two tickets are removed at random (no replacements). Show that the expected value for the product of the numbers is $\frac{1}{12}(n + 1)(3n + 2)$. Use the fact that

$$\sum_{k=1}^{n} k^2 = \tfrac{1}{6} n(n + 1)(2n + 1).$$

8. An urn contains m white and n black balls. The balls are removed one at a time until a white ball is removed. What is the mean number of black balls removed until this event occurs? [Hint: $n = X_1 + X_2 + \ldots + X_{m+1}$, with X_i the number of black balls withdrawn between the $(i-1)$st and ith white balls.]

9. Show that the generalized Pascal distribution has a mean given by $\mu = m/p$, see Example 4, Section 3.5.

10. Let μ be the mean number of trials until a failure follows a success for the case of Bernoulli trials. Show that $\mu = 1/pq$.

11. An urn contains m zeros and n ones. The numbers are withdrawn at random without replacements, yielding sequences of zeros and ones. Show that the mean number of runs is $\mu = 1 + 2pqN$, with $p = m/(m + n)$, $q = n/(m + n)$, and $N = m + n$.

12. Each of n people has a probability p of yielding a positive blood test. The blood samples can be pooled and if the test is negative all blood types are negative and the test is over. If the pooled sample is positive then each of the n people must be tested separately. Find the mean number of tests necessary to determine the blood type (positive or negative) of each of the n individuals.

13. For the Gambler's Ruin problem, $p \neq q$ (see Example 9, this section), show that the mean number of games played before A or B is ruined is

$$\mu = \frac{a}{q-p} + \frac{a+b}{p-q} \frac{1 - \left(\frac{q}{p}\right)^a}{1 - \left(\frac{q}{p}\right)^{a+b}}.$$

14. Using the notation of Section 3.6, let

$$f_{ij} = \Pr\{X = x_i; \ Y = y_j\},$$
$$g_i = \Pr\{X = x_i\},$$
$$h_i = \Pr\{Y = y_i\},$$
$$k_i|_j = \Pr\{X = x_i | Y = y_j\} = f_{ij}/h_j.$$

The expected value of X, given that $Y = y_j$ has occurred, is defined by

$$E(X|Y = y_j) = \sum_i x_i k_{i|j}$$
$$= (1/h_j) \sum_i x_i f_{ij}.$$

Returning to Example 3, Section 3.6, show that $E(X|Y = 2) = 3$.

15. For a Poisson process let $\mu(t)$ be the mean number of occurrences up to time t. Explain why $\mu(t + dt) \approx \mu(t) + \lambda\, dt$, and deduce that $\mu = \lambda t$.

16. Referring to Example 5, this section, let

$$S_r = X_1 + X_2 + \cdots + X_r,$$

with X_i the number of trials after the $(i-1)$st new element has been obtained up to and including the observation of the ith new element. Show that

$$E(X_i) = \frac{n}{n-i+1}, \quad \text{and} \quad E(S_r) = n\sum_{i=1}^{r} \frac{1}{n-i+1}.$$

17. Let $Z = XY$, so that Z takes on the values $x_i y_j$ with probability f_{ij}. Some of the values $x_i y_j$ may be repeated. Explain why

$$E(Z) = \sum_j \sum_i x_i y_j f_{ij}.$$

18. Justify the result of Example 1, this section, as follows: Let X_n represent the number of successes in n Bernoulli trials (X_n is a random variable). Then

$$X_{n+1} = X_n + 1 \quad \text{with probability } p$$
$$= X_n \quad \text{with probability } q.$$

The expected value of X_{n+1}, given X_n successes on the first n trials, is denoted by $\mathscr{E}(X_{n+1})$. Show that $\mathscr{E}(X_{n+1}) = p + X_n$. Averaging over all possible outcomes X_n, show that $\mu_{n+1} = p + \mu_n$.

19. Returning to Problem 18, show that

$$\mathscr{E}(X_{n+1}^2) = X_n^2 + 2p\, X_n + p.$$

Let $\mu_n^{(2)} = E(X_n^2)$, the mean square number of successes in n trials. Show that

$$\mu_{n+1}^{(2)} - \mu_n^{(2)} = 2p^2 n + p$$

and that

$$\mu_n^{(2)} = pqn + p^2 n^2.$$

20. Consider the following game: Each time a success occurs in a Bernoulli trial one unit is won. Moreover, whenever a success immediately follows a success an additional unit is won. The occurrence of a failure incurs the loss of a unit. We wish to determine the mean number of units gained in n trials, say μ_n. For $k > 1$, let $U_k = 1$ if a success occurs on the kth trial and a failure occurred on the previous trial; let $V_k = 2$ if successes occur on the $(k-1)$st and kth trials; and let $W_k = -1$ if a failure occurs on the kth trial. Show that

$$E(U_k + V_k + W_k) = 2p^2 - q^2,$$
$$\mu_n = p - q + (2p^2 - q^2)(n - 1).$$

21. Urn I contains two red and three white balls. Urn II contains three red and two white balls. A ball is chosen at random from urn I and placed in urn II. Then a ball is chosen from urn II and placed in urn I. At no stage is the color of the ball noted. Find the mean number of red balls in urn I after k transfers to urn I.

22. Suppose m people enter an elevator. If the building has n floors above the lobby, show that the mean number of stops is

$$\mu = n\left[1 - \left(1 - \frac{1}{n}\right)^m\right],$$

if the *a priori* probability of any one person stopping on the kth floor is $1/n$ for $1 \le k \le n$.

23. A, B, C have equal ability in playing a game against one another. A plays against B, and the loser is replaced by C. Each time the loser is replaced by the opponent who sits out the previous game. The match ends when one of the players defeats the other two players consecutively.

   a) Find the probability that A will win the contest if he defeats B on the first game.
   b) Find the probability that C will win the contest.
   c) Find the mean number of games played until the contest terminates.

24. Among n keys there are k which fit a door. One key at a time is tried at random without replacements. Show that the mean number of trials until a fit occurs is

$$\mu = \frac{n + 1}{k + 1}.$$

Hint: Let X_1 be the number of trials before the first fit, X_2 the number of trials before the second fit, etc., so that

$$n - k = \sum_{i=1}^{k+1} X_i.$$

25. Consider an urn containing the n integers 1, 2, 3, ..., n. The integers are sampled at random without replacements, yielding the sequence $X_1, X_2, ..., X_n$. If $X_i > X_{i+1}$ no point is scored, and if $X_i < X_{i+1}$ one point is scored. Show that $(n - 1)/2$ is the mean number of points scored.

26. In Problem 25, m integers are picked at random, $m \leq n$, with no replacements. Let Z be the maximum integer chosen. Show that

$$E(Z) = \frac{m}{1 + m}(1 + n).$$

27. Show that for a sequence of Bernoulli trials, the mean number of trials until at least m successes and n failures occur is

$$\mu = \sum_{N=m+n}^{\infty} N\binom{N-1}{m-1} p^m q^{N-m} + \sum_{N=m+n}^{\infty} N\binom{N-1}{n-1} q^n p^{N-n}$$

$$= \frac{m}{p} + \frac{n}{q} - mp^m \sum_{r=0}^{n-1} \binom{m+r}{m} q^r - nq^n \sum_{r=0}^{m-1} \binom{n+r}{n} p^r$$

28. Independent games are played as follows: With probability p_1, one unit is gained and the play continues; with probability p_2, no units are lost or gained and the play continues; with probability p_3, the play ends with no loss or gain; $p_1 + p_2 + p_3 = 1$. Show that the mean number of games played is $\mu = 1/p_3$, and the mean units won is p_1/p_3.

29. A sequence of n questions are ordered such that p_i, $i = 1, 2, ..., n$, are the probabilities of correctly answering these questions, $p_1 > p_2 > p_3 > \cdots > p_n$. The reward for answering the ith question correctly is R_i, with $R_1 < R_2 < \cdots < R_n$. If the first k questions have been answered correctly the quizee may quit and receive an amount R_k. However, if any question is answered incorrectly the game terminates and the net winning is zero.

Let F_k be the expected (average) return using an optimal strategy (quit or go on) if the kth question has been answered correctly. Obviously $F_n = R_n$. Show that

$$F_k = \max(R_k, p_{k+1} F_{k+1}).$$

For the special case $R_1 = 1$, $R_2 = 10$, $R_3 = 9{,}000$, $p_1 = 0.9$, $p_2 = 0.2$, $p_3 = 0.001$, show that $F_2 = 10$, $F_1 = 2$, $F_0 = 1.8$. This shows that if the first two questions have been answered correctly one should quit. What type of person would do this?

30. A gambler can make n bets. If he bets x units he wins x units with probability p and loses x units with probability $q = 1 - p$. Let $R_k(y)$ be the expected return for the gambler if he has y units and if, by his use of an optimal strategy, k bets remain. Show that

$$R_k(y) = \max R_{k-1}[y + x(2p - 1)],$$
$$0 \leq x \leq y$$

with $R_0(y) = y$. Show that if $p > \frac{1}{2}$ the gambler should bet his total capital on any game.

Suppose the gambler has y units and bets x units, $0 \le x \le y$, with $p > \frac{1}{2}$. The average of the logarithm of his return is

$$pln(y + x) + (1 - p) \, ln(y - x).$$

Show that $x = (2p - 1)y$ maximizes this quantity.

31. Consider n coins, each having a probability p of yielding a head and $q = 1 - p$ of yielding a tail. The n coins are tossed and all heads are removed. The remaining coins are tossed again and all heads are removed and so on. Show that the probability that no coins remain after k tosses is

$$P_k = (1 - q^k)^n - (1 - q^{k-1})^n.$$

Show that the mean number of tosses until no coins remain is

$$\mu_n = \sum_{r=1}^{n} \binom{n}{r} (- 1)^r \frac{1}{q^r - 1}.$$

32. Consider a sequence of Bernoulli trials with $p > q$. Show that the mean number of trials until the successes outnumber the failures is $\mu = 1/(p - q)$ (see Problem 17 of Section 3.5).

3.8 HIGHER MOMENTS · VARIANCE · CORRELATION

Let us consider the random variable $Y = X^2$ where X is a discrete random variable which takes the distinct values $x_1, x_2, \ldots, x_n, \ldots$ with corresponding probabilities $f_1, f_2, \ldots, f_n, \ldots$. If the x_i are all positive, or all negative, then clearly Y takes on the distinct values $x_1^2, x_2^2, \ldots$ with respective probabilities $f_1, f_2, \ldots$, so that

$$E(Y) = E(X^2) = \sum_n x_n^2 f_n. \tag{1}$$

It is not difficult to see that this equation still holds if the restriction on the sign of the x_i is removed.

In general, to each function $\phi(x)$ defined on the range of X, there corresponds a new discrete random variable $Y = \phi(X)$, and it can be shown that

$$E(Y) = E[\phi(X)] = \sum_k \phi(x_k)f_k, \tag{2}$$

provided the sum converges absolutely. Let the reader deduce that for any constant a, $E(a) = a$, $E[a\phi(X)] = aE[\phi(X)]$.

The quantity, $E(X^2)$, is called the second moment of X. It is analogous to the moment of inertia about the origin for a set of mass points lying on a line, say the x-axis. The rth moment of a discrete random variable is defined by

$$\nu_r = E[X^r] = \sum_k (x_k)^r f_k, \tag{3}$$

provided the series converges absolutely.

We let the reader show that if $\nu_2 < \infty$, then $\nu_1 = \mu < \infty$, by considering the values of X less than 1 in absolute value and the values of X greater than 1 in absolute value.

In analytic mechanics the moment of inertia about the center of mass plays an important role. Analogously, in statistics, the second moment about the mean is a quantity of fundamental importance. We call this quantity the *variance* or *dispersion* of X, written $\sigma^2 \equiv V(X)$, and defined by

$$\sigma^2 = E[(X - \mu)^2] = \sum_k (x_k - \mu)^2 f_k, \tag{4}$$

provided the sum converges. It follows immediately that

$$\sigma^2 = E[X^2 - 2\mu X + \mu^2]$$

$$= E(X^2) - 2\mu E(X) + \mu^2$$

$$= E(X^2) - \mu^2 = v_2 - v_1^2. \tag{5}$$

Thus the variance is the second moment less the square of the mean. The positive square root of $V(X)$, namely σ, is called the *standard deviation* of X.

Let X be a random variable which takes on the single value, a, with probability one. Then $\mu = E(X) = a$, $E(X^2) = a^2$, and $V(X) = a^2 - a^2 \equiv 0$. Thus we may expect that if $V(X) \ll 1$, there must be a small probability that X assumes any value far from its mean. If for some value j, $|x_j - \mu|$ is large, so is $|x_j - \mu|^2$, and f_j must be very small in order that $\sigma^2 \ll 1$ (see Eq. 4). Thus the variance, in a sense, is a measure of the spread or dispersion of the distribution.

Let us consider the following example. Let X be a discrete random variable with mean μ and variance σ^2. Suppose we have n independent random variables $X_1, X_2, \ldots, X_n$ defined on the same sample space as X and having the same probability distribution, and therefore the same mean μ and variance σ^2. Such *identically distributed* random variables appear in random sampling from a fixed population, as we shall see later in our study of statistics.

Now consider the random variable

$$Z_n = \frac{X_1 + X_2 + \cdots + X_n}{n}. \tag{6}$$

We note that $E(Z_n) = \mu$ from the summation rule for expectations. It is natural to call Z_n the *sample mean*. Now

$$Z_n - \mu = \frac{(X_1 - \mu) + \cdots + (X_n - \mu)}{n},$$

$$(Z_n - \mu)^2 = \frac{1}{n^2}[(X_1 - \mu)^2 + \cdots + (X_n - \mu)^2$$

$$+ 2(X_1 - \mu)(X_2 - \mu) + \cdots]. \tag{7}$$

Since X_1 and X_2 are assumed independent, we have

$$E(X_1 X_2) = E(X_1)E(X_2),$$

and so

$$E[(X_1 - \mu)(X_2 - \mu)] = E(X_1 X_2) - \mu E(X_1) - \mu E(X_2) + \mu^2$$
$$= \mu^2 - \mu^2 - \mu^2 + \mu^2 \equiv 0.$$

Thus,

$$V(Z_n) = E[(Z_n - \mu)^2] = \frac{n\sigma^2}{n^2} = \frac{\sigma^2}{n}. \tag{8}$$

As $n \to \infty$, $V(Z_n) \to 0$, so that it is not surprising that we will be able to prove that the sample mean Z_n approaches the true mean μ with probability one, as n becomes infinite.

Next, let us drop the restriction that the random variables X_i have the same mean and variance, but retain the assumption that the variables are statistically independent. Let

$$Z = \sum_{i=1}^{n} X_i,$$

and let the reader deduce that

$$V(Z) \equiv V(X_1 + \cdots + X_n) = V(X_1) + V(X_2) + \cdots + V(X_n). \tag{9}$$

Equation (9) is a most useful and important result.

Before proceeding with examples let us determine the second moment about any fixed point $x = \xi$. Thus

$$E[(X - \xi)^2] = E[(X - \mu + \mu - \xi)^2]$$
$$= E[(X - \mu)^2] + 2(\mu - \xi)E(X - \mu) + (\mu - \xi)^2$$
$$= \sigma^2 + (\mu - \xi)^2. \tag{10}$$

We have proved the following.

Translation theorem. For a discrete random variable the second moment about any point is the variance (second moment about the mean) plus the square of the distance from the mean to the point in question, provided the variance exists.

Example 1. Let X assume the values $-1, 0, 1$, with probabilities $\frac{1}{4}, \frac{1}{2}, \frac{1}{4}$, respectively. Then

$$E(X) = \tfrac{1}{4}(-1) + \tfrac{1}{2}(0) + \tfrac{1}{4}(1) = 0,$$
$$E(X^2) = \tfrac{1}{4}(-1)^2 + \tfrac{1}{2}(0)^2 + \tfrac{1}{4}(1)^2 = \tfrac{1}{2},$$

so that

$$\sigma^2 = V(X) = \tfrac{1}{2} - 0^2 = \tfrac{1}{2}.$$

Example 2. For the Poisson random variable X we have

$$E(X^2) = e^{-\mu} \sum_{k=0}^{\infty} \frac{k^2 \mu^k}{k!} = e^{-\mu} \sum_{k=1}^{\infty} \frac{k\mu^k}{(k-1)!}$$

$$= e^{-\mu} \sum_{k=1}^{\infty} \frac{(k-1+1)\mu^k}{(k-1)!}$$

$$= e^{-\mu}\mu^2 \sum_{k=2}^{\infty} \frac{\mu^{k-2}}{(k-2)!} + e^{-\mu}\mu \sum_{k=1}^{\infty} \frac{\mu^{k-1}}{(k-1)!}$$

$$= e^{-\mu}\mu^2 e^{\mu} + e^{-\mu}\mu e^{\mu} = \mu^2 + \mu,$$

so that $V(X) = \mu^2 + \mu - \mu^2 = \mu$, since $E(X) = \mu$. Thus the mean and variance have the same value.

Example 3. Let X be of the class $B(p, n)$. Then

$$E(X^2) = \sum_{k=0}^{n} k^2 \binom{n}{k} p^k q^{n-k}$$

$$= n(n-1)p^2 + np,$$

which follows from

$$(x + q)^n = \sum_{k=0}^{n} \binom{n}{k} x^k q^{n-k}$$

by differentiating with respect to x, multiplying by x, and differentiating again with respect to x, finally setting $x = p$ with $p + q = 1$. Since $\mu = np$, it follows that

$$V(X) = n(n-1)p^2 + np - n^2 p^2$$

$$= np - np^2 = np(1-p) = npq. \tag{11}$$

We can obtain this result by letting $S = X_1 + X_2 + \cdots + X_n$ with $X_1 = 1$ if a success occurs, $X_1 = 0$ otherwise, with a similar remark for $X_2, X_3, \ldots, X_n$. Then

$$E(X_1) = 1 \cdot p + 0 \cdot q = p$$

$$E(X_1^2) = 1^2 \cdot p + 0^2 \cdot q = p$$

$$V(X_1) = p - p^2 = p(1-p) = pq.$$

Since the X_i are statistically independent, Eq. (9) yields

$$V(S) = pq + pq + \ldots + pq = npq.$$

Example 4. *Random walk problem.* To find the variance for the random variable S of Example 7, Section 3.7 we note that

$$E(X_i^2) = p(1)^2 + q(-1)^2 = 1,$$

so that

$$V(X_i) = 1 - (p - q)^2 = 4pq,$$
$$V(S) = 4pqn,$$

since

$$V(S) = V(X_1) + V(X_2) + \cdots + V(X_n).$$

Now suppose that each move in time Δt is either $+(\Delta x)$ with probability $\frac{1}{2}$, or $-(\Delta x)$ with probability $\frac{1}{2}$, so that after n moves, $t = n\Delta t$, or $n = t/\Delta t$. Furthermore,

$$V(S) = \sigma^2 = n(\Delta x)^2 = t\,\frac{(\Delta x)^2}{\Delta t}.$$

We now let $\Delta t \to 0$ in such a manner that

$$\lim_{\Delta t \to 0}\,\frac{(\Delta x)^2}{\Delta t} = 2D.$$

$D = $ constant, so that $\sigma^2 \to 2Dt$. In this analysis we are dealing, essentially, with a continuous random walk problem (Brownian motion) such that the variance increases linearly with time (Fig. 7).

Before letting $\Delta t \to 0$, let $P(x, t)$ be the probability of being at the level x at time t. Then

$$P(x, t + \Delta t) = \tfrac{1}{2}P(x - \Delta x, t) + \tfrac{1}{2}P(x + \Delta x, t), \tag{12}$$

since we must either be at $x - \Delta x$ at time t and then move a distance Δx with probability $\frac{1}{2}$ in time Δt, or be at $x + \Delta x$ at time t and then move a distance $-(\Delta x)$ with probability $\frac{1}{2}$ in time Δt.

Expanding Eq. (12) in a Taylor series, including terms of the type $(\Delta x)^2$, yields

$$P(x, t) + \frac{\partial P}{\partial t}\,\Delta t = \tfrac{1}{2}\left[P(x, t) - \frac{\partial P}{\partial x}\,\Delta x + \tfrac{1}{2}\frac{\partial^2 P}{\partial x^2}\,(\Delta x)^2\right]$$
$$+ \tfrac{1}{2}\left[P(x, t) + \frac{\partial P}{\partial x}\,\Delta x + \tfrac{1}{2}\frac{\partial^2 P}{\partial x^2}\,(\Delta x)^2\right]$$
$$= P(x, t) + \tfrac{1}{2}\frac{\partial^2 P}{\partial x^2}\,(\Delta x)^2,$$

so that

$$\frac{\partial P}{\partial t} = \tfrac{1}{2}\frac{\partial^2 P}{\partial x^2}\lim_{\Delta t \to 0}\frac{(\Delta x)^2}{\Delta t}$$
$$= D\,\frac{\partial^2 P}{\partial x^2}. \tag{13}$$

Equation (13) is the Fokker-Planck diffusion equation, analogous to the heat equation

$$\frac{\partial T}{\partial t} = k\,\frac{\partial^2 T}{\partial x^2}.$$

Example 5. In Example 8 of Section 3.7 it was found that the mean number of Bernoulli trials to obtain two consecutive successes is

$$\mu = \frac{p + 1}{p^2}.$$

Let us apply the translation theorem to find the variance σ^2. A failure occurs on the first trial with probability q, requiring an average of $\xi = \mu + 1$ trials to obtain two consecutive successes, a distance of one unit from μ. A failure follows a success with probability pq, requiring an average of $\xi = \mu + 2$ trials to obtain two consecutive successes, a distance of two units from μ. The probability that one has two consecutive successes on the first two trials, is p^2, so $\xi = 2$, a distance of $2 - (p + 1)/p^2$ units from the mean $\mu = (p + 1)/p^2$. Hence the translation theorem states that

$$\sigma^2 = q(\sigma^2 + 1^2) + pq(\sigma^2 + 2^2) + p^2\left[2 - \frac{p + 1}{p^2}\right]^2,$$

yielding

$$\sigma^2 = \frac{(1 + 2p - 2p^2 - p^3)}{p^4}.$$

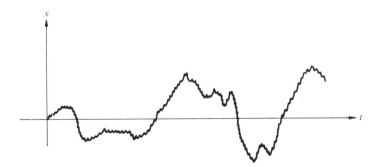

Figure 3.7

Example 6. *Card matching problem.* Consider N cards labeled $1, 2, \ldots, N$ which are placed at random into N cells labeled $1, 2, \ldots, N$, one card to each cell. Find the mean number of times that the number of a card matches the number of the cell, and find the variance.

Solution. Let

$$S = X_1 + X_2 + \cdots + X_N,$$

with $X_i = 1$ if the ith numbered card falls into the ith numbered cell, $X_i = 0$ otherwise, $i = 1, 2, \ldots, N$. Now

$$\Pr(X_i = 1) = \frac{1}{N},$$

so that

$$E(X_i) = 1 \cdot \frac{1}{N} + 0 \cdot \left(1 - \frac{1}{N}\right) = \frac{1}{N}$$

and $E(S) = 1$, independent of N. This is the same result one would obtain if the N numbers are on balls in an urn; you guess the number that will be withdrawn, and perform the experiment N times with replacements.

To find the variance we note that

$$S^2 = \sum_{i=1}^{N} X_i^2 + 2 \sum \sum_{i > j} X_i X_j.$$

Now

$$E(X_i^2) = \frac{1}{N} 1^2 + \left(1 - \frac{1}{N}\right) 0^2 = \frac{1}{N}.$$

To find $E(S^2)$ we need to compute $E(X_i X_j)$, $i \neq j$. We have $X_i X_j = 1$ if a match occurs for both balls, $X_i X_j = 0$ otherwise. The probability that a match occurs for both balls is $1/N \cdot 1/(N - 1)$, so that

$$E(X_i X_j) = \frac{1}{N(N - 1)}.$$

Hence

$$E(S^2) = N \cdot \frac{1}{N} + 2 \binom{N}{2} \frac{1}{N(N - 1)} = 2,$$

yielding

$$V(S) = 2 - 1^2 = 1 = E(S).$$

The example above suggests a study of expectations of the type $E(XY)$. Let $Z = X + Y$ be a sum of two discrete random variables X, Y, not necessarily statistically independent. Then

$$\mu_z = E(Z) = E(X) + E(Y) = \mu_x + \mu_y,$$

so that

$$Z - \mu_z = (X - \mu_x) + (Y - \mu_y),$$

$$(Z - \mu_z)^2 = (X - \mu_x)^2 + (Y - \mu_y)^2 + 2(X - \mu_x)(Y - \mu_y), \qquad (14)$$

$$\sigma_z^2 = \sigma_x^2 + \sigma_y^2 + 2 \sum_j \sum_i (x_i - \mu_x)(y_j - \mu_y) f_{ij},$$

with

$$\sigma_z^2 = E[(Z - \mu_z)^2],$$

etc., assuming the series exist. The quantity

$$\text{Cov}(X, Y) \equiv \sum_j \sum_i (x_i - \mu_x)(y_j - \mu_y) f_{ij} \qquad (15)$$

is analogous to the cross-product of inertia in analytic mechanics. It is called the covariance of X and Y, written $\text{Cov}(X, Y)$.

The correlation coefficient, $\rho = \rho_{xy}$, is defined by $\rho\sigma_x\sigma_y = \text{Cov}(X, Y)$,

$$\rho_{xy} = \frac{1}{\sigma_x\sigma_y} \sum_j \sum_i (x_i - \mu_x)(y_j - \mu_y) f_{ij}$$

$$= \frac{1}{\sigma_x\sigma_y} E[(X - \mu_x)(Y - \mu_y)]$$

$$= \frac{1}{\sigma_x\sigma_y} [E(XY) - E(X)E(Y)]. \tag{16}$$

We note that $\rho = 0$ if X and Y are statistically independent, since $E(XY) = E(X)E(Y)$ for this case. We then say that X and Y are also uncorrelated. However, $\rho = 0$ does not imply that X and Y are statistically independent (see the example at the end of Section 3.7). The role of ρ will become more evident in Chapter 4, Section 6.

Since

$$W = [\lambda(X - \mu_x) - (Y - \mu_y)]^2 \geq 0$$

for all real λ, it follows that $E(W) \geq 0$, yielding

$$\lambda^2\sigma_x^2 - 2\lambda\rho\sigma_x\sigma_y + \sigma_y^2 \geq 0$$

for all real λ. Choosing $\lambda = \sigma_y/\sigma_x$ yields $\sigma_y^2 - 2\rho\sigma_y^2 + \sigma_y^2 \geq 0$, and $\rho \leq 1$. Choosing $\lambda = -\sigma_y/\sigma_x$ yields $\rho \geq -1$, so that $|\rho| \leq 1$. In conclusion,

$$\Lambda = \begin{bmatrix} \sigma_x^2 & \rho\sigma_x\sigma_y \\ \rho\sigma_x\sigma_y & \sigma_y^2 \end{bmatrix} \tag{17}$$

is called the covariance matrix. For the moment we will not be concerned with this matrix.

Example 7. Referring back to Table 1, page 74, we have

$$\text{Cov}(X, Y) = E(XY) - E(X)E(Y).$$

Now

$$E(X) = \tfrac{1}{4}(1 + 2 + 3 + 4) = \tfrac{5}{2},$$

$$E(Y) = \tfrac{1}{4}(1 + 2 + 3 + 4) = \tfrac{5}{2},$$

$$E(XY) = \sum_{j=1}^{4} \sum_{i=1}^{4} ij f_{ij}$$

$$= \tfrac{1}{12} [1\cdot2 + 1\cdot3 + 1\cdot4 + 2\cdot1 + 2\cdot3 + 2\cdot4$$

$$+ 3\cdot1 + 3\cdot2 + 3\cdot4 + 4\cdot1 + 4\cdot2 + 4\cdot3]$$

$$= \tfrac{35}{6},$$

$$\text{Cov}(X, Y) = \tfrac{35}{6} - \tfrac{25}{4} = -\tfrac{5}{12}.$$

From
$$E(X^2) = \tfrac{1}{4}(1^2 + 2^2 + 3^2 + 4^2) = \tfrac{15}{2} = E(Y^2)$$
we have
$$\sigma_x^2 = \sigma_y^2 = \tfrac{15}{2} - \tfrac{25}{4} = \tfrac{5}{4}.$$
Hence the correlation is
$$\rho = -\frac{\tfrac{5}{12}}{\tfrac{5}{4}} = -\tfrac{1}{3}.$$

Let us observe that if $X = 1$, the average value of Y is
$$\tfrac{2+3+4}{3} = \tfrac{9}{3};$$
if $X = 2$, the average value of Y is $\tfrac{8}{3}$; if $X = 3$, the average value of Y is $\tfrac{7}{3}$; and if $X = 4$ the average value of Y is $\tfrac{6}{3}$. The larger the observed value of X, the smaller the mean value of the observed Y. This is why ρ is negative in this example.

In concluding this section, let Z be the sum of n discrete random variables (not necessarily independent). From
$$Z = \sum_{i=1}^{n} X_i,$$
$$\mu = E(Z) = \sum_{i=1}^{n} E(X_i) = \Sigma\mu_i,$$
we obtain
$$Z - \mu = \sum_{i=1}^{n} (X_i - \mu_i).$$

To find the variance of Z we note that
$$(Z - \mu)^2 = \sum_{i=1}^{n} (X_i - \mu_i)^2 + 2 \sum_{i>j} (X_i - \mu_i)(X_j - \mu_j).$$
Taking expected values yields
$$V(Z) = \sum_{i=1}^{n} V(X_i) + 2 \sum_{i>j} \text{Cov}(X_i, X_j) \tag{18}$$
as the simple extension of Eq. (9).

PROBLEMS

1. X takes on the values $-1, 0, 1$ with equal probabilities. Show that the variance is $\sigma^2 = \tfrac{2}{3}$.

2. Let X be the number of points scored on the cast of n independent dice. Show that $V(X) = 35n/12$.

3. For a discrete random variable X show that if $E(X^2)$ exists then $E(X)$ exists. From $E[(\lambda X - 1)^2] \geq 0$ for all real λ, show that

$$[E(X)]^2 \leq E(X^2).$$

Under what conditions does the equality hold?

4. If $E(X^4)$ exists for a discrete random variable, show that $E(X^2)$ exists, and that

$$[E(X^2)]^2 \leq E(X^4).$$

5. For Problem 5 of Section 3.7, show that the variance of the sum of the tickets is

$$\sigma^2 = \tfrac{1}{12} m(n + 1)(n - m)$$

Why is $\sigma^2 = 0$ for $n = m$?

6. X is a discrete random variable with mean $E(X)$ and variance $V(X)$. Let $Y = aX + b$, a and b constants. Show that $E(Y) = aE(X) + b$, $V(Y) = a^2 V(X)$.

7. If X is of the class $B(p, n)$, show that

$$E(X^3) = n(n - 1)(n - 2) p^3 + 3n(n - 1) p^2 + np.$$

8. For Bernoulli trials let X represent the number of trials until the kth success occurs. Show that

$$V(X) = \frac{qk}{p^2}.$$

9. For the Gambler's Ruin problem, $p = q = \tfrac{1}{2}$, show that the variance for the number of games played until a ruin occurs is

$$\sigma^2 = \tfrac{1}{3} ab(a^2 + b^2 - 2).$$

10. Two fair dice are tossed. Let X be the score on the first die and Y the larger of the two scores. Find the means, the variances, the covariance, and the correlation coefficient.

11. Let X be a discrete random variable with mean μ and variance $V(X)$. Let S be the set of x's for which $(X - \mu)^2 \geq k^2$, so that

$$\Pr\{|X - \mu| \geq k\} = \sum_{s} f_i.$$

From

$$E[(X - \mu)^2] = \sum_{s} (x_j - \mu)^2 f_j + \sum_{s'} (x_j - \mu)^2 f_j$$

show that

$$\Pr\{|X - \mu| \geq k\} \leq \frac{V(X)}{k^2}. \tag{19}$$

This is Chebyshev's inequality. Apply this result to

$$\bar{X} = \frac{1}{n} \sum_{i=1}^{n} X_i,$$

the X_i being independent, $E(X_i) = \mu$, $V(X_i) = \sigma^2$ for all i. Show that

$$\Pr\{|\bar{X} - \mu| \geq \epsilon\} \leq \frac{\sigma^2}{n\epsilon^2}.$$

What happens as $n \to \infty$ for any fixed $\epsilon > 0$?

12. A has three coins and B has two coins. They toss their coins at random. Whoever tosses the most number of heads wins. If a tie occurs the game continues until a winner emerges.

a) Find the probability that A is the winner.
b) Find the probability that A wins on the nth game.
c) Let X be the number of games played until a winner emerges. Find $E(X)$, $V(X)$.

13. Referring to Problem 24 of Section 3.7, find the variance for the number of trials until a fit occurs.

3.9 GENERATING FUNCTIONS

Consider a sequence of constants $f_0, f_1, f_2, \ldots, f_n, \ldots$ The function

$$F(s) = f_0 + f_1 s + f_2 s^2 + \cdots + f_n s^n + \cdots$$

$$= \sum_{k=0}^{\infty} f_k s^k \tag{1}$$

is called the generating function for the sequence $\{f_n\}$ in the sense that if $F(s)$ is known and has a Taylor series development in s, then the coefficient of s^n yields f_n, $n = 0, 1, 2, 3, \ldots$

For example, the sequence of constants $1, 1, 1, \ldots, 1, \ldots$, each term being one, has the generating function

$$F(s) = 1 + s + s^2 + \cdots + s^n + \cdots = 1/(1 - s),$$

provided $|s| < 1$. Conversely, $F(s) = 1/(1 - s)$ yields the Taylor series above, so that $f_n \equiv 1$ for all nonnegative integers, n. The function

$$F(s) = e^s = \sum_{n=0}^{\infty} \frac{1}{n!} s^n$$

generates the sequence $1, 1, 1/2!, \ldots, 1/n!, \ldots$

If, in particular, X is a random variable which attains nonnegative integral values such that $f_k = \Pr(X = k)$, then $F(s)$ of Eq. (1) is called the *probability generating function* (pgf). From

$$\sum_{k=0}^{\infty} f_k = 1$$

it follows that $F(s)$ converges for $|s| \leq 1$. Furthermore, since $f_k \geq 0$ for all k, it follows that $F(s) \geq F(t)$ for $s \geq t \geq 0$.

Example 1.

a) The generating function for the binomial distribution, $B(p, N)$, is

$$F(s) = \sum_{k=0}^{N} \binom{N}{k} p^k q^{N-k} s^k$$

$$= \sum_{k=0}^{N} \binom{N}{k} (ps)^k q^{N-k} = (ps + q)^N. \tag{2}$$

b) The generating function for the Poisson distribution is

$$F(s) = \sum_{n=0}^{\infty} e^{-\lambda} \frac{\lambda^n}{n!} s^n = e^{-\lambda} \sum_{n=0}^{\infty} \frac{(\lambda s)^n}{n!}$$

$$= e^{-\lambda} e^{\lambda s} = e^{\lambda(s-1)}. \tag{3}$$

c) The generating function for the Pascal distribution is

$$F(s) = \sum_{n=1}^{\infty} pq^{n-1} s^n = ps \sum_{n=1}^{\infty} q^{n-1} s^{n-1}$$

$$= \frac{ps}{1 - qs}. \tag{4}$$

d) The generating function for the generalized Pascal distribution is (see Eq. (6), Section 3.5)

$$F(s) = \sum_{k=m}^{\infty} \binom{k-1}{m-1} p^m q^{k-m} s^k$$

$$= (ps)^m \sum_{r=0}^{\infty} \binom{r+m-1}{m-1} (qs)^r = \left(\frac{ps}{1-qs} \right)^m. \tag{5}$$

From

$$F'(s) = \sum_{k=0}^{\infty} kf_k s^{k-1} \tag{6}$$

it follows that if $E(X)$ exists, then

$$E(X) = F'(1). \tag{7}$$

Applying this result to the examples above yields,

a) $F'(s) = Np(ps + q)^{N-1}$,   so that $\mu = Np$

b) $F'(s) = \lambda e^{\lambda(s-1)}$,   so that $\mu = \lambda$

c) $F'(s) = \dfrac{(1 - qs)p + pqs}{(1 - qs)^2} = \dfrac{p}{(1 - qs)^2}$,   so that $\mu = \dfrac{1}{p}$ (8)

d) $F'(s) = m \left(\dfrac{ps}{1 - qs} \right)^{m-1} \dfrac{p}{(1 - qs)^2}$,   so that $\mu = \dfrac{m}{p}$

From Eq. (6) it follows that

$$\frac{d}{ds}(sF'(s)) = \frac{d}{ds}\sum_{k=0}^{\infty} kf_k s^k = \sum k^2 f_k s^{k-1}. \tag{9}$$

Thus

$$\nu_2 = E(X^2) = \frac{d}{ds}(sF'(s))|_{s=1} = F''(1) + F'(1) \tag{10}$$

and

$$\sigma^2 = V(X) = \nu_2 - \nu_1^2 = F''(1) + F'(1) - [F'(1)]^2, \tag{11}$$

provided $E(X^2)$ exists.

Applying this result to the examples above yields

a) $F''(s) = N(N-1)p^2(ps+q)^{N-2}$

$F''(1) = N(N-1)p^2$

$\sigma^2 = N(N-1)p^2 + Np - N^2p^2 = Npq$

b) $F''(s) = \lambda^2 e^{\lambda(s-1)}, \qquad F''(1) = \lambda^2$

$\sigma^2 = \lambda^2 + \lambda - \lambda^2 = \lambda$

c) $F''(s) = \dfrac{2pq}{(1-qs)^3}, \qquad F''(1) = \dfrac{2q}{p^2}$

$\sigma^2 = \dfrac{2q}{p^2} + \dfrac{1}{p} - \dfrac{1}{p^2} = \dfrac{q}{p^2}$

d) $\ln F'(s) = \ln(mp) + (m-1)[\ln p + \ln s]$

$\qquad - (m+1)\ln(1-qs) \tag{12}$

$\dfrac{F''(s)}{F'(s)} = \dfrac{m-1}{s} + \dfrac{(m+1)q}{1-qs}$

$F''(1) = \dfrac{m}{p}\left[m - 1 + \dfrac{(m+1)q}{p}\right]$

$\qquad = \dfrac{m}{p^2}[m+q-p]$

$\sigma^2 = \dfrac{m}{p^2}(m+q-p) + \dfrac{m}{p} - \dfrac{m^2}{p^2}$

$\qquad = \dfrac{mq}{p^2}$

Example 2. If X is a discrete random variable such that $f_k = \Pr(X = k)$ for $k = 0$, $1, 2, \ldots$, we may be interested in the generating function for the random variable $Y = 2X + 3$, given $F(s)$, the generating function of X. Let

$$g_n = \Pr(Y = n) = \Pr(2X + 3 = n)$$

$$= \Pr\left(X = \frac{n-3}{2}\right) = f_{(n-3)/2}.$$

Then

$$G(s) = \sum_{n=0}^{\infty} g_n s^n = \sum_{n=0}^{\infty} f_{(n-3)/2}\, s^n$$

$$= \sum_{m=0}^{\infty} f_m s^{2m+3} = s^3 \sum f_m (s^2)^m = s^3 F(s^2).$$

Example 3. Find the generating function for the sequence $\{g_n\}$, with $g_n = \Pr(X > n)$, and

$$F(s) = \sum_{n=0}^{\infty} f_n s^n,$$

the pgf of X.

Solution. We have

$$g_n = f_{n+1} + f_{n+2} + f_{n+3} + \cdots, \qquad n \geq 0,$$

$$g_{n+1} = \qquad\quad f_{n+2} + f_{n+3} + \cdots, \qquad n \geq 0,$$

so that

$$g_n - g_{n+1} = f_{n+1},$$

$$g_n s^n - \frac{1}{s} g_{n+1} s^{n+1} = \frac{1}{s} f_{n+1} s^{n+1}, \tag{13}$$

$$\sum_{n=0}^{\infty} g_n s^n - \frac{1}{s} \sum_{n=0}^{\infty} g_{n+1} s^{n+1} = \frac{1}{s} \sum_{n=0}^{\infty} f_{n+1} s^{n+1}.$$

Now we note that

$$\sum_{n=0}^{\infty} f_{n+1} s^{n+1} = F(s) - f_0,$$

$$\sum_{n=0}^{\infty} g_{n+1} s^{n+1} = G(s) - g_0,$$

with $g_0 = \Pr(X > 0) = 1 - f_0$. Hence Eq. (13) yields

$$G(s) - \frac{1}{s}[G(s) - 1 + f_0] = \frac{1}{s}[F(s) - f_0], \tag{14}$$

$$G(s) = \frac{1 - F(s)}{1 - s}.$$

From $F(1) = 1$, we note that

$$\lim_{s \to 1} G(s) = F'(1) = E(X),$$

provided $E(X)$ exists, by applying L'Hospital's rule. If $E(X) = 1$, then we may set $G(1) = 1$, and $G(s)$ is a pgf. In all other cases the elements of $\{g_n\}$ are not the components of a frequency function.

If we are interested in the generating function for the sequence $\{h_n\}$ such that $h_n = \Pr(X \geq n)$, we note that $h_n = \Pr(X = n) + \Pr(X > n) = f_n + g_n$, so that $H(s) = F(s) + G(s)$. From Eq. (14) it follows that

$$H(s) = \frac{1 - sF(s)}{1 - s}, \tag{15}$$

Let the reader deduce that

$$\lim_{s \to 1} H(s) = E(X) + 1,$$

provided $E(X)$ exists.

Example 4. Let us consider the product of two generating functions. Thus

$$H(s) = F(s)G(s) = \sum_{k=0}^{\infty} f_k s^k \cdot \sum g_r s^r$$

$$= [f_0 + f_1 s + f_2 s^2 + \cdots] \cdot [g_0 + g_1 s + g_2 s^2 + \cdots]$$

$$= f_0 g_0 + (f_0 g_1 + f_1 g_0)s + (f_0 g_2 + f_1 g_1 + f_2 g_0)s^2 +$$

$$+ \cdots + (f_0 g_n + f_1 g_{n-1} + f_2 g_{n-2} + \cdots + f_n g_0)s^n + \cdots$$

If we write

$$H(s) = \sum_{n=0}^{\infty} h_n s^n,$$

it follows that

$$h_n = f_0 g_n + f_1 g_{n-1} + f_2 g_{n-2} + \cdots + f_n g_0 \tag{16}$$

for $n = 0, 1, 2, \ldots$. Whenever a sequence $\{h_n\}$ is obtained from two sequences $\{f_n\}$, $\{g_n\}$ by means of Eq. (16) we say that the sequence $\{h_n\}$ is the convolution of these two sequences, written $h = f*g = g*f$. Conversely, whenever $h = f*g$, it follows that $H(s) = F(s)G(s)$.

The result above is applicable to the following situation. Let X and Y be statistically independent random variables which assume the values $0, 1, 2, \ldots$, $n, \ldots$ with respective probabilities $\{f_n\}$ and $\{g_n\}$. Let $Z = X + Y$, so that $Z = n$ occurs for the mutually exclusive cases

$$(X = 0, Y = n), (X = 1, Y = n - 1), \ldots, (X = n, Y = 0).$$

Thus

$$h_n = \Pr(Z = n)$$

$$= f_0 g_n + f_1 g_{n-1} + \cdots + f_n g_0, \qquad n \geq 0,$$

since X and Y are statistically independent random variables. We note that $h = f*g$, so that

$$H(s) = F(s)G(s). \tag{17}$$

As an immediate generalization we have the following theorem.

Convolution theorem. If Z is the sum of a finite number of statistically independent random variables $X_1, X_2, \ldots, X_n$ which assume nonnegative integral values

$$Z = \sum_{i=1}^{n} X_i,$$

then the pgf associated with the random variable Z is the product of the pgf's associated with $X_1, X_2, \ldots, X_n$; i.e.,

$$H(s) = F_1(s)F_2(s) \ldots F_n(s). \tag{18}$$

Two examples come to mind immediately. For a single Bernoulli trial, $F(s) = q + ps$, so that for X of the class $B(p, n)$, we have $(q + ps)^n$ as the pgf of X. The pgf for the sum of n statistically independent Poisson processes with means $\lambda_1, \lambda_2, \ldots, \lambda_n$, is

$$H(s) = \exp[\lambda_1(s - 1)] \exp[\lambda_2(s - 1)] \cdots \exp[\lambda_n(s - 1)]$$

$$= \exp[\sum_{i=1}^{n} \lambda_i(s - 1)] = \exp[\lambda(s - 1)],$$

which yields a new Poisson process with mean

$$\lambda = \sum_{i=1}^{n} \lambda_i.$$

Example 5. Let $g_n = \Pr(X \leq n)$, so that

$$g_n = f_0 + f_1 + f_2 + \cdots + f_n, \qquad n \geq 0,$$

$$= 1 \cdot f_0 + 1 \cdot f_1 + 1 \cdot f_2 + \cdots + 1 \cdot f_n.$$

Hence $g = 1*f$, and

$$G(s) = \frac{1}{1 - s} \cdot F(s) = \frac{F(s)}{1 - s},$$

since the generating function for the sequence $\{1\}$ is $1/(1 - s)$.

Example 6. Let $S = X_1 + X_2 + \cdots + X_N$, with the X_i, $i = 1, 2, \ldots, N$, independent random variables with a common distribution; i.e., $\Pr(X_i = k) = f_k$ for $i = 1, 2, \ldots, N$, and all integers k. The pgf associated with S is

$$H(s) = [F(s)]^N. \tag{19}$$

This result is useful when one considers the following problem. Let N also be a random variable such that $\Pr(N = n) = g_n$, with

$$G(s) = \sum_{n=0}^{\infty} g_n s^n.$$

We note that

$$h_k = \Pr(S = k)$$

$$= \sum_{n=0}^{\infty} \Pr(N = n) \Pr(X_1 + X_2 + \cdots + X_n = k) \tag{20}$$

by applying Bayes' formula. Hence

$$H(s) = \sum_{k=0}^{\infty} h_k s^k$$

$$= \sum_{n=0}^{\infty} g_n \sum_{k=0}^{\infty} \Pr(X_1 + X_2 + \cdots + X_n = k) s^k$$

$$= \sum_{n=0}^{\infty} g_n [F(s)]^n = G(F(s)). \tag{21}$$

We note that $H(1) = G(F(1)) = G(1) = 1$. Also

$$H'(s) = G'(F(s))F'(s), \qquad \text{so that} \qquad H'(1) = G'(F(1))F'(1),$$

and

$$H'(1) = G'(1)F'(1), \qquad \text{so that} \qquad E(S) = E(N)E(X).$$

Equation (21) is the important compound formula applicable to problems of the following types.

Death Rates. Let N be the number of people who catch a certain disease, with N a random variable. Let $X_i = +1$ if the ith individual succumbs to this disease, $X_i = 0$ otherwise, with respective probabilities p and $q = 1 - p$. Then $S = X_1 + X_2 + \cdots + X_N$ is a random variable denoting the number of people who succumb to this disease. Let us assume that N is Poisson distributed, so that $G(s) = e^{\lambda(s-1)}$. Since $F(s) = q + ps$, the compound formula yields

$$H(s) = \exp \{\lambda[q + ps - 1]\} = \exp [\lambda p(s - 1)],$$

so that S is also Poisson distributed with a mean λp, and

$$h_k = \Pr(S = k) = \exp (-\lambda p) \frac{(\lambda p)^k}{k!}$$

is the probability that k people will succumb to the disease. We have assumed that the healing ability is an independent event as regards each individual.

Branching Processes. Let $f_k = \Pr(X = k)$ represent the probability that an individual can generate k new individuals for the next generation. Beginning with a single individual, we wish to determine the frequency function for the number of individuals present at the nth generation. Now suppose that N individuals are present at the nth generation, N a random variable with a pgf given by $F_n(s)$. The number of individuals present at the $(n + 1)$st generation is

$$R = X_1 + X_2 + \cdots + X_N,$$

with X_i, $i = 1, 2, \ldots, N$, the random variable designating the number of individuals produced by the ith individual. The compound formula yields

$$F_{n+1}(s) = F_n(F(s)), \tag{22}$$

with

$$F(s) = \sum_{k=0}^{\infty} f_k s^k$$

and $F(s) = F_1(s)$. Thus

$$F_2(s) = F_1(F(s)) = F(F(s)) = F(F_1(s)),$$
$$F_3(s) = F_2(F(s)) = F[F_1(F(s))] = F(F_2(s)),$$
$$F_4(s) = F_3(F(s)) = F[F_2(F(s))] = F(F_3(s)),$$

and by mathematical induction one can show that

$$F_{n+1}(s) = F(F_n(s)). \tag{23}$$

A differentiation yields

$$F'_{n+1}(s) = F'(F_n(s))F'_n(s),$$
$$F'_{n+1}(1) = F'(F_n(1))F'_n(1) = F'(1)F'_n(1), \tag{24}$$
$$\mu_{n+1} = \mu\mu_n,$$

with μ_n the mean number of individuals present at the nth generation, μ the mean number of individuals produced by a single individual*, $\mu = \mu_1$. It follows that $\mu_n = \mu^n$, so that

$$\lim_{n \to \infty} \mu_n = 0 \quad\quad \text{for} \quad\quad \mu < 1$$
$$= 1 \quad\quad \text{for} \quad\quad \mu = 1$$
$$= \infty \quad\quad \text{for} \quad\quad \mu > 1. \tag{25}$$

From Eq. (25) one would not be surprised that for $\mu > 1$ the probability of extinction of the species is zero.

Now let X_n be the probability that the species is extinct on the nth generation. Of course, if it is extinct before the nth generation, it is obvious that the species is

---

* It is fairly evident that if Y_n individuals are present at the nth generation, then the average number of individuals present at the next generation is $\mathscr{E}(Y_{n+1}) = \mu Y_n$. An average over all Y_n yields $\mu_{n+1} = \mu\mu_n$.

extinct on the nth generation. Thus $X_{n+1} \geq X_n$, which may also be proved by means of Eq. (23). Now the sequence $X_2, X_3, X_4, \ldots, X_n, \ldots$ is bounded above, $X_n \leq 1$, and is monotonic nondecreasing. From real variable theory it follows that

$$\lim_{n \to \infty} X_n = \xi \quad \text{with} \quad 0 < \xi \leq 1.$$

Since $X_n = F_n(0)$, and since $F_n(s)$ is continuous at $s = 0$, it follows from Eq. (23) that

$$\lim_{n \to \infty} X_{n+1} = \lim_{n \to \infty} F(X_n) = F(\lim_{n \to \infty} X_n),$$

$$\xi = F(\xi). \tag{26}$$

Of course, $\xi = 1$, satisfies Eq. (26). Let us see if there are any other values of ξ which may satisfy this equation. The graph of $y = s$ and $y = F(s)$ is shown in Fig. 8.

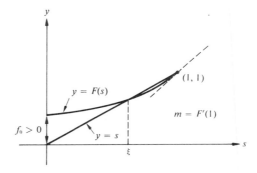

Figure 3.8

We know that $F(s)$ is monotonic in s, and that $F''(s) > 0$. Hence the curve is concave up, and a unique $\xi < 1$ exists, if and only if $\mu = F'(1) > 1$. Hence for $\mu > 1$ the probability that the species does not become extinct is $1 - \xi > 0$. For $\mu \leq 1$, we have $\xi = 1$, so that with probability one the species will eventually become extinct.

Before concluding this section, we show the use of generating functions in solving elementary difference equations. Consider the difference equation

$$f_{n+2} - 2f_{n+1} + f_n = 1, \qquad n = 0, 1, 2, 3, \ldots,$$

with $f_0 = 1, f_1 = 2$. Let

$$F(s) = \sum_{n=0}^{\infty} f_n s^n.$$

be the generating function for the sequence $\{f_n\}$. Hence,

$$\frac{1}{s^2} \sum_0^\infty f_{n+2} s^{n+2} - \frac{2}{s} \sum_0^\infty f_{n+1} s^{n+1} + \sum_0^\infty f_n s^n = \sum_0^\infty s^n,$$

$$\frac{1}{s^2}[F(s) - 1 - 2s] - \frac{2}{s}[F(s) - 1] + F(s) = \frac{1}{1 - s},$$

so that

$$F(s) = \frac{s^2}{(1 - s)^3} + \frac{1}{(1 - s)^2}. \tag{27}$$

Since

$$(1 - s)^{-2} = \sum_0^\infty n s^{n-1}, \qquad (1 - s)^{-3} = \sum_0^\infty \frac{n(n - 1)}{2} s^{n-2},$$

it follows that

$$F(s) = \sum_{n=0}^\infty \frac{n^2 + n + 2}{2} s^n, \tag{28}$$

yielding

$$f_n = \tfrac{1}{2}(n^2 + n + 2), \qquad n = 0, 1, 2, \ldots$$

Example 7. Consider the difference equation

$$f_{n+2} - 5f_{n+1} + 6f_n = 0, \qquad n \geq 0,$$

with $f_0 = 0, f_1 = 1$. Thus,

$$\sum_{n=0}^\infty f_{n+2} s^{n+2} - 5s \sum_{n=0}^\infty f_{n+1} s^{n+1} + 6s^2 \sum_{n=0}^\infty f_n s^n = 0$$

$$F(s) - s - 5sF(s) + 6s^2 F(s) = 0$$

$$F(s) = \frac{s}{(1 - 3s)(1 - 2s)} = \frac{A}{1 - 3s} + \frac{B}{1 - 2s}$$

We note that

$$A = \lim_{s \to 1/3} \frac{s}{1 - 2s} = 1, \qquad B = \lim_{s \to 1/2} \frac{s}{1 - 3s} = -1,$$

so that

$$F(s) = \frac{1}{1 - 3s} - \frac{1}{1 - 2s} = \sum_0^\infty 3^n s^n - \sum_0^\infty 2^n s^n,$$

yielding $f_n = 3^n - 2^n$ for $n = 0, 1, 2, 3, \ldots$

PROBLEMS

1. The random variable X assumes the values $0, 1, 2, \ldots, N - 1$ with probability $1/N$ at each value. Show that the pgf of X is

$$F(s) = \frac{1}{N} \frac{1 - s^N}{1 - s},$$

and show that

$$\lim_{s \to 1} F(s) = 1.$$

2. X is a discrete random variable such that

$$f_k = \Pr(X = k) = \frac{1}{k(k + 1)}, \qquad k = 1, 2, 3, \ldots$$

Show that

$$\sum_{k=1}^{\infty} f_k = 1.$$

Show that

$$F(s) = \frac{s - (1 + s) \ln (1 - s)}{s}.$$

Hint:

$$\frac{1}{n(n + 1)} = \frac{1}{n} - \frac{1}{n + 1}, \qquad \text{and} \qquad \sum_{1}^{\infty} s^{n-1} = \frac{1}{1 - s},$$

so that

$$\sum_{1}^{\infty} \frac{s^n}{n} = - \ln(1 - s) \qquad \text{for} \qquad |s| < 1.$$

3. Let X be a discrete random variable with a pgf given by $F(s)$. Find the generating functions of $Y = 3X + 1$.

4. Let $g_n = \Pr(X < n)$. Show that

$$G(s) = \sum_{0}^{\infty} g_n s^n = \frac{s F(s)}{(1 - s)}.$$

5. In a sequence of Bernoulli trials let f_n be the probability that two consecutive successes occur for the first time on trials $n - 1$ and n. Show that

$$f_n = q f_{n-1} + p q f_{n-2}$$

for $n \geq 3$, with $f_0 = f_1 = 0$, $f_2 = p^2$. Show that

$$F(s) = \frac{p^2 s^2}{1 - qs - pqs^2}.$$

Show that the mean is $(1 + p)/p^2$, and find the variance.

6. Solve the difference equation of Problem 5 above by means of the pgf for $p = q = \frac{1}{2}$.

7. N is a Poisson random variable with mean λ. If $N = n$ occurs we place n balls at random into r cells. Let $S = X_1 + X_2 + \cdots + X_n$, with $X_i = 1$ if ball i is placed into cell 1, $X_i = 0$ otherwise, $i = 1, 2, \ldots, n$. Hence S is a random variable designating the number of balls placed into cell 1. Show that the pgf associated with S is

$$H(s) = \exp[\tfrac{\lambda}{r}(s - 1)],$$

and that

$$f_k = \frac{\exp(-\tfrac{\lambda}{r}) \left(\dfrac{\lambda}{r}\right)^k}{k!}$$

is the probability that k balls are placed in cell 1.

8. Referring to Problem 7 above, show that

$$g_k = \binom{r}{k} \exp(-\tfrac{\lambda k}{r}) [1 - \exp(-\tfrac{\lambda}{r})]^{r-k}$$

is the probability of having exactly k cells empty.

9. Referring to Problem 1 above, let $S = X_1 + X_2 + \cdots + X_n$, with the X_k's independent, each of the same type as X. Show that the pgf of S is

$$G(s) = \frac{1}{N^n} \frac{(1 - s^N)^n}{(1 - s)^n}.$$

Show that

$$\Pr(S = r) = \sum_{k=0}^{n} (-1)^k \binom{n}{k} \binom{r - Nk + n - 1}{n - 1}.$$

10. The number, N, of animals trapped is a random variable such that $g_n = P(N = n) = qp^n$, $n = 0, 1, 2, \ldots$, with $0 < p < 1$. If an animal is trapped, the probability of not escaping is P, $0 < P < 1$. Show that

$$h_k = \frac{q}{1 - pQ} \left(\frac{pP}{1 - pQ}\right)^k$$

is the probability that k animals do not escape from their traps, with $P + Q = 1$.

11. Let $F(s)$ be a pgf, with

$$F(s) = f_0 + f_1 s + f_2 s^2 + \cdots + f_N s^N + R_N,$$
$$R_N = f_{N+1} s^{N+1} + f_{N+2} s^{N+2} + \cdots .$$

Show that

$$R_N < \frac{s^{N+1}}{1 - s} \qquad \text{for} \qquad 0 \le s < 1.$$

Next show that an integer N_0 exists such that for $N \ge N_0$, $R_N < \epsilon$ for arbitrary $\epsilon > 0$, ϵ fixed. Next consider a sequence of probability generating functions $G_r(s)$, $r = 1, 2, \ldots$, with

$$G_r(s) = \sum_{k=0}^{\infty} g_k(r) s^k.$$

Show that if $\lim_{r \to \infty} g_k(r) = f_k$, then

$$\lim_{r \to \infty} G_r(s) = F(s) \equiv \sum_{k=0}^{\infty} f_k \, s^k.$$

Conversely, it can be shown that if $\lim_{r \to \infty} G_r(s) = F(s)$, then $\lim_{r \to \infty} g_k(r) = f_k$, $k = 0, 1, 2, \ldots$

This is the continuity theorem for discrete random variables. As an example, consider X to be of the class $B(p, n)$, with $G_n(s) = [1 - p + ps]^n$. Let $n \to \infty$, $p \to 0$, such that $np = \lambda$. Then

$$G_n(s) = \left[1 - \frac{\lambda(1 - s)}{n} \right]^n$$

and

$$\lim_{n \to \infty} G_n(s) = e^{-\lambda(1-s)}.$$

Thus X approaches the Poisson distribution as a limiting case.

3.10 RECURRENT EVENTS · RANDOM WALK PROBLEM

Consider a sequence of Bernoulli trials with p the probability of a success and $q = 1 - p$ the probability of a failure on any trial. Let E be the event that two consecutive successes occur. Once E occurs we continue the trials and the game proceeds again. Thus in the sequence

$$SFFSFSS|SFFSFSS|SS|FSFFSS|S$$

the event E has occurred four times.

The example above leads us to a general study of recurrent events. We assume that once the event E occurs the game proceeds in the same manner under the equivalent initial probability considerations. Thus the trials need not be Bernoulli trials.

Now let f_n be the probability that a specific event E occurs for the first time on the nth transmission. In the above example the event E occurred for the first time on the seventh transmission. Let u_n be the probability that the event E occurs on the nth transmission but not necessarily for the first time.

For example, in the random walk problem discussed previously, let E be the event of a return to the origin. Then f_{10} would be the probability of a first return to the origin after 10 moves, whereas u_{10} would be a return to the origin after 10 moves but not necessarily for the first time. It is apparent that $u_n \geq f_n$. Moreover $f_0 = 0$, since if no trial has occurred the event E cannot have occurred.

Now the event E can occur on the nth trial in the following mutually exclusive ways. The event E can occur for the first time on the first trial, and subsequently occur on the $(n - 1)$st trial following this trial, not necessarily for the first time, or the event E can occur for the first time on the second trial followed by an occurrence of E on the subsequent $(n - 2)$nd trial, again not necessarily for the first time, and so on. Thus

$$u_n = f_1 u_{n-1} + f_2 u_{n-2} + \cdots + f_{n-1} u_1 + f_n \tag{1}$$

for $n \geq 1$. Equation (1) is not quite a convolution of the sequences $\{f_n\}$, $\{g_n\}$. Let us choose $u_0 = 1$. Since $f_0 = 0$ we have

$$u_n = f_0 u_n + f_1 u_{n-1} + f_2 u_{n-2} + \cdots + f_{n-1} u_1 + f_n u_0 \tag{2}$$

for $n \geq 1$. Now let $v_n = u_n$ for $n \geq 1$, $v_0 = 0$. Then

$$v_n = f_0 u_n + f_1 u_{n-1} + f_2 u_{n-2} + \cdots + f_n u_0 \tag{3}$$

for $n \geq 0$, so that the convolution theorem yields

$$V(s) = F(s)U(s), \tag{4}$$

with $F(s)$, $U(s)$, $V(s)$, the generating functions for the sequences $\{f_n\}$, $\{u_n\}$, $\{v_n\}$. Moreover, $V(s) = U(s) - u_0 = U(s) - 1$, so that

$$U(s) = \frac{1}{1 - F(s)} . \tag{5}$$

Now let

$$f = F(1) = \sum_{k=0}^{\infty} f_k, \tag{6}$$

$$u = U(1) = \sum_{k=0}^{\infty} u_k.$$

If $f = 1$, we say that the event E is *persistent*; and if $f < 1$, we say that the event E is *transient*. But from Eq. (5) it is clear that if $f = 1$, then $u = \infty$, and conversely. Thus, a necessary and sufficient condition that the event be persistent is that the series $\sum_0^{\infty} u_n$ diverges. If the series $\sum_0^{\infty} u_n$ converges, then u is finite and $f < 1$, a transient condition.

Since for most events it is simpler to compute u_n than to compute f_n, the above result is useful in determining whether an event is persistent or transient.

Example 1. For Bernoulli trials let E be the event that two consecutive successes occur. It is apparent that $u_n = qp^2$ for $n \geq 3$, $u_2 = p^2$. For $0 < p < 1$ the series $\sum_2^{\infty} u_n$ diverges so that the event E is persistent. For $p = 1$, $u_n = 1$ for $n \geq 2$, and again the event is persistent, an obvious fact. Let the reader deduce that for Bernoulli trials, $0 < p < 1$, that any event E composed of a finite sequence of successes and failures must be a persistent event.

Example 2. *Random walk problem.* Starting at the origin, let p be the probability of a unit step to the right and $q = 1 - p$ the probability of a unit step to the left. Then

$$u_{2n} = \binom{2n}{n} (pq)^n \tag{7}$$

is the probability of a return to the origin after $2n$ moves. From Stirling's approximation, namely

$$k! \approx \sqrt{2\pi k}\left(\frac{k}{e}\right)^k, \qquad k \gg 1, \tag{8}$$

we have

$$u_{2n} = \frac{(2n)!}{(n!)^2}(pq)^n \approx \frac{(4pq)^n}{\sqrt{n\pi}}. \tag{9}$$

For $p = q = \frac{1}{2}$,

$$u_{2n} \approx \frac{1}{\sqrt{n\pi}},$$

and the series $\sum_0^\infty u_{2n}$ diverges since the series $\sum_1^\infty 1/\sqrt{n}$ diverges. Hence $u = \infty$ and $f = 1$ so that the event is persistent.

For $p \neq q$ we have $4pq < 1$ which is left to the reader to verify. Since the series $\sum_0^\infty \alpha^n$ converges for $|\alpha| < 1$ with $\alpha = 4pq < 1$, it follows that $\sum_0^\infty u_{2n}$ converges, since each term is less than a convergent geometric series. Hence u is finite so that $f < 1$, and the event is transient. There is a nonzero probability of never returning to the origin.

We now derive a simple method for obtaining the mean number of trials until a persistent event E occurs. Suppose that u_n approaches a limit $\lambda \neq 0$ as $n \to \infty$. Thus $u_n = \lambda + \epsilon_n$, $\lim_{n\to\infty} \epsilon_n = 0$. Thus for every $\epsilon > 0$, there exists an integer $N = N(\epsilon)$ such that $|\epsilon_n| < \epsilon$ for $n \geq N$. Now choose $\epsilon \ll \lambda$. Then

$$U(s) = \sum_0^\infty u_n s^n$$

$$= \sum_0^\infty \lambda s^n + \sum_{n=0}^{N-1} \epsilon_n s^n + \sum_{n=N}^\infty \epsilon_n s^n$$

$$= \frac{\lambda}{1-s} + \sum_{n=0}^{N-1} \epsilon_n s^n + \sum_{n=N}^\infty \epsilon_n s^n, \qquad |s| < 1. \tag{10}$$

The middle term of Eq. (10) is a polynomial in s of degree at most $N - 1$. Moreover,

$$\left|\sum_{n=N}^\infty \epsilon_n s^n\right| \leq \epsilon \sum_{n=N}^\infty s^n = \frac{\epsilon s^N}{1-s} \leq \frac{\epsilon}{1-s}, \qquad 0 \leq s < 1. \tag{11}$$

Thus we note that

$$U(s) \approx \frac{\lambda}{1-s}, \qquad s < 1,$$

s close to one. It is also easily verified that

$$U'(s) \approx \frac{\lambda}{(1-s)^2}$$

for s close to unity, $s < 1$. From

$$F(s) = 1 - \frac{1}{U(s)},$$ (12)

(see Eq. 5) it follows that

$$\mu = F'(1) = \lim_{s \to 1} F'(s) = \lim_{s \to 1} \frac{U'(s)}{[U(s)]^2}$$

$$= \frac{1}{\lambda} = \frac{1}{\lim_{n \to \infty} u_n}.$$ (13)

One also notes that for $\lambda \neq 0$, $U(1) = \infty$, and the event E is persistent.

Example 3. For Bernoulli trials let E be the event that two consecutive successes occur. For $n \gg 1$ it is apparent that E will occur on the nth trial if the end of the sequence is FSS, or $FSSSS$, or $FSSSSSS$, etc., so that

$$\lambda = \lim_{n \to \infty} u_n = p^2 q + p^4 q + p^6 q + \cdots$$

$$= \frac{p^2 q}{1 - p^2} = \frac{p^2}{1 + p},$$

and

$$\mu = \frac{1 + p}{p^2}.$$

We conclude this section with a more sophisticated approach to the elementary random walk problem. Starting at the origin let p and q be the probabilities of moving a unit to the right and a unit to the left, respectively, or equivalently, of gaining and losing a unit, $p + q = 1$. Now let f_n be the probability of being one unit ahead for the first time on the nth game, see Fig. 9. Let g_n be the probability of being two units ahead for the first time after n games or moves.

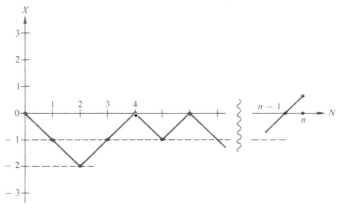

Figure 3.9

We note that $f_n = qg_{n-1}$, since we must lose the first game and subsequently gain two units for the first time in the remaining $(n-1)$ games. Moreover, $f_0 = 0$, $f_1 = p, f_2 = 0, f_3 = qp^2$, with $g_0 = g_1 = 0, g_2 = p^2$, so that $f_n = qg_{n-1}$ for $n \geq 3$. Hence

$$\sum_{n=3}^{\infty} f_n s^n = qs \sum_{n=3}^{\infty} g_{n-1} s^{n-1},$$

$$F(s) - ps = qsG(s). \tag{14}$$

We note also that

$$g_n = f_1 f_{n-1} + f_2 f_{n-2} + \cdots + f_{n-1} f_1, \qquad n \geq 1, \tag{15}$$

since a net gain of two units for the first time on the nth game can be accomplished only by a net gain of one unit for the first time on the kth game followed by another net gain of one unit for the first time in the subsequent $(n - k)$ games, $k = 1, 2, \ldots,$ $n - 1$. Of course $f_2, f_4, f_6, \ldots,$ all vanish, but this does not affect the analysis. Since $f_0 = g_0 = 0$ it follows that Eq. (15) also holds for $n = 0$, so that $g = f{*}f$, and $G(s) = [F(s)]^2$. Equation (14) now yields

$$F(s) - ps = qs[F(s)]^2,$$

so that

$$F(s) = \frac{1 - \sqrt{1 - 4pqs^2}}{2qs}, \tag{16}$$

with $F(0) = f_0 = 0$. We note that

$$F(1) = \frac{1 - \sqrt{1 - 4pq}}{2q} = \frac{1 - \sqrt{1 - 4p(1-p)}}{2q}$$

$$= \frac{1 - \sqrt{(1-2p)^2}}{2q} = \frac{1 - |1 - 2p|}{2q}$$

$$= \frac{1 - |p - q|}{2q}. \tag{17}$$

For the case $p \geq q$ we have $F(1) = 1$ and the event E is persistent (reaching the level one). For $p < q$, $F(1) = p/q < 1$, and the event is transient. If we interchange p and q we obtain the generating function for the sequence of probabilities involved in reaching a level $x = -1$ for the first time, so that

$$F_{-1}(s) = \frac{1 - \sqrt{1 - 4pqs^2}}{2ps}. \tag{18}$$

If h_n is the probability of a first return to the origin $(x = 0)$ on the nth game, then

$$h_n = qf_{n-1} + pf_{n-1}^{(-1)},$$

so that

$$H(s) = qsF(s) + psF_{-1}(s)$$

$$= 1 - \sqrt{1 - 4pqs^2}. \tag{19}$$

We observe that $H(1) = 1 - |p - q|$, so that the event concerning a first return to the origin is transient for $p \neq q$ and is persistent for $p = q = \frac{1}{2}$, a result noted previously. If u_n is the probability of a return to the origin (a return to $x = 0$) on the nth game, not necessarily for the first time, we have from Eq. (5),

$$U(s) = \frac{1}{1 - H(s)} = (1 - 4pqs^2)^{-1/2}. \tag{20}$$

Example 4. Let the probability that no zero occurs up to time n, be v_n, for the case $p = q = \frac{1}{2}$. Then

$$v_n = f_{n+1} + f_{n+2} + f_{n+3} + \cdots,$$

with f_n the probability of a first return to zero on the nth game. Equation (19) applies, so that

$$V(s) = \frac{1 - H(s)}{1 - s} = \frac{\sqrt{1 - s^2}}{1 - s}$$

$$= (1 + s) \frac{1}{\sqrt{1 - s^2}} = (1 + s)U(s).$$

We note that $v_{2n} = u_{2n}$ (coefficients of s^{2n}), so the probability that no zero occurs up to time $2n$ is the same as the probability of a return to zero at time $2n$.

PROBLEMS

1. Show that the mean number of Bernoulli trials for the occurrence of three consecutive successes is

$$\mu = \frac{(1 + p + p^2)}{p^3}.$$

2. A fair die is tossed repeatedly. The event E is the equal occurrence of the numbers 1 to 6. Show that E is transient.

3. Two fair coins are tossed repeatedly. The event E is the equal occurrence of the total number of heads thrown by the two coins. Show that E is persistent with an infinite mean recurrence time.

4. Consider the two dimensional random walk problem such that if the particle is at (m, n) the probabilities of moving to the points $(m + 1, n)$ $(m - 1, n)$ $(m, n + 1)$, $(m, n - 1)$ are all $\frac{1}{4}$. Starting at the origin show that the probability of returning to the origin after $2n$ moves (not necessarily for the first time), is

$$u_{2n} = \frac{1}{4^{2n}} \binom{2n}{n}^2.$$

Then show that the event is persistent.

5. For $p = q = \frac{1}{2}$, show that the generating function for the event that a return to zero occurs on the $(2n)$th game while never falling below the zero level, is

$$W(s) = [1 - \tfrac{1}{2}H(s)]^{-1}.$$

BIBLIOGRAPHY

1. W. FELLER, *An Introduction to Probability Theory and Its Applications*, Vol. I, 3rd ed., John Wiley & Sons, New York, 1968. A complete discussion of discrete probability theory on a sophisticated level. Highly recommended for the mathematically mature reader who should be fascinated by the extensive applications, many of which are rather difficult.

2. W. MENDENHALL, *Introduction to Probability and Statistics*, 2nd ed., Wadsworth Publishing Company, Belmont, California, 1967. An excellent introduction on an elementary level.

3. M. E. MUNROE, *Theory of Probability*, McGraw-Hill Book Company, New York, 1951. A readable elementary text.

4. E. PARZEN, *Modern Probability Theory and Its Applications*, John Wiley & Sons, New York, 1960.

5. J. V. USPENSKI, *Introduction to Mathematical Probability*, McGraw-Hill Book Company, New York, 1937. A highly recommended discussion of discrete probability theory.

CHAPTER 4

CONTINUOUS PROBABILITY THEORY

4.1 INTRODUCTION

In Chapter 3 we studied the subject of discrete probability theory wherein a random variable X could take on discrete values with nonzero probabilities. In the case of a fair coin, X was assigned the values ± 1, with equal probabilities $\frac{1}{2}$, the occurrence of a head represented by $X = +1$, and the occurrence of a tail represented by $X = -1$. For Δx small, the probability ΔP that X takes on a value between $1 - \Delta x/2$ and $1 + \Delta x/2$ is also $\frac{1}{2}$, so that ΔP does not approach zero as Δx tends to zero. It is this result which distinguishes discrete probability theory from continuous probability theory.

Let us consider an idealized spinner whose pointer can assume any one of the directions $0 \le x < 2\pi$, with x measured in radians and all values of x being equally likely. It makes very little sense to ask for the probability that the spinner will stop at the direction x_0, since x_0 is one possible outcome of an infinite number of equally likely outcomes. What does make sense is to ask for the probability that X will take on a value between x_0 and $x_0 + dx$, $dx > 0$. We define this probability as $dP = 1/(2\pi)\,dx$ for an idealized spinner. Note that $dP \to 0$ as $dx \to 0$. Furthermore dP is the ratio of dx to 2π (the total range of x).

We are now in a position to define a continuous random variable. Let X be a random variable which takes on the numerical values x, $-\infty < x < \infty$, and let a nonnegative function, $p(x)$, exist such that

$$1) \qquad\qquad dP = p(x)dx$$

is the probability that X will assume a value in the interval $(x, x + dx)$, except for infinitesimals of higher order. The value one obtains for X is the result of an experiment.

$$2) \qquad\qquad dP \to 0 \quad \text{as} \quad dx \to 0,$$

which, from (1) above, implies that $p(x)$ is finite for any real x.

$$3) \qquad\qquad \int_{-\infty}^{\infty} p(x)dx = 1,$$

which assures us that a definite value of X will occur as the outcome of an experiment. If the three conditions hold, we say that X is a one-dimensional continuous random variable. Moreover, we call $p(x)$ the probability density function associated with the random variable X, henceforth abbreviated as pdf.

It is not necessary that we denote the outcomes of X by the letter x, for if we had so desired we could designate these outcomes by the symbol t, $-\infty < t < \infty$, with $\int_{-\infty}^{\infty} p(t)dt = 1$, or by any other appropriate symbol. It follows immediately that for a single experiment,

$$\int_{a}^{b} p(x)dx \equiv \Pr(a \leq X \leq b) \tag{1}$$

is the probability that the random variable X lies in the interval (a, b).

Example 1. *The uniform PDF, $U(a, b)$.* The random variable X, with a pdf given by

$$p(x) = \frac{1}{b - a}, \qquad a \leq x \leq b, \qquad b > a,$$
$$= 0 \qquad\qquad \text{otherwise,} \tag{2}$$

is said to be a uniform random variable on the interval (a, b), and henceforth said to be of the class $U(a, b)$. The probability that X takes on a value in the interval (c, d), with $a \leq c \leq d \leq b$, is

$$P = \int_{c}^{d} p(x)dx = \frac{d - c}{b - a}. \tag{3}$$

We call P of Eq. (3) an interval function.

The graph of $p(x)$ versus x is shown in Fig. 1. Note that $p(x)$ is discontinuous at $x = a$ and at $x = b$, although X is a continuous random variable. The random variable X defined above is said to have a uniform distribution. Thus, in subsequent examples, we will deal with the exponential distribution, the Rayleigh distribution, the Cauchy distribution, the normal distribution, etc., which refer to the types of continuous random variables having special pdf's.

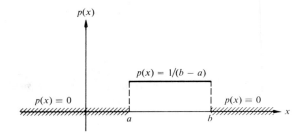

Figure 4.1

Example 2. Let us consider two trains A, B which arrive at random times between twelve and one o'clock, $0 \leq t \leq 1$. Let us assume that the arrival times of A and B are "independent," each with a uniform pdf, of the class $U(0, 1)$. By independent we mean that the arrival of train A in no way influences the arrival time of train B, and conversely. Subsequently we will give a mathematical definition of independent random variables. If T_A and T_B are the random variables associated with the arrival times of the two trains, we may be interested in the arrival time of the earlier train designated by the random variable $T = \min(T_A, T_B)$. It is our purpose to determine the pdf associated with T. From the analysis below it follows that to a first approximation

$$\Pr\{t \le T \le t + dt\} = \Pr\{t \le T_A \le t + dt, T_B > t\} + \Pr\{t \le T_B \le t + dt, T_A > t\}.$$

The probability that both trains arrive in the interval $(t, t + dt)$ is $(1\,dt)(1\,dt) = dt^2$, an infinitesimal of higher order, so we neglect this case. The probability that train A will arrive in the time interval $(t, t + dt)$ is dt, and the probability that train B will arrive after train A, in the time interval $(t + dt, 1)$ is $1 - (t + dt)$. From our assumption of independence we note that $dP_1 = dt(1 - t - dt) \approx (1 - t)\,dt$, is the probability that train A is the earlier of the two trains arriving in the interval $(t, t + dt)$. From symmetry it is apparent that the same result applies for the case in which B is the earlier train. Hence $dP = 2(1 - t)dt$ is the probability that the earlier train will arrive in the time interval $(t, t + dt)$, neglecting infinitesimals of higher order. Note that $dP \to 0$ as $dt \to 0$. The pdf of T is $p(t) = 2(1 - t)$ for $0 \le t \le 1$, $p(t) = 0$ otherwise. Furthermore

$$\int_0^1 p(t)dt = 2 \int_0^1 (1 - t)dt = 1.$$

The graph of $p(t)$ versus t is shown in Fig. 2.

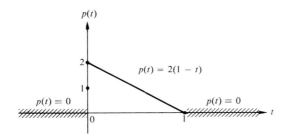

Figure 4.2

We can obtain the same result for $p(t)$ as follows. The probability that both trains arrive after time t is $(1 - t)^2$, and the probability that both trains arrive after time $t + dt$ is $(1 - t - dt)^2$. Thus

$$dP = (1 - t)^2 - (1 - t - dt)^2 = 2(1 - t)dt - dt^2$$

is the probability that the earlier train will arrive in the time interval $(t, t + dt)$. It follows that

$$p(t) = \lim_{dt \to 0} \frac{dP}{dt} = 2(1 - t).$$

Example 3. *The Exponential PDF.* Suppose that an electron tube begins to function at $t = 0$. We assume, further, that if the tube has functioned properly up to time $t > 0$, then $(1/\mu)dt$ is the probability that the tube will fail to function in the time interval $(t, t + dt)$, with μ a positive constant. Now let $p(t)dt$ be the probability that the tube will fail to function in the time interval $(t, t + dt)$. To accomplish this result the tube must function properly up to time t and then must fail to function in the time interval $(t, t + dt)$.

Since $\int_0^t p(\tau)d\tau$ is the probability that the tube fails in the interval $(0, t)$, of necessity, $1 - \int_0^t p(\tau)d\tau$ is the probability that the tube functions properly up to time t. Hence

$$p(t)dt = \left[1 - \int_0^t p(\tau)d\tau \right]\frac{dt}{\mu},$$

$$\mu p(t) = 1 - \int_0^t p(\tau)d\tau.$$
(4)

Assuming that $p(t)$ is continuous, we obtain upon differentiating that $\mu p'(t) = -p(t)$, so that $p(t) = Ke^{-t/\mu}$. From $\int_0^\infty p(t)dt = 1$ (the tube fails eventually), we obtain $K = 1/\mu$, so that

$$p(t) = \frac{1}{\mu} e^{-t/\mu} U(t),$$
(5)

with $U(t) = 1$ for $t \geq 0$, $U(t) = 0$ for $t < 0$, the unit step function. The graph of the exponential distribution $\mathscr{E}(\mu)$ is shown in Fig. 3. The single parameter μ characterizes this pdf.

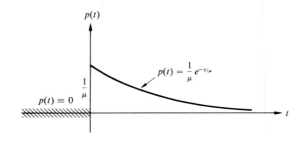

Figure 4.3

Example 4. *The Rayleigh PDF.* If in Example 3 we assume that $t \, (dt/\alpha^2)$ is the probability that the tube will fail to function in the time interval $(t, t + dt)$, given that it has functioned properly up to time t, then, as above, we obtain

$$1 - \int_0^t p(\tau)d\tau = \frac{\alpha^2 p(t)}{t}.$$

A differentiation yields

$$\alpha^2 \frac{d}{dt}\left(\frac{p(t)}{t} \right) = -p(t).$$

Let the reader show that

$$p(t) = \frac{t}{\alpha^2} \exp\left(-\frac{t^2}{2\alpha^2}\right) U(t). \tag{6}$$

The graph of the Rayleigh pdf is shown in Fig. 4.

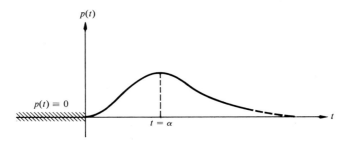

Figure 4.4

Example 5. *The Cauchy PDF.* In Fig. 5, Θ is a random variable which takes on the values $-\pi/2 \le \theta \le \pi/2$ uniformly, so that $p(\theta) = 1/\pi$ for $-\pi/2 \le \theta \le \pi/2$, $p(\theta) = 0$ otherwise. The values of Θ can be obtained by means of a spinner. The line OP is extended to the point Q on the x-axis. Each value of θ yields a unique value of x. The set of all x obtained in this fashion yields a random variable X whose pdf we wish to obtain.

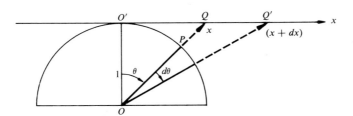

Figure 4.5

Now we note that if X lies in the range $(x, x + dx)$, then Θ lies in the range $(\theta, \theta + d\theta)$, and conversely, with $\theta = \tan^{-1} x$. Consequently

$$q(x)dx = p(\theta)d\theta = \frac{1}{\pi} d\theta.$$

From $d\theta = dx/(1 + x^2)$, it follows that

$$q(x) = \frac{1}{\pi} \frac{1}{1 + x^2}, \qquad -\infty < x < \infty,$$

with $q(x)$ the pdf associated with X. The most general Cauchy pdf is given by

$$p(x) = \frac{b}{\pi} \frac{1}{(x - \mu)^2 + b^2}, \qquad -\infty < x < \infty, \tag{7}$$

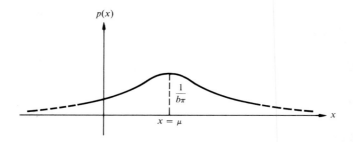

$p(x)$

$\frac{1}{b\pi}$

$x = \mu$

x

Figure 4.6

which is characterized by the two parameters μ, b. The graph of $p(x)$ versus x is shown in Fig. 6.

Example 6. *The Normal, or Gaussian, PDF:* $N(\mu, \sigma^2)$. We will note subsequently that

$$p(x) = \frac{1}{\sqrt{2\pi}\sigma} \exp\left(-\frac{(x-\mu)^2}{2\sigma^2}\right), \qquad -\infty < x < \infty, \qquad (8)$$

is the most important pdf of probability theory and statistics. The random variable X with this pdf is called the normal or Gaussian random variable. At present we note some simple properties of $p(x)$. Since $\ln p$ is monotonic in p (i.e., $\ln p_1 > \ln p_2$ whenever $p_1 > p_2$), it follows that $p(x)$ is a maximum when $\ln p(x)$ is a maximum. Now

$$\ln p(x) = \ln\left(\frac{1}{\sqrt{2\pi}\sigma}\right) - \frac{(x-\mu)^2}{2\sigma^2},$$

$$\frac{1}{p(x)} \frac{d}{dx} p(x) = -\frac{(x-\mu)}{\sigma^2}, \qquad (9)$$

$$\frac{1}{p} \frac{d^2p}{dx^2} - \frac{1}{p^2}\left(\frac{dp}{dx}\right)^2 = -\frac{1}{\sigma^2}.$$

Setting $p'(x) = 0$ yields $x = \mu$, which is the point at which $p(x)$ is a maximum (see Eq. 8). Moreover,

$$p''(x) = \frac{p(x)}{\sigma^4}[-\sigma^2 + (x-\mu)^2],$$

so that $p''(x) = 0$ at the two points $x = \mu \pm \sigma$. These are the inflection points each located at a distance σ from μ. The graph of $p(x)$ versus x is shown in Fig. 7.

Example 7. *The Dirac Delta Function.* There are random variables which are neither discrete nor continuous. Consider a random variable X which takes on the value $X = -1$ with probability $\frac{1}{2}$, and the values $0 \le x \le 1$ with pdf $p(x) = \frac{1}{2}$, i.e., for any subinterval $(x_1, x_2) \subset (0, 1)$,

$$\Pr(x_1 < X < x_2) = \tfrac{1}{2}(x_2 - x_1).$$

(The values of X might be determined by the following (idealized) experiment. A fair coin is tossed; if a tail appears, set $X = -1$; if a head appears, spin an unbiased pointer with uniform circular scale running from 0 to 1, and set X equal to the number indicated by the pointer.)

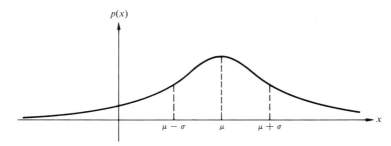

Figure 4.7

The random variable X is neither a discrete nor a continuous random variable. The Dirac delta function discussed in Section 12 of the Appendix enables us to express the pdf of X in a simple fashion. Consider

$$p(x) = \tfrac{1}{2}\delta(x + 1) + \tfrac{1}{2}[U(x) - U(x - 1)] \tag{10}$$

with $U(x)$ the unit step function, so that

$$U(x) - U(x - 1) = 0 \qquad \text{for} \qquad x < 0,$$
$$= 1 \qquad \text{for} \qquad 0 < x < 1,$$
$$= 0 \qquad \text{for} \qquad x > 1.$$

Thus

$$\int_{-\infty}^{\infty} p(x)dx = \tfrac{1}{2} \int_{-\infty}^{\infty} \delta(x + 1)dx + \tfrac{1}{2}\int_0^1 dx$$
$$= \tfrac{1}{2} + \tfrac{1}{2} = 1.$$

The graph of $p(x)$ versus x is shown in Fig. 8. The spike at $x = -1$ represents a discrete occurrence.

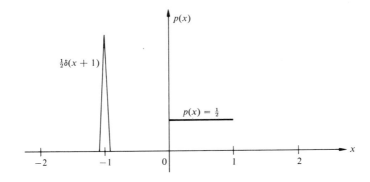

Figure 4.8

PROBLEMS

1. Let X be of the class $U(0, 1)$. Expressing the value of X in decimal notation, what is the probability that the digit in the seventh position is a 5?

2. Show that for the exponential distribution

$$\Pr(X \geq \alpha) = e^{-\alpha/\mu}, \qquad \alpha \geq 0.$$

3. Three trains arrive independently in the time interval ($0 \leq t \leq 1$), each arrival time being a random variable of the class $U(0, 1)$. Show that $p(t) = 3(1 - t)^2, 0 \leq t \leq 1$, $p(t) = 0$ otherwise, is the pdf for the arrival time T of the earliest of the three trains.

4. Referring to Problem 3, show that $p(t) = 3t^2, 0 \leq t \leq 1$, $p(t) = 0$ otherwise, is the pdf for the arrival time T of the latest of the three trains.

5. Referring to Problem 3, show that $p(t) = 6t(1 - t), 0 \leq t \leq 1$, $p(t) = 0$ otherwise, is the pdf for the arrival time T of the middle train.

6. For what values of x does the Cauchy pdf of Eq. (7) reach a maximum value? Are there any points of inflection?

7. For what value of x does the Rayleigh pdf of Eq. (6) reach a maximum value?

8. Referring to Example 7, show that

$$\Pr(X \leq \tfrac{1}{4}) = \tfrac{5}{8},$$
$$\Pr(X \leq -\tfrac{1}{2}) = \tfrac{1}{2},$$
$$\Pr(X \geq 2) = 0.$$

9. Show that Eq. (6) holds.

10. Show that for the Cauchy distribution,

$$\lim_{R \to \infty} \int_{\mu-R}^{\mu+R} x \, p(x) \, dx = 0,$$

but that $\int_{-\infty}^{\infty} x \, p(x) \, dx$ does not exist.

11. Show that $p(x) = 1/(2\sqrt{x}), 0 < x \leq 1$, $p(x) = 0$ otherwise, represents the pdf of a continuous random variable.

12. Sketch

$$p(x) = \frac{1}{2\sqrt{2\pi}\sigma} \left[\exp\left(-\frac{(x - \mu)^2}{2\sigma^2} \right) + \exp\left(-\frac{(x + \mu)^2}{2\sigma^2} \right) \right],$$

$-\infty < x < \infty$, with $\mu > 0, \sigma > 0$.

13. Consider

$$\int_{-\infty}^{\infty} \exp(-x^2/2) \, dx \int_{-\infty}^{\infty} \exp(-y^2/2) \, dy = \int_{-\infty}^{\infty} \int_{-\infty}^{\infty} \exp\left(-\frac{(x^2 + y^2)}{2} \right) dy \, dx$$

$$= \int_{0}^{\infty} \int_{0}^{2\pi} \exp(-r^2/2) \, r \, dr \, d\theta.$$

Show that

$$\int_{-\infty}^{\infty} \exp(-x^2/2) \, dx = \sqrt{2\pi}.$$

14. The probability that a tube fails to function in the time interval $(t, t + dt)$ is $\phi(t)\,dt$, provided the tube has functioned properly up to time t. Given $\int_0^\infty \phi(t)\,dt = \infty$, show that

$$p(t) = \phi(t)\,\exp[-\textstyle\int_0^t \phi(\tau)\,d\tau]\,U(t)$$

is the pdf for the time at which the tube first fails to function.

15. The angle $\Theta = \theta$ is a random variable, $U(0, \pi)$. A line is drawn through the point (a, b) of the x-y plane, making an angle θ with the y-axis and intersecting the x-axis at the point $X = x$. Find the pdf for the random variable X; see Eq. (7).

16. A number is chosen at random from the interval $(0, 1)$ by virtue of a uniform pdf. Find the probability that the first decimal place of the square of the number is the integer k. *Hint:* Let A_k be the set of numbers on the unit interval whose squares are such that the first decimal is the integer k, so that the probability of the occurrence of the set A_k is

$$P(A_k) = \Pr\left(\frac{k}{10} \le X^2 < \frac{k+1}{10}\right).$$

Show that

$$P(A_k) = \sqrt{\frac{k+1}{10}} - \sqrt{\frac{k}{10}}, \qquad \sum_{k=0}^{9} p(A_k) = 1.$$

17. In Problem 16 let B_k be the set for which the second decimal place of $\sqrt{X}$ is the integer k. Find $P(B_k)$. [*Hint:* If $\sqrt{X} = 0.mk\cdots$, then $100\sqrt{X} = mk.\cdots \ge 10m + k$, and $100\sqrt{X} < 10m + (k + 1)$, for $m = 0, 1, 2, \ldots, 9$.] Show that

$$P(B_k) = \sum_{m=0}^{9} \Pr\left[\frac{1}{100}\left(m + \frac{k}{10}\right)^2 \le X \le \frac{1}{100}\left(m + \frac{k+1}{10}\right)^2\right]$$

$$= \frac{1}{10{,}000} \sum_{m=0}^{9} (20m + 2k + 1)$$

$$= 0.091 + 0.002k.$$

Then obtain

$$\sum_{k=0}^{9} P(B_k) = 1.$$

4.2 THE CUMULATIVE DISTRIBUTION FUNCTION: CDF

Let X be a real valued random variable with a pdf given by $f(x)$, $-\infty < x < \infty$. It follows that $f(t)dt$ is the probability that X will lie in the interval $(t, t + dt)$ as the result of a single experiment. Thus

$$F(x) = \int_{-\infty}^{x} f(t)dt = \Pr(X \le x) \tag{1}$$

represents the probability that for a single experiment the random variable X takes

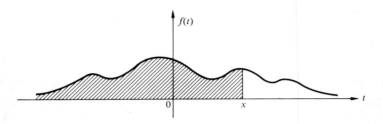

Figure 4.9

on a value less than or equal to the real parameter x. We call $F(x)$ the cumulative distribution function of X, abbreviated as the cdf of X.

In Fig. 9, $F(x)$ represents the accumulated area under the curve $f(t)$ from $t = -\infty$ to $t = x$. Before proceeding with examples let us note that

$$F(-\infty) = 0,$$
$$F(\infty) = 1.$$
$$\Pr(x \le X \le y) = \int_x^y f(t)dt = \int_{-\infty}^y f(t)dt - \int_{-\infty}^x f(t)dt$$
$$= F(y) - F(x), \tag{2}$$
$$F(y) \ge F(x) \qquad \text{for} \qquad y \ge x.$$

The fundamental theorem of the integral calculus applied to Eq. (1) yields

$$\frac{dF(x)}{dx} = f(x), \tag{3}$$

whenever f is continuous at the point x. This is a most important result regarding the cdf. A knowledge of the cdf enables one to obtain the pdf by a simple differentiation for those values of x for which $f(x)$ is continuous.

Example 1. Referring to the pdf of Example 1 we note that $F(x) = 0$ for $x < a$ since $f(t) = 0$ for $-\infty < t < a$. For $a < x < b$ we have

$$F(x) = \int_{-\infty}^a 0 \cdot dt + \int_a^x \frac{1}{b-a} dt = \frac{x-a}{b-a},$$

and for $x \ge b$ it is apparent that $F(x) = 1$. The graph of $F(x)$ versus x is shown in Fig. 10.

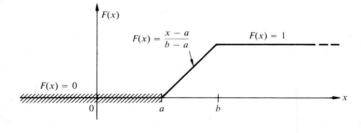

Figure 4.10

We note that $F(x)$ is continuous everywhere, but $F(x)$ is not differentiable at $x = a$ and at $x = b$. We obtain

$$f(x) = F'(x) = 0 \qquad \text{for} \quad x < a,$$

$$= \frac{1}{b - a} \qquad \text{for} \quad a < x < b, \tag{4}$$

$$= 0 \qquad \text{for} \quad x > b.$$

We cannot obtain the value of $f(x)$ at $x = a$ and at $x = b$, since $f(x)$ is discontinuous at these points. The value of $f(x)$ at $x = a$ and $x = b$ need not concern us, since X is a continuous random variable. As a matter of fact, two random variables X and Y are equivalent if their pdf's differ only at a countable number of points.

Example 2. Referring to the exponential pdf of Example 3 of Section 4.1, we note that $F(x) = 0$ for $x < 0$. For $x \geq 0$ we have

$$F(x) = \int_{-\infty}^{0} 0 \cdot dt + \frac{1}{\mu} \int_{0}^{x} e^{-t/\mu} \, dt$$

$$= 1 - e^{-x/\mu}, \qquad x \geq 0. \tag{5}$$

Note that $F(0) = 0$, and that $\lim_{x \to \infty} F(x) = 1$. The graph of $F(x)$ versus x is shown in Fig. 11. $F(x)$ is continuous everywhere but is not differentiable at $x = 0$. Furthermore,

$$f(x) = F'(x) = 0 \qquad \text{for} \quad x < 0,$$

$$= \frac{1}{\mu} e^{-x/\mu} \qquad \text{for} \quad x > 0,$$

which yields the pdf of X except at $x = 0$.

Example 3. Referring to the Rayleigh pdf of Example 4, Section 4.1, we note that $F(x) = 0$ for $x < 0$, and for $x \geq 0$,

$$F(x) = \frac{1}{\alpha^2} \int_{0}^{x} t \exp\left(-t^2/2\alpha^2\right) dt$$

$$= 1 - \exp\left(-x^2/2\alpha^2\right).$$

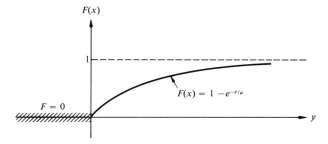

$F(x)$

1

$F = 0$

$F(x) = 1 - e^{-x/\mu}$

y

Figure 4.11

The graph of $F(x)$ versus x is shown in Fig. 12. The point of inflection occurs at $x = \alpha$. Furthermore,

$$f(x) = F'(x) = \frac{x}{\alpha^2} \exp\left(-x^2/2\alpha^2\right) \qquad \text{for} \qquad x \geq 0,$$

or

$$f(t) = \frac{t}{\alpha^2} \exp\left(-t^2/2\alpha^2\right) \qquad \text{for} \qquad t \geq 0.$$

Let the reader show that for $t_2 > t_1 > 0$,

$$\Pr(t_1 \leq T \leq t_2) = \exp\left(-t_1^2/2\alpha^2\right) - \exp\left(-t_2^2/2\alpha^2\right).$$

Example 4. Referring to the normal pdf of Example 6, Section 4.1, we obtain

$$F(x) = \frac{1}{\sqrt{2\pi}\sigma} \int_{-\infty}^{x} \exp\left[-(t - \mu)^2/2\sigma^2\right] dt \tag{6}$$

for $-\infty < x < \infty$. Although we cannot evaluate this integral in closed form, the change of variable of integration, $t - \mu = \sigma\xi$, yields an integral for $F(x)$ amenable to evaluation from a table of the incomplete error function. Thus

$$F(x) = \frac{1}{\sqrt{2\pi}} \int_{-\infty}^{(x-\mu)/\sigma} \exp\left(-\xi^2/2\right) d\xi = E\left(\frac{x - \mu}{\sigma}\right), \tag{7}$$

with $E(y)$ defined by

$$E(y) = \frac{1}{\sqrt{2\pi}} \int_{-\infty}^{y} \exp\left(-\xi^2/2\right) d\xi. \tag{8}$$

To find an approximate value of $E(y)$ for large y we note that

$$\begin{aligned}
E(y) &= 1 - \frac{1}{\sqrt{2\pi}} \int_{y}^{\infty} \exp\left(-\xi^2/2\right) d\xi \\
&= 1 - \frac{1}{\sqrt{2\pi}} \int_{y}^{\infty} \frac{1}{\xi} d[-\exp\left(-\xi^2/2\right)] \\
&= 1 + \frac{1}{\sqrt{2\pi}} \frac{1}{\xi} \exp\left(-\xi^2/2\right) \Big|_{y}^{\infty} + \frac{1}{\sqrt{2\pi}} \int_{y}^{\infty} \frac{1}{\xi^2} \exp\left(-\xi^2/2\right) d\xi \\
&= 1 - \frac{1}{\sqrt{2\pi}} \frac{1}{y} \exp\left(-y^2/2\right) + \frac{1}{\sqrt{2\pi}} \int_{y}^{\infty} \frac{1}{\xi^2} \exp\left(-\xi^2/2\right) d\xi
\end{aligned} \tag{9}$$

upon integrating by parts. Now

$$\int_{y}^{\infty} \frac{1}{\xi^2} \exp\left(-\xi^2/2\right) d\xi < \frac{1}{y^2} \int_{y}^{\infty} \exp\left(-\xi^2/2\right) d\xi,$$

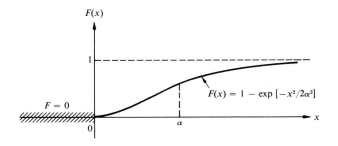

Figure 4.12

so that for $y \gg 1$ we may neglect this term and obtain

$$E(y) \approx 1 - \frac{1}{\sqrt{2\pi}}\frac{1}{y} \exp(-y^2/2). \qquad (10)$$

A repeated integration by parts of the last integral of Eq. (9) yields

$$E(y) \approx 1 - \frac{1}{\sqrt{2\pi}} \exp(-y^2/2)\left(\frac{1}{y} - \frac{1}{y^3}\right). \qquad (11)$$

It can be shown that integrating by parts indefinitely produces an infinite series which does not converge. This does not destroy the validity of the first few terms in the expansion as an approximate value of $E(y)$ for y large. A short table for $E(y)$ is listed below.

y	1	1.282	1.645	1.960	2.326	2.576	3.090
$E(y)$	0.84	0.90	0.95	0.975	0.99	0.995	0.999

Example 5. Let $f(x) = 1 - |x|$, $-1 \le x \le 1$, $f(x) = 0$ otherwise, be the pdf of a random variable X. The graph of $f(x)$ versus x is shown in Fig. 13.

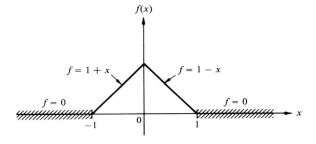

Figure 4.13

Since the form of $f(x)$ changes, we must be careful in obtaining the cdf, $F(x)$. We observe that

$$F(x) = \int_{-\infty}^{x} f dt = \int_{-\infty}^{x} 0 dt = 0 \quad \text{for} \quad x < -1,$$

$$F(x) = \int_{-\infty}^{-1} f dt + \int_{-1}^{x} f(t) dt = \int_{-1}^{x} (1 + t) dt$$
$$= \tfrac{1}{2}(1 + x)^2 \quad \text{for} \quad -1 \le x \le 0,$$

$$= F(0) + \int_{0}^{x} (1 - t) dt = \frac{1}{2} + x - \frac{x^2}{2} \quad \text{for} \quad 0 \le x \le 1,$$

$$= 1 \quad \text{for} \quad x \ge 1.$$

The graph of $F(x)$ versus x is shown in Fig. 14.

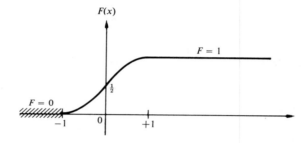

Figure 4.14

Example 6. Let $\lambda(t)dt$ be the probability that a piece of equipment will fail to function in the time interval $(t, t + dt)$, given that it has functioned properly up to time t. If $f(t)dt$ represents the probability that the equipment first fails in the time interval $(t, t + dt)$, then

$$f(t)dt = [1 - F(t)]\lambda(t)dt, \tag{12}$$

since $1 - F(t)$ is the probability that there is no failure up to time t, with $F(t)$ the cdf of $f(t)$. From $f(t) = \lambda(t)[1 - F(t)]$ we obtain, by differentiating, that

$$f'(t) = \lambda'(t)[1 - F(t)] - \lambda F'(t)$$
$$= f(t) \frac{\lambda'(t)}{\lambda(t)} - \lambda f(t), \tag{13}$$

so that

$$\frac{f'(t)}{f(t)} = \frac{\lambda'(t)}{\lambda(t)} - \lambda(t). \tag{14}$$

A simple integration yields

$$\ln f(t) = \ln \lambda(t) - \int \lambda(t) dt,$$

and

$$f(t) = K\lambda(t) \exp\left[-\int_{0}^{t} \lambda(\tau) d\tau\right].$$

We may deduce from $\int_0^\infty f(t)dt = 1$ and the assumption that $\int_0^\infty \lambda(\tau)d\tau = \infty$, that $K \equiv 1$. Hence

$$f(t) = \lambda(t) \exp\left[-\int_0^t \lambda(\tau)d\tau\right]. \tag{15}$$

The Exponential and Rayleigh pdf's are special cases of the above result, with $\lambda(t) = 1/\mu$, $\lambda(t) = t/\alpha^2$, respectively.

Example 7. Let X be $U(0, 1)$. Let us sample n times (independent samples), and consider the n-tuple of values obtained, say $(x_1, x_2, \ldots, x_n)$. Each time we sample n times we obtain an n-tuple of values. It is in this sense that we may consider the random variable $Z = \max(X_1, X_2, \ldots, X_n)$ with X_i, $i = 1, 2, \ldots, n$, each of the class $U(0, 1)$. Let us determine the cdf of Z, say $F(z)$. In order that $\max(x_1, x_2, \ldots, x_n) \leq z$, of necessity $x_1 \leq z$, $x_2 \leq z, \ldots, x_n \leq z$, and conversely. The probability that $X_i \leq z$ is z for $i = 1, 2, \ldots, n$, so that $F(z) = z^n$, and $f(z) = F'(z) = nz^{n-1}$, $0 \leq z \leq 1$, $f(z) = 0$ otherwise, is the pdf of Z. We emphasize again that

$$F(z) = \Pr(Z \leq z) = \Pr\{X_i \leq z, i = 1, 2, \ldots, n\} = [\Pr(X_1 \leq z)]^n = z^n.$$

Example 8. Let X be a random variable defined as follows. If a head occurs $(p = \tfrac{1}{2})$ we obtain $x = 2$. If a tail occurs we choose x from $U(0, 1)$. Thus

$$f(x) = \tfrac{1}{2}\delta(x - 2) + \tfrac{1}{2}[U(x) - U(x - 1)].$$

The graph of $F(x)$ versus x is shown in Fig. 15. The discontinuity at $x = 2$ occurs because X takes on the value $x = 2$ with nonzero probability $(\tfrac{1}{2})$. The jump in the discontinuity of $F(x)$ at $x = 2$ is precisely $\tfrac{1}{2}$, the probability that $X = 2$. In general, when $F(x)$ is discontinuous at $x = x_0$, the jump in the discontinuity at x_0 is the probability that $X = x_0$.

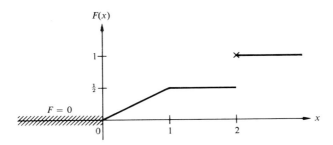

Figure 4.15

Example 9. Let X be of the class $U(0, 1)$. Consider the new random variable $Y = \sqrt{X}$. To find the cdf of Y we note that

$$\Pr(Y \leq y) = \Pr(\sqrt{X} \leq y)$$
$$= \Pr(X \leq y^2) = y^2, \qquad 0 \leq y \leq 1,$$

so that $F(y) = y^2$, $0 \leq y \leq 1$, is the cdf of Y, with $F(y) = 0$ or 1, otherwise. The pdf of Y is simply $f(y) = F'(y) = 2y$, $0 \leq y \leq 1$, $f(y) = 0$ otherwise.

Example 10. Let X be $N(0, 1)$ and $Y = X^2$. We wish to determine the pdf of Y. Now for $y > 0$,

$$
\begin{aligned}
F(y) = \Pr(Y \le y) &= \Pr(X^2 \le y) \\
&= \Pr(-\sqrt{y} \le X \le \sqrt{y}) \\
&= \frac{1}{\sqrt{2\pi}} \int_{-\sqrt{y}}^{\sqrt{y}} \exp\left(-x^2/2\right) dx = \frac{2}{\sqrt{2\pi}} \int_{0}^{\sqrt{y}} \exp\left(-x^2/2\right) dx
\end{aligned}
$$

is the cdf of Y. Hence

$$
\begin{aligned}
f(y) = F'(y) &= \frac{2}{\sqrt{2\pi}} \exp\left(-y/2\right) \frac{d\sqrt{y}}{dy} \\
&= \frac{1}{\sqrt{2\pi y}} \exp\left(-y/2\right) U(y)
\end{aligned}
$$

is the pdf of Y, with $f(y) = 0$ for $y < 0$.

In the previous two examples we have seen how the cdf enables one to find the pdf of a new random variable. Let X be a random variable with a pdf given by $p(x)$, $-\infty < x < \infty$. Now let $Y = \phi(X)$ represent a new random variable, and let us assume that $\phi'(x)$ exists, $\phi'(x) > 0$, so that to each real y there exists a unique x, given by $x = \psi(y)$. Then

$$
\begin{aligned}
F(y) = \Pr(Y \le y) &= \Pr(\phi(x) \le y) \\
&= \Pr(x \le \psi(y)) \\
&= \int_{-\infty}^{\psi(y)} p(x) dx
\end{aligned} \tag{16}
$$

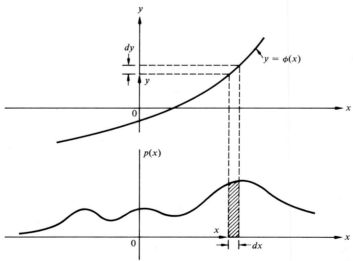

Figure 4.16

is the cdf of Y. From the calculus we have

$$q(y) = F'(y) = p[x = \psi(y)] \, (d\psi/dy) \tag{17}$$

as the pdf of the random variable Y. Equation (17) may be obtained from the following graphical point of view (Fig. 16).

From Fig. 16 we note that the probability that Y will lie in the region $(y, y + dy)$ is precisely the probability that X will lie in the region $(x, x + dx)$, which is $p(x)dx$. Hence

$$q(y)dy = p(x)dx.$$

Now $x = \psi(y)$, the inverse transformation of $y = \phi(x)$, so that $dx = \psi'(y)dy$. Hence $q(y) = p[x = \psi(y)]\psi'(y)$, the result of Eq. (17). We note also that $dy = \phi'(x)dx$, so that

$$q(y) = \frac{p(x)}{\phi'(x)}\bigg|_{x=\psi(y)} \tag{18}$$

is an alternative expression for $q(y)$.

If the inverse transformation of $y = \phi(x)$ is not single-valued; i.e., if for a given value of y there exist k values of x, say $x_1, x_2, \ldots, x_k$, such that $y = \phi(x_j)$, $j = 1, 2, \ldots, k$, then Eq. (17) must be modified into the form

$$q(y) = \sum_{j=1}^{k} p(x_j) \left|\frac{d\psi}{dy}\right|_{x=x_j} , \tag{19}$$

since each $x_j, j = 1, 2, \ldots, k$, yields a contribution to $q(y)$ (see Fig. 17). Note

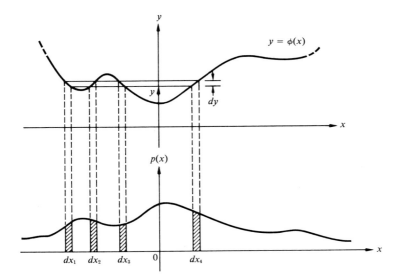

Figure 4.17

that $p(x_j)$ is obtained by replacing x_j in terms of y. We note from Fig. 17 that

$$q(y)dy = p(x_1)dx_1 + p(x_2)dx_2 + p(x_3)dx_3 + p(x_4)dx_4,$$

$$q(y) = p(x_1)\left|\frac{dx_1}{dy}\right| + p(x_2)\left|\frac{dx_2}{dy}\right| + p(x_3)\left|\frac{dx_3}{dy}\right| + p(x_4)\left|\frac{dx_4}{dy}\right|$$

$$= \sum_{j=1}^{4} p(x_j)\left|\frac{dx_j}{dy}\right|$$

as a special case of Eq. (19).

PROBLEMS

1. Show that the cdf for the Cauchy pdf given by

$$f(x) = \frac{1}{\pi}(1 + x^2)^{-1}, \qquad -\infty < x < \infty,$$

is

$$F(x) = \frac{1}{\pi}\left[\tan^{-1} x + \frac{\pi}{2}\right], \qquad -\infty < x < \infty.$$

2. Let X be a random variable with a pdf given by

$$f(x) = \tfrac{1}{2} e^{-|x|}, \qquad -\infty < x < \infty.$$

Show that the cdf is given by

$$F(x) = \tfrac{1}{2} e^x \qquad \text{for} \qquad x < 0,$$

$$= 1 - \frac{e^{-x}}{2} \qquad \text{for} \qquad x \geq 0.$$

3. Referring to Example 7 of this section, let $U = \min(X_1, X_2, \ldots, X_n)$. Show that $F(u) = 1 - (1 - u)^n$ for $0 \leq u \leq 1$, $F(u) = $ constant otherwise. Then show that the pdf of U is $f(u) = n(1 - u)^{n-1}$ for $0 \leq u \leq 1$, $f(u) = 0$ otherwise. Show that $\int_0^1 f(u)\,du = 1$.

4. Referring to Problem 2, show that the pdf for the random variable $Y = X^2$ is

$$p(y) = \tfrac{1}{2} y^{-1/2} e^{-\sqrt{y}} U(y).$$

5. A random variable X has a pdf given by

$$p(x) = 0 \qquad \text{for} \qquad x < 0,$$

$$= \tfrac{3}{4}x^2 \qquad \text{for} \qquad 0 \leq x \leq 1,$$

$$= A e^{-x} \quad \text{for} \qquad x > 1.$$

Find the value of A. Find the cdf, $P(x)$, and sketch $P(x)$ versus x.

6. A random variable X has a pdf given by

$$f(x) = axe^{-\alpha x} \quad \text{for} \quad x \geq 0,$$
$$= 0 \qquad \text{for} \quad x < 0.$$

with a and α positive constants. Determine a in terms of α. Find the cdf, $F(x)$, and plot $F(x)$ versus x.

7. Let X be a random variable with a pdf given by $f(x)$, $-\infty < x < \infty$. Let $Y = \int_{-\infty}^{x} f(x)\, dx$ define a new random variable Y. What is the range of Y? Show that Y is of the class $U(0, 1)$. This is a fundamental result which states that the cdf of any continuous random variable is always of the class $U(0, 1)$.

8. A random variable X has a pdf given by

$$p(x) = 0 \qquad \text{for} \quad x < 0,$$
$$= \tfrac{1}{2} \qquad \text{for} \quad 0 < x < 1,$$
$$= \frac{3}{2x^4} \quad \text{for} \quad x > 1.$$

Show that $\int_{-\infty}^{\infty} p(x)\, dx = 1$. Find the cdf of X and sketch $P(x)$ versus x.

9. The pdf for a random variable X is

$$p(x) = \frac{1}{2(\beta - \alpha)} \qquad \text{for} \quad -\beta \leq x \leq -\alpha,$$
$$= \frac{1}{2(\beta - \alpha)} \qquad \text{for} \quad \alpha < x < \beta,$$
$$= 0 \qquad\qquad \text{otherwise,}$$

with $\beta > \alpha > 0$. Find the cdf of X and graph $P(x)$ versus x.

10. X is of the class $U(-1, 1)$. Find the pdf of $Y = X^2$.

11. Let

$$Y = \left[\int_{-\infty}^{x} p(x)\, dx \right]^2.$$

Find the pdf of Y.

12. The probability that one will be served at a restaurant within t units of time is

$$P(t) = \left(\frac{t}{t + \tau} \right)^2,$$

with τ a constant. Show that $p(t)dt = 2t\tau(t + \tau)^{-3}\, dt$ is the probability that one will be served in the interval $(t, t + dt)$.

13. The cdf for a random variable X is

$$F(x) = 0 \qquad\qquad\qquad\qquad\qquad \text{for} \quad x < 0,$$
$$= 1 - \tfrac{1}{2}e^{-x/2} - \tfrac{1}{2}e^{-[x/2]} \quad \text{for} \quad x \geq 0,$$

in which $[x/2]$ denotes the largest integer less than or equal to $x/2$. Sketch $F(x)$ versus x. Is $F(x)$ continuous for all x? Find $\Pr(2 < X < 4)$, $\Pr(2 \leq X \leq 4)$, $\Pr(X > 4)$.

14. The cdf for a random variable X is given by

$$
\begin{aligned}
F(x) &= 0 && \text{for} && x < 0, \\
&= x && \text{for} && 0 \leq x < \tfrac{1}{2}, \\
&= \tfrac{5}{8} && \text{for} && \tfrac{1}{2} \leq x < \tfrac{3}{4}, \\
&= x && \text{for} && \tfrac{3}{4} \leq x \leq 1, \\
&= 1 && \text{for} && x > 1.
\end{aligned}
$$

Sketch $F(x)$ versus x. Find $\Pr(X = \tfrac{1}{2})$, $\Pr(X = \tfrac{3}{4})$, $\Pr(\tfrac{1}{2} < X < \tfrac{3}{4})$, $\Pr(X > \tfrac{1}{4})$, $\Pr(X \geq \tfrac{1}{4})$.

15. Let $p(x)$ be the pdf of a continuous random variable X. Let $Y = \phi(X)$ denote a new random variable. Consider

$$
F(y) = \int_{-\infty}^{\infty} \int_{-\infty}^{y} \delta(\xi - \phi(x)) \, p(x) \, d\xi \, dx, \tag{20}
$$

with δ the Dirac-delta function. Show that

$$
F(y) = \int_{S} p(x) \, dx,
$$

where S is the set of X such that $\phi(x) < y$. Hence, deduce that $F(y)$ is the cdf of Y. Show that the pdf of Y is

$$
q(y) = \int_{-\infty}^{\infty} \delta(y - \phi(x)) \, p(x) \, dx. \tag{21}
$$

As a special case let $p(x) = e^{-x} U(x)$, $Y = \sqrt{X}$, so that

$$
q(y) = \int_{0}^{\infty} \delta(y - \sqrt{x}) \, e^{-x} \, dx, \qquad y \geq 0.
$$

Let $x = u^2$ and show that $q(y) = 2y \exp(-y^2) U(y)$.

4.3 MOMENTS · MEAN · VARIANCE

Analogous to the case of discrete probability theory, we define the kth moment of a continuous random variable X with a pdf given by $p(x)$, by

$$
\nu_k = \int_{-\infty}^{\infty} x^k p(x) dx, \qquad k = 0, 1, 2, \ldots, \tag{1}
$$

provided the integral converges absolutely. For the special case $k = 1$ we obtain the first moment or mean, defined by

$$
\mu \equiv \nu_1 = \int_{-\infty}^{\infty} x p(x) dx = E(X). \tag{2}
$$

We also call the mean, μ, the expected value of X, written $E(X)$.

The kth moment about the mean is defined as the kth *central moment*, given by

$$\mu_k = \int_{-\infty}^{\infty} (x - \mu)^k p(x)dx, \qquad k = 0, 1, 2, 3, \ldots \tag{3}$$

It follows that

$$\mu_0 = 1,$$
$$\mu_1 = \int_{-\infty}^{\infty} (x - \mu)p(x)dx$$
$$= \int_{-\infty}^{\infty} xp(x)dx - \mu \int_{-\infty}^{\infty} p(x)dx$$
$$= \mu - \mu = 0.$$

Of great importance to the theory of statistics is the second central moment, written as

$$\sigma^2 = \int_{-\infty}^{\infty} (x - \mu)^2 p(x)dx = V(X). \tag{4}$$

The quantity σ^2 is called the variance or dispersion of X, written also as $V(X)$. Note that $\sigma^2 > 0$ unless $p(x) = \delta(x - \mu)$, in which case X assumes the value μ with probability one. Thus σ^2 is a measure of the dispersion of X from its mean μ. We call σ (the positive square root of σ^2) the *standard deviation*. From Eq. (4) it follows that

$$\sigma^2 = \int_{-\infty}^{\infty} x^2 p(x)dx - 2\mu \int_{-\infty}^{\infty} xp(x)dx + \mu^2 \int_{-\infty}^{\infty} p(x)dx$$
$$= \nu_2 - 2\mu^2 + \mu^2 = \nu_2 - \mu^2, \tag{5}$$

or $\nu_2 = \sigma^2 + \mu^2$, which is the same result obtained in discrete probability theory.

Example 1. Let X be of the class $U(a, b)$. Then

$$\mu = \nu_1 = \int_a^b x \frac{1}{b-a} dx = \frac{1}{b-a} \int_a^b xdx$$
$$= \frac{1}{b-a} \left(\frac{b^2 - a^2}{2} \right) = \frac{a+b}{2},$$

the obvious mean. Furthermore,

$$\nu_2 = \frac{1}{b-a} \int_a^b x^2 dx = \frac{1}{b-a} \frac{b^3 - a^3}{3} = \frac{a^2 + ab + b^2}{3},$$
$$\sigma^2 = \nu_2 - \nu_1^2 = \frac{a^2 + ab + b^2}{3} - \frac{a^2 + 2ab + b^2}{4}$$
$$= \tfrac{1}{12} (a^2 - 2ab + b^2) = \tfrac{1}{12} (b - a)^2.$$

Let the reader show that

$$\nu_k = \frac{b^{k+1} - a^{k+1}}{(k+1)(b-a)}. \tag{6}$$

Example 2. Let

$$p(x) = \frac{1}{\mu} e^{-x/\mu} U(x)$$

the exponential pdf. We have no assurance that the parameter μ is the actual mean. Now

$$\nu_k = \frac{1}{\mu} \int_0^\infty x^k e^{-x/\mu} \, dx = (k!)\mu^k,$$

so that $\nu_1 = \mu$, $\nu_2 = 2\mu^2$, $\sigma^2 = 2\mu^2 - \mu^2 = \mu^2$, and the variance is the square of the mean, with $E(X) = \mu$.

Example 3. Let $p(x) = (1/2a) e^{-|x|/a}$, $-\infty < x < \infty, a > 0$, be the pdf of a random variable X. Then

$$\nu_k = \frac{1}{2a} \int_{-\infty}^\infty x^k e^{-|x|/a} dx$$

$$= \frac{1}{2a} \int_{-\infty}^0 x^k e^{x/a} dx + \frac{1}{2a} \int_0^\infty x^k e^{-x/a} dx$$

$$= \frac{1}{2a} \int_0^\infty (-y)^k e^{-y/a} dy + \frac{1}{2a} \int_0^\infty x^k e^{-x/a} dx$$

$$= \frac{(k!)a^k}{2} [(-1)^k + 1],$$

so that

$$\nu_{2k+1} \equiv 0, \qquad \nu_{2k} = a^{2k}(2k)!.$$

From $\nu_0 = 1$ we have

$$\int_{-\infty}^\infty p(x)dx = 1.$$

Furthermore, $\nu_1 = \mu = 0$, so that $\sigma^2 = \nu_2 = 2a^2$, $a = \sigma/\sqrt{2}$, and

$$p(x) = \frac{1}{\sigma\sqrt{2}} \exp\left(-\frac{\sqrt{2}|x|}{\sigma}\right), \qquad -\infty < x < \infty.$$

The most general two-sided exponential pdf is given by

$$p(x) = \frac{1}{\sigma\sqrt{2}} \exp\left(-\frac{\sqrt{2}|x - \mu|}{\sigma}\right), \qquad -\infty < x < \infty, \tag{7}$$

which is completely characterized by its mean μ and its standard deviation $\sigma > 0$.

Example 4. Let X be a continuous random variable with a pdf given by $p(x)$, $-\infty < x < \infty$. Let $Y = \phi(X)$ be a new random variable, and assume that $\phi'(X) > 0$. We have seen that the pdf of Y is

$$q(y) = p[x = \psi(y)] \frac{d\psi}{dy},$$

with $\psi(Y) = X$. Thus

$$E(Y) = \int_{-\infty}^{\infty} yq(y)dy = \int_{-\infty}^{\infty} yp(x)\frac{d\psi}{dy}\,dy. \tag{8}$$

Let $y = \phi(x)$ be a change of variable of integration, so that $dy = \phi'(x)dx$, and $\psi'(y)dy = \psi'(y)\phi'(x)dx = dx$, since $\psi'(y) = 1/\phi'(x)$. Thus

$$E(Y) = \int_{-\infty}^{\infty} \phi(x)p(x)dx. \tag{9}$$

If X is a random variable we define the expected value of $\phi(X)$ by

$$E[\phi(X)] \equiv \int_{-\infty}^{\infty} \phi(x)p(x)dx, \tag{10}$$

which is consistent with the above derivation (see Eq. 9).

We introduce now a method for generating the moments of a random variable. Consider the Taylor series expansion

$$e^{\theta x} = 1 + \theta x + \frac{\theta^2}{2!}x^2 + \cdots + \frac{\theta^n}{n!}x^n + \cdots,$$

with θ a parameter. Quite formally we multiply by $p(x)$ and integrate term-by-term over the range $(-\infty, \infty)$. This yields

$$E(e^{\theta x}) = M(\theta) \equiv \int_{-\infty}^{\infty} p(x)e^{\theta x}dx = \sum_{n=0}^{\infty}\frac{\theta^n}{n!}\int_{-\infty}^{\infty} x^n p(x)dx$$

$$= \sum_{n=0}^{\infty}\frac{\nu_n}{n!}\,\theta^n. \tag{11}$$

The coefficient of $\theta^n/n!$ is precisely the nth moment, ν_n. It is for this reason that $M(\theta)$ is called the *moment generating function.* If

$$M(\theta) = \int_{-\infty}^{\infty} p(x)e^{x\theta}dx$$

exists and has a convergent Taylor series about $\theta = 0$, then

$$M(\theta) = \sum_{n=0}^{\infty}\left(\frac{d^n M}{d\theta^n}\right)_{\theta=0}\frac{\theta^n}{n!}, \tag{12}$$

so that

$$\nu_n = \left(\frac{d^n M}{d\theta^n}\right)_{\theta=0}, \qquad n = 0, 1, 2, \ldots \tag{13}$$

We note that in all cases,

$$M(0) = \int_{-\infty}^{\infty} p(x)dx = 1$$

for a random variable X. The Cauchy random variable is such that $M(\theta)$ exists for only one real value of θ, namely $\theta = 0$, whereas for $\theta \neq 0$, $M(\theta)$ is a divergent integral.

However, if θ is a pure imaginary number, $\theta = jt$, with $j = \sqrt{-1}$ and t real, then

$$F(t) = M(\theta = jt) = \int_{-\infty}^{\infty} p(x)e^{jtx}dx \tag{14}$$

exists for all real t, $-\infty < t < \infty$, since

$$|F(t)| \leq \int_{-\infty}^{\infty} p(x) |e^{jtx}|dx = \int_{-\infty}^{\infty} p(x)dx = 1. \tag{15}$$

The function $F(t)$ is called the characteristic function, CF, associated with the random variable X with a pdf given by $p(x)$. The reader should recognize that $F(t)$ is the Fourier transform of $p(x)$, whereas $M(\theta)$ is the two-sided Laplace transform of $p(x)$.

Example 5. Consider X of the class $U(a, b)$. Then

$$M(\theta) = \frac{1}{b-a} \int_{a}^{b} e^{x\theta}dx = \frac{1}{b-a} \frac{e^{b\theta} - e^{a\theta}}{\theta}$$

$$= \frac{1}{b-a} \sum_{n=1}^{\infty} \frac{(b^n - a^n)\theta^{n-1}}{n!}$$

$$= \frac{1}{b-a} \sum_{n=0}^{\infty} \frac{(b^{n+1} - a^{n+1})}{n+1} \frac{\theta^n}{n!},$$

so that (see Eq. 6),

$$\nu_n = \frac{1}{b-a} \frac{b^{n+1} - a^{n+1}}{n+1}.$$

Example 6. Let

$$p(x) = \frac{1}{\mu} e^{-x/\mu} U(x).$$

Then

$$M(\theta) = \frac{1}{\mu} \int_{0}^{\infty} e^{-x/\mu}e^{x\theta}dx = \frac{1}{\mu} \int_{0}^{\infty} e^{-x(1/\mu - \theta)}dx$$

$$= \frac{1}{\mu} \frac{1}{1/\mu - \theta} = \frac{1}{1 - \mu\theta}, \qquad |\mu\theta| < 1$$

$$= \sum_{n=0}^{\infty} \mu^n\theta^n = \sum_{n=0}^{\infty} n!\mu^n \frac{\theta^n}{n!}.$$

Hence $\nu_n = \mu^n n!$, see Example 2.

Example 7. Let X be normal, $N(\mu, \sigma^2)$. Then

$$M(\theta) = \frac{1}{\sqrt{2\pi}\sigma} \int_{-\infty}^{\infty} \exp(x\theta) \exp\left(-\frac{(x-\mu)^2}{2\sigma^2}\right)dx$$

$$= \frac{1}{\sqrt{2\pi}\sigma} \int_{-\infty}^{\infty} \exp\left\{-\frac{1}{2\sigma^2}[x^2 - 2(\mu + \sigma^2\theta)x + \mu^2]\right\}dx.$$

Now

$$x^2 - 2(\mu + \sigma^2\theta)x + \mu^2 = [x - (\mu + \sigma^2\theta)]^2 - 2\mu\sigma^2\theta - \sigma^4\theta^2,$$

so that the change of variable of integration,

$$y = \frac{1}{\sigma}[x - (\mu + \sigma^2\theta)],$$

yields

$$M(\theta) = \exp(\mu\theta)\exp\left(\frac{\sigma^2\theta^2}{2}\right)\frac{1}{\sqrt{2\pi}}\int_{-\infty}^{\infty} \exp(-y^2/2)dy$$

$$= \exp(\mu\theta)\exp(\sigma^2\theta^2/2) \qquad\qquad (16)$$

$$F(t) = \exp(j\mu t)\exp(-\sigma^2 t^2/2).$$

We note that $M(0) = 1$. Furthermore,

$$\ln M(\theta) = \mu\theta + \frac{\sigma^2\theta^2}{2},$$

$$\frac{1}{M}M'(\theta) = \mu + \sigma^2\theta, \qquad M'(0) = \mu = v_1,$$

$$\frac{1}{M}M''(\theta) - \frac{1}{M^2}[M'(\theta)]^2 = \sigma^2,$$

$$M''(\theta = 0) = \sigma^2 + \mu^2 = v_2,$$

so that the parameters μ and σ^2 are indeed the mean and variance of X, respectively.

Example 8. We note that if $Y = bX$, b a constant, then $E(Y) = E(bX) = bE(X)$, since

$$E(bX) = \int_{-\infty}^{\infty} bxp(x)dx = bE(X).$$

Now $Y^2 = b^2 X^2$, so that $E(Y^2) = b^2 E(X^2)$. Hence

$$V(Y) = E(Y^2) - [E(Y)]^2 = b^2 E(X^2) - b^2[E(X)]^2$$

$$= b^2\{E(X^2) - [E(X)]^2\} = b^2 V(X). \qquad\qquad (17)$$

Example 9. Let X be a discrete random variable taking on the values $x_1, x_2, \ldots, x_n$ with respective probabilities $p_1, p_2, \ldots, p_n$, $\sum_{i=1}^{n} p_i = 1$. The pdf of X can be expressed as

$$p(x) = \sum_{i=1}^{n} p_i\delta(x - x_i)$$

by virtue of the Dirac δ-function. The MGF of X is

$$M(\theta) = E(e^{x\theta}) = \sum_{i=1}^{n} p_i \int_{-\infty}^{\infty} (x - x_i)e^{\theta x} \, dx = \sum_{i=1}^{n} p_i e^{\theta x_i}.$$

PROBLEMS

1. Referring to Problem 8 of Section 4.2, find the mean, second moment, and variance.

2. Referring to Problem 9 of Section 4.2, find the moment generating function, $M(\theta)$. Then determine the mean and the variance from $M(\theta)$.

3. Let

$$p(x) = \frac{1}{\sigma\sqrt{2}} \exp\left(-\frac{\sqrt{2}}{\sigma} |x|\right), \qquad -\infty < x < \infty.$$

Show that

$$M(\theta) = \frac{1}{1 - \dfrac{\sigma^2 \theta^2}{2}}, \qquad \left|\frac{\sigma^2 \theta^2}{2}\right| < 1,$$

is the moment generating function. Then show that

$$\nu_{2n} = \frac{(2n)! \, \sigma^{2n}}{2^n}, \qquad n = 0, 1, 2, 3, \dots,$$

$$\nu_{2n+1} = 0.$$

4. Let $p(x) = \alpha^2 \, x \, e^{-\alpha x} \, U(x)$ be the pdf of a continuous random variable X. Find the moment generating function and determine the mean and the variance.

5. Show directly that if X is $N(\mu, \sigma^2)$, then $E(X) = \mu$, $V(X) = \sigma^2$.

6. A continuous random variable X has a pdf given by $p(x) = 1 - |x|$ for $-1 \le x \le 1$, $p(x) = 0$ otherwise. Show that the moment generating function is

$$M(\theta) = \frac{e^\theta + e^{-\theta} - 2}{\theta^2} = 2 \sum_{n=0}^{\infty} \frac{\theta^{2n}}{(2n + 2)!}.$$

Show that

$$\mu_{2n} = \frac{1}{(n + 1)(2n + 1)}, \qquad \mu_{2n+1} = 0, \qquad n = 0, 1, 2, 3, \dots$$

7. For the train problem of Example 2, Section 4.1, show that the mean time of arrival of the earlier train is $\mu = \frac{1}{3}$.

8. Find the mean value of the Rayleigh random variable whose pdf is given in Eq. (6) of Section 4.1.

9. Show that the Cauchy random variable has no mean.

10. Show that if $\int_{-\infty}^{\infty} x^2 \, p(x)dx$ exists, then $\int_{-\infty}^{\infty} xp(x)dx$ exists.

11. Show that the moment generating function associated with the random variable X whose pdf is $p(x) = \frac{1}{2}\delta(x + 1) + \frac{1}{2}\delta(x - 1)$ is $M(\theta) = \cosh\theta$. Show that $\mu = 0$, $V(X) = 1$. Show that the CF is $F(t) = \cos t$.

12. Show that the CF of the random variable X which is uniform on the range $(-1, 1)$ is

$$F(t) = \frac{\sin t}{t} = \sum_{n=0}^{\infty} \frac{(-1)^n t^{2n}}{(2n + 1)!}.$$

Determine the moments ν_n, $n = 0, 1, 2, 3, \ldots$.

13. From $F_X(t) = E[e^{jXt}]$ show that the CF of the random variable $Y = aX + b$ is

$$F_Y(t) = E[e^{jYt}] = e^{jbt} F_X(at).$$

14. Given $F(t)$ as the CF of a random variable X, show that

$$\left.\frac{d^n F(t)}{dt^n}\right|_{t=0} = j^n \nu_n$$

provided the nth moment exists. If the Taylor series

$$F(t) = \sum_{n=0}^{\infty} a_n t^n$$

converges to $F(t)$ for $|t| > 0$, show that $\nu_n = (-1)^n j^n a_n n!$.

15. Show that the CF of a random variable X, whose pdf is given by $p(x) = \frac{1}{2}|x|e^{-|x|}$, $-\infty < x < \infty$, is

$$F(t) = \frac{(1 - t^2)}{(1 + t^2)^2}.$$

Then show that

$$F(t) = 1 + \sum_{n=1}^{\infty} (-1)^n (2n + 1)t^{2n},$$

and deduce that $\nu_{2n+1} = 0, \nu_{2n} = (2n + 1)!$ for all integers n (see Problem 14 above).

16. Let $p(t)dt$ represent the probability that an event will occur in the time interval $(t, t + dt)$. The instant the event occurs the process starts anew with the same pdf, $p(t)$. Let $\mu(T)$ be the mean number of successes in time T. Show that

$$\mu(T) = \int_0^T p(t)[1 + \mu(T - t)]dt$$
$$= \int_0^T p(t)\,dt + \int_0^T p(t)\,\mu(T - t)dt.$$

Assuming that $\mu'(T)$ exists, show that

$$\frac{d\mu(T)}{dT} = p(T) + \int_0^T p(t)\,\mu'(T - t)dt.$$

Given $\mu(T) \equiv T/\lambda$, show that

$$p(t) = \frac{1}{\lambda}e^{-t/\lambda}, \qquad t \geq 0.$$

Assume that the Laplace transform of $\mu(T)$ exists, i.e.,

$$\bar{\mu}(s) = \int_0^\infty e^{-sT} \mu(T)dT < \infty .$$

Show that

$$\bar{\mu}(s) = \frac{1}{s} \frac{\bar{p}(s)}{1 - \bar{p}(s)}$$

with

$$\bar{p}(s) = \int_0^\infty e^{-st} p(t)dt .$$

For an Erlangian distribution,

$$p(t) = \frac{4t}{\lambda^2} \exp\left(- \frac{2t}{\lambda}\right) U(t) ,$$

show that

$$\bar{\mu}(s) = \frac{1}{\lambda} \frac{1}{s^2} - \frac{1}{4s} + \frac{1}{4} \frac{1}{s + 4/\lambda} ,$$

so that

$$\mu(T) = \frac{1}{\lambda} T + \frac{1}{4} \left[\exp\left(- \frac{4T}{\lambda}\right) - 1\right] .$$

17. At any stage of a process you are allowed to pick a number at random from a pdf given by $p(x)$, $- \infty < x < \infty$. You have N draws available. If on the kth draw you obtain the number x_k, you may quit and receive x_k units (if $x_k < 0$ you lose an amount $- x_k$), or go on with no gain or loss. If n draws are still available and you drew the number x on the previous draw, let $F_n(x)$ be the average value of the process using an optimal decision procedure. Show that

$$F_n(x) = \max [x, \int_{-\infty}^\infty F_{n-1} (y) p(y) dy] ,$$

with $F_0(x) = x$. What is $F_1(x)$?

18. Let X be a continuous random variable which takes on only nonnegative values. Assume that $E(X)$ exists and that the pdf, $f(x)$, is continuous for $x \geq 0$, $f(x) = 0$ for $x < 0$. Since $\mu = \int_0^\infty xf(x)dx < \infty$, for any $\epsilon > 0$ there exists a T_0 such that $\int_T^\infty xf(x)dx < \epsilon$ for $T \geq T_0$. Show that $T[1 - F(T)] < \epsilon$ for $T \geq T_0$, with $F(x)$ the cdf of X. Thus $\lim_{T\to\infty} T[1 - F(T)] = 0$.
Next consider

$$\int_0^T xf(x)dx = \int_0^T xdF(x) = xF(x)\Big|_0^T - \int_0^T F(x)dx$$

$$= T[F(T) - 1] + \int_0^T [1 - F(x)]dx .$$

Show that

$$\mu = E(X) = \int_0^\infty [1 - F(x)]dx .$$

4.4 JOINT DENSITY FUNCTIONS ·
STATISTICALLY INDEPENDENT RANDOM VARIABLES

Imagine that one is throwing darts at a board. Because of the inaccuracy of the tosses there is a probability, dP, that the dart will fall in the area (region) $dA = dydx$ centered about the point (x, y). We define

$$p(x, y) = \lim_{dA \to 0} \frac{dP}{dA} \qquad (1)$$

as the joint pdf of the pair of random variables (X, Y). Thus

$$dP = p(x, y)dydx \qquad (2)$$

is the probability that the dart will fall in the two dimensional region ($x \leq X \leq x + dx, y \leq Y \leq y + dy$), except for infinitesimals of higher order. In order that $p(x, y)$ be a joint pdf, of necessity

$$p(x, y) \geq 0 \qquad \text{for all} \qquad x, y,$$

$$\int_{-\infty}^{\infty} \int_{-\infty}^{\infty} p(x, y)dydx = 1. \qquad (3)$$

Furthermore, we say that X and Y are a joint pair of continuous random variables if dP approaches zero whenever $dA = dydx$ approaches zero.

The generalization to any number of random variables is simple. The random variables $X_1, X_2, \ldots, X_n$ are said to have a joint pdf given by $p(x_1, \ldots, x_n)$ if

$$p(x_1, x_2, \ldots, x_n) \geq 0 \qquad \text{for all} \qquad x_1, x_2, \ldots, x_n,$$

$$\int_{-\infty}^{\infty} \cdots \int_{-\infty}^{\infty} p(x_1, x_2, \ldots, x_n)dx_1 dx_2 \cdots dx_n = 1, \qquad (4)$$

with

$$dP = p(x_1, x_2, \ldots, x_n)dx_1 dx_2 \cdots dx_n \qquad (5)$$

the probability that $X_1, X_2, \ldots, X_n$ assume values in the intervals

$$(x_1 \leq X_1 \leq x_1 + dx_1, x_2 \leq X_2 \leq x_2 + dx_2, \ldots, x_n \leq X_n \leq x_n + dx_n).$$

Returning to the two dimensional case, one may plot $z = p(x, y)$ as a surface in the xyz space. Since $p(x, y) \geq 0$, the surface does not lie below the xy plane. Furthermore, from

$$\int_{-\infty}^{\infty} \int_{-\infty}^{\infty} p(x, y)dydx = 1,$$

the total volume between the surface and the xy plane is unity. The volume of the stick shown in Fig. 18 represents the probability that ($x \leq X \leq x + dx, y \leq Y \leq y + dy$) except for infinitesimals of higher order. Fortunately one need not construct such surfaces to determine the various properties of the pair of random variables (X, Y).

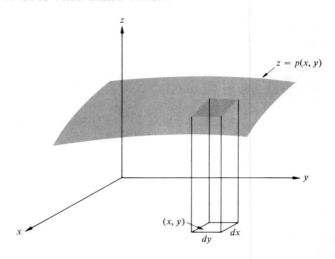

Figure 4.18

Example 1. Let $p(x, y) = x + y$ for the region $0 \leq x \leq 1, 0 \leq y \leq 1, p(x, y) = 0$ otherwise. We note that $p(x, y) \geq 0$ for all x, y. Furthermore

$$\int_{-\infty}^{\infty} \int_{-\infty}^{\infty} p(x, y)dy \, dx = \int_0^1 \int_0^1 (x + y)dy \, dx = 1,$$

so that $p(x, y)$ is a pdf for the pair of random variables (X, Y).

Example 2. Let

$$p(x, y) = xy \exp\left[-(x^2 + y^2)/2\right]U(x)U(y),$$

so that $p(x, y) \geq 0$ for all x, y. Moreover,

$$\begin{aligned}
\int_{-\infty}^{\infty} \int_{-\infty}^{\infty} p(x, y)dy \, dx &= \int_0^{\infty} \int_0^{\infty} x \exp(-x^2/2)y \exp(-y^2/2)dy \, dx \\
&= \int_0^{\infty} x \exp(-x^2/2)dx \int_0^{\infty} y \exp(-y^2/2)dy \\
&= 1 \cdot 1 = 1,
\end{aligned}$$

so that $p(x, y)$ is a pdf for a pair of random variables (X, Y).

Example 3. Let $p(x, y) = 1/x$ for the region $0 < y \leq x \leq 1$ (see Fig. 19), $p(x, y) = 0$ otherwise.

Certainly $p(x, y) \geq 0$ for all (x, y). Moreover,

$$\begin{aligned}
\int_{-\infty}^{\infty} \int_{-\infty}^{\infty} p(x, y)dy \, dx &= \int_{x=0}^{x=1} \int_{y=0}^{y=x} \frac{1}{x} \, dy \, dx \\
&= \int_0^1 \frac{x}{x} \, dx = 1,
\end{aligned}$$

so that $p(x, y)$ represents the joint pdf of a pair of random variables (X, Y).

Example 4. *Marginal density function.* Given a joint pdf, say $p(x, y)$, of a pair of random variables (X, Y), one may ask what is the probability that any experiment is such that the random variable X will lie in the interval $(x, x + dx)$? Recall that for each experiment a pair of numbers (x, y) arise. It is apparent that this is just the probability that the dart will fall in the vertical strip of Fig. 20. [Whenever the random variables X, Y assume the values x, y as the result of an experiment, one may imagine that a dart has been thrown at a board and that the dart has struck the point (x, y).]

    Thus

$$f(x)\, dx = \left[\int_{-\infty}^{\infty} p(x, y)\, dy \right] dx, \tag{6}$$

except for infinitesimals of higher order, since $p(x, y)dy\, dx$ is the probability that the dart will fall in the region $(x, x + dx)$, $(y, y + dy)$, and $f(x)dx$ is obtained by summing over all possible values of y. Hence

$$f(x) = \int_{-\infty}^{\infty} p(x, y)dy \tag{7}$$

is the pdf of the random variable X. We call $f(x)$ the marginal pdf associated with the random variable X, although the word "marginal" is redundant.

    Similarly,

$$g(y) = \int_{-\infty}^{\infty} p(x, y)dx \tag{8}$$

is the marginal pdf associated with the random variable Y.

Example 5. Referring to Example 1 we have

$$f(x) = \int_{0}^{1} (x + y)dy = x + \tfrac{1}{2} \qquad \text{for} \qquad 0 \le x \le 1,$$
$$= 0 \qquad\qquad\qquad\qquad\qquad \text{otherwise,}$$
$$g(y) = \int_{0}^{1} (x + y)dx = y + \tfrac{1}{2} \qquad \text{for} \qquad 0 \le y \le 1,$$
$$= 0 \qquad\qquad\qquad\qquad\qquad \text{otherwise.}$$

We note that

$$p(x, y) = x + y \ne f(x)g(y) = (x + \tfrac{1}{2})(y + \tfrac{1}{2}).$$

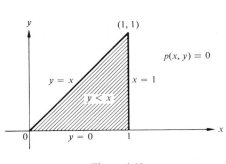

Figure 4.19

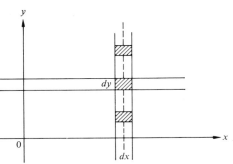

Figure 4.20

However, for Example 2 we note that

$$f(x) = \int_0^\infty xy \exp\left(-\tfrac{1}{2}x^2\right) \exp\left(-\tfrac{1}{2}y^2\right) U(x)\, dy = x \exp\left(-\tfrac{1}{2}x^2\right) U(x),$$

$$g(y) = \int_0^\infty xy \exp\left(-\tfrac{1}{2}x^2\right) \exp\left(-\tfrac{1}{2}y^2\right) U(y)\, dx = y \exp\left(-\tfrac{1}{2}y^2\right) U(y),$$

so that $p(x, y) = f(x)g(y)$ for all (x, y).

Definition.   Whenever

$$p(x, y) = f(x)g(y)$$

$$= \int_{-\infty}^\infty p(x, y)dy \int_{-\infty}^\infty p(x, y)dx \qquad (9)$$

for all (x, y), we say that X and Y are statistically independent random variables.

Conversely, if X and Y are statistically independent random variables with pdf's given by $f(x)$ and $g(y)$, respectively, then the joint pdf of (X, Y) is given by $p(x, y) = f(x)g(y)$. If Eq. (9) fails to hold for at least one pair (x, y) we say that X and Y are statistically dependent random variables.   Henceforth the word "independent" will mean "statistically independent" as regards random variables.

Example 6.   Returning to Example 3 we note that

$$f(x) = \int_0^x \frac{1}{x}\, dy = 1 \qquad \text{for} \quad 0 \le x \le 1,$$

$$= 0 \qquad\qquad\qquad \text{otherwise},$$

so that X is of the class $U(0, 1)$.   However,

$$g(y) = \int_{x=y}^{x=1} \frac{1}{x}\, dx = -\ln y \qquad \text{for} \quad 0 < y \le 1,$$

$$= 0 \qquad\qquad\qquad\qquad \text{otherwise}.$$

We note that

$$\int_{-\infty}^\infty g(y)dy = \int_0^1 -\ln y\, dy = -[y \ln y - y]_0^1 = 1,$$

since $\lim_{y \to 0} y \ln y = 0$, so that $g(y)$ is a pdf for the random variable Y.   However,

$$p(x, y) = (1/x) \ne 1(-\ln y) = f(x)g(y)$$

for the region of interest, so that X and Y are dependent random variables.   This result will be apparent in Example 1 of Section 4.5.

Example 7.   Let us imagine that one throws a dart at a board in an attempt to hit the center of the board ($x = 0$, $y = 0$).   Inaccuracy in the toss of the dart leads us to discuss the pdf of the pair of random variables (X, Y).   We assume that this pdf depends only on the distance to the origin and that X and Y are independent random variables. Hence

$$p(x^2 + y^2) = f(x)g(y). \tag{10}$$

We assume further that $f(x)$ and $g(y)$ are differentiable and that $f(x)$, $g(y)$ approach zero as $|x| \to \infty$, $|y| \to \infty$. Differentiating Eq. (10) with respect to x and y yields the pair of equations

$$p'(x^2 + y^2)2x = f'(x)g(y),$$
$$p'(x^2 + y^2)2y = f(x)g'(y), \tag{11}$$

so that

$$\frac{f'(x)}{x f(x)} = \frac{g'(y)}{y g(y)} \tag{12}$$

holds for all x and y, provided $x f(x)$ and $y g(y)$ are different from zero. If we set $y = 1$ we have $f'(x)/xf(x) = $ constant for all x. Hence,

$$\frac{f'(x)}{x f(x)} = \frac{g'(y)}{y g(y)} = -\frac{1}{\sigma^2}, \tag{13}$$

with σ^2 a constant. An integration yields

$$f(x) = K \exp(-x^2/2\sigma^2),$$
$$g(y) = L \exp(-y^2/2\sigma^2), \tag{14}$$
$$p(x, y) = A \exp[-(1/2\sigma^2)(x^2 + y^2)].$$

From

$$\int_{-\infty}^{\infty} \int_{-\infty}^{\infty} p(x, y)dy \, dx = 1$$

we obtain

$$A \int_{-\infty}^{\infty} \int_{-\infty}^{\infty} \exp[-(1/2\sigma^2)(x^2 + y^2)]dy \, dx = A \int_{0}^{\infty} \int_{0}^{2\pi} \exp(-r^2/2\sigma^2) \, r \, dr \, d\theta$$
$$= 2\pi A \left[-\sigma^2 \exp(-r^2/2\sigma^2)\right]\big|_{0}^{\infty}$$
$$= 2\pi A \sigma^2 = 1$$

by changing to polar coordinates. Hence $A = 1/2\pi\sigma^2$, so that

$$p(x, y) = \frac{1}{\sqrt{2\pi}\sigma} \exp(-x^2/2\sigma^2) \frac{1}{\sqrt{2\pi}\sigma} \exp(-y^2/2\sigma^2), \tag{15}$$

and we see that X and Y are both normal, $N(0, \sigma^2)$.

The pdf, $p(x, y)$, given by

$$p(x, y) = \frac{1}{2\pi\sigma^2} \exp\left[-\frac{1}{2}\frac{(x^2 + y^2)}{\sigma^2}\right] \tag{16}$$

is a special case of the bivariate normal distribution to be discussed subsequently.

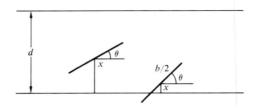

Figure 4.21

Example 8. *The Buffon needle problem.* Consider a set of parallel lines in a plane at a distance d apart, and let $b < d$ be the length of a needle which is tossed at random on the plane. We ask for the probability that the needle will intersect one of the lines. The position of the needle is completely specified by the distance of the center of the needle to the nearest line, say x, and by the direction of the needle, say θ (see Fig. 21).

The random variables (X, Θ) are assumed to be independent and uniform, so that

$$p(x, \theta) = \frac{1}{d/2} \frac{1}{\pi} = \frac{2}{\pi d}, \qquad \begin{array}{l} 0 \le x \le d/2 \\ 0 \le \theta \le \pi, \end{array}$$

$p(x, \theta) = 0$ otherwise. Now, if $\dfrac{b}{2} \sin \theta \ge x$ the needle will intersect the line. The region of success is the shaded region of Fig. 22. Thus

$$P = \frac{2}{\pi d} \int_0^\pi \int_0^{(b/2)\sin\theta} dx \, d\theta = \frac{b}{\pi d} \int_0^\pi \sin\theta \, d\theta = \frac{2b}{\pi d}. \tag{17}$$

It is interesting to note that Buffon threw a great number of sticks, determined the ratio of success to the total number of trials, approximately P, and determined a value close to π, from $\pi = 2b/dP$.

Example 9. Let X be of the class $U(0, 1)$. Let us suppose that we sample n times ((independent samples from $U(0, 1)$)), and consider the random sequence $(X_1, X_2, \ldots, X_n)$. Let U and V denote the minimum and maximum values of the elements of this sequence,

$$U = \min(X_1, X_2, \ldots, X_n),$$
$$V = \max(X_1, X_2, \ldots, X_n). \tag{18}$$

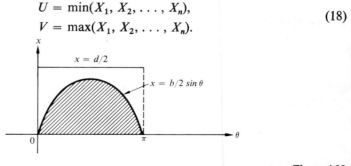

Figure 4.22

Thus U and V are random variables, since $X_1, X_2, \ldots, X_n$ are random variables. We wish to determine the joint pdf of (U, V). Let $p(u, v)du\, dv$ represent the probability that U lies in the interval $(u, u + du)$ and that V lies in the interval $(v, v + dv)$, jointly, with $v > u$.

First we note that the probability that X_j lies in the interval $(u, u + du)$ is du; the probability that X_k lies in the interval $(v, v + dv)$ is dv; and the probability that the remaining $(n - 2)$ X's lie in the interval (u, v) is $(v - u)^{n-2}$. The probability of occurrence of these events is $(v - u)^{n-2}\, du\, dv$. Now there are n choices for the X that falls in the interval $(u, u + du)$, followed by $(n - 1)$ choices for the X which falls in the interval $(v, v + dv)$. Hence $p(u, v)du\, dv = n(n - 1)\,(v - u)^{n-2}\, du\, dv$, so that

$$p(u, v) = n(n - 1)\,(v - u)^{n-2}, \qquad 0 \le u \le v \le 1,$$
$$= 0 \qquad \text{otherwise.} \tag{19}$$

Next we determine the probability that $V - U \ge \beta$, $0 \le \beta \le 1$. Now if $v - u \ge \beta$, then v must lie between $u + \beta$ and 1. Furthermore, u cannot be greater than $1 - \beta$, for if $u > 1 - \beta$, then $v \ge u + \beta > 1 - \beta + \beta = 1$, an impossibility. Thus

$$\Pr(V - U \ge \beta) = n(n - 1) \int_0^{1-\beta} \int_{u+\beta}^1 (v - u)^{n-2}\, dv\, du$$

$$= n \int_0^{1-\beta} (v - u)^{n-1}\Big|_{u+\beta}^1 du$$

$$= n \int_0^{1-\beta} [(1 - u)^{n-1} - \beta^{n-1}]du \tag{20}$$

$$= -(1 - u)^n \Big|_0^{1-\beta} - n\beta^{n-1}\,(1 - \beta)$$

$$= 1 - \beta^n - n\beta^{n-1}\,(1 - \beta).$$

Example 10. Returning to the n independent samples of the previous example, let us order $X_1, X_2, \ldots, X_n$ into $Y_1 \le Y_2 \le Y_3 \le \cdots \le Y_{j-1} \le Y_j \le Y_{j+1} \le \cdots \le Y_n$. Let $Z = Y_j$ be the jth ordered statistic. We wish to determine the pdf of Z. Now if Z is to fall in the interval $(z, z + dz)$, then exactly $(j - 1)$ of the X's must fall in the interval $(0, z)$, one of the X's must fall in the interval $(z, z + dz)$, and the remaining $(n - j)$ X's must fall in the interval $(z + dz, 1)$. There are $n\binom{n-1}{j-1}$ ways of accomplishing this result, each outcome occurring with probability $z^{j-1}(1 - z)^{n-j}dz$, so that

$$p(z) = n\binom{n-1}{j-1}z^{j-1}\,(1 - z)^{n-j}, \qquad 0 \le z \le 1,$$
$$= 0 \qquad \text{otherwise.} \tag{21}$$

Since

$$\int_0^1 p(z)dz = 1,$$

we obtain

$$n\binom{n-1}{j-1} \int_0^1 z^{j-1}(1 - z)^{n-j}\, dz = 1.$$

Now let $j = k + 1, n = k + 1 + l$, so that

$$\int_0^1 z^k(1 - z)^l \, dz = \frac{1}{(k + l + 1) \binom{k+l}{k}}$$

$$= \frac{k!l!}{(k + l + 1)!} \tag{22}$$

$$= \frac{\Gamma(k + 1) \, \Gamma(l + 1)}{\Gamma(k + l + 2)}$$

for integers k, l. The integral above is the well-known beta integral.

The sum of two random variables. Let $p(x, y)$ be the joint pdf of a pair of random variables X, Y. Now let $Z = X + Y$ be a new random variable whose numerical values are $z = x + y$. It is seen from Fig. 23 that the probability that Z will lie in the interval $(z, z + dz)$ is just the probability that (x, y) lies in the strip bounded by $x + y = z$ and $x + y = z + dz$.

Thus

$$g(z)dz \approx \left[\int_{-\infty}^{\infty} p(x, z - x)dx \right] dz, \tag{23}$$

since for $dz \ll 1, y \approx z - x$, and the area of the shaded region is $dz \, dx$. As $dz \to 0$ we obtain

$$g(z) = \int_{-\infty}^{\infty} p(x, z - x)dx = \int_{-\infty}^{\infty} p(z - y, y) \, dy \tag{24}$$

as the pdf of Z.

It is often convenient to find the cdf of $Z = X + Y$, defined by

$$F(z) = \Pr(Z \leq z) = \Pr(X + Y \leq z).$$

Once $F(z)$ has been obtained one can determine the pdf of Z from $g(z) = F'(z)$. This procedure for determining $g(z)$ is quite often simpler than evaluating the

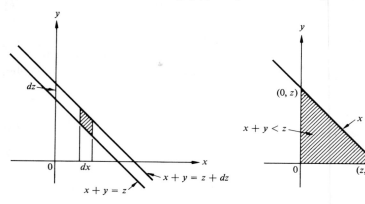

Figure 4.23   Figure 4.24

integral of Eq. (24). On the other hand, Eq. (24) proves useful in deriving important results in connection with the expected value of a sum of random variables, and in determining the characteristic function associated with a sum of independent random variables.

Example 11. Let $p(x, y) = e^{-(x+y)} U(x)U(y)$ be the joint pdf of a pair of random variables (X, Y). We are interested in the cdf of $Z = X + Y$. The line $x + y = z$, z fixed, separates the x, y plane into two regions, one for which $x + y < z$ and the other for which $x + y > z$. We are interested in the region $x + y < z$.

For $z < 0$ the line $x + y = z$ will not intersect the first quadrant of the x-y plane [the region where $p(x, y) \neq 0$]. Hence $F(z) = 0$ for $z < 0$. The shaded region of Fig. 24 is the region for which $x + y < z$, and for which $p(x, y) \neq 0$. Hence

$$F(z) = \int_0^z \int_0^{z-x} e^{-(x+y)} \, dy \, dx, \qquad z \geq 0$$

$$= \int_0^z e^{-x} [1 - e^{-(z-x)}] dx$$

$$= 1 - e^{-z} - ze^{-z}.$$

It follows that

$$g(z) = F'(z) = 0 \qquad \text{for} \qquad z < 0$$

$$= F'(z) = z\,e^{-z} \qquad \text{for} \qquad z \geq 0.$$

Note that

$$\int_{-\infty}^{\infty} g(z)dz = \int_0^{\infty} z\,e^{-z} = 1.$$

We can also solve for $g(z)$ by means of Eq. (24). Thus

$$g(z) = \int_{-\infty}^{\infty} e^{-(x+z-x)} U(x)U(z-x)dx = e^{-z} \int_{-\infty}^{\infty} U(x)U(z-x)dx.$$

For $z \geq 0$ we have $g(z) = e^{-z} \int_0^z dx = z\,e^{-z}$. Let the reader show that $g(z) = 0$ for $z < 0$.

Example 12. Let $p(x, y) = 2x$ for the unit square $0 \leq x \leq 1, 0 \leq y \leq 1, p(x, y) = 0$ otherwise. The cdf of $Z = X + Y$ will depend on the value of $Z = z$, since $x + y = z$ does not intersect the unit square (the region for which $p(x, y) \neq 0$) for $z < 0$ and for $z > 2$. It should be apparent that

$$F(z) = \Pr(X + Y < z) = 0 \qquad \text{for} \qquad z < 0,$$

$$= \Pr(X + Y < z) = 1 \qquad \text{for} \qquad z > 2.$$

From Fig. 25a we have

$$F(z) = \int_0^z \int_0^{z-x} 2x \, dy \, dx, \qquad 0 < z < 1,$$

$$= \tfrac{1}{3} z^3.$$

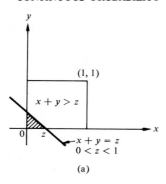 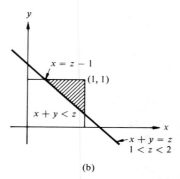

(a)   (b)

Figure 4.25

The shaded region of Fig. 25b is the region for which $X + Y > z$, for $1 < z < 2$. Hence

$$1 - F(z) = \int_{z-1}^{1} \int_{z-x}^{1} 2x \, dy \, dx, \qquad 1 < z < 2,$$

$$= \tfrac{5}{3} - z + \tfrac{1}{3}(z - 1)^3,$$

so that

$$F(z) = -\tfrac{2}{3} + z - \tfrac{1}{3}(z - 1)^3 \qquad \text{for} \qquad 1 \le z \le 2.$$

Note that $F(1) = \tfrac{1}{3}$, $F(2) = 1$. It follows that

$$\begin{aligned} q(z) = F'(z) &= 0 & \text{for} & \quad z < 0, \\ &= z^2 & \text{for} & \quad 0 \le z \le 1, \\ &= 1 - (z - 1)^2 & \text{for} & \quad 1 \le z \le 2, \\ &= 0 & \text{for} & \quad z > 2. \end{aligned}$$

The graph of $q(z)$ versus z is shown in Fig. 26.

Returning to Eq. (24) we note that

$$E(Z) = \int_{-\infty}^{\infty} zq(z)dz = \int_{-\infty}^{\infty} \int_{-\infty}^{\infty} zp(z - y, y)dy \, dz, \tag{25}$$

provided the integral converges absolutely.

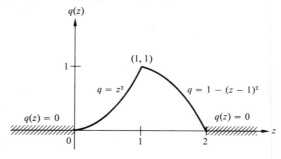

Figure 4.26

In the double integral of Eq. (25) we perform the change of variable $z = y + x$, $dz = dx$, interchange the limits of integration, permissible if $\int_{-\infty}^{\infty} |z| q(z) \, dz$ exists, and obtain

$$
\begin{aligned}
E(Z) &= \int_{-\infty}^{\infty} \int_{-\infty}^{\infty} (x + y) p(x, y) dx \, dy \\
&= \int_{-\infty}^{\infty} \int_{-\infty}^{\infty} x \, p(x, y) dy \, dx + \int_{-\infty}^{\infty} \int_{-\infty}^{\infty} y \, p(x, y) dx \, dy \\
&= \int_{-\infty}^{\infty} x f(x) dx + \int_{-\infty}^{\infty} y \, g(y) dy \\
&= E(X) + E(Y).
\end{aligned}
\tag{26}
$$

Since $Z = X + Y$, we have proved the important result that

$$
E(X + Y) = E(X) + E(Y),
\tag{27}
$$

which holds whether or not X and Y are independent random variables. In general, the expected value of a finite sum of random variables is the sum of the expected values of the individual random variables, provided these expected values exist.

From Eq. (24) we note that if X and Y are independent random variables, $p(x, y) = f(x)g(y)$, then $Z = X + Y$ has a pdf given by

$$
\begin{aligned}
q(z) &= \int_{-\infty}^{\infty} f(x) g(z - x) dx \\
&= \int_{-\infty}^{\infty} f(z - y) g(y) dy,
\end{aligned}
\tag{28}
$$

which are the convolution integrals of $f(x)$ and $g(y)$. The CF for Z is

$$
\begin{aligned}
F_z(t) &= \int_{-\infty}^{\infty} q(z) \, e^{jzt} \, dz \\
&= \int_{-\infty}^{\infty} \int_{-\infty}^{\infty} f(x) g(z - x) \, e^{jzt} \, dx \, dz,
\end{aligned}
\tag{29}
$$

provided X and Y are independent random variables.

Interchanging the order of integration, and letting $z = x + y$, $dz = dy$, yields

$$
\begin{aligned}
F_z(t) &= \int_{-\infty}^{\infty} \int_{-\infty}^{\infty} f(x) g(y) \, e^{j(x+y)t} \, dy \, dx \\
&= \int_{-\infty}^{\infty} f(x) \, e^{jxt} \, dx \int_{-\infty}^{\infty} g(y) \, e^{jyt} \, dy \\
&= F_x(t) \, F_y(t).
\end{aligned}
\tag{30}
$$

This result is of extreme importance. It states that if X and Y are independent random variables, then the CF associated with their sum, $Z = X + Y$, is the product of the CF's associated with X and Y.

Example 13. If X and Y are normal, $N(\mu_1, \sigma_1^2)$, $N(\mu_2, \sigma_2^2)$, then their CF's are given by

$$
\begin{aligned}
F_X(t) &= \exp(j\mu_1 t) \exp(-\sigma_1^2 t^2 / 2), \\
F_Y(t) &= \exp(j\mu_2 t) \exp(-\sigma_2^2 t^2 / 2).
\end{aligned}
$$

In particular if X and Y are independent random variables, then the CF of $Z = X + Y$ is

$$F_z(t) = \exp[j(\mu_1 + \mu_2)t] \exp[-\tfrac{1}{2}(\sigma_1^2 + \sigma_2^2)t^2].$$

Thus Z is also normal, $N(\mu_1 + \mu_2, \sigma_1^2 + \sigma_2^2)$, and the sum of a finite number of independent normal random variables is also normal, $N(\mu, \sigma^2)$, with

$$\mu = \sum_{i=1}^{n} \mu_i, \qquad \sigma^2 = \sum_{i=1}^{n} \sigma^2.$$

Example 14. *The product of two random variables.* Let $Z = XY$ be a new random .variable. Let the reader deduce that

$$q(z) = \int_{-\infty}^{\infty} \frac{1}{|x|} p(x, z/x)dx \tag{31}$$

is the pdf of Z, see Fig. 27.
Now

$$E(Z) = \int_{-\infty}^{\infty} zq(z)dz = \int_{-\infty}^{\infty} \int_{-\infty}^{\infty} \frac{z}{|x|} p(x, z/x)dx \, dz. \tag{32}$$

Let $z = xy$, $dz = |x| \, dy$, interchange the order of integration, so that

$$E(Z) = \int_{-\infty}^{\infty} \int_{-\infty}^{\infty} xy \, p(x, y)dy \, dx = E(XY). \tag{33}$$

In particular, if X and Y are independent random variables, then $p(x, y) = f(x)g(y)$, so that

$$\begin{aligned}
E(Z) &= \int_{-\infty}^{\infty} \int_{-\infty}^{\infty} xy \, f(x)g(y)dy \, dx \\
&= \int_{-\infty}^{\infty} x f(x)dx \int_{-\infty}^{\infty} y \, g(y)dy \\
&= E(X)E(Y). \tag{34}
\end{aligned}$$

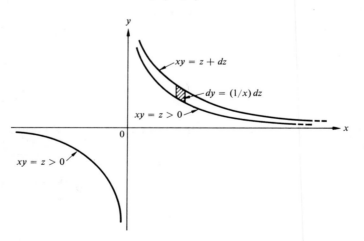

Figure 4.27

We have obtained the important result that if X and Y are independent random variables, then

$$E(XY) = E(X)E(Y). \tag{35}$$

The converse is not true. If Eq. (35) holds, we cannot conclude that X and Y are independent random variables. For example, let X be of the class $U(-1, 1)$ and let $Y = X^2$. Certainly X and Y are not independent random variables. However, $E(XY) = E(X^3) = 0$, $E(X) = 0$, $E(Y) = E(X^2) = \frac{1}{3}$. Thus, $E(XY) = E(X)E(Y)$, since $0 \cdot \frac{1}{3} = 0$.

In Example 1 of this section we have

$$E(X) = \tfrac{7}{12}, \qquad E(Y) = \tfrac{7}{12},$$

$$E(XY) = \int_0^1 \int_0^1 x\, y(x + y)dy\, dx = \tfrac{1}{3} \neq E(X)E(Y) = (\tfrac{7}{12})^2.$$

Hence X and Y cannot be independent random variables.

We conclude this section with a note that the cdf for a joint pair of random variables (X, Y) is defined by

$$F(x, y) = \Pr(X \leq x, Y \leq y)$$

$$= \int_{-\infty}^{y} \int_{-\infty}^{x} p(\zeta, \eta)d\zeta\, d\eta, \tag{36}$$

from which it follows that

$$p(x, y) = \frac{\partial^2 F}{\partial x \partial y} \tag{37}$$

whenever $p(x, y)$ is continuous in both x and y.

PROBLEMS

1. X and Y are joint random variables with a pdf given by $p(x, y) = 8xy$ for $0 \leq y \leq x \leq 1$, $p(x, y) = 0$ otherwise. Show that the marginal pdf's are $f(x) = 4x^3$, $0 \leq x \leq 1$, $f(x) = 0$ otherwise, and $g(y) = 4y\,(1 - y^2)$, $0 \leq y \leq 1$, $g(y) = 0$ otherwise. Are X and Y independent random variables?

2. The joint pdf for the pair of random variables (X, Y) is

$$p(x, y) = \tfrac{1}{2}(x + y)\, e^{-x}\, e^{-y}\, U(x)\, U(y).$$

Show that

$$f(x) = \tfrac{1}{2}(x + 1)\, e^{-x}\, U(x),$$

$$g(y) = \tfrac{1}{2}(y + 1)\, e^{-y}\, U(y)$$

are the pdf's of X and Y, respectively. For $x > 0$, $y > 0$, show that

$$F(x, y) = \Pr(X \leq x, Y \leq y)$$

$$= \tfrac{1}{2}[(1 - e^{-y})(1 - e^{-x} - x\, e^{-x}) + (1 - e^{-x})(1 - e^{-y} - y\, e^{-y})],$$

and show that

$$\frac{\partial^2 F}{\partial x \, \partial y} = p(x, y) \qquad \text{for} \qquad x > 0, y > 0 \,.$$

3. The joint pdf of X and Y is

$$p(x, y) = e^{-(x+y)} U(x) \, U(y) \,.$$

Show that the cdf of $Z = X + Y$ is $F(z) = 1 - e^{-z} - ze^{-z}$ for $z \geq 0$, $F(z) = 0$ for $z < 0$. Then show that the pdf for Z is $f(z) = ze^{-z} U(z)$.

4. X and Y are independent random variables, both of the class $U(0, 1)$. Show that $\Pr(Y \geq X^3) = \frac{3}{4}$ by considering the region $y \geq x^3$ in the xy plane.

5. Referring to Problem 3, let $Z = Y - X$. Show that the cdf of Z is

$$F(z) = 1 - \tfrac{1}{2} e^{-z}, \qquad z \geq 0,$$
$$= \tfrac{1}{2} e^{z}, \qquad z < 0,$$

and that

$$f(z) = \tfrac{1}{2} e^{-|z|}, \qquad -\infty < z < \infty,$$

is the pdf of Z.

6. Given that X_1 and X_2 are independent random variables each with a pdf given by $p(x) = xe^{-x} U(x)$, show that the CF of $Z = X_1 + X_2$ is $F_z(t) = (1 - jt)^{-4}$. Find the mean and variance of Z.

7. X and Y are independent random variables; show from $F_z(t) = F_x(t) \, F_y(t)$ that $V(X + Y) = V(X) + V(Y)$, with $Z = X + Y$. [Hint: differentiate!]

8. Two points are chosen independently on the line segment $0 \leq x \leq 1$. The unit line is cut at these two points, yielding three line segments. Show that the probability that a triangle can be formed from these line segments is $P = \frac{1}{4}$.

9. Referring to Example 9, show that for $n = 4$, $\Pr(V - U \geq \frac{1}{2}) = \frac{11}{16}$.

10. Let Y be linearly dependent on X so that $Y = a + bX$ with probability one. If $f(x)$ is the pdf of X, then $p(x, y) = \delta(y - a - bx)f(x)$ is the joint pdf of (X, Y), with δ the Dirac delta function. Show that

$$\mu_y = a + b \, \mu_x,$$
$$\sigma_y^2 = b^2 \, \sigma_x^2,$$

so that

$$Y - \mu_y = \pm \frac{\sigma_y}{\sigma_x} (X - \mu_x) \,.$$

11. Let X and Y be independent random variables with X of the class $U(0, 2)$ and Y of the class $U(0, 1)$. Find the joint pdf of X, Y. Let $Z = X + Y$ and find the cdf of Z for the regions $0 < z < 1$, $1 < z < 2$, $2 < z < 3$. Then find the pdf of Z.

12. X is a random variable with a pdf given by

$$f(x) = \frac{1}{\alpha^2} x \, e^{-x/\alpha} U(x), \qquad \alpha > 0 \,.$$

If $X = x$ is observed, then Y is chosen uniformly on the interval $(0, x)$. Let $Z = X + Y$. For $z > 0$ show that

$$\Pr(Z \leq z) = (1 - e^{-z/2\alpha})^2.$$

Show that

$$p(z) = \frac{1}{\alpha} (e^{-z/2\alpha} - e^{-z/\alpha}) \, U(z)$$

is the pdf of Z. Show that

$$E(Z) = 3\alpha = E(X) + E(Y) = 2\alpha + \alpha .$$

4.5 CONDITIONAL PROBABILITY DENSITY FUNCTIONS

Let $p(x, y)$ be the joint pdf for the pair of random variables (X, Y). If A is the event that X falls in the interval $(x, x + dx)$, and if B is the event that Y falls in the interval $(y, y + dy)$, it follows that

$$P(AB) = p(x, y)dy \, dx,$$
$$P(A) = f(x)dx, \tag{1}$$
$$P(B) = g(y)dy,$$

except for infinitesimals of higher order. From Bayes' theorem we have

$$P(AB) = P(A|B)P(B) = P(B|A)P(A),$$

so that

$$P(A|B) = \frac{P(AB)}{P(B)} = \frac{p(x, y)dy \, dx}{g(y)dy}$$

$$= \frac{p(x, y)dx}{g(y)}, \qquad g(y) \neq 0. \tag{2}$$

If we let $dy \to 0$ we obtain

$$\Pr(x \leq X \leq x + dx | Y = y) = \frac{p(x, y)}{g(y)} \, dx. \tag{3}$$

The left-hand side of Eq. (3) represents the probability that X lies in the interval $(x, x + dx)$, given that we have observed the value $Y = y$. Hence

$$f(x|y) \equiv \frac{p(x, y)}{g(y)}, \qquad g(y) \neq 0, \tag{4}$$

is defined as the *conditional* pdf of X, given that $Y = y$ has been observed. We note that

$$\int_{-\infty}^{\infty} f(x|y)dx = \frac{1}{g(y)} \int_{-\infty}^{\infty} p(x, y)dx = \frac{g(y)}{g(y)} = 1. \tag{5}$$

This result is to be expected, for if $Y = y$ has been observed, of necessity some value of X must have occurred as the outcome of an experiment. Thus $f(x|y)$ of

Eq. (4) is a pdf in X. Similarly, the conditional pdf of Y, given that $X = x$ has been observed, is

$$g(y|x) \equiv \frac{p(x, y)}{f(x)}, \qquad f(x) \neq 0, \tag{6}$$

with

$$\int_{-\infty}^{\infty} g(y|x)dy = 1.$$

Thus Bayes' formula for continuous random variables may be expressed by

$$p(x, y) = f(x|y)g(y)$$
$$= g(y|x)f(x). \tag{7}$$

Now if X and Y are independent random variables, $p(x, y) = f(x)g(y)$, it follows that

$$f(x|y) = f(x),$$
$$g(y|x) = g(y) \tag{8}$$

for all x, y. This means that the conditional pdf of X given $Y = y$ does not depend on which value of Y has been observed, so that the *a posteriori* probability that X will fall in the region $(x, x + dx)$ is the same as the *a priori* probability that X will fall in the region $(x, x + dx)$. The fact that $Y = y$ has occurred yields no new information about the random variable X. Similar statements hold by interchanging the roles of X and Y.

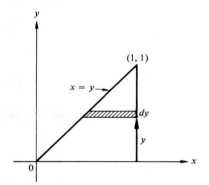

Figure 4.28

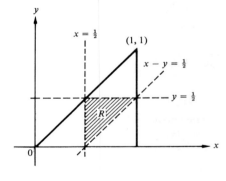

Figure 4.29

Example 1. Let X be a random variable of the class $U(0, 1)$. Whenever $X = x$ is obtained as the result of an experiment, we consider the interval $(0, x)$ and let Y be a new random variable of class $U(0, x)$. Thus our second experiment yields a value of Y in the interval $(0, x)$, so that $0 \leq y \leq x$, and $g(y|x) = 1/x$, $x \neq 0$. If $X = 0$, then $Y = 0$ with probability 1.

The joint pdf of (X, Y) is obtained from Eq. (7) with $f(x) = 1$ for $0 \leq x \leq 1$, $f(x) = 0$ otherwise. Hence

$$p(x, y) = \frac{1}{x} \qquad \text{for} \qquad 0 < y \leq x \leq 1,$$

$$= 0 \qquad \text{otherwise.} \tag{9}$$

From Fig. 28 it follows that

$$g(y) = \int_{x=y}^{x=1} p(x, y)dx = \int_y^1 \frac{1}{x} dx = -\ln y, \qquad 0 < y \leq 1.$$

We observe that

$$\int_0^1 g(y)dy = -\int_0^1 \ln y \, dy = -[y \ln y - y]_0^1 = 1,$$

$$E(Y) = \int_0^1 -y \ln y \, dy = -\left[\frac{y^2}{2} \ln y - \frac{y^2}{4}\right]_0^1 = \tfrac{1}{4},$$

since

$$\lim_{y \to 0} y \ln y = \lim_{y \to 0} y^2 \ln y = 0.$$

It is not surprising that $E(Y) = \tfrac{1}{4}$ since $E(X) = \tfrac{1}{2}$, and $E(Y)$ will be $\tfrac{1}{2}$ of this value.

Continuing with this example we ask for the probability that the three line segments of lengths y, $x - y$, $1 - x$ (of total length unity) will form a triangle. Since the sum of any two sides of a triangle is greater than the third side, each of the sides $y, x - y, 1 - x$ must be less than $\tfrac{1}{2}$. Conversely, if $y < \tfrac{1}{2}, x - y < \tfrac{1}{2}, 1 - x < \tfrac{1}{2}$, a triangle can be formed. The region of interest, R, is shown in Fig. 29.

Hence

$$P = \int_R \int p(x, y)dy \, dx = \int_{\frac{1}{2}}^1 \int_{x-\frac{1}{2}}^{\frac{1}{2}} \frac{1}{x} dy \, dx$$

$$= \int_{\frac{1}{2}}^1 \frac{\tfrac{1}{2} - (x - \tfrac{1}{2})}{x} dx = \int_{\frac{1}{2}}^1 \frac{1 - x}{x} dx$$

$$= (\ln x - x)\Big|_{\frac{1}{2}}^1 = \ln 2 - \tfrac{1}{2}.$$

Example 2. Let $p(x, y)$ be the joint pdf for the pair of random variables (X, Y). Let us consider the random variable X as a random signal and the random variable Y as a random noise source. We consider a new random variable, Z, composed of signal plus noise, $Z = X + Y$.

If we observe $Z = z$, we may wish to estimate the signal by means of the conditional pdf of X given $Z = z$. Now the joint probability that X will lie in the range $(x, x + dx)$ and that Z will lie in the range $(z, z + dz)$ is simply the probability that Y will lie in the range $(z - x, z - x + dz)$ along with the requirement that X lie in the range $(x, x + dx)$. Hence $p(x, z - x)$ is the joint pdf of X and Z.

From Bayes' formula, Eq. (4), we obtain

$$f(x|Z = z) \equiv f(x|z) = \frac{p(x, z - x)}{\int_{-\infty}^{\infty} p(x, z - x)dx}, \tag{10}$$

since $\int_{-\infty}^{\infty} p(x, z - x)dx$ is the pdf of Z.

If the signal plus noise has yielded a value $Z = z$, we may be interested in estimating the original signal. Now $f(x|Z = z) \, dx$ is the probability that X lie in the interval $(x, x+dx)$ given that $Z = z$ has occurred. It is clear that this proba-bility is a maximum when $f(x|Z = z)$ is a maximum. The most likely value of x which occurred is that $\hat{x} = x$ for which $f(x|Z = z)$ is a maximum, and hence for which $p(x, z - x)$ is a maximum since only the numerator of Eq. (10) depends on x.

For example, suppose that X and Y are normal independent random variables, $N(0, \sigma_x^2)$, $N(0, \sigma_y^2)$. Then

$$p(x, z - x) = \frac{1}{2\pi\sigma_x\sigma_y} \exp\left\{-\left[\frac{x^2}{2\sigma_x^2} + \frac{(z - x)^2}{2\sigma_y^2}\right]\right\}.$$

Thus $p(x, z - x)$ is a maximum (z fixed) when

$$L' = \frac{x^2}{2\sigma_x^2} + \frac{(z - x)^2}{2\sigma_y^2}$$

is a minimum. Now

$$\frac{\partial L'}{\partial x} = \frac{x}{\sigma_x^2} - \frac{(z - x)}{\sigma_y^2} = 0$$

yields

$$\hat{X} = \frac{1}{1 + (\sigma_y/\sigma_x)^2} Z \tag{11}$$

as the maximum *a posteriori* estimate of X given $Z = z$.

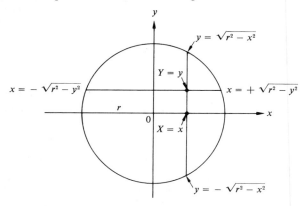

Figure 4.30

Example 3. Consider a circle of radius r centered at the origin. We choose $X = x$ uniformly on the interval $-r \leq x \leq r$, so that $f(x) = 1/2r$ for this region. Having obtained $X = x$ as the result of an experiment we draw a chord perpendicular to the x-axis at the point $X = x$ and then choose $Y = y$ uniformly on this chord of length $2\sqrt{r^2 - x^2}$, so that

$$g(y|x) = \frac{1}{2\sqrt{r^2 - x^2}}, \qquad -\sqrt{r^2 - x^2} \leq y \leq \sqrt{r^2 - x^2},$$

$$= 0 \qquad \text{otherwise}$$

(see Fig. 30).

The joint pdf of (X, Y) is

$$p(x, y) = f(x)g(y|x)$$

$$= \frac{1}{4r}(r^2 - x^2)^{-1/2}, \qquad x^2 + y^2 \leq r^2,$$

$$= 0 \qquad \text{otherwise,}$$

and the pdf of Y is

$$g(y) = \frac{1}{4r} \int_{-\sqrt{r^2 - y^2}}^{\sqrt{r^2 - y^2}} (r^2 - x^2)^{-1/2} \, dx$$

$$= \frac{1}{2r} \int_0^{\sin^{-1} \sqrt{1 - y^2/r^2}} d\theta$$

$$= \frac{1}{2r} \sin^{-1} \sqrt{1 - y^2/r^2}, \qquad -r \leq y \leq r,$$

by letting $x = r \sin \theta$, $dx = r \cos \theta \, d\theta$. We let the reader show that $E(y) = 0$.

Example 4. *Conditional means.* The mean value of X, given that $Y = y$ has been observed, is defined by

$$E(X|y) = \int_{-\infty}^{\infty} x f(x|y) dx \tag{12}$$

and the mean value of Y, given that $X = x$ has been observed, is defined by

$$E(Y|x) = \int_{-\infty}^{\infty} y g(y|x) dy. \tag{13}$$

In Example 1 of Section 4.4 we have $p(x, y) = x + y$ over the unit square $0 \leq x \leq 1, 0 \leq y \leq 1, p(x, y) = 0$ otherwise, as the joint pdf of a pair of random variables (X, Y). The marginal pdf's are (see Example 5 of Section 4.4)

$$f(x) = \int_0^1 (x + y)dy = x + \tfrac{1}{2}, \qquad 0 \leq x \leq 1,$$

$$g(y) = \int_0^1 (x + y)dx = y + \tfrac{1}{2}, \qquad 0 \leq y \leq 1,$$

with $f(x)$ and $g(y)$ zero, otherwise. We note that X and Y are not independent random variables since $(x + \frac{1}{2})(y + \frac{1}{2}) \not\equiv x + y$. The conditional pdf's are

$$f(x|y) = \frac{x + y}{y + \frac{1}{2}}, \qquad g(y|x) = \frac{x + y}{x + \frac{1}{2}}$$

for the unit square. We observe that

$$\int_0^1 f(x|y)dx = \frac{1}{y + \frac{1}{2}}\int_0^1 (x + y)dx = \frac{y + \frac{1}{2}}{y + \frac{1}{2}} = 1,$$

$$\int_0^1 g(y|x)dy = \frac{1}{x + \frac{1}{2}}\int_0^1 (x + y)dy = \frac{x + \frac{1}{2}}{x + \frac{1}{2}} = 1.$$

Furthermore,

$$E(X|y) = \int_0^1 x f(x|y)dx$$

$$= \frac{1}{y + \frac{1}{2}}\int_0^1 (x^2 + xy)dx$$

$$= \frac{1}{3}\frac{1 + 3y}{1 + 2y}, \qquad 0 \leq y \leq 1,$$

$$E(Y|x) = \int y g(y|x)dy$$

$$= \frac{1}{3}\frac{2 + 3x}{1 + 2x}, \qquad 0 \leq x \leq 1.$$

Show that

$$\max E(X|y) = \tfrac{2}{3},$$

$$\min E(Y|x) = \tfrac{5}{9}.$$

PROBLEMS

1. Referring to Example 1 in this Section, show that the conditional pdf, $f(x|y)$, is given by $f(x|y) = -1/x \ln y$ for $0 < y \leq x \leq 1$, $f(x|y) = 0$ otherwise. Show that

$$E(X|y) = \frac{y - 1}{\ln y}, \qquad 0 < y \leq 1.$$

Why is $E(X|y) \leq 1$? Hence deduce that $y - 1 \geq \ln y$ for $0 < y \leq 1$. What is $E(X|y = 1)$?

2. The joint pdf for (X, Y) is given by $p(x, y) = \frac{3}{2}(x^2 + y^2)$ for the unit square $0 \leq x \leq 1$, $0 \leq y \leq 1$, $p(x, y) = 0$ otherwise. Find the conditional pdf's, $f(x|y)$, $g(y|x)$. Find $E(Y|x)$, $E(X|y)$.

3. The joint pdf for (X, Y) is
$$p(x, y) = \tfrac{1}{2}(x + y) e^{-(x+y)} U(x) U(y).$$
   Show that
$$E(X|y) = \frac{y + 2}{y + 1}, \qquad 0 \le y < \infty.$$

4. Let $f(x|y) = ye^{-xy} U(x)$ be the conditional pdf of X, given $Y = y > 0$, and let $g(y) = e^{-y} U(y)$ be the pdf of the random variable Y. Show that $f(x) = (x + 1)^{-2}$ $U(x)$ is the pdf for the random variable X.

5. Let
$$f(x|y) = \frac{1}{\alpha} e^{-(x-y)/\alpha} U(x) \qquad \text{for} \qquad x > y,$$
$$f(x|y) = 0 \qquad\qquad\qquad \text{otherwise},$$
   be the conditional pdf of X, given $Y = y$, and let $g(y) = (1/\beta) e^{-y/\beta} U(y)$ be the pdf of Y, $\alpha > 0$, $\beta > 0$. Find the joint pdf of (X, Y). Find the conditional pdf of Y given $X = x$. Find the pdf of X. In what region of the xy plane is the joint pdf of (X, Y) nonzero?

6. Referring to Problem 4, find $E(X|y)$, $E(Y|x)$.

7. Referring to Problem 5, find $E(X|y)$, $E(Y|x)$.

8. If
$$M_1(\theta) \equiv \int_{-\infty}^{\infty} f(x|y) e^{\theta x} \, dx,$$
$$M_2(\theta) = \int_{-\infty}^{\infty} g(y|x) e^{\theta y} \, dy,$$
   how can one determine $E(X|y)$, $E(Y|x)$? Apply this result to Problem 4 and check the results of Problem 6.

4.6 CORRELATION · COVARIANCE · REGRESSION

Given a joint pdf of (X, Y), say $p(x, y)$, we can obtain the marginal pdf's, $f(x)$, $g(y)$, and the conditional pdf's, $f(x|y)$, $g(y|x)$. Then

$$\mu_x = E(X) = \int_{-\infty}^{\infty} x f(x) dx = \int_{-\infty}^{\infty}\int_{-\infty}^{\infty} x\, p(x, y) dy\, dx,$$

$$\mu_y = E(Y) = \int_{-\infty}^{\infty} y\, g(y) dy = \int_{-\infty}^{\infty}\int_{-\infty}^{\infty} y\, p(x, y) dx\, dy,$$

$$\sigma_x^2 = V(X) = \int_{-\infty}^{\infty} (x - \mu_x)^2 f(x) dx = \int_{-\infty}^{\infty}\int_{-\infty}^{\infty} (x - \mu_x)^2\, p(x, y) dy\, dx,$$

$$\sigma_y^2 = V(Y) = \int_{-\infty}^{\infty} (y - \mu_y)^2 g(y) dy = \int_{-\infty}^{\infty}\int_{-\infty}^{\infty} (y - \mu_y)^2\, p(x, y) dx\, dy, \tag{1}$$

$$E(X|y) = \int_{-\infty}^{\infty} x f(x|y) dx = \frac{1}{g(y)}\int_{-\infty}^{\infty} x\, p(x, y) dx, \qquad g(y) \neq 0,$$

$$E(Y|x) = \int_{-\infty}^{\infty} y\, g(y|x) dy = \frac{1}{f(x)}\int_{-\infty}^{\infty} y\, p(x, y) dy, \qquad f(x) \neq 0.$$

The following integral, which corresponds to the cross-product of inertia in mechanics, defines the covariance of (X, Y) and the correlation coefficient of (X, Y), written ρ_{xy}.

$$\text{cov}(X, Y) \equiv \rho_{xy}\sigma_x\sigma_y = \int_{-\infty}^{\infty}\int_{-\infty}^{\infty} (x - \mu_x)(y - \mu_y)\, p(x, y)dy\, dx$$

$$= \int_{-\infty}^{\infty}\int_{-\infty}^{\infty} xy\, p(x, y)dy\, dx - \mu_x\mu_y, \tag{2}$$

provided the double integral converges absolutely. We call $\rho_{xy} \equiv \rho$ the correlation coefficient associated with the random variables (X, Y). To show that $\rho^2 \leq 1$ we consider the random variable

$$W^2 = [\lambda(X - \mu_x) - (Y - \mu_y)]^2 \geq 0 \tag{3}$$

with λ an arbitrary constant. Since $E(W^2) \geq 0$, of necessity

$$E(W^2) = \lambda^2\sigma_x^2 - 2\lambda\rho\sigma_x\sigma_y + \sigma_y^2 \geq 0 \tag{4}$$

for all real values of λ. If we choose

$$\lambda = \rho\frac{\sigma_y}{\sigma_x}$$

we obtain $\rho^2 \leq 1$ from Eq. (4). If $\rho = 1$ we obtain

$$E(W^2) = (\lambda\sigma_x - \sigma_y)^2,$$

which shows that $E(W^2) = 0$ for $\lambda = \sigma_y/\sigma_x$. This means that $W \equiv 0$ with probability unity. Hence

$$y - \mu_y = \frac{\sigma_y}{\sigma_x}(x - \mu_x) \tag{5}$$

from Eq. (3), setting $\lambda = \sigma_y/\sigma_x$. Thus X and Y are linearly related (highly correlated). For $\rho = -1$ (negative correlation) we may deduce that

$$y - \mu_y = -\frac{\sigma_y}{\sigma_x}(x - \mu_x). \tag{6}$$

Hence for $\rho^2 = 1$ we can say that the pair of random variables (X, Y) are linearly related, or linearly dependent, and their joint pdf is given by

$$p(x, y) = \delta\left[y - \mu_y \mp \frac{\sigma_y}{\sigma_x}(x - \mu_x)\right]f(x), \tag{7}$$

with $f(x)$ the pdf of X, and δ the Dirac delta function (see Problem 10, Section 4).

If $\rho = 0$, we say that X and Y are uncorrelated. This always occurs when X and Y are statistically independent, since

$$\rho\sigma_x\sigma_y = \int_{-\infty}^{\infty}\int_{-\infty}^{\infty} (x - \mu_x)(y - \mu_y)\, f(x)\, g(y)dy\, dx$$

$$= \int_{-\infty}^{\infty} (x - \mu_x)\, f(x)dx \int_{-\infty}^{\infty} (y - \mu_y)\, g(y)dy = 0. \tag{8}$$

However, if $\rho = 0$ we cannot say that X and Y are statistically independent. For example, let X be of the class $U(-1, 1)$, and let $Y = X^2$. Then $E(X) = 0$ and $E(Y) = E(X^2) = \frac{1}{3}$, yielding

$$E[(X - \mu_x)(Y - \mu_y)] = E(XY) = E(X^3)$$
$$= \frac{1}{2} \int_{-1}^{1} x^3 \, dx = 0,$$

so that $\rho = 0$, although X and Y are not statistically independent (the occurrence of $X = x$ specifies the occurrence of $Y = x^2$).

Example 1. Let $p(x, y) = 1/x$ for $0 < y \le x \le 1$, $p(x, y) = 0$ otherwise. Then

$$\mu_x = \int_0^1 \int_0^x x \frac{1}{x} \, dy \, dx = \frac{1}{2},$$

$$\mu_y = \int_0^1 \int_0^x y \frac{1}{x} \, dy \, dx = \frac{1}{4},$$

$$\sigma_x^2 = \int_0^1 \int_0^x (x - \tfrac{1}{2})^2 \frac{1}{x} \, dy \, dx = \frac{1}{12},$$

$$\sigma_y^2 = \int_0^1 \int_0^x (y - \tfrac{1}{4})^2 \frac{1}{x} \, dy \, dx = \frac{7}{144},$$

$$\rho \sigma_x \sigma_y = \int_0^1 \int_0^x xy \frac{1}{x} \, dy \, dx - \frac{1}{2} \cdot \frac{1}{4} = \frac{1}{24},$$

so that $\rho = \sqrt{3/7}$, a positive correlation between X and Y.

Let us consider now the following problem. Let (X, Y) be a pair of random variables. Given that $X = x$ has occurred, we may wish to estimate the value of Y. For example, if we know someone's mathematical ability (as judged by a test given by a psychologist) we may desire to estimate his I.Q. without giving that person an I.Q. test.

Let $\hat{Y}$ be an estimate of Y given that $X = x$ has occurred. Since linear equations can be manipulated most readily, we assume that

$$\hat{Y} = aX + b, \tag{9}$$

with a and b unknown constants. The mean-square error is

$$E[(\hat{Y} - Y)^2] = \int_{-\infty}^{\infty} \int_{-\infty}^{\infty} (ax + b - y)^2 \, p(x, y) dy \, dx \tag{10}$$

(see Fig. 31).

Next, we determine the constants a, b, which minimize the mean-square error. Note that

$$E[(\hat{Y} - Y)^2] = \int_{-\infty}^{\infty} \int_{-\infty}^{\infty} [a(x - \mu_x) - (y - \mu_y) + a\mu_x + b - \mu_y]^2 \, p(x, y) \, dy \, dx$$
$$= a^2 \sigma_x^2 + \sigma_y^2 - 2a\rho \, \sigma_x \sigma_y + (a\mu_x + b - \mu_y)^2. \tag{11}$$

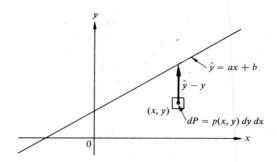

Figure 4.31

Since $(a\mu_x + b - \mu_y)^2 \geq 0$, we choose $b = \mu_y - a\mu_x$ to minimize $E[(\hat{Y} - Y)^2]$. Then a is chosen to minimize

$$a^2\sigma_x^2 + \sigma_y^2 - 2a\rho\sigma_x\sigma_y \equiv (a\sigma_x - \rho\sigma_y)^2 + \sigma_y^2(1 - \rho^2). \tag{12}$$

Hence we choose $a\sigma_x - \rho\sigma_y = 0$, yielding

$$a = \rho\frac{\sigma_y}{\sigma_x},$$

$$b = \mu_y - \rho\mu_x\frac{\sigma_y}{\sigma_x}. \tag{13}$$

Substituting into Eq. (9) yields the *line of regression* of Y on X, given by

$$\frac{\hat{y} - \mu_y}{\sigma_y} = \rho\frac{x - \mu_x}{\sigma_x}. \tag{14}$$

The line of regression always passes through the mean (μ_x, μ_y) of the distribution. Note that Eqs. (5) and (6) correspond to $\rho = 1$ and $\rho = -1$, respectively. The line of regression of X on Y (estimating X, given that $Y = y$ has occurred) is

$$\frac{\hat{x} - \mu_x}{\sigma_x} = \rho\frac{y - \mu_y}{\sigma_y} \tag{15}$$

by interchanging the roles of X and Y.

The results above hold also for joint random variables in discrete probability theory, using the corresponding definitions of μ_x, μ_y, σ_x, σ_y, ρ, see Section 3.8.

Example 2. Referring to Example 1, the line of regression of Y on X is

$$\hat{y} - \tfrac{1}{4} = \frac{\sqrt{\tfrac{3}{7}}\sqrt{\tfrac{7}{144}}}{\sqrt{\tfrac{1}{12}}}(x - \tfrac{1}{2}) = \tfrac{1}{2}(x - \tfrac{1}{2}),$$

so that $\hat{y} = \tfrac{1}{2}x$. There is nothing remarkable about this result. Recall that X was of the class $U(0, 1)$ and that Y was chosen uniformly on the interval $(0, x)$. Given that $X = x$ has occurred, the best linear estimate of Y is to choose $\hat{y} = \tfrac{1}{2}x$, the average value of Y, given $X = x$.

Example 3. Consider the pdf of Example 1 of Section 4.4. We have

$$\mu_x = \int_0^1 x(x + \tfrac{1}{2})dx = \tfrac{7}{12} = \mu_y,$$

$$\sigma_x^2 = \int_0^1 (x - \tfrac{7}{2})^2 (x + \tfrac{1}{2})dx = \tfrac{11}{144} = \sigma_y^2,$$

$$\rho\sigma_x\sigma_y = \int_0^1\int_0^1 xy(x + y)dy\,dx - \tfrac{49}{144} = -\tfrac{1}{144},$$

so that

$$\hat{y} - \tfrac{7}{12} = -\tfrac{1}{11}(x - \tfrac{7}{12})$$

is the line of regression of Y on X.

Before proceeding to a more general consideration of estimating Y given that $X = x$ has occurred, let us note that

$$E(Y|x) = \int_{-\infty}^{\infty} y\,g(y|x)dy,$$

so that

$$E[\psi(X)\,E(Y|x)] = \int_{-\infty}^{\infty} \psi(x)\,E(Y|x)\,f(x)dx$$

$$= \int_{-\infty}^{\infty}\int_{-\infty}^{\infty} y\,\psi(x)\,g(y|x)\,f(x)dx\,dy$$

$$= \int_{-\infty}^{\infty}\int_{-\infty}^{\infty} y\,\psi(x)\,p(x, y)dy\,dx$$

$$= E[\psi(X)\,Y]. \tag{16}$$

Now let $\hat{Y} = \phi(X)$ be the best estimate of Y, given that $X = x$ has occurred, in the sense that $E[(\hat{Y} - Y)^2] = E\{[\phi(X) - Y]^2\}$ is to be a minimum. We wish to determine the unknown function $\phi(X)$ which yields the minimum mean-square error. Now

$$E\{[\phi(X) - Y]^2\} = \int_{-\infty}^{\infty}\int_{-\infty}^{\infty} [\phi(x) - y]^2\,p(x, y)dy\,dx$$

$$= \int_{-\infty}^{\infty}\int_{-\infty}^{\infty} [\phi(x) - E(Y|x) + E(Y|x) - y]^2\,p(x, y)dy\,dx$$

$$= \int_{-\infty}^{\infty}\int_{-\infty}^{\infty} [\phi(x) - E(Y|x)]^2\,p(x, y)dy\,dx \tag{17}$$

$$+ \int_{-\infty}^{\infty}\int_{-\infty}^{\infty} [E(Y|x) - y]^2\,p(x, y)dy\,dx$$

$$+ 2\int_{-\infty}^{\infty}\int_{-\infty}^{\infty} \psi(x)\,[E(Y|x) - y]\,p(x, y)dy\,dx,$$

with $\psi(x) = \phi(x) - E(Y|x)$.

From Eq. (16) the last integral vanishes. Furthermore, the second integral is a constant independent of $\phi(x)$. Hence the mean-square error is a minimum when the first integral is a minimum. This occurs, obviously, when $\phi(x) \equiv E(Y|x)$. Thus the curve of regression of Y on X is given by

$$\hat{y} = E(Y|x) = \phi(x). \tag{18}$$

It should be clear to the reader that whenever $\phi(x)$ is linear in x, the curve of regression becomes the line of regression. For other cases the curve of regression need not pass through the center (μ_x, μ_y) of the distribution.

Example 4. In Example 1 we have $g(y|x) = 1/x$ for $0 < y \leq x \leq 1$, $g(y|x) = 0$ otherwise. Hence

$$E(Y|x) = \int_0^x y \frac{1}{x} dy = \frac{x}{2} = \phi(x),$$

so that $\hat{y} = x/2$ is both the line and curve of regression of Y on X.

Example 5. In Example 4 of Section 4.5 we have $p(x, y) = x + y$ for the unit square $0 \leq x \leq 1, 0 \leq y \leq 1$, $p(x, y) = 0$ otherwise. Hence

$$f(x) = \int_0^1 (x + y)dy = x + \tfrac{1}{2},$$

so that

$$g(y|x) = \frac{(x + y)}{(x + \tfrac{1}{2})}$$

and

$$\phi(x) = E(Y|x) = \int_0^1 \frac{y(x + y)}{x + \tfrac{1}{2}} dy$$

$$= \frac{1}{3} \frac{3x + 2}{2x + 1}$$

$$\hat{y} = \frac{1}{3} \frac{3x + 2}{2x + 1}, \qquad 0 \leq x \leq 1.$$

The curve of regression of Y on X is a branch of a hyperbola in the $x, \hat{y}$ plane. For $x = \mu_x = \tfrac{7}{12}$ we have

$$\hat{y} = \tfrac{55}{78} \neq \mu_y = \tfrac{7}{12}.$$

Example 6. *The variance of a sum of random variables.* Let

$$Y = \sum_{i=1}^n X_i$$

be a sum of random variables. We compute the variance of Y, say $V(Y)$. Now

$$\bar{Y} = E(Y) = \sum_{i=1}^n E(X_i) = \sum \bar{X}_i,$$

so that

$$Y - \bar{Y} = \sum_{i=1}^n (X_i - \bar{X}_i)$$

$$(Y - \bar{Y})^2 = \sum_{i=1}^n (X_i - \bar{X}_i)^2 + \sum\sum_{i \neq j} (X_i - \bar{X}_i)(X_j - \bar{X}_j).$$

Taking expected values yields

$$V(Y) = \sum_{i=1}^{n} V(X_i) + \sum_{i \neq j} \sum \text{Cov}(X_i, X_j), \qquad (19)$$

provided the variances and covariances exist. If the X_i, $i = 1, 2, \ldots, n$, are independent in pairs, then $\text{Cov}(X_i, X_j) = 0$ for $i \neq j$, and

$$V(Y) = \sum_{i=1}^{n} V(X_i). \qquad (20)$$

Thus we state the important

Theorem. The variance of a sum of independent random variables (independent in pairs) is the sum of the individual variances of the random variables.

Thus, if $X_1, X_2, \ldots, X_n$ are independent random samples from a common distribution, the sample mean random variable defined by

$$S_n = \frac{1}{n}(X_1 + X_2 + \cdots + X_n)$$

yields a variance

$$V(S_n) = \frac{1}{n^2}[V(X_1) + V(X_2) + \cdots + V(X_n)]$$

$$= \frac{n\sigma^2}{n^2} = \frac{\sigma^2}{n},$$

with $\sigma^2 = V(X_1) = V(X_2) = \cdots = V(X_n)$.

As $n \to \infty$ we note that $V(S_n) \to 0$, which suggests that as $n \to \infty$ the sample mean approaches a constant value, namely $E(S_n) = \mu_x$, with probability one. This conclusion will be discussed further, together with other implications of the "laws of large numbers," in Chapter 5.

PROBLEMS

1. The joint pdf of (X, Y) is $p(x, y) = e^{-y}$ for the region $y \geq x > 0$, $p(x, y) = 0$ otherwise. Show that $E(X) = 1$, $E(Y) = 2$, $V(X) = 1$, $V(Y) = 2$, $E(X|y) = y/2$, $E(Y|x) = x + 1$, $\rho = \sqrt{2}/2$. Find the line and curve of regression of Y on X.

2. X is a random variable with a pdf given by

$$p(x) = \frac{1}{\alpha^2} x \, e^{-x/\alpha} \, U(x).$$

If $X = x$ has been obtained as the result of an experiment, then Y is chosen uniformly on $(0, x)$, so that $f(y|x) = 1/x$ for $x \geq y > 0$. Show that $E(X) = 2\alpha$, $E(Y) = \alpha$, $V(X) = 2\alpha^2$, $V(Y) = \alpha^2$, $\rho = \sqrt{2}/2$, $E(Y|x) = x/2$, $E(X|y) = y + \alpha$. Find the line and the curve of regression of Y on X, of X on Y.

3. Let $p(x, y) = \frac{4}{5}(x + y + xy)$ for the unit square $0 \le x \le 1, 0 \le y \le 1, p(x, y) = 0$ otherwise, be the pdf of (X, Y). Find the line and curve of regression of Y on X.

4. Let X and Y be dependent random variables with the same variance. Show that the correlation coefficient of the random variables $U = X + Y$, $V = X - Y$, is zero. [*Hint:* Show that $E(UV) - E(U) E(V) = 0$.]

4.7 COORDINATE TRANSFORMATIONS

Let $p(x, y)$ be the joint pdf for the pair of random variables (X, Y). Now consider the coordinate transformation

$$u = u(x, y),$$
$$v = v(x, y), \tag{1}$$

such that for every point $P(x, y)$ in a region of the xy plane there corresponds a unique point $P'(u, v)$ in the uv plane. Thus every time a dart falls at the point $P(x, y)$ we may imagine that a dart has fallen at the point $P'(u, v)$. Since X and Y are random variables we may consider U and V, whose values are u and v respectively, as a joint pair of random variables. Let us determine their joint pdf, say $q(u, v)$.

In Section A.10 of the Appendix, dealing with Jacobians, we have seen that an area dA in the xy plane will map into an area dA' in the uv plane, such that

$$dA = \left| J\left(\frac{x, y}{u, v}\right) \right| dA'. \tag{2}$$

Since probability must be conserved,

$$dP = q(u, v)dA' = p(x, y)dA, \tag{3}$$

so that

$$q(u, v) = \left| J\left(\frac{x, y}{u, v}\right) \right| p(x, y). \tag{4}$$

If the points $(x_1, y_1), \ldots, (x_j, y_j), \ldots, (x_k, y_k)$ map into the single point (u, v), then

$$q(u, v) = \sum_{j=1}^{k} \left| J\left(\frac{x, y}{u, v}\right) \right|_{\substack{x = x_j \\ y = y_j}} p(x_j, y_j). \tag{5}$$

The result of Eq. (5) applies to n-dimensional coordinate transformations as well.

Example 1. Let $p(x, y) = x + y$ inside the unit square $0 \le x \le 1, 0 \le y \le 1$, $p(x, y) = 0$ otherwise, be the joint pdf of the random variables (X, Y). We are interested in the random variable $U = XY$. Let $u = xy, v = y$ be a coordinate transformation. The fact that we set $v = y$ is purely arbitrary.

Let us determine the region R' in the uv plane which the unit square, R, maps into under the coordinate transformation $u = xy, v = y$. The line $x = 1, 0 \le y \le 1$, maps into $u = y$, $v = y$, which is the straight line $v = u$, $0 \le u \le 1$; the line $x = 0$, $0 \le y \le 1$, maps into the line $u = 0$, $0 \le v = y \le 1$; the line $y = 1$, $0 \le x \le 1$, maps into the line $v = 1$, $0 \le u = x \le 1$; the line $y = 0$, $0 \le x \le 1$, maps into the point $(u = 0, v = 0)$. The region R' is shown in Fig. 32.

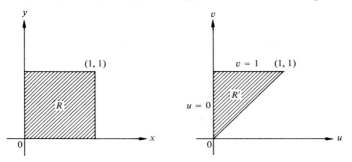

Figure 4.32

Since

$$J\left(\frac{u, v}{x, y}\right) = \begin{vmatrix} y & x \\ 0 & 1 \end{vmatrix} = y,$$

$$J\left(\frac{x, y}{u, v}\right) = \frac{1}{y} = \frac{1}{v},$$

we obtain from Eq. (4) that

$$q(u, v) = \frac{1}{v}(x + y) = \frac{1}{v}(u/v + v) = 1 + \frac{u}{v^2}$$

for the region $R'(v \ne 0)$, $q(u, v) = 0$ otherwise. To find the pdf of U we determine the marginal density function

$$h(u) = \int_{v=u}^{v=1} q(u, v)dv = \int_u^1 \left(\frac{u}{v^2} + 1\right)dv$$

$$= \left[-\frac{u}{v} + v \right]_u^1 = 2(1 - u), \qquad 0 \le u \le 1,$$

with $h(u) = 0$ otherwise. Let the reader show that $k(v) = v + \frac{1}{2}$, $0 \le v \le 1$, $k(v) = 0$ otherwise, is the marginal pdf of V, which is of the same form as $g(y)$, since $Y = V$.

Example 2. For $p(x, y)$ defined in Example 1, let $U = X/Y$, $V = Y$. The reader can easily verify that the unit square R maps into the region R', shown in Fig. 33.

To find $h(u)$ we must consider two cases, namely $0 \le u \le 1$ and $u > 1$, since in the first case v must be integrated from zero to one, and in the second case v

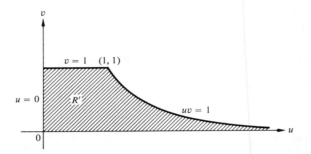

Figure 4.33

must be integrated from zero to $1/u$. Furthermore,

$$J\left(\frac{u, v}{x, y}\right) = \begin{vmatrix} 1/y & -x/y^2 \\ 0 & 1 \end{vmatrix} = \frac{1}{y} = \frac{1}{v},$$

$$J\left(\frac{x, y}{u, v}\right) = v,$$

so that

$$q(u, v) = v(uv + v) = v^2(u + 1),$$

$$h(u) = \int_0^1 v^2(u + 1)dv = \tfrac{1}{3}(u + 1), \qquad 0 \le u \le 1,$$

$$= \int_0^{1/u} v^2(u + 1)dv = \frac{u + 1}{3u^3}, \qquad u > 1,$$

with $h(u) = 0$ for $u < 0$. Let the reader show that

$$\int_{-\infty}^{\infty} h(u)du = 1.$$

We note that

$$k(v) = \int_0^{1/v} v^2(u + 1)du$$

$$= v^2\left(\frac{1}{2v^2} + \frac{1}{v}\right) = v + \frac{1}{2}, \qquad 0 \le v \le 1,$$

$k(v) = 0$ otherwise, as expected, since $V = Y$.

Example 3. Let X and Y have a joint pdf given by

$$p(x, y) = e^{-(x+y)} U(x) U(y),$$

and consider the new random variables $U = X/Y$, $V = Y$. The reader can show that the first quadrant of the xy plane maps into the first quadrant of the uv plane by considering the lines $y = kx$, which map into the lines $u = 1/k$, $0 < k < \infty$. Hence

$$q(u, v) = v e^{-v(1+u)} U(u) U(v),$$

$$h(u) = U(u) \int_0^{\infty} v e^{-v(1+u)}dv = \frac{1}{(1 + u)^2} U(u).$$

Note that

$$\int_{-\infty}^{\infty} h(u)\,du = \int_0^\infty \frac{du}{(1+u)^2} = -\frac{1}{1+u}\Big|_0^\infty = 1.$$

Example 4. Let $p(x, y) = xy\, e^{-(x^2+y^2)/2}\, U(x)\, U(y)$ be the joint pdf of (X, Y). Let $U = X/Y$, $V = Y$. From previous considerations we have

$$q(u, v) = uv^3 \exp\left[-\frac{v^2}{2}(u^2 + 1)\right] U(u)\, U(v),$$

$$h(u) = u \int_0^\infty v^3 \exp\left[-\frac{v^2}{2}(u^2 + 1)\right] dv\, U(u).$$

Let

$$v^2 = \frac{2w}{u^2 + 1}, \qquad v\,dv = \frac{dw}{u^2 + 1},$$

so that

$$h(u) = \frac{2u}{(u^2 + 1)^2} \int_0^\infty w\, e^{-w}\, dw\, U(u)$$

$$= \frac{2u}{(u^2 + 1)^2}\, U(u)$$

is the pdf of $U = X/Y$.

PROBLEMS

1. X and Y are independent random variables both of the class $U(0, 1)$. Let $U = X - Y$, $V = Y$ be a new pair of random variables. Show that

$$q(u) = 1 - |u|, \qquad -1 \le u \le 1,$$
$$q(u) = 0 \qquad \text{otherwise},$$

is the pdf of U.

2. Let $p(x, y) = e^{-(x+y)}\, U(x)\, U(y)$ be the pdf of (X, Y). Let $Z = X/Y$, $W = X - Y$. Show that the joint pdf of (Z, W) is

$$q(z, w) = w(z - 1)^{-2} \exp\left(-\frac{z+1}{z-1}\, w\right)$$

for the shaded region of Fig. 34. Then show that

$$f(z) = \frac{1}{(z+1)^2}\, U(z), \qquad g(w) = \frac{1}{2} e^{-|w|}, \qquad -\infty < w < \infty,$$

are the pdf's of Z and W, respectively.

3. Let $p(x, y) = \frac{1}{4}$ inside the square with vertices at $(-1, 1)$, $(1, 1)$, $(1, -1)$, $(-1, -1)$, $p(x, y) = 0$ otherwise, be the pdf of (X, Y). Let $U = X + Y$, $V = X - Y$. Find the pdf's of U and V.

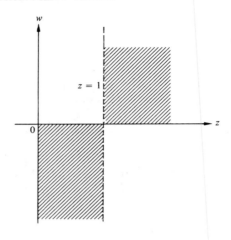

Figure 4.34

4. Let

$$p(x, y) = \frac{1}{2\pi} \exp[- \tfrac{1}{2}(x^2 + y^2)], \qquad - \infty < x < \infty, \qquad - \infty < y < \infty,$$

be the pdf of (X, Y). Let $X = R \cos \Theta$, $Y = R \sin \Theta$. Show that the pdf of (R, Θ) is

$$p(r, \theta) = \frac{r}{2\pi} \exp(- \tfrac{1}{2}r^2), \qquad 0 \le r < \infty, \qquad 0 \le \theta \le 2\pi.$$

Then show that

$$q(\theta) = \frac{1}{2\pi}, \qquad 0 \le \theta \le 2\pi, \qquad h(r) = r \exp(- \tfrac{1}{2}r^2) \, U(r)$$

are the pdf's of Θ, R, respectively.

5. Let $p(x, y) = \tfrac{1}{4}$ for the shaded region of Fig. 35, $p(x, y) = 0$ otherwise, be the pdf of (X, Y). Find the pdf's of $U = X + Y$, $V = X - Y$.

6. Let $p(x, y) = 2x$ for the unit square in the first quadrant, $p(x, y) = 0$ otherwise, be the pdf of (X, Y). Show that the pdf of $Z = X + Y$ is

$$
\begin{aligned}
f(z) &= z^2 & &\text{for} & &0 \le z \le 1, \\
f(z) &= 1 - (z - 1)^2 & &\text{for} & &1 \le z \le 2, \\
f(z) &= 0 & &\text{otherwise.}
\end{aligned}
$$

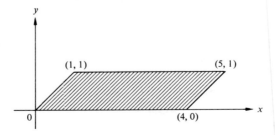

Figure 4.35

7. Let

$$p(x, y) = \frac{1}{2\pi\sigma^2} \exp\left[-\frac{1}{2\sigma^2}(x^2 + y^2)\right] \qquad -\infty < x < \infty, \qquad -\infty < y < \infty,$$

be the joint pdf of a pair of independent normal random variables (X, Y). Find the pdf's for the pair of random variables (U, V) defined by

$$U = (X^2 + Y^2)^{1/2}, \ V = X/Y.$$

8. The joint pdf of the random variables (X, Y) is

$$p(x, y) = \frac{1}{\alpha\beta} e^{-x/\alpha} e^{-y/\beta} U(x) U(y).$$

Find the pdf of the random variable $S = X - Y$ for $X \geq Y$, $S = 0$ for $X < Y$.

9. Referring to Problem 8, find the pdf's of $V = X + Y$, $W = X/(X + Y)$.

10. The joint pdf of the random variables (X, Y, Z) is

$$p(x, y, z) = \frac{1}{(2\pi)^{3/2}\sigma^3} \exp\left[-\frac{1}{2\sigma^2}(x^2 + y^2 + z^2)\right]$$

for the entire x-y-z space. The coordinate transformation to spherical coordinates is $x = r \sin\theta \cos\phi$, $y = r \sin\theta \sin\phi$, $z = r \cos\theta$. Show that

$$J\left(\frac{x, y, z}{r, \theta, \phi}\right) = r^2 \sin\theta, \qquad \begin{array}{l} 0 \leq r < \infty, \\ 0 \leq \theta \leq \pi, \\ 0 \leq \phi \leq 2\pi, \end{array}$$

and that the pdf associated with the random variable R is

$$p(r) = \sqrt{\frac{2}{\pi}} \frac{1}{\sigma^3} r^2 \exp(-r^2/2\sigma^2) U(r).$$

4.8 THE CHI-SQUARE (χ^2), STUDENT, AND F DISTRIBUTIONS

Let $X_1, X_2, \ldots, X_n$ be independent random variables, all $N(0, 1)$. The random variable

$$Y_n = X_1^2 + X_2^2 + \cdots + X_n^2 \tag{1}$$

is called the chi-square random variable with n degrees of freedom. We determine now the pdf of Y_n. The joint pdf of $X_1, X_2, \ldots, X_n$, is

$$p(x_1, x_2, \ldots, x_n) = \frac{1}{(2\pi)^{n/2}} \exp\left(-\tfrac{1}{2}\sum_{i=1}^{n} x_i^2\right). \tag{2}$$

Next consider the coordinate transformations

$$y_1 = x_1$$
$$y_2 = x_2,$$
$$y_3 = x_3, \tag{3}$$
$$\vdots$$
$$y_{n-1} = x_{n-1}$$
$$y_n = x_1^2 + x_2^2 + \cdots + x_n^2,$$

whose Jacobian is

$$J\left(\frac{y_1, y_2, \ldots, y_n}{x_1, x_2, \ldots, x_n}\right) = \begin{vmatrix} 1 & 0 & 0 & & 0 \\ 0 & 1 & 0 & \cdots & 0 \\ 0 & 0 & 1 & & 0 \\ & & \vdots & & \\ 2x_1 & 2x_2 & & \cdots & 2x_n \end{vmatrix} = 2x_n. \tag{4}$$

$$\left| J\left(\frac{x_1, x_2, \ldots, x_n}{y_1, y_2, \ldots, y_n}\right) \right| = \frac{1}{2|x_n|} = \frac{1}{2}[y_n - y_1^2 - y_2^2 - \cdots - y_{n-1}^2]^{-1/2}.$$

The joint pdf for the random variables $Y_1, Y_2, \ldots, Y_n$ is

$$q(y_1, y_2, \ldots, y_n) = \frac{1}{(2\pi)^{n/2}}[y_n - y_1^2 - y_2^2 - \cdots - y_{n-1}^2]^{-1/2} \exp(-y_n/2). \tag{5}$$

The factor of $\frac{1}{2}$ in the Jacobian is dropped, since both $\pm x_n$ contribute to y_n^2. Thus the marginal pdf of Y_n is

$$p_n(y_n) = \frac{\exp(-y_n/2)}{(2\pi)^{n/2}} \int\int \cdots \int [y_n - y_1^2 - y_2^2 \cdots - y_{n-1}^2]^{-1/2} \, dy_1 \cdots dy_{n-1}, \tag{6}$$

the region of integration given by $y_1^2 + y_2^2 + \cdots + y_{n-1}^2 \leq y_n$, with $y_n \geq 0$, $p_n(y_n) = 0$ for $y_n < 0$. Now, the change of variable $y_k = \sqrt{y_n}\, z_k$, $dy_k = \sqrt{y_n}\, dz_k$, $k = 1, 2, \ldots, n - 1$, $y_n = y$, yields

$$p_n(y) = \left[\frac{1}{(2\pi)^{n/2}} \int\int \cdots \int_{\sum_{i=1}^{n-1} z_i^2 \leq 1} [1 - z_1^2 - \cdots - z_{n-1}^2]^{-1/2} dz_1 \cdots dz_{n-1}\right] y^{(n/2)-1} e^{-y/2}$$

$$= K_n\, y^{(n/2)-1}\, e^{-y/2}\, U(y). \tag{7}$$

We need not evaluate the integral of Eq. (7) directly since $p_n(y)$ is a pdf, which implies that

$$K_n \int_0^\infty y^{(n/2)-1} e^{-y/2} \, dy = 1. \tag{8}$$

We can obtain a more convenient relation by changing the variable of integration,

$$\frac{y}{2} = w, \qquad dy = 2\,dw,$$

so that Eq. (8) becomes

$$K_n\,2^{n/2} \int_0^\infty w^{(n/2)-1}\,e^{-w}\,dw = 1. \tag{9}$$

The integral in this expression is simply the well-known gamma function defined by the general relation

$$\Gamma(p) = \int_0^\infty x^{p-1}\,e^{-x}\,dx.$$

We can, therefore, express the result of Eq. (9) as

$$K_n \equiv \frac{1}{(2\pi)^{n/2}} \underset{\sum_1^{n-1} z_i^2 \,\leq\, 1}{\int \cdots \int} [1 - z_1^2 \cdots - z_{n-1}^2]^{-1/2} dz_1 \cdots dz_{n-1} = \frac{1}{2^{n/2}\Gamma(n/2)}, \tag{10}$$

and

$$p_n(y) = \frac{1}{2^{n/2}\Gamma(n/2)}\,y^{(n/2)-1}\,e^{-y/2}\,U(y) \tag{11}$$

is the pdf for the χ^2 random variable with n degrees of freedom.
    We note that

$$p_1(y) = \frac{1}{\sqrt{2\pi}}\,y^{-1/2}\,e^{-y/2}\,U(y),$$

$$p_2(y) = \frac{1}{2}\,e^{-y/2}\,U(y),$$

$$p_3(y) = \frac{1}{\sqrt{2\pi}}\,y^{1/2}\,e^{-y/2}\,U(y), \tag{12}$$

$$p_4(y) = \frac{1}{4}\,y\,e^{-y/2}\,U(y),$$

$$p_5(y) = \frac{1}{3\sqrt{2\pi}}\,y^{3/2}\,e^{-y/2}\,U(y),$$

$$\vdots$$

with $p_1(y)$ the pdf of the square of a single normal random variable, $N(0, 1)$, and $p_2(y)$ the pdf of an exponential random variable. The cdf associated with χ_n^2 is

$$P_n(x) = \frac{1}{2^{n/2}\Gamma(n/2)} \int_0^x y^{(n/2)-1}\,e^{-y/2}\,dy \tag{13}$$

for $x \geq 0$, $F_n(x) = 0$ for $x < 0$, $P_n(x) = \Pr(Y_n \leq x)$.

The CF associated with χ_n^2 is

$$F_n(t) = \frac{1}{2^{n/2}\,\Gamma(n/2)} \int_0^\infty y^{(n/2)-1}\, e^{-y/2}\, e^{jyt}\, dy.$$

The change of variable $y(\tfrac{1}{2} - jt) = z$, $dy = (\tfrac{1}{2} - jt)^{-1}\, dz$, yields

$$F_n(t) = \frac{1}{2^{n/2}\,\Gamma(n/2)} \frac{1}{(\tfrac{1}{2} - jt)^{n/2}} \int_0^\infty z^{(n/2)-1}\, e^{-z}\, dz$$

$$= (1 - 2jt)^{-n/2}. \tag{14}$$

Hence

$$E(Y_n) = \mu_n = \frac{1}{j}\,\frac{d\,F_n(t)}{dt}\bigg|_{t=0} = n,$$

$$E(Y_n^2) = -\left(\frac{d^2\,F_n}{dt^2}\right)_{t=0} = n(n+2), \tag{15}$$

$$V(Y_n) = \sigma_n^2 = 2n.$$

If Y_n and Z_m are χ^2 independent random variables with n and m degrees of freedom, respectively, then the CF associated with $W = Y_n + Z_m$ is

$$F_W(t) = F_{Y_n}(t)\, F_{Z_m}(t)$$

$$= (1 - 2jt)^{-n/2}(1 - 2jt)^{-m/2} = (1 - 2jt)^{-(n+m)/2},$$

so that W is a χ^2 random variable with $(n + m)$ degrees of freedom. Why is this an obvious result?

Example 1. *The Student (Gossett) distribution.* Let X be normal, $N(0, 1)$ and let Y be a χ^2 random variable with n degrees of freedom. If X and Y are independent random variables, then the random variable defined by

$$T = \frac{X}{\sqrt{Y/n}} = \sqrt{n}\,\frac{X}{\sqrt{Y}} \tag{16}$$

is called the Student I random variable. The joint pdf of (X, Y) is given by

$$p(x, y) = \frac{1}{\sqrt{2\pi}\, 2^{n/2}\,\Gamma(n/2)} \exp\left(-x^2/2\right) y^{(n/2)-1} \exp\left(-y/2\right) \tag{17}$$

for the region $-\infty < x < \infty$, $y \geq 0$, $p(x, y) = 0$ otherwise.
The coordinate transformation

$$t = \sqrt{n}\,\frac{x}{\sqrt{y}},$$

$$s = y$$

yields

$$J\left(\frac{t, s}{x, y}\right) = \sqrt{\frac{n}{s}}, \qquad \left|J\left(\frac{x, y}{t, s}\right)\right| = \sqrt{\frac{s}{n}},$$

so that

$$q(t, s) = \sqrt{\frac{s}{n}} \frac{1}{\sqrt{2\pi}} \frac{1}{2^{n/2} \Gamma(n/2)} s^{(n/2)-1} \exp\left(-\frac{s}{2}\right) \exp\left(-\frac{st^2}{2n}\right) \qquad (18)$$

is the joint pdf of (T, S) for $-\infty < t < \infty$, $s \geq 0$. The pdf of T is

$$p_n(t) = \frac{1}{2^{n/2} \Gamma(\frac{n}{2})\sqrt{2\pi n}} \int_0^\infty s^{(n-1)/2} \exp\left(-\frac{s}{2}\right) \exp\left(-\frac{st^2}{2n}\right) ds$$

$$= \frac{1}{2^{n/2} \Gamma(\frac{n}{2})\sqrt{2\pi n}} \int_0^\infty s^{(n-1)/2} \exp\left[-\frac{s}{2}\left(1 + \frac{t^2}{n}\right)\right] ds. \qquad (19)$$

The change of variable of integration

$$s = 2w\left(1 + \frac{t^2}{n}\right)^{-1},$$

yields

$$p_n(t) = \frac{\Gamma(\frac{n+1}{2})}{\Gamma(\frac{n}{2})\sqrt{n\pi}} \frac{1}{\left(1 + \frac{t^2}{n}\right)^{(n+1)/2}}, \qquad -\infty < t < \infty, \qquad (20)$$

as the pdf of the Student random variable, T_n. By applying Stirling's formula to $\Gamma(\frac{n}{2})$, $\Gamma(\frac{n+1}{2})$, for large n it is a simple matter to show that

$$\lim_{n\to\infty} p_n(t) = \frac{1}{\sqrt{2\pi}} \exp(-t^2/2). \qquad (21)$$

Hence, for large n, the random variable T_n is approximately normal, $N(0, 1)$. The cdf associated with T_n is

$$P_n(x) = \Pr(T \leq x)$$

$$= \frac{\Gamma\left(\frac{n+1}{2}\right)}{\Gamma\left(\frac{n}{2}\right)\sqrt{n\pi}} \int_{-\infty}^x \frac{dt}{\left(1 + \frac{t^2}{n}\right)^{(n+1)/2}}. \qquad (22)$$

Let the reader deduce that

$$\int_{-x}^x p_n(t)dt = 2P_n(x) - 1. \qquad (23)$$

Example 2. *The F distribution (Snedecor).* Of importance to statistics is the random variable F defined by

$$F = \frac{Y/m}{Z/n}, \qquad (24)$$

with Y and Z independent χ^2 random variables having m and n degrees of freedom, respectively. The joint pdf of (Y, Z) is

$$p(y, z) = \frac{1}{2^{(n+m)/2} \; \Gamma\!\left(\dfrac{m}{2}\right) \Gamma\!\left(\dfrac{n}{2}\right)} \, y^{(m/2)-1} \, z^{(n/2)-1} \exp\left(-\frac{y+z}{2}\right) U(y) \, U(z). \quad (25)$$

The coordinate transformation

$$f = \frac{ny}{mz} \qquad y = \frac{m}{n} fg$$

$$g = z \qquad z = g$$

yields

$$J\left(\frac{y, z}{f, g}\right) = \frac{m}{n} g,$$

so that

$$h(f, g) = \frac{\left(\dfrac{m}{n}\right)^{m/2} f^{(m/2)-1}}{2^{(n+m)/2} \; \Gamma\!\left(\dfrac{m}{2}\right) \Gamma\!\left(\dfrac{n}{2}\right)} \, g^{(m+n)/2-1} \exp\left[-\frac{1}{2}\left(1 + \frac{m}{n} f\right) g\right] \quad (26)$$

is the joint pdf of (F, G) for f and g nonnegative. The pdf for F is

$$p_{m/n}(f) = \frac{\left(\dfrac{m}{n}\right)^{m/2} f^{(m/2)-1}}{2^{(m+n)/2} \; \Gamma\!\left(\dfrac{m}{2}\right) \Gamma\!\left(\dfrac{n}{2}\right)} \int_0^\infty g^{[(m+n)/2]-1} \exp\left[-\frac{1}{2}\left(1 + \frac{m}{n} f\right) g\right] dg. \quad (27)$$

The change of variable of integration given by

$$g = 2\left(1 + \frac{m}{n} f\right)^{-1} w,$$

$$dg = 2\left(1 + \frac{m}{n} f\right)^{-1} dw$$

yields

$$p_{m/n}(f) = \frac{\left(\dfrac{m}{n}\right)^{m/2} f^{(m/2)-1} \, 2^{(m+n)/2}}{2^{(n+m)/2} \; \Gamma\!\left(\dfrac{m}{2}\right) \Gamma\!\left(\dfrac{n}{2}\right) \left(1 + \dfrac{m}{n} f\right)^{(m+n)/2}} \int_0^\infty w^{[(m+n)/2]-1} e^{-w} \, dw$$

$$= \frac{m^{m/2} \, n^{n/2} \, \Gamma\!\left(\dfrac{m+n}{2}\right) f^{(m-2)/2}}{\Gamma\!\left(\dfrac{m}{2}\right) \Gamma\!\left(\dfrac{n}{2}\right) (n + mf)^{(m+n)/2}} \, U(f) \quad (28)$$

as the pdf of F (m degrees of freedom in the numerator and n degrees of freedom in the denominator).

The cdf of F is given by

$$P(x) = \Pr(F \leq x) \tag{29}$$

$$= \frac{m^{m/2} \, n^{n/2} \, \Gamma\left(\dfrac{m+n}{2}\right)}{\Gamma\left(\dfrac{m}{2}\right)\Gamma\left(\dfrac{n}{2}\right)} \int_0^x \frac{f^{(m-2)/2}}{(n+mf)^{(m+n)/2}} \, df.$$

It should be clear that the random variable $F' = 1/F$ has the same pdf and cdf as F, with the roles of m and n interchanged (see Eq. 24).

Let us write $F = F_{m/n}$, $F' = F_{n/m}$. If from a set of tables involving the cdf of F we find two constants a, b such that

$$\Pr(F_{m/n} \leq a) = 0.95, \qquad \Pr(F_{n/m} \leq b) = 0.95,$$

it follows that $\Pr(F_{m/n} \geq a) = 0.05$, and $\Pr(F_{n/m} \geq b) = 0.05$. Since $F_{n/m} = 1/F_{m/n}$ we obtain

$$\Pr\left(\frac{1}{F_{m/n}} \geq b\right) = 0.05, \qquad \Pr\left(F_{m/n} \leq \frac{1}{b}\right) = 0.05,$$

and

$$\Pr\left[\frac{1}{b} \leq F_{m/n} \leq a\right] = 0.90.$$

Applications of the distributions discussed in this section occur in Chapter 7.

PROBLEMS

1. Derive Eq. (20) from Eq. (19).
2. Derive the result of Eq. (21).
3. Derive Eq. (23).
4. Derive the pdf for the Student t random variable by first determining the cdf of $T = X/\sqrt{Y/n}$.
5. Let $X = \sqrt{Y/n}$ with Y a χ^2 random variable with n degrees of freedom. Show that the pdf of X is

$$p(x) = \frac{2(n/2)^{n/2}}{\Gamma(n/2)} \, x^{n-1} \exp(-nx^2) \, U(x),$$

which is the pdf for the χ random variable.

6. Let X be a χ^2 random variable with n degrees of freedom. Show that the CF of $Y = -X$ is $F(t) = (1 + 2jt)^{-n}$.

7. X and Y are independent random variables. It is known that X and $Z = X + Y$ are χ^2 random variables with m and n degrees of freedom respectively, $m < n$. Show that Y is a χ^2 random variable with $n-m$ degrees of freedom. [*Hint: Fz(t) = Fx(t) Fy(t).*]

4.9 THE n-DIMENSIONAL NORMAL PDF, ITS COVARIANCE MATRIX

Consider the following function of n variables $x_1, x_2, \ldots, x_n$ given by

$$p(x_1, x_2, \ldots, x_n) = K \exp\left(-\tfrac{1}{2}\mathbf{X}^T \mathbf{A} \mathbf{X}\right), \tag{1}$$

with $\mathbf{X}^T$ the row vector $(x_1, x_2, \ldots, x_n)$ and $\mathbf{A}$ an $n \times n$ symmetric matrix of real constants,

$$\mathbf{A} = \begin{bmatrix} a_{11} & a_{12} & \cdots & a_{1n} \\ a_{21} & a_{22} & \cdots & a_{2n} \\ & & \vdots & \\ a_{n1} & a_{n2} & \cdots & a_{nn} \end{bmatrix} \quad (a_{ij} = a_{ji}).$$

From matrix theory we know that $\mathbf{X}^T \mathbf{A} \mathbf{X}$ is a quadratic form in the variables $x_1, x_2, \ldots, x_n$. If we desire that $p(x_1, x_2, \ldots, x_n)$ be a joint pdf of a set of random variables $X_1, X_2, \ldots, X_n$ with $-\infty < x_i < \infty$, $i = 1, 2, \ldots, n$, of necessity the quadratic form must be positive definite, for otherwise the n-fold integral

$$\int_{-\infty}^{\infty} \cdots \int_{-\infty}^{\infty} p \, dx_1 \cdots dx_n$$

would fail to exist. Hence the eigenvalues associated with the matrix $\mathbf{A}$ must be positive.

We recall that in matrix theory a rotation matrix $\mathbf{R}$ exists such that the transformation $\mathbf{X} = \mathbf{R}\mathbf{Y}$ reduces the quadratic form $\mathbf{X}^T \mathbf{A} \mathbf{X}$ to a new canonical form in the variables $y_1, y_2, \ldots, y_n$, given by

$$\begin{aligned} Q = \mathbf{X}^T \mathbf{A} \mathbf{X} &= \mathbf{Y}^T (\mathbf{R}^T \mathbf{A} \mathbf{R}) \mathbf{Y} \\ &= \mathbf{Y}^T (\mathbf{R}^{-1} \mathbf{A} \mathbf{R}) \mathbf{Y} \\ &= \sum_{i=1}^{n} \frac{1}{\sigma_i^2} y_i^2 \end{aligned} \tag{2}$$

so that

$$\mathbf{R}^{-1}\mathbf{A}\mathbf{R} = \begin{bmatrix} \dfrac{1}{\sigma_1^2} & 0 & 0 & \cdots & 0 \\ 0 & \dfrac{1}{\sigma_2^2} & 0 & & 0 \\ & & \vdots & & \\ 0 & 0 & 0 & \cdots & \dfrac{1}{\sigma_n^2} \end{bmatrix}. \tag{3}$$

The positive numbers $1/\sigma_i^2$, $i = 1, 2, \ldots, n$ are the eigenvalues of the matrix

A. Fortunately we need not determine these eigenvalues, nor need we find the rotation matrix R for the analysis below.

Since

$$J\left(\frac{x_1, x_2, \ldots, x_n}{y_1, y_2, \ldots, y_n}\right) = |R^{-1}| = 1,$$

it follows that the joint pdf of the random variables $Y_1, Y_2, \ldots, Y_n$ (related to the random variables $X_1, X_2, \ldots, X_n$ by the set of linear transformations $Y = R^{-1}X$) is

$$q(y_1, y_2, \ldots, y_n) = K \exp\left(-\frac{1}{2}\sum_{i=1}^{n}\frac{y_i^2}{\sigma_i^2}\right). \tag{4}$$

Hence the new random variables are normal, $N(0, \sigma_i^2)$, $i = 1, 2, \ldots, n$, and independent. We note that

$$\int_{-\infty}^{\infty}\cdots\int_{-\infty}^{\infty} q(y_1, y_2, \ldots, y_n)dy_1\, dy_2\cdots dy_n = K(\sqrt{2\pi})^n\, \sigma_1\sigma_2\cdots\sigma_n = 1,$$

so that

$$K = \frac{1}{(\sqrt{2\pi})^n}\,(\sigma_1\,\sigma_2\cdots\sigma_n)^{-1}.$$

From Eq. (3) we obtain

$$|R^{-1}\,AR| = |R^{-1}|\,|A|\,|R| = |A| = (\sigma_1\,\sigma_2\cdots\sigma_n)^{-2}$$

so that

$$K = \frac{|A|^{1/2}}{(\sqrt{2\pi})^n}.$$

Returning to Eq. (1) yields

$$p(x_1, x_2, \ldots, x_n) = \frac{1}{(2\pi)^{n/2}\,|A|^{-1/2}}\exp\left(-\tfrac{1}{2}X^T\,AX\right) \tag{5}$$

as the multi-dimensional normal pdf of the random variables $X_1, X_2, \ldots, X_n$.

The expected value of the matrix

$$XX^T = \begin{bmatrix} x_1 \\ x_2 \\ \vdots \\ x_n \end{bmatrix}[x_1 x_2\cdots x_n] = \begin{bmatrix} x_1^2 & x_1x_2 & \cdots & x_1x_n \\ x_2x_1 & x_2^2 & \cdots & x_2x_n \\ & & \vdots & \\ x_nx_1 & x_nx_2 & \cdots & x_n^2 \end{bmatrix}$$

is called the covariance matrix of the random variables $X_1, X_2, \ldots, X_n$. It is expressed as the matrix

$$E(XX^T) = [E(X_iX_j)] = \begin{bmatrix} E(X_1^2) & \cdots & E(X_1X_n) \\ & \vdots & \\ E(X_nX_1) & \cdots & E(X_n^2) \end{bmatrix}, \tag{6}$$

and is of fundamental importance in linear estimation theory.

To determine this matrix we note that $\mathbf{X} = \mathbf{RY}$, $\mathbf{X}^T = Y^T\mathbf{R}^T$ yields

$$E(\mathbf{XX}^T) = E[\mathbf{R}YY^T\mathbf{R}^{-1}]$$
$$= \mathbf{R}E(YY^T)\mathbf{R}^{-1} \tag{7}$$

Since the Y_i, $i = 1, 2, \ldots, n$ have been shown to be independent normal random variables, it follows that

$$E(YY^T) = \begin{bmatrix} \sigma_1^2 & 0 & 0 \\ 0 & \sigma_2^2 & 0 \\ & & \ddots & \\ 0 & 0 & \sigma_n^2 \end{bmatrix} = (\mathbf{R}^{-1}\mathbf{AR})^{-1} = \mathbf{R}^{-1}\mathbf{A}^{-1}\mathbf{R}, \tag{8}$$

by virtue of Eq. (3). Thus

$$E(\mathbf{XX}^T) = \mathbf{R}(\mathbf{R}^{-1}\mathbf{A}^{-1}\mathbf{R})\mathbf{R}^{-1} = \mathbf{A}^{-1}. \tag{9}$$

We recognize that the covariance matrix associated with the joint normal random variables $X_1, X_2, \ldots, X_n$, is simply the inverse of the matrix $\mathbf{A}$ associated with the quadratic form $\mathbf{X}^T\mathbf{AX}$. The most general n-dimensional normal multivariate pdf is

$$p(x_1, x_2, \cdots, x_n) = \frac{1}{(2\pi)^{n/2}|\mathbf{A}|^{-1/2}} \exp \{-\tfrac{1}{2}[(\mathbf{X}^T - \boldsymbol{\mu}^T)\mathbf{A}(\mathbf{X} - \boldsymbol{\mu})]\}, \tag{10}$$

with $\boldsymbol{\mu}$ a column vector,

$$\boldsymbol{\mu}^T = [E(X_1), E(X_2), \ldots, E(X_n)].$$

Furthermore,

$$\mathbf{A}^{-1} = E[(\mathbf{X} - \boldsymbol{\mu})\,(\mathbf{X}^T - \boldsymbol{\mu}^T)] \tag{11}$$

is the covariance matrix given by

$$\mathbf{A}^{-1} = \begin{bmatrix} \sigma_1^2 & \rho_{12}\sigma_1\sigma_2 & \cdots & \rho_{1n}\sigma_1\sigma_n \\ \rho_{21}\sigma_2\sigma_1 & \sigma_2^2 & \cdots & \rho_{2n}\sigma_2\sigma_n \\ \vdots & & & \\ \rho_{n1}\sigma_n\sigma_1 & \rho_{n2}\sigma_n\sigma_2 & \cdots & \sigma_n^2 \end{bmatrix}, \tag{12}$$

with ρ_{ij} the correlation coefficient of the pair of random variables (X_i, X_j), $\sigma_j^2 = V(X_j)$.

Example 1. Let X and Y be joint normal random variables, and let

$$\mathbf{A}^{-1} = \begin{bmatrix} \sigma_x^2 & \rho\sigma_x\sigma_y \\ \rho\sigma_x\sigma_y & \sigma_y^2 \end{bmatrix} (\rho^2 < 1) \tag{13}$$

be the covariance matrix associated with X and Y, $\rho = \rho_{xy}$. Hence

$$|A^{-1}| = (1 - \rho^2)\sigma_x^2\sigma_y^2, \qquad \rho^2 < 1,$$

$$A = \frac{1}{1 - \rho^2} \begin{bmatrix} \dfrac{1}{\sigma_x^2} & -\dfrac{\rho}{\sigma_x\sigma_y} \\ -\dfrac{\rho}{\sigma_x\sigma_y} & \dfrac{1}{\sigma_y^2} \end{bmatrix}, \tag{14}$$

$$Q = (x, y)A\begin{pmatrix} x \\ y \end{pmatrix} = \frac{1}{1 - \rho^2}\left[\frac{x^2}{\sigma_x^2} - \frac{2\rho xy}{\sigma_x\sigma_y} + \frac{y^2}{\sigma_y^2}\right].$$

Thus the most general bivariate normal pdf is

$$p(x, y) = \frac{1}{2\pi\sigma_x\sigma_y\sqrt{1 - \rho^2}}$$

$$\exp\left\{-\frac{1}{2(1 - \rho^2)}\left[\left(\frac{x - \mu_x}{\sigma_x}\right)^2 - \frac{2\rho(x - \mu_x)(y - \mu_y)}{\sigma_x\sigma_y} + \left(\frac{y - \mu_y}{\sigma_y}\right)^2\right]\right\}, \tag{15}$$

with $-\infty < x < \infty$, $-\infty < y < \infty$, $\mu_x = E(X)$, $\mu_y = E(Y)$.

Example 2. Let

$$p(x, y) = \frac{1}{2\pi(\frac{2}{7}\sqrt{7})} \exp\left\{-\frac{1}{2}[x^2 + xy + 2y^2]\right\}$$

be a bivariate normal pdf. To find the covariance matrix we note that

$$A = \begin{bmatrix} 1 & \frac{1}{2} \\ \frac{1}{2} & 2 \end{bmatrix}, \qquad |A| = \frac{7}{4}, \qquad A^{-1} = \frac{4}{7}\begin{bmatrix} 2 & -\frac{1}{2} \\ -\frac{1}{2} & 1 \end{bmatrix} = \begin{bmatrix} \frac{8}{7} & -\frac{2}{7} \\ -\frac{2}{7} & \frac{4}{7} \end{bmatrix},$$

so that $\sigma_x^2 = \frac{8}{7}$, $\sigma_y^2 = \frac{4}{7}$, $\rho\sigma_x\sigma_y = -\frac{2}{7}$.

Example 3. Let $X_1, X_2, \ldots, X_n$ be independent identically distributed random variables, all of the class $N(0, 1)$. The joint pdf for these random variables is

$$p(x_1, x_2, \ldots, x_n) = \frac{1}{(\sqrt{2\pi})^n} \exp\left(-\frac{1}{2}X^TX\right).$$

Now let $Y_1, Y_2, \ldots, Y_n$ be a set of random variables related linearly to $X_1, X_2, \ldots, X_n$ by means of a rotation matrix R such that $Y = RX$. From

$$Y^TY = X^TR^TRX = X^TR^{-1}RX = X^TX$$

it follows that the joint pdf of $Y_1, Y_2, \ldots, Y_n$ is

$$q(y_1, y_2, \ldots, y_n) = \frac{1}{(\sqrt{2\pi})^n} \exp\left(-\frac{1}{2}\sum_{i=1}^{n} y_i^2\right),$$

so that the random variables Y_1, Y_2, ... , Y_n are also statistically independent. An alternative proof is obtained by noting that

$$E(\mathbf{YY}^T) = E(\mathbf{RXX}^T\mathbf{R}^T) = \mathbf{R}E(\mathbf{XX}^T)\mathbf{R}^{-1} = \mathbf{RIR}^{-1} = \mathbf{I}$$

the unit matrix.

PROBLEMS

1. Given that X and Y are jointly normal, show that $\rho = 0$ is a necessary and sufficient condition that they be independent.

2. Given that X_1, X_2, ... , X_n are jointly normal random variables, explain why the set of random variables Z_1, Z_2, ... , Z_m, $m \leq n$, which depend linearly on X_1, X_2, ... , X_n are also jointly normal random variables.

3. From the result of Problem 2 show that $U = X - Y$, $V = X + Y$ are independent normal random variables, provided that $V(X) = V(Y)$, and that X and Y are jointly normal random variables.

4. For $p(x, y)$ given by Eq. (15), show that

$$\int_{-\infty}^{\infty} p(x, y) \, dy = \frac{1}{\sqrt{2\pi}\,\sigma_x} \exp\left[-\frac{1}{2}\left(\frac{x - \mu_x}{\sigma_x}\right)^2 \right].$$

5. Let X_1, X_2, ... , X_n be independent normal random variables with the same mean and variance, say μ and σ^2. Consider the random variables

$$S_n = \frac{1}{n}(X_1 + X_2 + \cdots + X_n),$$

$$Y = S_n - X_1.$$

Show that

$$E(S_n^2) = \frac{\sigma^2}{n} + \mu^2 = E(X_1 S_n).$$

Then show that

$$E[(S_n - \mu)Y] = 0$$

and deduce that S_n and Y are normal independent random variables.

6. Let X and Y be independent normal random variables, both of the class $N(0, 1.)$ Show that the CF of $Z = XY$ is $F(t) = \sqrt{1 + t^2}$ by considering

$$F(t) = E[e^{jXYt}]$$

$$= \frac{1}{2\pi} \int_{-\infty}^{\infty} \int_{-\infty}^{\infty} e^{jxyt} \exp[-\tfrac{1}{2}(x^2 + y^2)] \, dy \, dx.$$

7. Let

$$\mathbf{A} = \begin{bmatrix} 1 & 0 & -1 \\ 0 & 3 & 1 \\ -1 & 1 & 5 \end{bmatrix}$$

for a three-dimensional normal pdf given by Eq. (1). Find the covariance matrix.

8. Let X_1 and X_2 be jointly normal random variables with parameters μ_1, μ_2, σ_1, σ_2, ρ. Show that $U = X_1 - \mu_1$ and

$$V = Y - \mu_2 - \rho \frac{\sigma_2}{\sigma_1} (X - \mu_1)$$

are independent random variables by showing that $E(UV) = 0$, since $E(U) = E(V) = 0$.

9. Let X and Y be independent normal random variables, both of the class $N(0, 1)$. Show that the pdf of $Z = X/Y$ is

$$p(z) = \frac{1}{\pi} (1 + z^2)^{-1},$$

the Cauchy distribution.

4.10 THE CENTRAL LIMIT THEOREM

Let us consider the random variable X which takes on only two values, $X = 1$ with probability $\frac{1}{2}$, and $X = -1$ with probability $\frac{1}{2}$. Now let $X_1, X_2, \ldots, X_n$ be n independent samples associated with the ff above, and consider the random variable

$$Y_n = \frac{X_1 + X_2 + \cdots + X_n}{\sqrt{n}}. \tag{1}$$

Since $E(X) = 0$, $V(X) = 1$, we note that

$$E(Y_n) = \frac{1}{\sqrt{n}} [E(X_1) + \cdots + E(X_n)] = 0,$$

$$V(Y_n) = \frac{1}{n} [V(X_1) + \cdots + V(X_n)] = 1,$$

for all integers $n \geq 1$.

The CF of the random variable X is

$$F_x(t) = \sum_{x=-1, 1} p(x) e^{jtx}$$

$$= \tfrac{1}{2}[e^{-jt} + e^{jt}] = \cos t.$$

Hence, the CF associated with the random variable Y_n is

$$F_{Y_n}(t) = \left(\cos \frac{t}{\sqrt{n}} \right)^n.$$

Of interest is the limiting form of $F_{Y_n}(t)$ as $n \to \infty$.

We have

$$\ln F_{Y_n}(t) = n \ln\left[\cos \frac{t}{\sqrt{n}}\right],$$

$$\lim_{n\to\infty} \ln F_{Y_n}(t) = \lim_{n\to\infty} \frac{\ln[\cos t/\sqrt{n}]}{1/n}$$

$$= \lim_{n\to\infty} -\frac{\sin t/\sqrt{n}}{t/\sqrt{n}} \frac{t^2}{2}$$

$$= -\frac{t^2}{2}$$

by applying L'Hospital's rule. Hence

$$\lim_{n\to\infty} F_{Y_n}(t) = \exp(-t^2/2),$$

which is precisely the CF of a normal random variable, $N(0, 1)$.

Returning to Eq. (1) we note that for $n = 10^4$, Y_n ranges from -10^2 to 10^2 at intervals of length $2 \cdot 10^{-2}$. For $n = 10^{10}$, Y_n ranges from 10^{-5} to 10^5 at intervals of length $2 \cdot 10^{-5}$. As $n \to \infty$, the range of Y_n becomes infinite in both the negative and positive directions, and the lengths of the intervals tend to zero, so that Y_n approaches a continuous random variable with mean zero and variance one. It should not be too surprising that Y_n tends to $N(0, 1)$ as $n \to \infty$.

Example 1. Let X be a random variable with a pdf given by $p(x) = \frac{1}{2} e^{-|x|}$, $-\infty < x < \infty$. The CF associated with X is

$$F_x(t) = \frac{1}{2} \int_{-\infty}^{0} e^x e^{jxt}\, dx + \frac{1}{2} \int_{0}^{\infty} e^{-x} e^{jtx}\, dx$$

$$= \frac{1}{2} \int_{0}^{\infty} e^{-x} e^{-jxt}\, dx + \frac{1}{2} \int_{0}^{\infty} e^{-x} e^{jtx}\, dx$$

$$= \frac{1}{2}\left[\frac{1}{1+jt} + \frac{1}{1-jt}\right] = \frac{1}{1+t^2}.$$

Now, let

$$Y_n = \frac{X_1 + X_2 + \cdots + X_n}{\sqrt{2}\sqrt{n}},$$

with the X_i, $i = 1, 2, \ldots, n$, independent random variables having the same pdf as X. From $E(X) = 0$, $V(X) = 2$, we obtain $E(Y_n) = 0$, $V(Y_n) = 1$, for all integers $n \geq 1$. The CF of Y_n is

$$F_{Y_n}(t) = \left(1 + \frac{t^2}{2n}\right)^{-n},$$

so that

$$\lim_{n\to\infty} F_{Y_n}(t) = \exp(-t^2/2),$$

which is the CF of the normal random variable, $N(0, 1)$.

Example 2. Let $p(x) = \frac{1}{2}$ for the interval $-1 \le x \le 1$, $p(x) = 0$ otherwise, be the pdf of a random variable X, with $E(X) = 0$, $V(X) = \frac{1}{3}$. Consider the random variable

$$Y_n = \frac{X_1 + X_2 + X_3 + \cdots + X_n}{\sqrt{\frac{1}{3}}\sqrt{n}},$$

with the X_i independent random variables associated with the pdf above. The CF of X is

$$F_x(t) = \frac{1}{2}\int_{-1}^{1} e^{jtx}\, dx = \frac{1}{2}\frac{e^{jtx}}{jt}\bigg|_{-1}^{1}$$

$$= \frac{1}{2jt}[e^{jt} - e^{-jt}] = \frac{\sin t}{t}.$$

Hence, the CF of Y_n is

$$F_{Y_n}(t) = \left(\frac{\sin\dfrac{t}{\sqrt{\frac{n}{3}}}}{\dfrac{t}{\sqrt{\frac{n}{3}}}}\right)^n = \left(1 - \frac{t^2}{2n} + \cdots\right)^n.$$

By means of the L'Hospital's rule it can be shown that

$$\lim_{n\to\infty} F_{Y_n}(t) = \exp(-t^2/2).$$

Example 3. The Cauchy random variable X, with

$$p(x) = \frac{1}{\pi}\frac{1}{1 + x^2}, \qquad -\infty < x < \infty,$$

has no variance. The CF of X can be shown to be $F_X(t) = e^{-|t|}$. The random variable $Y_n = (1/n)(X_1 + X_2 + \cdots + X_n)$, with the X_i independent, has a CF given by

$$F_{Y_n}(t) = \left[\exp\left(-\left|\frac{t}{n}\right|\right)\right]^n = e^{-|t|},$$

so that Y_n is also a Cauchy random variable for all integers $n \ge 1$.

One may ask why we have dealt with the CF of a random variable rather than with the moment generating function. The answer is that the moment generating function may not exist other than for $\theta = 0$. This situation will prevail when at least one of the moments of the random variable fails to exist, as happens in the case of the Cauchy random variable. The proof below, of one form of the central limit theorem, depends essentially on the assumption that the random variable X has a finite third central moment, v_3. Indeed, Eq. (2) below is simply the Taylor series expansion of $F_{X-\mu}(t)$ with $R_3 = K(t)t^3$, the remainder after three terms.

The simplest form of the *central limit theorem* is obtained as follows: Let

X be a random variable such that $E(X) = \mu$, $V(X) = \sigma^2$, exist. We assume, further, that the CF of the random variable $X - \mu$ has a bounded third derivative, so that

$$F_{X-\mu}(t) = 1 - \frac{\sigma^2 t^2}{2} + K(t)t^3, \tag{2}$$

with $|K(t)| < A < \infty$ for all t.

Now let

$$Y_n = \frac{(X_1 - \mu) + (X_2 - \mu) + \cdots + (X_n - \mu)}{\sigma\sqrt{n}} \tag{3}$$

be a new random variable, with $X_1, X_2, \ldots, X_n$ independent random variables of the type X. The CF of Y_n is

$$F_{Y_n}(t) = \left[1 - \frac{t^2}{2n} + K\left(\frac{t}{\sigma\sqrt{n}}\right)\frac{t^3}{\sigma^3 n^{3/2}} \right]^n. \tag{4}$$

By applying L'Hospital's rule it is a simple matter to show that

$$\lim_{n \to \infty} F_{Y_n}(t) = \exp(-t^2/2). \tag{5}$$

In advanced texts it is shown that if a sequence of random variables $\{Y_n\}$ exists such that Eq. (5) holds, then the pdf of Y_n approaches the pdf associated with the normal random variable, $N(0, 1)$. This result, in essence, is the central limit theorem. It follows that for $n \gg 1$,

$$\Pr\left(a \le \frac{(X_1 - \mu) + (X_2 - \mu) + \cdots + X_n - \mu)}{\sigma\sqrt{n}} \le b \right) \approx \frac{1}{\sqrt{2\pi}} \int_a^b \exp(-x^2/2)\,dx. \tag{6}$$

From Eq. (6) we note that

$$\Pr\left(\frac{a\sigma}{\sqrt{n}} \le S_n - \mu \le \frac{b\sigma}{\sqrt{n}} \right) \approx \frac{1}{\sqrt{2\pi}} \int_a^b \exp(-x^2/2)dx, \tag{7}$$

where S_n is the sample mean random variable defined by

$$S_n = \frac{X_1 + X_2 + \cdots + X_n}{n}. \tag{8}$$

Example 4. From tables of the normal distribution we find that

$$\frac{1}{\sqrt{2\pi}} \int_{-1.96}^{1.96} \exp(-x^2/2)dx = 0.95.$$

If X is a random variable such that $V(X) = \sigma^2 = 0.01$, $\sigma = 0.1$, then the number of independent samples required, such that the sample mean will differ from the true mean by less than 0.01 with 95% probability, must satisfy

$$\frac{b\sigma}{\sqrt{n}} = 0.01,$$

with $b = 1.96$, $\sigma = 0.1$, so that $n \approx (19.6)^2 \approx 384$.

In other words, the random variable

$$S_{384} = \frac{1}{384} \sum_{i=1}^{384} X_i$$

has a 95 % probability of yielding a value within 0.01 unit of the true mean, $\mu = E(X)$.

PROBLEMS

1. Consider a discrete random variable X such that

$$\Pr(X = -1) = \tfrac{1}{4},$$
$$\Pr(X = 0) = \tfrac{1}{2},$$
$$\Pr(X = +1) = \tfrac{1}{4}.$$

Let

$$Y_n = \sqrt{\frac{2}{n}} (X_1 + X_2 + \cdots + X_n),$$

with $X_1, X_2, \ldots, X_n$ independent random variables of the type X. Show that the CF of Y_n approaches $\exp(-t^2/2)$ as $n \to \infty$.

2. Let $p(x) = |x|$ for $-1 \le x \le 1$, $p(x) = 0$ otherwise, be the pdf of a random variable X. Show that the CF of $Y_n = \sqrt{2/n} (X_1 + X_2 + \cdots X_n)$ approaches $\exp(-t^2/2)$ as $n \to \infty$ for $X_1, X_2, \ldots, X_n$ independent random variables of the type X.

3. Given that $\sigma = 0.05$ for a random variable X, determine the number of independent samples required in order that the sample mean random variable will differ from the true mean by no more than 0.01 unit, with 95 % probability.

4. Give a plausible argument why the random variable represented by the I.Q. of individuals should be, essentially, a normal random variable.

4.11 GEOMETRICAL PROBABILITIES

Many so-called paradoxes occur in connection with geometrical problems which arise in probability theory. For example, suppose you were asked to determine the mean distance of all points in the interior of a circle from its center. If you had never studied probability theory you might reason as follows: The points on any radial line are, on the average, at a distance of $\frac{1}{2}a$ from the center (a is the radius of the circle). But each point lies on some radial line, so that $\bar{r} = \frac{1}{2}a$. Now, this answer is perfectly correct if the determination of the random points is obtained by first choosing $\Theta = \theta$ from $U(0, 2\pi)$, which determines a line, and then choosing the point at a distance $R = r$ from the center, with R of the class $U(0, a)$. Thus

$$\bar{r} = \frac{1}{2\pi a} \int_0^a \int_0^{2\pi} r \, d\theta \, dr = \frac{a}{2}.$$

On the other hand, if the point P were obtained by throwing a dart at the circle, and if we assume that the probability that the dart will strike inside a given area is proportional to that area, then

$$dP = \frac{1}{\pi a^2} r \, dr \, d\theta,$$

so that

$$\bar{r} = \int r \, dP = \frac{1}{\pi a^2} \int_0^{2\pi} \int_0^a r^2 \, dr \, d\theta,$$

$$= \tfrac{2}{3} a$$

which differs from our previous result.

It is clear, then, that the answer one obtains depends on how one performs the experiment of obtaining random points, lines, etc.

Example 1. Let Θ be of the class $U(0, 2\pi)$. Each choice of $\Theta = \theta$ determines a point P on the circle (see Fig. 36).

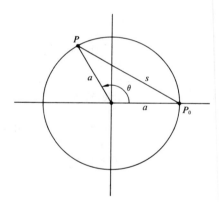

Figure 4.36

We wish to determine the mean length of the chord P_0P. Now, $s^2 = a^2 + a^2 - 2a^2 \cos \theta = 2a^2(1 - \cos \theta) = a^2 \sin^2 \theta/2$, so that

$$E(S) = \int_0^{2\pi} a \sin \theta/2 \, \frac{d\theta}{2\pi} = \frac{2a}{\pi}.$$

On the other hand, one can generate chords as follows: Let X be of the class $U(-a, a)$. Once $X = x$ has been obtained, construct a perpendicular at this point yielding a chord of length $s = 2\sqrt{a^2 - x^2}$. The average length of this chord is

$$E(S) = \int_{-a}^a 2\sqrt{a^2 - x^2} \, \frac{dx}{2a} = \frac{\pi a}{2} > \frac{2}{\pi} a.$$

Again we have obtained two different answers, but it must be remembered that in these two cases the methods for obtaining random chords have been different.

Example 2. Let X and Y be of the class $U(0, a)$. We wish to determine $E[|X - Y|^n]$, given by

$$E[|X - Y|^n] = \int_0^a \int_0^a |x - y|^n \frac{dy \, dx}{a^2}.$$

Let us solve this problem without evaluating the previous integral. Let $F_n(a)$ denote the desired mean value of $|X - Y|^n$. Then, for $\Delta \ll a$,

$$F_n(a + \Delta) = \left(\frac{a}{a + \Delta}\right)^2 F_n(a) + \frac{2\Delta}{a + \Delta} \int_0^{a+\Delta} \frac{|a - x|^n}{a + \Delta} dx, \tag{1}$$

except for infinitesimals of higher order. The reasoning is as follows: Both points may fall in the interval $(0, a)$ with probability $[a/(a + \Delta)]^2$, or one of them (two choices) may fall in the interval $(a, a + \Delta)$ with probability $\Delta/(a + \Delta)$, the other point falling in the interval $(x, x + dx)$ with probability $dx/(a + \Delta)$. Hence

$$F_n(a + \Delta) \approx \left(1 - \frac{2\Delta}{a}\right) F_n(a) + \frac{2\Delta}{a^2} \int_0^a (a - x)^n \, dx,$$

$$\frac{F_n(a + \Delta) - F_n(a)}{\Delta} = -\frac{2F_n(a)}{a} + \frac{2}{a^2} \frac{a^{n+1}}{n + 1},$$

except for infinitesimals of higher order. Letting $\Delta \to 0$ yields

$$\frac{dF_n(a)}{da} = -\frac{2F_n(a)}{a} + \frac{2a^{n-1}}{n + 1},$$

$$\frac{d}{da}(a^2 F_n) = \frac{2a^{n+1}}{n + 1}, \tag{2}$$

$$a^2 F_n = \frac{2a^{n+2}}{(n + 1)(n + 2)} + K.$$

Now for $a = 0$ we have $F_n = 0$, so that $K = 0$. Thus

$$F_n(a) = \frac{2a^n}{(n + 1)(n + 2)},$$

and $E[|X - Y|] = \frac{1}{3}a$, an expected result.

Example 3. *The Buffon needle problem.* Referring to Example 8 in Section 4.4, let $l < d$. Now let $p(l)$ be the probability that a needle of length l will intersect one of the ruled lines. If we choose a point P on the needle, dividing the needle into two lengths l_1, l_2, with $l = l_1 + l_2$, then $p(l) = p(l_1 \cup l_2) = p(l_1) + p(l_2) - p(l_1 \cap l_2)$. However, $p(l_1 \cap l_2) = 0$, since the needle cannot intersect the ruled lines in more than one point $(l < d)$. Hence $p(l_1 + l_2) = p(l_1) + p(l_2)$, with $p(0) = 0$. One can show that $p(l)$ must be linear in l, i.e., $p(l) = Kl$, K an unknown constant.

Now consider any polygon (n sides) of the lengths $l_1, l_2, \ldots, l_n$ all less than d, which is tossed at random on the plane containing the ruled lines. Let $Z_i = 1$ if the side of length l_i intersects one of the ruled lines, $Z_i = 0$ otherwise, $i = 1, 2, \ldots, n$, and consider the random variable

$$Z = Z_1 + Z_2 + \cdots + Z_n,$$

$$E(Z) = E(Z_1) + E(Z_2) + \cdots + E(Z_n).$$

Since

$$E(Z_i) = 1(Kl_i) + 0(1 - Kl_i) = Kl_i,$$

it follows that

$$E(Z) = Kl_1 + Kl_2 + \cdots + Kl_n$$

$$= K(l_1 + l_2 + \cdots + l_n) = KL,$$

with L the total perimeter of the polygon. By considering any convex curve as a limit of polygons we obtain $E(Z) = Kl$ with l the length of the curve.

Now consider a circle of diameter d, $L = \pi d$, tossed at random on the plane of ruled lines. This curve always intersects the lines in exactly two points, so that $E(Z) = 2 = K\pi d$, yielding $K = 2/\pi d$, and $p(l) = 2l/\pi d$, our previous answer. This ingenious proof is due to Barbier.

Example 4. *Laplace's problem.* A board is covered with a set of congruent rectangles of dimensions a, b, and a thin needle is thrown on the board. We assume that the length l of the needle is smaller than a and b. What is the probability that the needle will intersect a boundary of the rectangles?

Solution. Let A be the event that the needle intersects one of the horizontal lines (a units apart), and let B be the event that the needle intersects one of the vertical lines (b units apart). We are interested in $p(A + B)$. From Example 3 we know that

$$p(A) = \frac{2l}{\pi a}, \qquad p(B) = \frac{2l}{\pi b}.$$

Moreover,

$$P = p(A + B) = p(A) + p(B) - p(AB)$$

$$= \frac{2l(a + b)}{\pi ab} - p(AB),$$

with $p(AB)$ the probability that the needle intersects both a horizontal and vertical line. Let the reader show that

$$p(AB) = \int_0^{\pi/2} \frac{(l/2) \cos \theta}{b/2} \frac{(l/2) \sin \theta}{a/2} \frac{d\theta}{\pi/2}$$

$$= \frac{l^2}{\pi ab},$$

so that

$$P = \frac{2(a + b)l - l^2}{\pi ab}.$$

PROBLEMS

1. Solve the Buffon needle problem for the case $l = 2d$.

2. A point is chosen randomly on each of two adjacent sides of a rectangle. Show that the mean area of the triangle formed by the sides of the rectangle and the line joining the two points is $\frac{1}{3}$ the area of the rectangle.

3. We divide a line into three subintervals by choosing a point randomly from the first half of the line and a point randomly from the second half of the line. Find the probability that the three line segments thus formed could be made to form the sides of a triangle.

4. Two points are chosen at random on a line of length l. Show that the probability that their distance apart is greater than d, $d \le l$, is $P = [1 - (d/l)]^2$.

5. Let $p_n(l)$ be the probability that n points chosen at random on a line of length l will all be at least a distance d apart. Show that

$$p_n(l + \Delta) \approx \left(\frac{l}{l + \Delta}\right)^n p_n(l) + \frac{n\Delta}{l}\left(\frac{l - d}{l}\right)^{n-1} p_{n-1}(l - d)$$

for $\Delta \ll 1$. Then show that

$$\frac{d}{dl}[l^n p_n(l)] = n(l - d)^{n-1} p_{n-1}(l - d),$$

$$\frac{d}{dl}(g_n(l)) = n g_{n-1}(l - d),$$

with $g_n(l) = l^n p_n(l)$.
From

$$p_1(l) = 1, \qquad\qquad g_1(l) = l,$$
$$p_2(l = d) = 0, \qquad g_2(l = d) = 0,$$

show that $g_2(l) = (l - d)^2$. Show by mathematical induction that $g_n(l) = [l - (n - 1)d]^n$, so that

$$p_n(l) = \left[1 - (n - 1)\frac{d}{l}\right]^n.$$

6. Derive the final result of Example 4.

7. Solve Problem 5 from the following considerations: The probability that the n points all lie within a distance $l - (n - 1)d$ of the origin is $P_n = [1 - (n - 1)(d/l)]^n$. Let the ordered points be designated by $x_1 \leq x_2 \leq x_3 \leq \ldots \leq x_n$. Now consider the linear transformations $y_1 = x_1, y_2 = x_2 + d, y_3 = x_3 + 2d, \cdots, y_n = x_n + (n - 1)d$, with $y_1 < y_2 < y_3 \ldots < y_n \leq l$. Why are all the y's at least a distance d apart? Since the transformations have a unique inverse, explain why $P_n = p_n(l)$ of Problem 5.

8. Let n points be chosen at random on the circumference of a circle. Show that the probability that all the points will be at least θ radians apart, $\theta \leq 2\pi/n$, is

$$P_n(\theta) = \left(1 - \frac{n\theta}{2\pi}\right)^{n-1}.$$

BIBLIOGRAPHY

1. H. Cramér, *Mathematical Methods of Statistics*, Princeton University Press, Princeton, 1961. An excellent text for the mathematically mature reader.

2. W. Feller, *An Introduction to Probability Theory and Its Applications*, Vol. II, John Wiley & Sons, 1966. Extended treatment of many advanced topics, including the generalized version of the central limit theorem.

3. M. E. Munroe, *Theory of Probability*, McGraw-Hill Book Company, New York, 1951. A readable elementary text.

4. E. Parzen, *Modern Probability Theory and its Applications*, John Wiley & Sons, New York, 1960. A good discussion of all aspects of continuous probability theory.

5. H. G. Tucker, *A Graduate Course in Probability*, Academic Press, New York, 1967. A sophisticated discussion of the general principles, with a concise treatment of the central limit theorem.

6. J. V. Uspenski, *Introduction to Mathematical Probability*, McGraw-Hill Book Company, New York, 1937. A highly recommended discussion of continuous probability.

CHAPTER 5

PROPERTIES OF STATISTICAL SAMPLES

5.1 INTRODUCTION

Thus far we have been concerned mainly with the probability associated with events (subsets of a sample space) when the probability distribution over the basic sample space was known. For this purpose it has often been convenient to regard events as elements in the sample space of statements or conditions involving random variables (functions on the sample space). These techniques of probability theory were found to apply whether the random variables representing the events were continuous or discrete. In all cases, however, necessary information about the probability distribution was either given, or had been directly inferrable from the conditions of the problem.

In practice, however, we are more frequently faced with the task of estimating the probability of an event in the absence of relevant information about the probability distribution. The following examples illustrate this type of problem. The sample properties (called statistics) appropriate for these problems will be discussed in this chapter. The required rules of statistical inference will be discussed in subsequent chapters.

Example 1. *Quality control.* Consider a group of similar machines which produce items. We evaluate these machines by the percentage of defective items produced. When a machine produces more than some acceptable minimum percentage of defectives, it is taken out of production and overhauled. It is not economical, however, to inspect every item produced. So we sample only a fraction of the items and assume that if the sample is chosen in a random manner, it will be representative of the lot (which might be one day's production of a particular machine) from which it had been selected. We infer the percentage of defectives which the machine actually produces from the percentage of defectives in the randomly chosen sample.

Example 2. *Balls in an urn.* Consider an urn with red and black balls. Since we are unable to see the balls in the urn, and since it might not be convenient to remove all the balls, we must estimate the fraction of red balls in the urn by choosing a random sample from that urn and finding the fraction of red balls in that sample. Our solution to this problem, given later in the chapter, will include a discussion of the relative merits of sampling with and without replacement.

Example 3. *Evaluating students.* In order to determine how well they have learned subject material, students are asked questions in a series of examinations. Since it is impractical to ask questions in all subject material covered, the examinations represent only a fractional sample from the population of all possible questions. The percentage of correct answers on the examinations is used to estimate the fraction of the total subject which the student has actually learned.

For reasons of simplicity, this chapter and the two chapters following will be concerned with the analysis and use of unordered samples (all elements processed according to the same procedure, regardless of the magnitude of the parameter of interest). The additional techniques for utilizing the extra information contained in the detailed features of the sample (which element is largest, smallest, etc.) will be discussed in the subsequent chapter on order statistics.

5.2 SAMPLE MEAN

Consider a sample of n elements from a population with an unspecified distribution. Let the measurement of some parameter of interest associated with the ith element of the sample be denoted by x_i. The quality colloquially referred to as the average of these x_i's, for this particular sample, is

$$\bar{x} = \frac{1}{n} \sum_{i=1}^{n} x_i. \tag{1}$$

This average is actually the particular value of a random variable known as the sample mean, to be defined below, corresponding to this particular sample of n elements.

Example 1. Consider n balls sampled from an urn containing red and black balls. Let us define a color index x_i such that $x_i = 1$ if the ith ball drawn is red, and $x_i = 0$ if the ith ball is black. If the sample contains n_1 red balls and $n_2 = n - n_1$ black balls, then the value of this color index, averaged over the values of the elements of this particular sample, will be

$$\bar{x} = \frac{1}{n}(x_i + x_2 + \cdots + x_n) = \frac{n_1}{n}. \tag{2}$$

The reader should note that the x_i and, by inference, $\bar{x}$ have values which depend on the particular sample chosen. For any given sample these values are specified, but they generally change from one sample to another even though the samples are taken from the same original population. Consider an urn containing 60 red balls and 40 black ones. A particular sample of 10 balls could contain five red and five black balls, which would give $\bar{x} = 0.5$. Another 10-ball sample from the same urn might contain six red balls and four black balls, giving an average of $\bar{x} = 0.6$.

We recall, from Discrete Probability Theory (Chapter 3), that there will be probabilities associated with the two possible values of x_i for each i. In order to describe this probabilistic behavior, we define the random variable X_i, which takes on values of 0 or 1, with the appropriate probabilities. In the present example,

$$\Pr\{X_i = 1\} = 0.6,$$
$$\Pr\{X_i = 0\} = 0.4.$$

Using the random variables X_i, we can define the sample mean as

$$\bar{X} = \frac{1}{n} \sum_{i=1}^{n} X_i. \tag{3}$$

The reader should note the following observations connected with this definition:

a) Since $\bar{X}$ is defined as a weighted sum of random variables, it must itself be a random variable.

b) The random variables X_i (and by inference, $\bar{X}$) may be continuous or discrete, but the number n of elements in the sample is always finite.

c) Since the X_i represent samples from the same population, they will be identically distributed. (In other words, $\Pr\{X_i = k\}$ depends on k only, and not on i.)

d) If the population from which the sample is taken is finite, then the X_i (and by inference, $\bar{X}$) must be discrete. If the population is infinite with a continuum of shades for the property measured by X_i, then the random variables X_i and $\bar{X}$ will be continuous.

e) A random variable, such as $\bar{X}$, which is associated with a sample, is called a sample statistic. For a particular sample, the particular value of the sample statistic, such as $\bar{x}$, has no special name.

f) The particular value $\bar{x}$ of $\bar{X}$ is independent of the order in which the elements are chosen. Hence we speak of $\bar{X}$ as a statistic of an unordered sample.

In this section we have defined the random variable $\bar{X}$ (the sample mean) and described some of its properties. For any particular sample, this random variable takes on some particular value which we represent by $\bar{x}$. These notions and definitions should be somewhat familiar to the reader, since some properties of $\bar{X}$ have already been discussed in our treatment of Discrete and Continuous Probability. (See, particularly, Section 3.8, where $\bar{X}$ has been treated as an example of a random variable.) We will now provide a more extensive analysis of the properties of $\bar{X}$ in the context of the practical applications in which it arises.

5.3 EXPECTATION OF SAMPLE MEAN

The following computation of the expectation of the sample mean is merely a special case of the expectation of the sum of n random variables, which has been explained in Section 3.7. Since the expectation of a sum is the sum of the expectations, we can easily compute

$$E(\bar{X}) = \frac{1}{n} E\left(\sum_{i=1}^{n} X_i\right) = \frac{1}{n} \sum_{i=1}^{n} E(X_i). \tag{1}$$

Since the X_i are identically distributed, the definition of the first moment of a random variable, $\nu_1 = E(X_i)$, leads to

$$E(\bar{X}) = \frac{1}{n} n\nu_1 = \nu_1. \tag{2}$$

This equation merely states the fact that the expectation of the sample mean is the mean, or first moment, of the population distribution.

Example 1. Consider an urn containing N balls, N_1 red and $N_2 = N - N_1$ black. If we sample $n \leq N$ balls, the a priori probability of any given ball being red (regardless of whether we sample with or without replacement) is N_1/N. Let $X_i = 1$ for the occurrence of a red ball on the ith trial, and $X_i = 0$ if a black ball occurs. The mean number of red balls withdrawn will be

$$E(\bar{X}) = \nu_1 = E(X_i) = \Pr\{X_i = 1\} = N_1/N. \tag{3}$$

Example 2. Consider a sample of n points, randomly chosen from the interval $[0, 1]$, and let X_i be the coordinate of the ith chosen point. Obviously the original population is infinite, and the coordinate can assume any one of a continuum of values, so the random variable X_i is continuous with pdf $f(x) = 1$ for $0 \leq x \leq 1$, and $f(x) = 0$ otherwise. Thus

$$E(X_i) = \int_0^1 x \, dx = \tfrac{1}{2},$$

$$E(\bar{X}) = \nu_1 = E(X_i) = \tfrac{1}{2}. \tag{4}$$

These examples illustrate the fact that the expectation of the sample mean is equal to the true population mean. Because of this fact we say that the sample mean $\bar{X}$ is an unbiased estimator of the true population mean. The sample mean is one example of a sample statistic satisfying the following definition.

Definition. An unbiased estimator of a population parameter is a sample statistic (random variable) whose expected value (expectation) is equal to the true value of the population parameter.

This property of being unbiased does not guarantee that the particular sample mean $\bar{x}$ will be at all close to the true population mean ν_1. To determine the probability of the occurrence of this happy event we examine, in the next few sections, the behavior of the variance of the sample mean.

5.4 VARIANCE OF SAMPLE MEAN

The computation of the variance of the sample mean is of the same form as the computation of the variance of a sum of random variables, which should be recalled from probability theory (in particular Section 3.8).

$$\text{var}(\bar{X}) = E(\bar{X} - \nu_1)^2$$

$$= E\left(\frac{1}{n}\sum_{i=1}^{n} X_i - \nu_1\right)^2 = E\left[\frac{1}{n}\sum_{i=1}^{n}(X_i - \nu_1)\right]^2$$

$$= E\left[\frac{1}{n^2}\sum_{i,\,j=1}^{n}(X_i - \nu_1)(X_j - \nu_1)\right]$$

$$= \frac{1}{n^2}\sum_{i=1}^{n} E(X_i - \nu_1)^2 + \frac{1}{n^2}\sum_{i \neq j} E[(X_i - \nu_1)(X_j - \nu_1)]. \qquad (1)$$

Recall that

$$\text{var}(X_i) = E[(X_i - \nu_1)^2] = \mu_2 = \sigma^2$$

(since the X_i are identically distributed), and

$$E[(X_i - \nu_1)(X_j - \nu_1)] = \text{cov}(X_i, X_j) = \mu_{12}.$$

We may rewrite Eq. (1) as

$$\text{var}(\bar{X}) = \frac{1}{n^2}\sum_{i=1}^{n}\sigma^2 + \frac{1}{n^2}\sum_{i \neq j}\mu_{12} = \frac{\sigma^2}{n} + \frac{n-1}{n}\mu_{12}. \qquad (2)$$

Frequently, the X_i will be independent random variables, so $\mu_{12} = 0$ and the variance of the sample mean simplifies to (for independent samples)

$$\text{var}(\bar{X}) = \frac{\sigma^2}{n}. \qquad (3)$$

Example 1. Consider the urn problem, Example 1 of Section 5.3.

a) For sampling *with* replacement:

$$\nu_2 = E(X_i^2) = \frac{N_1}{N}.$$

If we use the obvious shorthand

$$\frac{N_1}{N} = p, \qquad \frac{N_2}{N} = q = 1 - p,$$

then

$$\sigma^2 = \text{var}(X_i) = p - p^2 = pq.$$

Sampling with replacement implies independent random variables, so

$$\mu_{12} = \text{cov}(X_i, X_j) = 0.$$

We can then compute

$$\text{var}(\bar{X}) = \frac{\sigma^2}{n} = \frac{pq}{n}.$$ (4)

b) For sampling *without* replacement:

$$E(X_i^2) = p,$$

$$E(X_i X_j) = \Pr\{X_i = 1, X_j = 1\} = \Pr\{X_1 = 1, X_2 = 1\}$$
$$\scriptstyle i \neq j \qquad\qquad\quad\, i \neq j$$

$$= \frac{N_1(N_1 - 1)}{N(N - 1)} = \frac{p(p - 1/N)}{1 - 1/N},$$

$$\mu_{12} = \text{cov}(X_i, X_j) = \text{cov}(X_1, X_2)$$
$$\scriptstyle\qquad\quad i \neq j$$

$$= \frac{p(p - 1/N)}{1 - 1/N} - p^2 = \frac{p^2 - p}{N - 1} = -\frac{pq}{N - 1},$$

$$\text{var}(\bar{X}) = \frac{\sigma^2}{n} + \frac{(n - 1)\mu_{12}}{n} = \frac{pq}{n}\left[1 - \frac{n - 1}{N - 1}\right].$$ (5)

As one would expect, the variance is smaller for sampling without replacement. In fact, if we sample the entire population, $n = N$, the variance is zero because we must obtain the same result every time we perform the experiment.

Example 2. Consider the uniform distribution problem of Example 2, Section 5.3. The points on the line are sampled with replacement so that the continuous random variables X_i are independent. Thus,

$$\text{var}(\bar{X}) = \frac{1}{n}\text{var}(X_i) = \frac{\sigma^2}{n} = \frac{\nu_2 - \nu_1^2}{n}$$

$$= \frac{1}{n}\left[\int_0^1 x^2\, dx - \left(\frac{1}{2}\right)^2\right]$$

$$= \frac{1}{n}\left(\frac{1}{3} - \frac{1}{4}\right) = \frac{1}{12n}.$$ (6)

In this section we have computed the variance of the sample mean for several particular types of samples. For most statistical applications we will be concerned vith independent sample elements which can be represented by independent random variables. For independent random variables Eq. (3) shows that the variance of the sample mean can be made small by making the number of sample elements, n, sufficiently large. We have also seen, from Example 1(b), that, in the particular case in which the variables are dependent because the sample is made without replacement from a finite population, the variance of the sample mean decreased even faster, with increasing n, than it did in the independent variable case. In the following sections we will show how a small variance implies a small probability for the random variable to deviate very far from its expected value.

PROBLEMS

1. Consider an experiment performed 10 times. Let the outcome for the ith experiment be characterized by the random variable X_i. If it is found that the experimental values of X_i turn out to be 10.4, 9.8, 9.7, 11.0, 10.9, 9.3, 9.2, 10, 9.7, 10, for $i = 1$ through 10:

   a) What is the sample mean?
   b) What is the sample variance?

2. Consider a sequence of 10 balls, sampled with replacement from a population of red and black balls. Let $X_i = 1$, if the ith choice is red, and $X_i = 0$ if it is black. If the actual sequence turns out to be R R B R B B B R B B, what are the sample mean and variance for this particular sample?

3. In the above example, assume that the probability of picking a red ball on any trial is p:

   a) What is the a priori probability of getting the particular sequence of Problem 2?
   b) What is the a priori probability of obtaining a sequence with the same value of the sample mean?

4. Consider a random variable sampled from an $N(2, 1)$ population.

   a) What is the minimum number of elements required to make the variance of the sample mean less than $\frac{3}{16}$?
   b) For a random sample of this many elements, what is the probability that they will all deviate from the mean by more than $\frac{3}{16}$?
   c) What is the probability that the average (or sample mean) will deviate from the mean by more than $\frac{3}{16}$? (Give numbers computed from the tabulated values of the CDF for the normal distribution.)

5. Consider a sample from an urn containing 10 red and 10 black balls. Let $X_i = 1$ if the ith ball is red, and $X_i = 0$ otherwise. Find the minimum number of elements which must be sampled so that var $(\bar{X}) < 0.1$ if:

   a) The sampling is done with replacement.
   b) The sampling is done without replacement.

6. Consider random samples from an urn containing n_1 red balls, n_2 white balls, and n_3 blue balls (with $n_1 + n_2 + n_3 = N$). Let $X_i = 1$ if the ith ball sampled is red, $X_i = 0$ if the ith ball is white, and $X_i = -1$ if the ith ball is blue. If m balls are sampled without replacement, find $E(\bar{X})$ and $E(\bar{X}^2)$ and show that

$$\text{var } (\bar{X}) = \frac{(n_1 + n_3)(N - m)}{m(N - 1)N} + \frac{(n_1 - n_3)^2 (m - N)}{mN^2(N - 1)}.$$

5.5 CHEBYSHEV'S INEQUALITY

The variance of a random variable can be used to set an upper bound on the probability of that variable taking on a value more than some particular distance from
its expected value $(E(X) = \nu_1)$. The actual mathematical relation involving those
quantities is known as Chebyshev's inequality and is derived from the following
general result, known as the Chebyshev–Bienaymé inequality.

Theorem. Let X be a random variable, and let $g(x)$ be an arbitrary nonnegative
integrable function of the values x which the random variable X can assume. Then
it follows that, for arbitrary positive τ,

$$\Pr\{g(X) \geq \tau\} \leq \frac{1}{\tau} \int_{-\infty}^{+\infty} g(x) f(x)\, dx = \frac{1}{\tau} E[g(x)], \tag{1}$$

where $f(x)$ is the pdf of the random variable X.

Proof. Divide the range of integration $(-\infty \leq x \leq +\infty)$ into the set of intervals
for which $g(x) \geq \tau$ (called S), and the set of intervals for which $g(x) < \tau$ (called S').
An illustration of a typical division into S and S' is shown in Fig. 1.

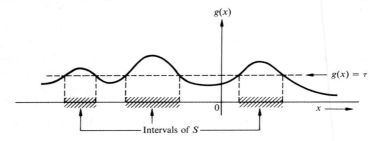

Figure 5.1

Now, since $g(x)$ is nonnegative, as is $f(x)$,

$$\int_{-\infty}^{+\infty} g(x) f(x)\, dx = \int_{S} g(x) f(x)\, dx + \int_{S'} g(x) f(x)\, dx$$

$$\geq \int_{S} g(x) f(x)\, dx. \tag{2}$$

Furthermore, since $g(x) \geq \tau$ over the intervals in the set S,

$$\int_{S} g(x) f(x)\, dx \geq \tau \int_{S} f(x)\, dx$$

$$\geq \tau \Pr\{X \in S\} = \tau \Pr\{g(X) \geq \tau\}. \tag{3}$$

Combining inequalities (2) and (3) and dividing through by τ gives the original form
of the theorem as stated in (1).

We can now obtain the usual form of Chebyshev's inequality by taking

$$g(x) = (x - \nu_1)^2.$$

The inequality (1) gives

$$\Pr\{(X - v_1)^2 \geq \tau\} \leq \frac{1}{\tau}\int_{-\infty}^{+\infty}(x - v_1)^2 f(x)\,dx = \frac{\sigma^2}{\tau}. \tag{4}$$

The standard form of this inequality is obtained by letting $\tau = t^2$, and observing that

$$\Pr\{(X - v_1)^2 \geq t^2\} = \Pr\{|X - v_1| \geq t\},$$

so that Eq. (4) can be rewritten as

$$\Pr\{|X - v_1| \geq t\} \leq \frac{\sigma^2}{t^2}. \tag{5}$$

The reader should note that this relationship depends only on the parameters v_1 and σ^2, and is independent of the other features of the distribution of the random variable X. We will use this general result to prove the law of large numbers in Section 5.7. First, however, we will illustrate the nature of this inequality for a few particular distributions.

Example 1. Consider the Gaussian pdf

$$f(x) = \frac{1}{\sqrt{2\pi}\,\sigma}\exp\left(-\frac{x^2}{2\sigma^2}\right).$$

The corresponding random variable X has $E(X) = 0$ and $E(X^2) = \text{var}(X) = \sigma^2$. Chebyshev's inequality (5) gives

$$\Pr\{|X| \geq t\} \leq \frac{\sigma^2}{t^2}. \tag{6}$$

It is interesting to compare this upper bound with the direct calculation of

$$\begin{aligned}
\Pr\{|X| \geq t\} &= \frac{1}{\sigma\sqrt{2\pi}}\int_t^\infty \exp\left(-x^2/2\sigma^2\right)dx \\
&\quad + \frac{1}{\sigma\sqrt{2\pi}}\int_{-\infty}^{-t}\exp\left(-x^2/2\sigma^2\right)dx \\
&= \frac{2}{\sigma\sqrt{2\pi}}\int_t^\infty \exp\left(-x^2/2\sigma^2\right)dx. \tag{7}
\end{aligned}$$

The last integral can be written in a more compact form by changing the integration variable $x = z\sigma$, $dx = \sigma\,dz$, and letting $t/\sigma = \alpha$;

$$\Pr\{|X| \geq \alpha\sigma\} = 2\sqrt{\frac{1}{2\pi}}\int_\alpha^\infty \exp\left(-z^2/2\right)dz. \tag{8}$$

This integral has been evaluated numerically and is tabulated in terms of the CDF of the $N(0, 1)$ distribution function

$$F(\alpha) = \int_{-\infty}^{\alpha}\frac{1}{\sqrt{2\pi}}\exp\left(-z^2/2\right)dz,$$

which is given, for various positive values of α, in Table 1 of Appendix D.
In terms of this function

$$\Pr\{|X| \geq \alpha\sigma\} = 2\sqrt{\frac{1}{2\pi}}\int_{\alpha}^{\infty} \exp\left(-z^2/2\right) dz$$

$$= 2[1 - F(\alpha)]. \tag{9}$$

For $\alpha \gg 1$ we saw in Section 4.2, that the integral in Eq. (8) could be approximated analytically. For this purpose the integral of (8) is rewritten as

$$\sqrt{\frac{2}{\pi}}\int_{\alpha}^{\infty} [z \exp\left(-z^2/2\right)]\left(\frac{1}{z}\right) dz = I. \tag{10}$$

This integral can be integrated by parts, integrating the first factor of the integrand and differentiating the second factor $(1/z)$. This procedure gives

$$I = -\sqrt{\frac{2}{\pi}}\frac{\exp\left(-z^2/2\right)}{z}\bigg|_{\alpha}^{\infty} - \sqrt{\frac{2}{\pi}}\int_{\alpha}^{\infty}\frac{\exp\left(-z^2/2\right)}{z^2} dz. \tag{11}$$

Since the integrand of the second term in this expression is positive, the integral is positive. Therefore, if this second term is removed from the equation we are left with the inequality

$$I \leq -\sqrt{\frac{2}{\pi}}\frac{\exp\left(-z^2/2\right)}{z}\bigg|_{\alpha}^{\infty} = \sqrt{\frac{2}{\pi}}\frac{\exp\left(-\alpha^2/2\right)}{\alpha}. \tag{12}$$

Substituting this result into Eq. (8) gives the inequality

$$\Pr\{|X| \geq \alpha\sigma\} \leq \sqrt{\frac{2}{\pi}}\frac{\exp\left(-\alpha^2/2\right)}{\alpha}. \tag{13}$$

(This result is equivalent to Eq. (10) of Section 4.2.) With the same notation the Chebyshev inequality (6) can be written as

$$\Pr\{|X| \geq \alpha\sigma\} \leq 1/\alpha^2. \tag{14}$$

A simple comparison of Eqs. (13) and (14) shows that the asymptotic approximation provides the stronger (smaller) upper bound.

Example 2. For the uniform distribution, $f(x) = 1$ for $0 \leq x \leq 1$, $f(x) = 0$ otherwise, we know that

$$v_1 = \tfrac{1}{2}, \qquad \sigma^2 = \tfrac{1}{12}.$$

Substituting these quantities into Chebyshev's inequality gives

$$\Pr\{|X - \tfrac{1}{2}| \geq t\} \leq 1/12t^2. \tag{16}$$

It is again interesting to compare this result with the exact calculation (which can be easily performed for this simple distribution), assuming $0 \leq t \leq \tfrac{1}{2}$. To perform this calculation, we note the inequality $|X - \tfrac{1}{2}| \geq t$ can only be satisfied by X in one of the sets $0 \leq X \leq \frac{1}{2} - t$ or $\frac{1}{2} + t \leq X \leq 1$. The probability of X being in these sets is simply the length of the set, since $f(x) = 1$, so

$$\Pr\{|X - \tfrac{1}{2}| \geq t\} = 2(\tfrac{1}{2} - t) = 1 - 2t. \tag{17}$$

A comparison of Eqs. (16) and (17) shows that Chebyshev's inequality will be a poor approximation for this distribution. Such a result might be expected, since Chebyshev's inequality only makes use of the variance, while higher moments are quite significant in the uniform distribution.

The reader should note that for distributions which do not have finite variances, the larger side of Chebyshev's inequality is infinite, and therefore the inequality does not provide a useful upper bound. For example, the variance of the Cauchy distribution, pdf $f(x) = 1/\pi(1 + x^2)$, is infinite, so the upper bound, given by Eq. (5), is useless.

In this section we have derived the general Chebyshev-Bienaymé inequality, and illustrated a few simple applications of the special Chebyshev's inequality. We will find these inequalities quite useful for placing upper bounds on the probability of random variables deviating from their expected values. They will be particularly useful when we wish to discuss the validity of general procedures without specifying any specific population distribution.

In order to gain some idea of the strength Chebyshev's inequality gives the upper bound we have compared the inequality for a few examples, with more precise calculations which happen to be feasible.

PROBLEMS

1. Consider a random variable X, with $\nu_1 = 5$ and $\sigma = 2$. Use Chebyshev's inequality to determine an upper bound for $\Pr\{X \geq 9\} + \Pr\{X \leq 1\}$.

2. Consider a sample with each element characterized by the random variable X_i. If the original population is such that $\sigma^2 = \mathrm{var}(X_i) = 4$, how many elements must be sampled so that $\Pr\{|\bar{X} - \nu_1| \geq 2\} \leq . 2$. (Use Chebyshev's inequality.)

3. Let $g(x, y)$ be an arbitrary positive function defined over the range of values of the random variables X and Y for which the joint pdf $f(x, y)$ exists. Generalize the Chebyshev-Bienaymé inequality to show that

$$\int_{-\infty}^{+\infty}\int_{-\infty}^{+\infty} g(x, y) f(x, y)\, dx\, dy \geq \tau \Pr\{g(X, Y) \geq \tau\}.$$

4. Let $u(x)$ and $v(y)$ be arbitrary positive functions defined over the same range of values as in the previous problem. Generalize the Chebyshev-Bienaymé inequality to show that

$$\int_{-\infty}^{+\infty}\int_{-\infty}^{\infty} u(x)\, v(y)\, f(x, y)\, dx\, dy \geq \tau_x\, \tau_y \Pr\{u(x) \geq \tau_x,\, v(y) \geq \tau_y\}.$$

5. Consider two random variables X, Y with means ν_x, ν_y and variances σ_x^2, σ_y^2. Show that a special case of the result of the previous example is

$$\Pr\{|X - \nu_x| \geq t, |Y - \nu_y| \geq t\} \leq \frac{\sigma_x^4 \sigma_y^4}{2t^4}.$$

6. Show that the right side of Eq. (13) is smaller than the right side of Eq. (14) for all positive values of α.

5.6 SPECIAL APPLICATIONS OF THE CHEBYSHEV-BIENAYME INEQUALITY

It is interesting to apply the general theorem of Eq. (1), Section 5.5, to other forms of $g(x)$ which might give stronger upper bounds for the probability of X deviating from ν_1 by a significant amount. For example, if $g(x) = (X - \nu_1)^4$, then Eq. (1) of Section 5.5 gives (letting $\tau = t^4$),

$$\Pr\{|X - \nu_1| \geq t\} \leq \frac{\mu_4}{t^4}. \tag{1}$$

This will give a stronger upper bound (smaller in numerical value) than the usual form of Eq. (5), Section 5.5, for those cases in which

$$\frac{\mu_4}{t^4} < \frac{\sigma^2}{t^2},$$

which can be rewritten as

$$t > \frac{\sqrt{\mu_4}}{\sigma} = \sqrt{\frac{\mu_4}{\mu_2}}. \tag{2}$$

Equation (2) implies that if a sufficiently large t is used, then Eq. (1) gives a smaller upper bound than does Eq. (5) of Section 5.5. Such a result is to be expected, since large values of t imply a concern with large deviations of X from ν_1, and large deviations are better characterized by μ_4 than by μ_2.

Example 1. Consider a distribution with $\mu_4 = \frac{1}{80}, \mu_2 = \frac{1}{12}$. (These values happen to result from the uniform distribution $U(0, 1)$, but this is immaterial since we generally resort to Chebyshev's inequality only when the complete distribution is unknown. The reader should note that there is actually an infinite family of distributions with these particular values of μ_2 and μ_4.) For

$$t > \sqrt{\frac{\mu_4}{\mu_2}} = \sqrt{\frac{12}{80}} = \frac{1}{2}\sqrt{\frac{3}{5}},$$

Eq. (1) will give a stricter upper bound than will Eq. (5) of Section 5.5. The probability upper bound associated with this value of t is

$$\frac{\mu_4}{t^4} = \frac{\mu_2^2}{\mu_4} = \frac{5}{9}.$$

If we know both μ_2 and μ_4, it is possible to obtain an upper bound on the probability of a deviation, by more than a specified value, of $(X - \nu_1)^2$ from the variance. If we let

$$g(x) = [(x - \nu_1)^2 - \mu_2]^2 \tag{3}$$

and substitute into Eq. (1) of Section 5.5, we get the inequality (letting $\tau = t^2$)

$$\Pr\{|(X - \nu_1)^2 - \mu_2| \geq t\} \leq \frac{1}{t^2} \int_{-\infty}^{+\infty} [(x - \nu_1)^2 - \mu_2]^2 f(x)\, dx$$

$$= \frac{\mu_4 - \mu_2^2}{t^2}. \tag{4}$$

There are two important observations which follow directly from this relation:

a) Since the integrand in (4) is non-negative, we always have $\mu_4 - \mu_2^2 \geq 0$.
b) If $\mu_4 - \mu_2^2$ is sufficiently small, then there will be only a very small probability that $(X - \nu_1)^2$ will be very far from μ_2. If μ_2 is sufficiently large, then $(X - \nu_1)^2$ being close to μ_2 implies that X cannot be close to ν_1. Such behavior is characteristic of a bimodal distribution (a pdf with two peaks).

Example 2. *Continuous bimodal distribution.* Let $f(x) = |x|$ for $-1 \leq x \leq 1$, $f(x) = 0$ otherwise. This pdf is illustrated in Fig. 2.
    We may write

$$E(X) = \int_{-1}^{1} x\,|x|\, dx$$

$$= -\int_{-1}^{0} x^2\, dx + \int_{0}^{1} x^2\, dx = 0.$$

Therefore, var $(X) = E(X^2)$, and

$$\mu_2 = \text{var}\,(X) = E(X^2)$$

$$= \int_{-1}^{+1} x^2\,|x|\, dx = 2\int_{0}^{1} x^3\, dx = \tfrac{1}{2}, \tag{5}$$

$$\mu_4 = E(X^4)$$

$$= \int_{-1}^{+1} x^4\,|x|\, dx = 2\int_{0}^{1} x^5\, dx = \tfrac{1}{3}, \tag{6}$$

$$\mu_4 - \mu_2^2 = \tfrac{1}{12}.$$

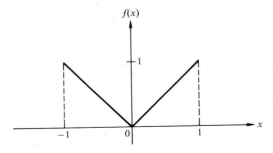

Figure 5.2

Equation (4) gives

$$\Pr\{|X^2 - \tfrac{1}{2}| \geq t\} \leq \frac{1}{12t^2},\tag{7}$$

while Eq. (5) of Section 5.5 gives the much weaker upper bound

$$\Pr\{|X| \geq t\} \leq \frac{1}{2t^2}.\tag{8}$$

Eqs. (9) and (10) strongly suggest, but do not prove, that this bimodal distribution has a much higher probability of X^2 being close to μ_2 than of X being close to $\nu_1 = 0$.

The examples given in this section serve to illustrate certain features of some interesting distributions. The reader who takes the trouble to follow the details of these analyses will also gain a better intuitive understanding of the behavior of the sample statistics involved.

PROBLEMS

1. Consider two distributions α, β which have zero mean and the second and fourth moments

$$\mu_{2\alpha} = 5, \qquad \mu_{2\beta} = 10,$$

$$\mu_{4\alpha} = 26, \qquad \mu_{4\beta} = 115.$$

   a) Use Chebyshev's inequality to determine an upper bound for $\Pr\{|x| \geq t\}$ for each distribution.
   b) Use the extended Chebyshev's inequality to determine an upper bound for $\Pr\{|X^2 - \mu_2| \geq t\}$ for each distribution.
   c) Which of these distributions would you expect to be bimodal?

2. Consider a random variable X distributed such that $E(X) = 0$, $E(X^2) = 5$, $E(X^4) = 80$. Find the strongest upper bound of $\Pr\{|X| \geq t\}$
   a) For $t = 3$,
   b) For $t = 6$.

3. Consider the discrete random variable X which takes on values $+1$ and -1, with equal probabilities of $\tfrac{1}{2}$. Compute μ_2 and μ_4, and use Eq. (4) to show that $X^2 = 1$ for all possible values of X. This result is, of course, self evident from the statement of the distribution of X.

4. Use Eqs. (1) and (4) to examine the bimodality of the distribution given by $f(x) = \tfrac{3}{2}x^2$ for $-1 \leq x \leq +1$.

5. Consider the bimodal pdf

$$f(x) = \frac{1}{2\sqrt{2\pi}\sigma_0}\left\{\exp\left[-\frac{(x-\mu)^2}{2\sigma_0^2}\right] + \exp\left[-\frac{(x+\mu)^2}{2\sigma_0^2}\right]\right\}.$$

a) Show that the moment generating function for the random variable X is

$$E[\exp(tx)] = \exp\left(\frac{\sigma_0^2\,t^2}{2}\right)\cosh\mu t\,.$$

b) Use this MGF to show that

$$\mu_4 = 3\sigma_0^4 + \mu^4 + 6\sigma_0^2\,\mu^2\,.$$

c) Use Chebyshev's inequality to show that

$$\Pr\{X^2 \geq t\} \leq \frac{\mu^2 + \sigma_0^2}{t}\,.$$

d) Use Eq. (4) of this section to show that

$$\Pr\{|X^2 - \sigma_0^2 - \mu^2| \geq t\} \leq \frac{2\sigma_0^4 + 4\sigma_0^2\,\mu^2}{t^2}\,.$$

e) How does the usefulness of the results in Parts (c) and (d) above depend on the ratio σ_0/μ? What does this imply, in terms of the distribution?

5.7 LAWS OF LARGE NUMBERS

Let us write the n element sample mean as

$$\bar{X}_n = \frac{1}{n}\sum_{i=1}^{n} X_i$$

to exhibit the explicit dependence of the sample mean upon n. If the population of the X_i has a mean ν_1 and a variance σ^2, the variance of the sample mean will be $\text{VAR}(\bar{X}) = \sigma^2/n$, and the application of Chebyshev's inequality gives

$$\Pr\{|\bar{X}_n - \nu_1| \geq t\} = \Pr\left\{\frac{|\bar{X}_n - \nu_1|}{\sigma/\sqrt{n}} \geq \frac{t}{\sigma/\sqrt{n}}\right\} \leq \frac{\sigma^2}{nt^2}\,. \tag{1}$$

As $n \to \infty$, this inequality becomes the mathematical statement of the Weak Law of Large Numbers,

$$\lim_{n\to\infty} \Pr\{|\bar{X}_n - \nu_1| \geq t\} = 0, \tag{2}$$

for any $t > 0$.

The interpretation of this weak law is:

"The probability that any particular $\bar{X}_n$ will deviate from the true population mean ν_1 by more than some (arbitrarily small) nonzero value t, can be made arbitrarily small by then choosing n sufficiently large."

With this interpretation we can say that $\bar{X}_n$ converges weakly to ν_1 in the limit $n \to \infty$. To understand the meaning of weak convergence (also called convergence in probability), we consider an experiment in which a large number n of elements is sampled and the sample mean $\bar{X}_n$ computed. Another element is then sampled and the new sample mean $\bar{X}_{n+1}$ is computed. If this process is repeated infinitely many times the weak law of large numbers implies that the probability of any of the computed $\bar{X}_k \, (k \geq n)$ deviating significantly from the mean can be made arbitrarily small by choosing n sufficiently large. The weak law does not imply that the infinite sum of these arbitrarily small probabilities can also be made arbitrarily small.

In other words, the weak law does not require that the probability of no significant deviation from the true population mean, each time we add a new sample element, tends to one. However, such a limitation is imposed by the Strong Law of Large Numbers. A somewhat heuristic derivation of the strong law can be obtained by invoking the central limit theorem so that $(\bar{X}_k - \nu_1)\sqrt{k}/\sigma$ is $N(0, 1)$ distributed. It was shown in Section 5.5 that the asymptotic approximation to the normal distribution provides a stronger upper bound on deviations than does Chebyshev's inequality. We therefore use Eq. (12) of Section 5.5 to write

$$\Pr\left\{\frac{|\bar{X}_k - \nu_1|\sqrt{k}}{\sigma} \geq \alpha\right\} \leq \sqrt{\frac{2}{\pi}} \, \frac{\exp\left(-\alpha^2/2\right)}{\alpha}. \tag{3}$$

For the present derivation it is convenient to let

$$\alpha = \sqrt{2b \ln k}, \tag{4}$$

and let A_k represent the event

$$\frac{|\bar{X}_k - \nu_1|\sqrt{k}}{\sigma} \geq \sqrt{2b \ln k},$$

or

$$|\bar{X}_k - \nu_1| \geq \frac{\sigma\sqrt{2b \ln k}}{\sqrt{k}}. \tag{5}$$

Since the right side of this inequality can be made arbitrarily small by taking k sufficiently large, the event A_k is the occurrence of an arbitrarily small deviation of $\bar{X}_k$ from the true population mean.

Using the form of α given by Eq. (4), Eq. (3) becomes

$$\Pr\{A_k\} \leq \sqrt{\frac{1}{\pi b \ln k}} \, e^{-b \ln k} = \frac{1}{k^b}\sqrt{\frac{1}{\pi b \ln k}}. \tag{6}$$

Summing over k we obtain

$$\sum_{k=n}^{\infty} \Pr\{A_k\} \leq \frac{1}{\sqrt{b\pi}} \sum_{k=n}^{\infty} \frac{1}{k^b \ln k}, \tag{7}$$

which, for large n, can be approximated by

$$\sum_{k=n}^{\infty} \Pr\{A_k\} \leq \frac{1}{\sqrt{b\pi \ln (n)}} \sum_{k=n}^{\infty} \frac{1}{k^b}$$

$$\approx \frac{1}{(b-1)n^{b-1}\sqrt{b\pi \ln (n)}}, \tag{8}$$

where we have approximated the discrete sum by an integral and have assumed $b > 1$. The right side of Eq. (8) can be made arbitrarily small by simply choosing n sufficiently large so that the probability of at least one significant deviation (as the sample size increases from n to infinity) is less than the left side of Eq. (8). Thus the probability of at least one significant deviation, in the infinite sequence of increasing size samples, can be made arbitrarily small by taking n sufficiently large. (This fact alone could also be obtained by simply observing that the series in Eq. (7) converges for $b > 1$). We can therefore state the strong law of large numbers as:

"For any pair of arbitrarily small numbers ϵ, δ, an n can always be found so that

$$\Pr\{|\bar{X}_k - \nu_1| \le \epsilon \quad \text{for all} \quad k \ge n\} \le 1 - \delta." \tag{9}$$

In the above derivation we would choose n and b according to Eqs. (5) and (7),

$$\epsilon \ge \frac{\sigma \sqrt{2b \ln (n)}}{\sqrt{n}},$$

$$\delta \ge \frac{1}{(b - 1)n^{b-1} \sqrt{b\pi \ln (n)}}. \tag{10}$$

It is easily seen that these inequalities can be satisfied for $b > 1$ by simply choosing n sufficiently large.

The above derivations of the strong and weak laws have relied heavily on the assumed finite variance of the random variable. Both laws can actually be shown to hold under the much less restrictive requirement of the finiteness of $E(|X|)$. The required proofs cannot simply rely on Chebyshev's inequality and the central limit theorem, and are beyond the scope of this text. Excellent proofs of these general theorems are given in references 3 and 5 listed at the end of the chapter.

The notion of convergence in probability (or weak convergence) is useful in defining the particular type of sample statistic known as a consistent estimator.

Definition. A sample statistic is said to be a *consistent estimator* for a true population parameter if it can be made to converge in probability to that particular parameter as the sample size tends to infinity.

If the variance of any sample statistic tends to zero as the sample size tends to infinity, Chebyshev's inequality guarantees convergence in probability. We can therefore use the following alternative definition of consistency.

Equivalent definition. A sample statistic is said to be a *consistent estimator* of a true population parameter if its variance tends to zero and its expectation tends to the true population parameter as the sample size tends to infinity.

From the above discussion it is evident that the smaller the variance of a sample statistic, the greater will be the reliance on estimates obtained from that statistic. It will be useful therefore to define the comparative notion of *efficiency*: If two different sample statistics have the same expectation, then the one with the smaller variance is said to be more efficient. Examples of such comparisons are given in Section 5.9.

PROBLEMS

1. Consider a sequence of 20 Bernoulli trials with $p = q = \frac{1}{2}$. Let $X_i = 1$ for a success and $X_i = 0$ for a failure on the ith trial. Compare the bounds on the probability $\Pr\{|\bar{X}_{20} - \frac{1}{2}| \geq 0.4\}$ computed from Chebyshev's inequality and from the asymptotic approximation to the normal distribution with the exact value.

2. Use Eqs. (10) to find the minimum value (approximate) of n which will satisfy Eq. (9) with $\epsilon = 0.01\,\sigma$ and $\delta = 0.01$, letting $b = 2$. Which of the two inequalities is the stronger?

5.8 SAMPLE VARIANCE

In most of the problems which require sampling, we know neither the mean nor the variance. It is therefore useful to define an additional random variable to characterize the fluctuations within the sample and to estimate the actual, unknown variance. The fluctuations within the sample are most easily characterized by the random variable

$$\mathscr{S}^2 = \frac{1}{n} \sum_{i=1}^{n} (X_i - \bar{X})^2 \,. \tag{1}$$

The reader should note that for any particular sample, $\mathscr{S}^2$ will have some particular value determined by

$$\mathscr{s}^2 = \frac{1}{n} \sum_{i=1}^{n} (x_i - \bar{x})^2 \tag{2}$$

where the x_i are, as defined previously, the values of the random variables X_i for that particular sample. It is evident that $\mathscr{s}^2$ characterizes the fluctuations within the particular sample. To determine whether $\mathscr{S}^2$ also serves as an unbiased estimator of the true population variance of the random variables X (all identically distributed), we compute its expectation

$$E(\mathscr{S}^2) = \frac{1}{n} E\left[\sum_{i=1}^{n} (X_i - \bar{X})^2 \right] = \frac{1}{n} \sum_{i=1}^{n} E(X_i - \bar{X})^2 \,. \tag{3}$$

To evaluate Eq. (3), we compute

$$E(X_i - \bar{X})^2 = E[(X_i - \nu_1) - (\bar{X} - \nu_1)]^2 = E\left[X_i - \nu_1 - \frac{1}{n} \sum_{j=1}^{n} (X_j - \nu_1) \right]^2 \tag{4}$$

If we separate out the term with $j = i$ from the summation in Eq. (4), we get

$$E(X_i - \bar{X})^2 = E\left[(X_i - \nu_1)\left(1 - \frac{1}{n}\right) - \frac{1}{n} \sum_{j \neq i} (X_j - \nu_1) \right]^2 . \tag{5}$$

Expanding the square in Eq. (5) will give square terms of the form $(X_j - \nu_1)^2$ and cross terms of the form $(X_j - \nu_1)(X_{j'} - \nu_1)$, where $j' \neq j$. If the sample elements are independent, then

$$E[(X_j - \nu_1)(X_{j'} - \nu_1)] = E(X_j - \nu_1) E(X_{j'} - \nu_1) = 0 .$$

Thus, when taking the expectation of the expanded square from Eq. (5), we need only consider the square terms so that Eq. (5) becomes

$$E(X_i - \bar{X})^2 = E(X_i - \nu_1)^2 \left(1 - \frac{1}{n}\right)^2 + \frac{1}{n^2} \sum_{j \neq i} E(X_j - \nu_1)^2 .$$

Since the X_i are identically distributed, $E(X_i - \nu_1)^2 = \sigma^2$ for all X_i, so this equation becomes

$$E(X_i - \bar{X})^2 = \sigma^2 \left(1 - \frac{1}{n}\right)^2 + \frac{1}{n^2}(n - 1)\sigma^2 = \frac{n - 1}{n} \sigma^2 \tag{6}$$

for all X_i.
  Substitution of this result into Eq. (3) gives

$$E(\mathscr{S}^2) = \frac{n - 1}{n} \sigma^2 . \tag{7}$$

Equation (7) shows that the expectation of $\mathscr{S}^2$ is not the actual variance of the random variable X_i, so $\mathscr{S}^2$ is a biased estimator for σ^2. In order to obtain an unbiased estimate of the actual variance, we use the random variable

$$S^2 = \left(\frac{n}{n - 1}\right)\mathscr{S}^2 = \frac{1}{n - 1} \sum_{i=1}^{n} (X_i - \bar{X})^2 . \tag{8}$$

The reader should verify that writing $\bar{X}$ as a sum of X_i leads to the alternative form

$$S^2 = \frac{1}{n - 1} \left[\sum_{i=1}^{n} X_i^2 - \frac{1}{n}\left(\sum_{i=1}^{n} X_i \right)^2 \right] = \frac{1}{n - 1}\left[\sum_{i=1}^{n} X_i^2 - n\bar{X}^2 \right] . \tag{9}$$

Note on terminology. Many textbooks call $\mathscr{S}^2$ the sample variance and S^2 the unbiased estimator of the variance. Strictly speaking, this notation does describe the actual mathematical operations involved. However, $\mathscr{S}^2$ is seldom used, and most formulas in statistics are more easily written in terms of S^2 than of $\mathscr{S}^2$. For this reason many textbooks do not use $\mathscr{S}^2$ at all, but refer to S^2 as the sample variance. We will use this terminology in the remainder of this volume. Both $\mathscr{S}^2$ and S^2 are further examples of random variables classified as sample statistics.

In the limit of large n, the biasedness of $\mathcal{S}^2$ vanishes so that it can become a consistent estimator. To determine the consistency of $\mathcal{S}^2$ and S^2 we must compute the variance of S^2.

5.9 VARIANCE OF SAMPLE VARIANCE

To compute the variance of S^2 we use the expression

$$\operatorname{var}(S^2) = E[(S^2)^2] - [E(S^2)]^2 = E(S^4) - [E(S^2)]^2 . \tag{1}$$

Now,

$$E(S^4) = E\left[\frac{1}{n-1} \sum_{i=1}^{n} (X_i - \bar{X})^2\right]^2$$

$$= E\left[\sum_{i=1}^{n} [(X_i - \nu_1) - (\bar{X} - \nu_1)]^2\right]^2 \frac{1}{(n-1)^2} \tag{2}$$

$$= \frac{1}{(n-1)^2} E\left(\sum_{i=1}^{n} [(X_i - \nu_1)^2 - 2(X_i - \nu_1)(\bar{X} - \nu_1) + (\bar{X} - \nu_1)^2]\right)^2 .$$

Substituting

$$\bar{X} - \nu_1 = \frac{1}{n} \sum_{j=1}^{n} (X_j - \nu_1)$$

gives

$$\sum_{i=1}^{n} (X_i - \nu_1)(\bar{X} - \nu_1) = \frac{1}{n} \sum_{i,j=1}^{n} (X_i - \nu_1)(X_j - \nu_1) \tag{3}$$

and

$$\sum_{i=1}^{n} (\bar{X} - \nu_1)^2 = n(\bar{X} - \nu_1)^2$$

$$= \frac{1}{n} \sum_{i,j} (X_i - \nu_1)(X_j - \nu_1) . \tag{4}$$

Substituting Eqs. (3) and (4) into Eq. (2) gives

$$E(S^4) = \frac{E}{(n-1)^2} \left[\sum_{i=1}^{n} (X_i - \nu_1)^2 - \frac{1}{n} \sum_{i,j=1}^{n} (X_i - \nu_1)(X_j - \nu_1)\right]^2 . \tag{5}$$

Expanding the square and interchanging the summation and expectation operations gives,

$$E(S^4) = \frac{1}{(n-1)^2}\left[\sum_{i,j=1}^{n} E\{(X_i - \nu_1)^2 (X_j - \nu_1)^2\}\right.$$

$$-\frac{2}{n}\sum_{i,j,k=1}^{n} E\{(X_i - \nu_1)^2 (X_j - \nu_1)(X_k - \nu_1)\} \tag{6}$$

$$\left. +\frac{1}{n^2}\sum_{i,j,k,l} E\{(X_i - \nu_1)(X_j - \nu_1)(X_k - \nu_1)(X_l - \nu_1)\}\right].$$

Assuming the sample elements to be independent, this expression can be reduced by evaluating the following expectations involving $E(X_i - \nu_1)^4 = \mu_4$ and $E(X_i - \nu_1)^2 = \sigma^2$, utilizing the Kronecker δ function, $\delta_{ij} = 1$ if $i = j$, $\delta_{ij} = 0$ if $i \neq j$,

$$E[(X_i - \nu_1)^2 (X_j - \nu_1)^2] = \mu_4 \delta_{ij} + \sigma^4(1 - \delta_{ij})$$

$$E[(X_i - \nu_1)^2 (X_j - \nu_1)(X_k - \nu_1)] = \mu_4 \delta_{ij}\delta_{jk} + \sigma^4(1 - \delta_{ij})\delta_{jk}$$

$$E[(X_i - \nu_1)(X_j - \nu_1)(X_k - \nu_1)(X_l - \nu_1)] = \mu_4 \delta_{ij}\delta_{jk}\delta_{kl} + \sigma^4[\delta_{ij}\delta_{kl}(1 - \delta_{ik})$$
$$+ \delta_{ij}\delta_{jl}(1 - \delta_{jk}) + \delta_{il}\delta_{jk}(1 - \delta_{ij})].$$

Substituting these expressions into Eq. (6), and noting that

$$\sum_{i,j=1}^{n} \delta_{ij} = n,$$

$$\sum_{i,j,k=1}^{n} \delta_{ij}\delta_{jk} = n,$$

$$\sum_{i,j,k,l=1}^{n} \delta_{ij}\delta_{jk}\delta_{kl} = n,$$

we obtain, after combining terms,

$$E(S^4) = \frac{\mu_4}{n} + \frac{\sigma^4}{n-1}\left(n - 2 + \frac{3}{n}\right). \tag{7}$$

Equation (7) can be substituted into Eq. (1) to give

$$\text{var}(S^2) = \frac{\mu_4}{n} - \frac{\sigma^4}{n}\left(\frac{n-3}{n-1}\right), \tag{8}$$

where the sample elements have been assumed to be independent.

This result shows that var $(S^2) \to 0$ as $n \to \infty$, so S^2 is a consistent estimator for σ^2. The reader can easily show that $\mathscr{S}^2$ is also a consistent estimator.

Example 1. Again, considering the uniform distribution problem discussed in Example 2 of Section 5.3, we may write

$$\mu_4 = \int_0^1 (x - \tfrac{1}{2})^4 \, dx = \int_{-\frac{1}{2}}^{+\frac{1}{2}} y^4 \, dy = \tfrac{2}{5}(\tfrac{1}{2})^5$$

$$= \frac{1}{(5)\,(16)} . \tag{9}$$

From Example 2 of Section 5.4, we found that $\sigma^2 = \tfrac{1}{12}$, and so

$$\text{var}(S^2) = \frac{1}{80n} - \frac{n-3}{144n(n-1)} . \tag{10}$$

The following example describes a sample statistic whose expectation is the true population variance, and which is generally easier to compute than S^2. Unfortunately, the variance of this statistic is larger than the variance of S^2. An example of another, similarly behaving statistic is given in Problem 4 of this section.

Example 2. Consider n elements sampled with replacement from a population of a random variable X, having the first four moments $\nu_1, \nu_2, \nu_3, \nu_4$. We compute the mean and variance of the sample statistic

$$V = \frac{1}{n}[X_1(X_1 - X_2) + X_2(X_2 - X_3) + \cdots + X_n(X_n - X_1)]. \tag{11}$$

Computing the expectation as a sum of expectations yields

$$E(V) = \frac{1}{n}[E(X_1^2) + E(X_2^2) + \cdots + E(X_n^2)] - \frac{1}{n}[E(X_1X_2) + E(X_2X_3) + \cdots$$
$$+ E(X_nX_1)] . \tag{12}$$

Since the sample elements are independent and identically distributed, $E(X_iX_{i+1}) = \nu_1^2$, and this equation simplifies to

$$E(V) = \nu_2 - \nu_1^2 = \sigma^2 . \tag{13}$$

To compute the variance of V we first write the product V^2 in the following form

$$\overbrace{n^2V^2 = X_1^2(X_1 - X_2)^2 + X_2^2(X_2 - X_3) + \cdots + X_n^2(X_n - X_1)^2}^{n \text{ terms}}$$

$$\overbrace{+ 2X_1X_2(X_1 - X_2)(X_2 - X_3) + 2X_2X_3(X_2 - X_3)(X_3 - X_4) + \cdots}^{n \text{ terms}}$$

$$+ 2X_nX_1(X_n - X_1)(X_1 - X_2)$$
$$+ \sum_{i>j+1} 2X_iX_j(X_i - X_{i+1})(X_j - X_{j+1}),$$

where the index $n + 1 \Rightarrow 1$. $\tag{14}$

The expectations of the first group of n terms are all identical and equal to

$$E[X_1^2(X_1 - X_2)^2] = E[X_1^4 - 2X_1^3X_2 + X_1^2X_2^2] = v_4 - 2v_3v_1 + v_2^2. \tag{15}$$

The expectations of each of the terms in the second group of n terms are all identical and equal to

$$E[X_1X_2(X_1 - X_2)(X_2 - X_3)] = E[X_1^2X_2^2 - X_1^2 X_2X_3 - X_2^3X_1 + X_1X_3X_2^2] \tag{16}$$
$$= v_2^2 - v_3v_1.$$

The expectations of each of the terms in the summation are identical and equal to

$$E[X_iX_j(X_i - X_{i+1})(X_j - X_{j+1})] = E[X_i^2X_j^2 - X_iX_{i+1}X_j^2 - X_i^2X_jX_{j+1}$$
$$+ X_iX_jX_{i+1}X_{j+1}] \tag{17}$$
$$= v_2^2 - 2v_1^2v_2 + v_1^4,$$

where we have used the fact that $i > j + 1$. Now in $n^2E(V^2)$ there are n terms of the form given in Eq. (15) and $2n$ terms of the form given in Eq. (16) (the n terms indicated in Eq. (14) times the factor of 2). Therefore there remain $n^2 - 3n$ terms of the form given in Eq. (17). Putting all these terms together, dividing by n^2, and subtracting $[E(V)]^2 = (v_2 - v_1^2)^2$, we obtain, after canceling terms and writing the answer in terms of the central moment, $\mu_4 = v_4 - 4v_3v_1 + 6v_1^2v_2 - 3v_1^4$,

$$\text{VAR} (V^2) = \frac{1}{n} \mu_4. \tag{18}$$

It is easily seen that the variance given by Eq. (18) is larger than that given by Eq. (8). Therefore, V is a less efficient estimator than is S^2. An actual numerical example for the computation of $E(V)$ is given in Problem 5.

PROBLEMS

1. Use the moment generating function for the normal distribution to show that the fourth central moment $\mu_4 = 3\sigma^4$. Then use this result to show that for a sample from a normally distributed population, the variance of the sample variance is $2\sigma^4/(n - 1)$.

2. Consider the random variable X, with the pdf

$$f(x) = \frac{2a^3}{\pi} \frac{1}{(x^2 + a^2)^2}.$$

   a) What is the expectation of the variance of an n-element sample taken from this population?
   b) What is the variance of the sample variance?

3. Consider an n-element sample from a joint population of two variables X, Y. Show that

$$\frac{1}{n - 1} E\left[\sum_{i=1}^{n} (X_i - \bar{X}) (Y_i - \bar{Y})\right] = \text{cov} (X, Y).$$

4. Consider the sample statistic formed from the sum of n squares

$$W = \frac{1}{n} [(X_1 - X_2)^2 + (X_2 - X_3)^2 + \cdots + (X_n - X_1)^2],$$

where the X_i are independent sample elements from some population with variance σ_0 and fourth central moment μ_4.

a) Show that

$$E(X_1^2 - 2X_1 X_2 + X_2^2) = 2\sigma_0^2.$$

b) Use the above result to show that

$$E\left(\frac{W}{2}\right) = \sigma_0^2.$$

c) Express W in the form

$$W = \frac{1}{n} \sum_{i=1}^{n} (Y_i - Y_{i+1})^2,$$

where $Y_i = X_i - \nu_1$ and, by definition, $Y_{n+1} = X_1 - \nu_1$.

Write W^2 in the form

$$W^2 = \frac{1}{n^2} \sum_{i,j=1}^{n} (Y_i - Y_{i+1})^2 (Y_j - Y_{j+1})^2,$$

and take expectations to show that

$$E\left(\frac{W^2}{4}\right) = \frac{\mu_4}{n} + \sigma_0^4.$$

d) What can you say about the efficiency of $W/2$ compared to S^2 and V?

5. Use the data of Problem 1 to compute

a) $E(V)$, defined in Example 2.

b) $E(W/2)$, defined in the previous problem.

5.10 DISTRIBUTION OF SAMPLE MEAN AND SAMPLE VARIANCE FOR SAMPLES FROM GAUSSIAN POPULATIONS

Our discussion of statistical samples has thus far included mainly the first and second moments of the sample statistics. When a sample is taken from a population having a normally distributed random variable, then we can also describe the probability distributions of the sample mean $\bar{X}$ and sample variance S^2.

We have already seen, in our discussion of continuous probability, that the sum of n independent random variables, each $N(\mu, \sigma^2)$ distributed, was itself $N(n\mu, n\sigma^2)$ distributed. Now, for an n-element sample from an $N(\nu_1, \mu_2)$ distributed population, $\bar{X}$ is the sum of n random variables, X_i/n, with each X_i/n being

$$N\left(\frac{\nu_1}{n}, \frac{\mu_2}{n^2}\right)$$

distributed. Therefore, the sum $\bar{X}$ is

$$N\left[n\left(\frac{\nu_1}{n}\right), n\left(\frac{\mu_2}{n^2}\right)\right] = N\left(\nu_1, \frac{\mu_2}{n}\right)$$

distributed.

To determine the probability distribution of S^2, we first examine the sum of squares of differences between n random variables X_i [each representing samples from the population $N(\nu_1, \sigma^2)$] and ν_1, namely

$$Y = \sum_{i=1}^{n} (X_i - \nu_1)^2. \tag{1}$$

From our discussion of continuous probability, we have seen that Y/σ^2 is chi-square distributed with n degrees of freedom, since the $(X_i - \nu_1)/\sigma$ are $N(0, 1)$ distributed and independent. We now express S^2 in terms of Y by noting that

$$Y = \sum_{i=1}^{n} [(X_i - \bar{X}) + (\bar{X} - \nu_1)]^2$$

$$= \sum_{i=1}^{n} [(X_i - \bar{X})^2 + 2(X_i - \bar{X})(\bar{X} - \nu_1) + (\bar{X} - \nu_1)^2]. \tag{2}$$

However, from the definition of sample mean,

$$\sum_{i=1}^{n} (X_i - \bar{X}) = 0, \tag{3}$$

so the middle term on the right-hand side of Eq. (2) drops out after summation over i. The equation then simplifies to

$$Y = \sum_{i=1}^{n} (X_i - \bar{X})^2 + n(\bar{X} - \nu_1)^2. \tag{4}$$

We can now express the result in terms of S^2 as

$$Y = (n - 1)S^2 + n(\bar{X} - \nu_1)^2. \tag{5}$$

We know that Y/σ^2 is chi-square distributed with n degrees of freedom, and we know that $(\bar{X} - \nu_1)$ is $N(0, \sigma^2/n)$ distributed, so that $\sqrt{n}(\bar{X} - \nu_1)/\sigma$ is $N(0, 1)$ distributed, and $n(\bar{X} - \nu_1)^2/\sigma^2$ is chi-square distributed with one degree of freedom. If we knew that S^2 and $(\bar{X} - \nu_1)^2$ were independent, we could easily determine the moment generating function of $(n - 1)S^2/\sigma^2$, by dividing the n degree of freedom, chi-square moment generating function of Y/σ^2 by the one degree of freedom, chi-square moment generating function of $n(\bar{X} - \nu_1)^2/\sigma^2$ to get the $(n - 1)$ degree of freedom, chi-square moment generating function of $(n - 1)S^2/\sigma^2$. The independence of $(\bar{X} - \nu_1)^2$ and S^2 is suggested (but not proved) by the results of Problems 1 and 2 at the end of this section. Assuming independence, the actual mathematics of the above derivation is left to the reader in Problem 3.

There are several methods to prove that $(\bar{X} - \nu_1)^2$ and S^2 are independent. The following method additionally gives the distribution of S^2 directly: Let

$$Z_i = \frac{(X_i - \nu_1)}{\sigma}, \qquad i = 1, 2, \ldots, n, \tag{6}$$

so that the Z_i are all $N(0, 1)$, and define

$$U_1 = \frac{1}{\sqrt{n}} \sum_{i=1}^{n} Z_i. \tag{7}$$

If we view the Z_i as the n components of a vector, denoted by $\mathbf{Z}$, then Eq. (7) can be viewed as defining the first component, U_1, of a vector $\mathbf{U}$, obtained by rotating the vector $\mathbf{Z}$, using a rotation matrix R which has $1/\sqrt{n}$ for each element of the first row. We then choose the elements of the remaining rows in any manner which will be consistent with R being a rotation matrix. In other words, the row vectors (vector formed by the elements of a row) must be normalized to 1, and must be orthogonal to each other. There is only one such matrix for $n = 2$, as shown in Problem 12, but there is a whole family of possible matrices for $n > 2$. This is illustrated in Problem 5 for $n = 3$.

Once we have selected the rotation matrix R, we have defined the remaining components of the vector $\mathbf{U}$, namely $U_2, U_3, U_4, \ldots, U_n$, by the equation

$$\mathbf{U} = R\mathbf{Z}. \tag{8}$$

The transpose of this equation is

$$\mathbf{U}^T = \mathbf{Z}^T R^T. \tag{9}$$

Equations (9) and (8) can be multiplied together to give

$$\mathbf{U}^T\mathbf{U} = \mathbf{Z}^T R^T R\mathbf{Z} = \mathbf{Z}^T\mathbf{Z}, \tag{10}$$

where we have used the fact that $R^T R = I$, since R is a rotation matrix. Now, Eq. (10) can be written, in terms of components, as

$$\sum_{i=1}^{n} U_i^2 = \sum_{i=1}^{n} Z_i^2. \tag{11}$$

We know from Example 3 of Section 4.9 that the transformation defined by Eq. (8) transforms the n independent $N(0, 1)$ components of $\mathbf{Z}$ into n independent $N(0, 1)$ random variables which are the components of $\mathbf{U}$. (See Problem 6 for illustrations of this property of the components of $\mathbf{U}$.)

From Eqs. (6) and (7) we see that

$$U_1^2 = \frac{n(\bar{X} - \nu_1)^2}{\sigma^2}, \tag{12}$$

$$\sum_{i=1}^{n} Z_i^2 = \frac{Y}{\sigma^2}. \tag{13}$$

Substituting these expressions into Eq. (11) we get

$$\frac{n(\bar{X} - \nu_1)^2}{\sigma^2} + \sum_{i=2}^{n} U_i^2 = \frac{Y}{\sigma^2}. \tag{14}$$

Comparing this result with Eq. (5) we see that

$$\frac{(n-1)S^2}{\sigma^2} = \sum_{i=2}^{n} U_i^2. \tag{15}$$

Since the U_i are independent $N(0, 1)$ distributed,

$$\sum_{i=2}^{n} U_i^2$$

is independent of U_1^2 and is chi-square distributed with $n - 1$ degrees of freedom, and so is $(n - 1)S^2/\sigma^2$, involving the parameter σ^2.

In this section we have shown that the sample mean $\bar{X}$ and the sample variance S^2 are independent whenever the samples are taken from a normally distributed population. We have also found that, for samples from normal populations, $\bar{X}$ is normally distributed, $[(n - 1)S^2]/\sigma^2$ is chi-square distributed, and they are independent. Thus

$$\frac{\frac{\sqrt{n}}{\sigma}(\bar{X} - \mu)}{\sqrt{\frac{(n-1)S^2}{\sigma^2(n-1)}}} \equiv \frac{(\bar{X} - \mu)\sqrt{n}}{S} \tag{16}$$

is a Student random variable with $(n - 1)$ degrees of freedom, as defined in Section 4.8.

PROBLEMS

1. Show that for independent, identically distributed, random variables

$$E[X_i - \nu_1)^2 (X_j - \nu_1)] = \delta_{ij} \mu_3,$$
$$E[(X_i - \nu_1)(X_j - \nu_1)(X_k - \nu_1)] = \delta_{ij} \delta_{jk} \mu_3, \tag{17}$$

where $\mu_3 = E(X_i - \nu_1)^3$. Use this result to show that

$$E[S^2(\bar{X} - \nu_1)] = 0 \tag{18}$$

for any symmetric distribution. Hint: Use the form

$$(n - 1)S^2 = \sum_{i=1}^{n} (X_i - \nu_1)^2 - n(\bar{X} - \nu_1)^2 . \tag{19}$$

2. Using the expectations derived in Section 5.8, compute

$$E[(n - 1)S^2 (\bar{X} - \nu_1)^2] .$$

   [*Hint:* Use the form given in Eq. (3). Use this result to show that in the special case of a Gaussian population, $\text{cov}[S^2, (\bar{X} - \nu_1)^2] = 0.$]

3. Write the moment generating function for Y/σ^2 as a chi-square distribution with n degrees of freedom, and the product of the MGF for $(n - 1)S^2/\sigma^2$ and the MGF for $n(\bar{X} - \nu_1)^2/\sigma^2$ (assuming independence between $(\bar{X} - \nu_1)^2$ and S^2). Use the equivalence of these two forms of the MGF for Y/σ^2 to determine that the MGF for $(n - 1)S^2/\sigma^2$ is

$$(1 - 2t)^{-(n-1)/2} .$$

4. Show that if the first row of a 2×2 rotation matrix has the elements $1/\sqrt{2}, 1/\sqrt{2},$ then the second row must have the elements $1/\sqrt{2}, -1/\sqrt{2}.$ (The signs in the second row could be interchanged.)

5. Consider the possible 3×3 rotation matrices with the first row having the elements $1/\sqrt{3}, 1/\sqrt{3}, 1/\sqrt{3}.$
   a) Show that if the second row is chosen to be $1/\sqrt{2}, -1/\sqrt{2}, 0$, then the third row must be $1/\sqrt{6}, 1/\sqrt{6}, -2/\sqrt{6}.$
   b) Show that if the second row is chosen to be $1/\sqrt{14}, 2/\sqrt{14}, -3/\sqrt{14}$, then the third row must be $5/\sqrt{42}, -4/\sqrt{42}, -1/\sqrt{42}.$

   (Note that any row could of course have all the elements multiplied by -1, corresponding to a rotation of the same magnitude, but in the opposite direction.)

6. Show that if in Problems 4 and 5, **Z** has independent $N(0, 1)$ components, then **U** will also have independent $N(0, 1)$ components. In other words, show that if Z_1, Z_2, Z_3 are independent $N(0, 1)$, then the following random variables are also $N(0, 1)$:

   a) $\dfrac{1}{\sqrt{2}}(Z_1 + Z_2), \qquad \dfrac{1}{\sqrt{2}}(Z_1 - Z_2)$

   (Verify that these two are independent.)

   b) $\dfrac{1}{\sqrt{3}}(Z_1 + Z_2 + Z_3), \qquad \dfrac{1}{\sqrt{2}}(Z_1 - Z_2), \qquad \dfrac{1}{\sqrt{6}}(Z_1 + Z_2 - 2Z_3)$

   (Verify that these three are independent.)

   c) $\dfrac{1}{\sqrt{14}}(Z_1 + 2Z_2 - 3Z_3), \qquad \dfrac{1}{\sqrt{42}}(5Z_1 - 4Z_2 - Z_3)$

   (Verify that these two are independent and that they are independent of the first of the three variables listed in (b) above.)

BIBLIOGRAPHY

1. H. D. BRUNK, *An Introduction to Mathematical Statistics*, 2nd ed., Blaisdell Publishing Company, Waltham, 1965.   A good introduction to sample theory, and the weak law of large numbers (referred to, somewhat misleadingly, as simply *the* law of large numbers).

2. H. CRAMER, *Mathematical Methods of Statistics*, Princeton University Press, Princeton, 1961.   An extremely well-written summary for the mathematically mature reader.

3. W. FELLER, *An Introduction to Probability Theory and Its Applications*, Vol. I, 3rd ed., John Wiley & Sons, New York, 1968.   Excellent discussions of strong and weak laws of large numbers including cases for which the variance is infinite.

4. P. G. HOEL, *Introduction to Mathematical Statistics*, John Wiley & Sons, New York, 1962.   A good elementary discussion of random sampling.

5. H. G. TUCKER, *A Graduate Course in Probability*, Academic Press, New York, 1967.   An excellent discussion of the laws of large numbers for the mature reader.

6. S. S. WILKS, *Mathematical Statistics*, John Wiley & Sons, New York, 1962.   One of the most comprehensive discussions of sampling theory available.   This advanced text is highly recommended for the student interested in further development of this topic.

CHAPTER 6

PARAMETRIC POINT ESTIMATION

6.1 INTRODUCTION

In the previous chapter we discussed sample statistics which turned out to be unbiased and consistent estimations of both the true population mean and the variance. In the present chapter we will show how probabilistic analysis leads to these estimators. We will also obtain other, more general types of estimators for population parameters. These estimation procedures are frequently divided into two broad categories: (1) point estimation procedures which lead to parameter estimates having one single value, and (2) interval estimation procedures which lead to estimates of the probability that certain intervals contain the true parameter.

The major portion of this chapter will be devoted to various types of point estimators. In the following chapter we will describe how the most frequently used of these estimators are extended to interval estimation. Such estimated intervals are usually called confidence intervals.

6.2 MAXIMUM A POSTERIORI AND MAXIMUM LIKELIHOOD ESTIMATORS FOR DISCRETE DISTRIBUTIONS

As an introduction to the type of logic involved in the deduction of statistical estimators, the reader will find it useful to consider the following example of the a posteriori reasoning described in Section 3.4.

Example 1. Consider three urns, each containing six balls. Let there be three red and three black balls in urn I, four red and two black in urn II, and two red and four black in urn III. Let one urn be selected at random according to the a priori probabilities $\Pr\{I\} = 0.38$, $\Pr\{II\} = 0.31 = \Pr\{III\}$. A ball is selected at random from the chosen urn (with the selection of all balls being equiprobable), and the observer is asked to estimate which urn the ball was actually chosen from, knowing only the color of the ball actually chosen and the given a priori probabilities for the selection of each urn. Let the color of the ball selected from the urn be red.

The logical procedure is to compute the a posteriori probability for having chosen each of the three urns. To use the Bayes' rule procedure described in Section 3.4 we first compute the marginal probability of selecting a red ball

$$\Pr\{r\} = \Pr\{r|I\}\Pr\{I\} + \Pr\{r|II\}\Pr\{II\} + \Pr\{r|III\}\Pr\{III\}$$
$$= (\tfrac{1}{2})(0.38) + (\tfrac{2}{3})(0.31) + (\tfrac{1}{3})(0.31) = \tfrac{1}{2}. \tag{1}$$

230

The straightforward computation of a posteriori probability gives

$$\Pr\{I|r\} = \frac{\Pr\{r|I\}\,\Pr\{I\}}{\Pr\{r\}} = 0.38,$$

$$\Pr\{II|r\} = 0.413,\ \Pr\{III|r\} = 0.207. \tag{2}$$

On the basis of the information given, the observer would estimate that urn II has been chosen, since it had the largest a posteriori probability.

Although the "maximum a posteriori probability" procedure described above is quite reasonable, the observer would be ill advised to continue with further operations on the selected urn solely on the assumption that it was, in actual fact, urn II. The potential pitfalls of such a procedure are illustrated by the following example.

Example 2. Consider the problem stated in Example 1 and let the observer attempt to predict the color of the next ball selected from the chosen, but still unknown urn. If it is assumed that urn II was actually selected, then the probability of selecting a second red ball from that urn is simply the number of red balls remaining after the first red ball is picked, divided by the total number remaining,

$$\Pr\{r_2|II\} = \tfrac{3}{5}. \tag{3}$$

However, since there is no certainty that urn II was actually selected, the correct probability, on the basis of all the information available (the red ball selected on the first pick and the a priori probabilities of selecting the three urns), will be

$$\Pr\{r_2|r_1\} = \Pr\{r_2|I\}\,\Pr\{I|r_1\} + \Pr\{r_2|II\}\,\Pr\{II|r_1\} + \Pr\{r_2|III\}\,\Pr\{III|r_1\}$$

$$= (\tfrac{2}{5})\,(0.38) + (\tfrac{3}{5})\,(0.413) + (\tfrac{1}{5})\,(0.207) = (0.44). \tag{4}$$

This correct result is not only different from the $\tfrac{3}{5}$ probability, which was obtained on the erroneous assumption that urn II was in fact chosen, but it also, having a probability less than $\tfrac{1}{2}$ for the second red, predicts that a black ball will most likely be chosen on the second try. The erroneous result, having a probability of greater than $\tfrac{1}{2}$ for the second red, predicts that the ball chosen on the second try will most likely be red.

The point of this example is that there are times when sample information should not be thrown away after the parameter of principal interest has been estimated. If we make the assumption that the maximum a posteriori probability estimate is the precise value of the unknown parameter (in this case the urn number), then we throw away information contained in the nonzero a posteriori probabilities of the other possible values of the unknown parameter.

We can summarize this discussion by noting that the estimator contains only a weighted average of the information available in the form of a posteriori probabilities; it does not contain the information itself. Subsequent estimation must be based on the detailed structure of all the prior information, so a knowledge of only the value of some previous estimator (or weighted average) will not be sufficient.

If the observer of the previous example were paid off according to whether he was right about the number of the urn chosen, then he would maximize his payoff by guessing urn II whenever a red ball was selected. If, on the other hand he were paid according to whether he was right about the color predicted for the next sampling, then his optimum strategy would require guessing black whenever the first ball selected was red. With this warning on the limited interpretation which must be placed on individual sample statistics as population estimators, we can proceed to the more conventional forms of sample estimation, utilizing a similar type of logic.

In many problems we do not have any knowledge of the a priori probabilities, and it may be reasonable to assume that they are all equal. Under such circumstances we can reap the benefit of the maximum a posteriori procedure without actually having to compute the a posteriori probability for each possible event. We demonstrate this simplification by considering the following modification of the problem of Examples 1 and 2 above. (For mathematical convenience, we will use the random variable notation.)

Example 3. Let the random variable x specify the number of one of three urns which is selected at random, $\Pr\{X = k\} = \frac{1}{3}$ for $1 \le k \le 3$, with urn I having three red and three black balls, urn II having four red and two black balls, and urn III having two red and four black balls. Let $Y = 1$ if a random sample from the chosen urn produces a red ball, and let $Y = 0$ if a black ball is drawn. The a posteriori probability of X can be written as

$$\Pr\{X = k \,|\, Y = j\} = \frac{\Pr\{Y = j \,|\, X = k\} \Pr\{X = k\}}{\Pr\{Y = j\}}. \tag{5}$$

Since for all k, $\Pr\{X = k\} = \frac{1}{3}$, the only real k dependence of the right hand side of this equation is contained in the factor $\Pr\{Y = j \,|\, X = k\}$. Therefore, the value of k which maximizes this factor will maximize the left hand side, $\Pr\{X = k \,|\, Y = j\}$. In other words, the value of k which maximizes the conditional probability $\Pr\{Y = j \,|\, X = k\}$ also maximizes the a posteriori probability $\Pr\{X = k \,|\, Y = j\}$. In the present problem we have $Y = 1$, and the largest value of the conditional probability occurs for $k = 2$,

$$\Pr\{Y = 1 \,|\, X = 2\} = \tfrac{2}{3}. \tag{6}$$

This immediately shows that the maximum a posteriori estimate of X is $X = 2$.

The estimate which maximizes the forward conditional probability $\Pr\{Y = j \,|\, X = k\}$ is called the *maximum likelihood estimate*, and the probability $\Pr\{Y = j \,|\, X = k\}$ is called the *likelihood function* when viewed as a function of the random variable X. (The reader should observe that $\Pr\{Y = j \,|\, X = k\}$ does not form a probability frequency function when viewed as a function of X. It must, therefore, be given a special name.) One frequently finds the informal statement that the value of k which maximizes the likelihood function is the most likely value of X.

The careful reader may be disturbed by our reliance on the computation of a posteriori probabilities of events which have already occurred, and are, therefore, no longer probabilistic. The justification for the logic of these procedures is that the repeated use over an ensemble of many such experiments will yield a reasonably large expectation for the number of correct guesses.

With the maximum a posteriori procedure we can specify this expectation to be simply the product of the a posteriori probability times the number of experiments performed. If the experiment of Example 1 were performed n times, the expected number of correct guesses, using the maximum a posteriori procedure, would be $(0.413)n$.

In this section we have described estimators for discrete parameters of discrete probability distributions. We saw that if an a priori frequency function is given for the unknown parameter, it is reasonable to estimate the parameter by finding the value which maximizes the a posteriori probability. If no a priori distribution is given, then it is natural to assume a uniform a priori distribution. Under such circumstances, we find the most likely value of the unknown parameter to be that value which maximizes the conditional probability.

$$\text{Pr\{Particular Value of Sample Statistic} \mid \text{Particular}$$
$$\text{Value of Unknown Parameter\}}$$

This conditional probability is called "likelihood function." As such, it is a function of the unknown parameter, even though the unknown parameter is *not* random variable.

PROBLEMS

1. Consider two urns. Urn I contains two red and four black balls. Urn II contains four red and two black balls. Assume that one urn is selected at random in such a manner that the probability of selecting urn I is $\frac{2}{3}$ and the probability of selecting urn II is $\frac{1}{3}$. Suppose a ball is sampled from the selected urn and the ball turns out to be red. What are the a posteriori probabilities of having selected urn I and urn II? What is the maximum a posteriori estimate of the urn actually chosen? If there were no knowledge of the a priori probabilities what would be the maximum likelihood estimate of the urn actually selected?

2. Consider the three-urn problem of Example 3, where all urns have equal a priori probabilities. Compute the a posteriori probabilities if a second ball is drawn and also turns out to be red. Show that the maximum a posteriori estimate of the urn actually selected is II.

3. Consider a lot of N items. We sample and inspect n of these items and find that k are defective. Show that the likelihood function for the estimator of the number of defectives D in the lot is

$$\text{Pr\{}k \text{ Defective in sample} \mid D \text{ Defective in lot\}} = \frac{\binom{D}{k}\binom{N-D}{n-k}}{\binom{N}{n}}.$$

Show that the maximum likelihood estimator $\hat{D}$ is the integer specified by the inequalities

$$\frac{k(N + 1)}{n} \geq \hat{D} > \frac{k(N + 1)}{n} - 1.$$

6.3 MAXIMUM A POSTERIORI AND MAXIMUM LIKELIHOOD ESTIMATION FOR CONTINUOUS DISTRIBUTIONS

In our discussion of continuous probability, we considered several examples of the computation of an a posteriori pdf. We found such functions to be useful for computing probabilities for the input distribution to a system in terms of the observed output of the system and some known properties of the system. It is natural to define the most probable value of the input to be the value which maximizes this a posteriori pdf.

To illustrate this maximum a posteriori procedure, we reconsider a problem already discussed in Section 4.5.

Example 1. Consider a system having signal input X and independent additive noise Y, where X is $N(0, \sigma_x^2)$ and Y is $N(0, \sigma_y^2)$ distributed. How does the observer best estimate the input if he can only observe the output, $Z = X + Y$?

From our previous discussion of this problem the reader should recall that the $N(0, \sigma_x^2)$ distribution for X specifies the a priori pdf

$$f_0(x) = \frac{1}{\sqrt{2\pi}\sigma_x} \exp\left(-\frac{x^2}{2\sigma_x^2}\right). \tag{1}$$

The $N(0, \sigma_y)$ distribution for Y specifies the conditional pdf for z

$$g_0(z|x) = \frac{1}{\sqrt{2\pi}\sigma_y} \exp\left(-\frac{(z - x)^2}{2\sigma_y^2}\right). \tag{2}$$

From these two expressions we compute the marginal pdf for z

$$f_1(z) = \int_{-\infty}^{+\infty} g_0(z|x) f_0(x)\, dx = \frac{1}{\sqrt{2\pi}\sigma_z} \exp\left(-\frac{z^2}{2\sigma_z^2}\right), \tag{3}$$

where $\sigma_z^2 = \sigma_x^2 + \sigma_y^2$. (This result also follows from the general result for the distribution of the sum of two normally distributed random variables.)

Using Bayes' rule we can compute the a posteriori pdf for x, given z,

$$g_1(x|z) = \frac{g_0(z|x) f_0(x)}{f_1(z)}$$

$$= \frac{\sigma_z}{\sqrt{2\pi}\sigma_x\sigma_z} \exp\left[-\frac{1}{2\sigma_y^2}\left(\frac{x\sigma_z}{\sigma_x} - \frac{z\sigma_x}{\sigma_z}\right)^2\right]. \tag{4}$$

Since the only dependence on x is in the exponent, it is easy to see that $g_1(x|z)$ will be maximized by the value of x which makes the exponent zero. Therefore, the maximum a posteriori probability estimator of X, the signal input, is the random variable

$$\hat{X} = \frac{\sigma_x^2}{\sigma_z^2} Z \tag{5}$$

(This is seen to be the same as Eq. (11) of Section 4.5.)

The reader should note that, if we were only interested in the maximum a posteriori estimate of X, we would not really need to compute the marginal pdf, $f_1(z)$, for use in the computation of $g_1(x|z)$. We could simply observe that Eq. (4) shows that the only x dependence of $g_1(z|x)$ is contained in the product $g_0(z|x)f_0(x)$. This implies that the maximum a posteriori estimate of x will simply be the value of x which maximizes the product $g_0(z|x)f_0(x)$.

In passing, it is interesting to interpret Eq. (5) by viewing σ_x^2/σ_y^2 as a signal-to-noise ratio. This is a natural assignment because a large σ for a random variable means that a large value of that variable is fairly likely. When there is little noise, the probability of the received signal deviating significantly from the transmitted signal becomes very small. As $\sigma_y \to 0$, we see that the pdf $g_0(z|x)$, given by Eq. (2), becomes the Dirac delta function which implies that $z = x$. Therefore, σ_y, as a measure of the noise, has the desired properties. Examining Eq. (5), we see that for a large signal-to-noise ratio, $\sigma_x^2/\sigma_y^2 \gg 1$, we have $\sigma_x^2/\sigma_z^2 \approx 1$, so that $\hat{X} \approx Z$. This is in agreement with our intuitive notion that the received signal should be quite similar to the transmitted signal whenever the noise is small in comparison with the signal.

If, on the other hand, the signal-to-noise ratio is small, $\sigma_x^2/\sigma_y^2 \ll 1$, then $\sigma_x^2/\sigma_z^2 \ll 1$, and Eq. (5) shows that the value of the estimator of the transmitted signal $\hat{X}$ will be much smaller than the value of the received signal Z. This result is also in agreement with our intuitive notion that whenever the noise is much larger than the transmitted signal, the received signal amplitude will be largely due to noise. Consequently, we would estimate that the transmitted signal amplitude was much smaller than the signal amplitude actually received.

The reader should note that, although there was an a priori distribution for X, there is really only one particular value of X for any given problem. Once this input is determined, the value of the output is dependent only on the random variable Y. In other words, for any given case the output Z is actually the result of a particular value of X. This means that in any given problem, X is not a random variable at all. However, the output Z is a random variable, and so the estimator $\hat{X}$ is also a random variable. We use a particular value of the random variable $\hat{X}$ as an estimate of the particular value of the input X. This state of affairs is completely analogous to the discrete situation illustrated in the examples of the previous section. In that problem the urn was selected at random, but once it had been selected, it was one particular urn. The color of the ball selected from that urn was a random variable which was used to estimate which urn was most likely to have been chosen.

The paradoxical feature of point estimation is that it must be interpreted probabilistically even though there may not be a probability associated with the final estimate. In fact, for continuous distributions, the a posteriori probability will be nonzero only over a finite interval. When the interval shrinks to zero length for a point estimation, the associated a posteriori probability must be zero. In other words, there is zero probability that the unknown parameter actually equals the particular sample value of the estimator, or any other particular value. This difficulty is overcome by considering a finite interval which has a significant a posteriori probability associated with it by integrating the a posteriori pdf. This nonzero a posteriori probability can then be interpreted in a manner analogous to the discrete case described in the previous section. A more precise description of these nonzero probability intervals will be given when this problem is re-examined in Chapter 7, dealing with confidence intervals.

As in the discrete case of the previous section, we can achieve a considerable simplification, leading directly to the maximum likelihood procedure, by assuming a uniform a priori distribution for the unknown parameter viewed as a random variable.

Most texts, however, give a simpler interpretation of the maximum likelihood procedure, which is most conveniently illustrated by reconsidering the signal transmission problem of Example 1. We again assume that the channel noise is $N(0, \sigma_y^2)$ distributed but that there is no a priori information concerning the input signal distribution. As before, Eq. (2) gives the conditional pdf of the output, z, given a particular value of the input, x. For illustration let us assume that the value of the signal received in $z = z_0$, and plot the conditional pdf for z, given $z = z_0$, as shown by the solid curve of Fig. 1. Also shown in Fig. 1 is the pdf for z given some other value, $x = x' \neq z_0$, for the input signal.

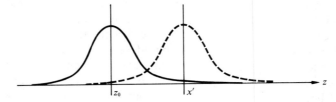

Fig. 6.1. Conditional pdf of output for two values of signal input.

Looking at this figure we would be inclined to choose z_0 over x' as the more likely input signal because it has a higher probability of yielding an output in the near vicinity of the actually observed output z. In other words, an input signal in the near vicinity of z_0 is more likely than an input signal in a vicinity of equal length centered about some other value of signal input, say x'.

Therefore, we say that $g_0(z|x)$ is the likelihood function, and the value of x which maximizes it, for some observed value of z, is called the maximum likelihood estimate of input x. In choosing $x = z_0$ over some other value $x = x'$, solely on the basis of which leads to a larger value of the pdf at the observed output z_0, we have tacitly assumed that in the absence of information concerning the input, all possible values of input x are equally likely. The actual value of output z_0 is, then, the sole criterion for choosing the most likely input.

In order to give the student further insight into the procedure we also give the explicit derivation from a posteriori reasoning using a uniform a priori distribution. The following example illustrates the application of this logic to the signal transmission problem discussed above.

Example 2. Consider the noisy transmission problem of Example 1, but take the a priori distribution of X to be uniform, so that

$$f_0(x) = \frac{1}{2M} \quad \text{for} \quad -M \le x \le M. \tag{6}$$

Using Bayes' rule, we can compute the a posteriori pdf

$$g_1(x|z) = \frac{f_0(x)g_0(z|x)}{f_1(z)} = \frac{1}{A} \exp\left[-\frac{1}{2\sigma_y^2}(z-x)^2 \right] \quad \text{for} \quad -M \le x \le M, \tag{7}$$

where we have simplified the notation by defining

$$A = \int_{-M}^{M} \exp\left[-\frac{1}{2\sigma_y^2}(z-x)^2 \right] dx. \tag{8}$$

Since A is independent of x, Eq. (7) shows that the x dependence of $g_1(x|z)$ is the same as the x dependence of $g_0(z|x)$, except for the additional obvious restriction on $g_1(x|z)$ that x lie in the range of the uniform a priori distribution. If we take M sufficiently large, the value of x which maximizes $g_1(x|z)$ will fall within this range. We therefore say that the maximum likelihood estimate of the transmitted signal is $\hat{x} = z$, in contrast with the estimate given in Eq. (5).

The above example suggests the use of the conditional pdf $g_0(z|x)$ as a likelihood function, in complete analogy with the simpler reasoning based on Fig. 1. The maximum likelihood estimate $\hat{x}$ is then the value of x which maximizes this pdf. Such a procedure is very useful for estimating from samples taken from populations with known distribution forms but containing unknown parameters.

The maximum a posteriori interpretation also permits us to extend the procedure to samples containing many elements, and represented by n-dimensional random variables.

To develop this general procedure, we define the conditional pdf for the n elements of a sample from a population with known pdf but unknown parameter θ: $g_0(x_1, x_2, x_3, \ldots, x_n|\theta)$. Of course, we know that the unknown parameter θ is not a random variable, but some specific number. The estimator for θ, however, will be a random variable, and the arguments regarding the validity of a posteriori reasoning, given previously, apply in this case. The computation of g_0 for several typical cases will be illustrated in examples below. First, however, it will be useful to develop the general procedure along the same lines as for the normally distributed single variable case of the previous example.

The a posteriori pdf for the unknown θ in terms of the n values x_i is a conditional pdf of the form $g_1(\theta|x_1, x_2, \ldots, x_n)$ for an n-element sample. This pdf is determined by the application of Bayes' rule;

$$g_1(\theta|x_1, x_2, \ldots, x_n) = \frac{g_0(x_1, x_2, \ldots, x_n|\theta)f_0(\theta)}{f_1(x_1, x_2, \ldots, x_n)}, \tag{9}$$

where

$$f_1(x_1, x_2, \ldots, x_n) = \int g_0(x_1, x_2, \ldots, x_n|\theta')f_0(\theta')\, d\theta'. \tag{10}$$

For the general maximum likelihood procedure, we assume a uniform distribution of the form

$$f_0(\theta) = \frac{1}{M_2 - M_1} \quad \text{for} \quad M_1 \le \theta \le M_2. \tag{11}$$

If Eq. (11) is substituted into Eq. (9), the factor $(M_2 - M_1)^{-1}$ in both numerator and denominator will cancel, leaving

$$g_1(\theta|x_1, x_2, \ldots, x_n) = \frac{g_0(x_1, x_2, \ldots, x_n|\theta)}{A}, \tag{12}$$

where

$$A = \int_{M_1}^{M_2} g_0(x_1, x_2, \ldots, x_n|\theta')\, d\theta', \tag{13}$$

in analogy with the single variable case of Eqs. (7) and (8).

We now simplify our procedure by observing that A is independent of θ, so that the value of θ which maximizes $g_0(x_1, x_2, \ldots, x_n|\theta)$ will also maximize the a posteriori pdf, $g_1(\theta|x_1, x_2, \ldots, x_n)$. If we are only interested in the most likely value of the parameter θ, we need only maximize $g_0(x_1, x_2, \ldots, x_n|\theta)$ with respect to θ, and thus automatically have the value of θ which maximizes $g_1(\theta|x_1, x_2, \ldots, x_n)$ even though these two functions are, in general, not equal. In other words, the value of θ_m which is the solution to the equation

$$\left. \frac{\partial g_0(x_1, x_2, \ldots, x_n|\theta)}{\partial \theta} \right|_{\theta=\theta_m} = 0 \tag{14}$$

will be the maximum likelihood estimate of the parameter θ. We can therefore use the conditional pdf $g_0(x_1, x_2, \ldots, x_n|\theta)$ as the likelihood function, just as we could in the single variable discrete case whenever there is no information concerning the unknown parameter. As mentioned previously, the maximum likelihood procedure is usually given without the above justification. The following examples show how this method can be used to obtain alternative derivations of some familiar estimators.

Example 3. *Gaussian distributions.* For estimation of variance, when the mean is known, consider n independent samples from a Gaussian distributed population with mean v_1 and variance θ. The pdf for the value of the random variable x_i for the ith sample element is then

$$g_0(x_i|\theta, v_1) = \frac{1}{\sqrt{2\pi\theta}} \exp\left[-\frac{(x_i - v_1)^2}{2\theta}\right]. \tag{15}$$

The joint pdf for the entire sample is

$$g_0(x_1, x_2, \ldots, x_n|\theta, v_1) = \frac{1}{(\sqrt{2\pi\theta})^n} \exp\left[-\frac{1}{2\theta}\sum_{i=1}^{n}(x_i - v_1)^2\right]. \tag{16}$$

If we regard v_1 as specified, then Eq. (16) is the likelihood function for the parameter θ. Rather than use this function directly in Eq. (14), it will be more convenient to note that the value of θ which maximizes the likelihood function will also maximize the natural logarithm of the likelihood function. Instead of differentiating Eq. (16) we will therefore use

$$\left.\frac{\partial \ln g_0(x_1, x_2, \ldots, x_n|\theta)}{\partial \theta}\right|_{\theta=\theta_m} = 0. \tag{17}$$

Using the pdf, given in Eq. (16), we may write

$$\ln g_0 = -\frac{n}{2}\ln 2\pi - \frac{n}{2}\ln \theta - \frac{1}{2\theta}\sum_{i=1}^{n}(x_i - v_1)^2. \tag{18}$$

Equation (17) then becomes

$$0 = \left.\frac{\partial \ln g_0}{\partial \theta}\right|_{\theta=\theta_m}$$

$$= -\frac{n}{2\theta_m} + \frac{1}{2\theta_m^2}\sum_{i=1}^{n}(x_i - v_1)^2, \tag{19}$$

which gives

$$\theta = \theta_m = \frac{1}{n}\sum_{i=1}^{n}(x_i - v_1)^2. \tag{20}$$

The reader should verify that the random variable, indicated by Eq. (20), is an unbiased and consistent estimator for the variance of the original population, provided the mean, v_1, of the original population is known.

Example 4. *Estimation of sample variance when mean is unknown.* If the actual population mean, v_1, were unknown in the above example, Eq. (20) would be of little use as a recipe for estimating. In this case we must find a pdf which uses the sample mean

$$\bar{x} = \frac{1}{n} \sum_{i=1}^{n} x_i \tag{21}$$

instead of ν_1. For this purpose we may rewrite the summation in the exponent of Eq. (20) as

$$\sum_{i=1}^{n} (x_i - \nu_1)^2 = \sum_{i=1}^{n} [(x_i - \bar{x}) + (\bar{x} - \nu_1)]^2$$

$$= \sum_{i=1}^{n} (x_i - \bar{x})^2 + 2(\bar{x} - \nu_1) \sum_{i=1}^{n} (x_i - \bar{x})$$

$$+ (\bar{x} - \nu_1)^2 \sum_{i=1}^{n} (1). \tag{22}$$

We now know that

$$\sum_{i=1}^{n} (x_i - \bar{x}) = 0,$$

$$\sum_{i=1}^{n} (1) = n,$$

so that Eq. (22) may be simplified to

$$\sum_{i=1}^{n} (x_i - \nu_1)^2 = \sum_{i=1}^{n} (x_i - \bar{x})^2 + n(\bar{x} - \nu_1)^2. \tag{23}$$

$$g_0(x_1, x_2, \ldots, x_n | \theta, \nu_1) = \frac{1}{(2\pi\theta)^{n/2}} \exp\left[-\frac{1}{2\theta} \sum_{i=1}^{n} (x_i - \bar{x})^2 - \frac{n}{2\theta} (\bar{x} - \nu_1)^2 \right]. \tag{24}$$

We know that

$$\sum_{i=1}^{n} (x_i - \bar{x})^2 \qquad \text{and} \qquad (\bar{x} - \nu_1)^2 \tag{25}$$

represent independent variables. Therefore, Eq. (24) can be interpreted as the product of a pdf for

$$\sum_{i=1}^{n} (x_i - \bar{x})^2$$

times a pdf for $(\bar{x} - \nu_1)^2$. In addition, we know that if the x_i are Gaussian distributed with mean ν_1 and variance θ, then $\bar{x} - \nu_1$ will also be Gaussian distributed with the pdf

$$h_0(\bar{x} | \theta, \nu_1) = \frac{1}{\sqrt{2\pi\theta}} \exp\left[-\frac{n}{2\theta} (\bar{x} - \nu_1)^2 \right]. \tag{26}$$

Since Eq. (23) is the product of the pdf for

$$\sum_{i=1}^{n} (x_i - \bar{x})^2$$

by the pdf for $(\bar{x} - \nu_1)^2$, we can obtain the pdf containing $\bar{x}$ instead of ν_1 by simply dividing Eq. (24) by (26):

$$u_0(x_1, x_2, \ldots, x_n, \bar{x} | \theta) = \frac{1}{(2\pi\theta)^{\frac{n-1}{2}}} \exp\left[-\frac{1}{2\theta} \sum_{i=1}^{n} (x_i - \bar{x})^2 \right]. \qquad (27)$$

Using this pdf in Eq. (17), we get the maximum likelihood estimate

$$\theta = \frac{1}{n-1} \sum_{i=1}^{n} (x_i - \bar{x})^2 . \qquad (28)$$

This result is just the estimator S^2, introduced in Chapter 5 and shown to be both unbiased and consistent.

The reader should verify that Eq. (16) can be derived directly by transforming the chi-square distribution with n degrees of freedom for the variable

$$Y = \frac{1}{\theta} \sum_{i=1}^{n} (x_i - \nu_1)^2 . \qquad (29)$$

Similarly, Eq. (27) can be derived directly by transforming the chi-square distribution with $n - 1$ degrees of freedom for the variable

$$Z = \frac{1}{\theta} \sum_{i=1}^{n} (X_i - \bar{X})^2 . \qquad (30)$$

Example 5. *Estimator of the upper limit of a uniformly distributed random variable.* Consider a random variable, uniformly distributed over the range $\alpha \leq X \leq \beta$. Let us assume that although we know the form of the distribution, we do not know the value of the upper limit, β, or the value of the lower limit, α. Let us take a n-element sample from this population, and estimate the value of β.

If we knew α and β, the joint pdf for the n uniformly distributed x_i could be viewed as a pdf conditioned upon α and β:

$$g_0(x_1, x_2, x_3, \ldots, x_n | \alpha, \beta) = \frac{1}{(\beta - \alpha)^n} \prod_{i=1}^{n} [U(x_i - \alpha) - U(x_i - \beta)], \qquad (31)$$

where $U(z)$ is the unit step function which is 1 for $z > 0$, and is 0 for $z < 0$. It is easily seen that $(\beta - \alpha)^{-n}$ will be maximized for β as small as possible, while the product of step functions will only be nonzero for $\beta > \max \{x_i\}$. We therefore conclude that the maximum likelihood estimator $\hat{\beta} = \max \{x_i\}$. We can verify this result by recalling that the CDF for the maximum, x_M, of n random variables is simply the probability that all elements will be less than, or equal to, x_M. Since we know that these variables are uniformly distributed,

$$F(x_M) = \left(\frac{x_M - \alpha}{\beta - \alpha}\right)^n. \tag{32}$$

Equation (32) leads to the pdf

$$f(x_M) = \frac{n}{\beta - \alpha} \left(\frac{x_M - \alpha}{\beta - \alpha}\right)^{n-1}. \tag{33}$$

This pdf will be maximized by the smallest value which β can assume, namely

$$\hat{\beta} = x_M. \tag{34}$$

To determine the biasedness of this estimator, we compute

$$E(X_M) = \frac{n}{\beta - \alpha} \int_\alpha^\beta \left(\frac{x_M - \alpha}{\beta - \alpha}\right)^{n-1} x_M \, dx_M$$

$$= \frac{n\beta}{n+1} + \frac{\alpha}{n+1}. \tag{35}$$

It is easily seen that this estimator is biased, unless $n \to \infty$. To check the consistency, we compute

$$E[(X_M - \beta)^2] = \int_\alpha^\beta (x_M - \beta)^2 f(x_M) \, dx_M$$

$$= \frac{2(\beta - \alpha)^2}{(n+1)(n+2)}, \tag{36}$$

which shows that this estimator is consistent.

PROBLEMS

1. Consider the signal transmission problem of Example 1 of this section. Let a second signal, identical to the first, be transmitted. Integrate $g_0(z_2|x)g_1(x|z_1)$ over x to obtain the conditional pdf of z_2 (the second received signal) for given z_1 (the first received signal). Show that the most probable value of z_2 is $\sigma_x^2 z_1/\sigma_z^2$. With Example 1 as a basis, why would you expect this answer intuitively?

2. Consider a sequence of n Bernoulli trials which yield k successes. Let the a priori pdf for the probability of success on a single trial be $f(p) = (r + 1)p^r$ for $0 \le p \le 1$, where r is positive. Show that the a posteriori pdf of p is

$$q(p|k) = f(p)\binom{n}{k} p^k (1 - p)^{n-k} A,$$

where

$$A^{-1} = \int_0^1 f(p) \binom{n}{k} p^k (1 - p)^{n-k} \, dp,$$

which is independent of p. Show that the value of p which maximizes $q(p|k)$ is

$$\hat{p} = \frac{r + k}{r + n}.$$

3. Consider the estimator for p obtained in the previous problem,

$$\hat{p} = \frac{r + k}{r + n}.$$

a) Show that

$$E(\hat{p}|p) = \frac{r + np}{r + n},$$

so that $\hat{p}$ is a biased estimator.

b) Show that the mean square deviation is

$$E[(\hat{p} - p)^2|p] = \frac{np(1 - p) + r^2 (1 - p)^2}{(r + n)^2},$$

which tends to zero as $n \to \infty$, so that the estimator is consistent.

4. Consider an experiment in which k trials are required to obtain the first success. Let the a priori pdf for the probability of success on a single trial be $f(p) = (r + 1)p^r$ for $0 \le p \le 1$. Show that the maximum a posteriori estimator for p is

$$\hat{p} = \frac{r + 1}{r + k}.$$

Can this estimator be obtained from the answer to Problem 2 by setting $k = 1$? Explain.

5. Let the random variable X, with negative exponential pdf $\mu e^{-\mu x}$, represent a transmitted signal, and let the random variable Y, with pdf $\lambda e^{-\lambda y}$, represent the noise added to the signal by a transmission channel. Then the random variable $Z = X + Y$ is the actual signal received.

a) Show that

$$f_0(x) g_0(z|x) = \lambda \mu e^{+x(\lambda - \mu) - \lambda z} U(z - x).$$

b) Show that

$$f_1(z) = \int f_0(x) g_0(z|x) \, dx$$

$$= \frac{\lambda \mu (e^{-\lambda z} - e^{-\mu z})}{\mu - \lambda}.$$

c) Show that the value of x which maximizes $g_1(x|z)$, i.e., the maximum a posteriori estimate of x, is

$$\hat{x} = 0 \text{ for } \lambda < \mu,$$

$$\hat{x} = z \text{ for } \lambda > \mu.$$

d) Show that, for $\lambda > \mu$

$$E(\hat{x}|x) = 1/\lambda + x,$$

so that $\hat{X}$ is a biased estimator of X.

6. Let the random variable X, $N(\mu, \sigma_0^2)$ distributed, be the transmitted signal. Let Y, $N(0, \sigma_1^2)$ distributed, be the noise in the transmission line. Let $Z = X + Y$ be the received signal. Compute $g_0(z|x)$, $f_1(z)$, $g_1(x|z)$, and find the value of x which maximizes $g_1(x|z)$.

7. Let the random variable X, with known a priori pdf $f_0(x) = 2x$, $0 \le x \le 1$, be the transmitted signal. Let the random variable Y, with the known a priori pdf $f_0(y) = 2y$, $0 \le y \le 1$, be the corrupting noise. Let the random variable $Z = X + Y$ be the received signal. Show that

a) $g_0(z|x) = 2(z - x)$.
b) $f_1(z) = \frac{2}{3} z^3$ for $0 \le z \le 1$,
    $f_1(z) = -2z(z - 1) + 2(z - 1)^2 + \frac{2}{3} z^3 - \frac{2}{3}(z - 1)^3$ for $1 \le z \le 2$.
c) the value of x, which maximizes $g_1(x|z)$, is $\hat{x} = z/2$.

8. Let the random variable X, with a priori pdf $f_0(x) = 2x$, $0 \le x \le 1$, be the transmitted signal. Let the random variable Y, with pdf $2(1 - y)$, $0 \le y \le 1$, be the corrupting noise. Let the random variable $Z = X + Y$ be the received signal. Show that

a) $g_0(z|x) = 2(1 - z + x)$.
b) the value of x, which maximizes $g_1(x|z)$, is given by

$$\hat{x} = \frac{z - 1}{2} \quad \text{for} \quad z \ge 1,$$

$$\hat{x} = 0 \quad \text{for} \quad z \le 1.$$

9. Consider an experiment to determine the probability p that a given coin will fall heads. Let us toss the coin n times and observe the number k of heads. Show that the likelihood function is $\binom{n}{k} p^k (1 - p)^{n-k}$, and show that this function is maximized for $\bar{p} = k/n$.

10. We wish to estimate the number R of red balls in an urn containing R red and B black balls. We sample n of these balls with replacement, and find that there are n_1 red balls in our sample.

a) Construct the likelihood function for estimating R.
b) Show that this function is maximized by

$$\bar{R} = \frac{n_1 B}{n - n_1}.$$

11. In Example 2 of Section 6.3, what is A in the limit $M \to \infty$? Show that in this limit the a posteriori pdf becomes a Gaussian in $z - x$.

12. Let each of the n outcomes of an experiment fall into one of k categories. Let $\hat{n}_i$ represent the number of experimentally observed outcomes which fall into category i, so that

$$\sum_{i=1}^{k} \hat{n}_i = n .$$

In the absence of more precise information we assume that the outcomes are multinomially distributed with ff

$$f_{n_1, n_2, n_3, \ldots, n_k} = \frac{n!}{\prod\limits_{i=1}^{k} n_i!} \prod_{i=1}^{k} (p_i)^{n_i} .$$

If we substitute the experimentally observed $\hat{n}_i$ for the n_i, then this function can serve as a likelihood function which we can maximize with respect to the unknown p_i's. Show that the maximization of this ff with respect to each of $k - 1$ independent p_i's requires that

$$\bar{p}_i = \frac{\hat{n}_i}{\hat{n}_k} \bar{p}_k , \qquad i < k ,$$

where

$$\bar{p}_k = 1 - \sum_{i=1}^{k-1} \bar{p}_i \qquad \text{and} \qquad \hat{n}_k = n - \sum_{i=1}^{k-1} \hat{n}_i .$$

Use these results to show that the maximum likelihood estimate for each p_i is

$$\bar{p}_i = \frac{\hat{n}_i}{n} .$$

13. Assume that we wish to estimate the probability of success p by counting the number of trials to the first success. Write the likelihood function for k trials to the first success with probability p for success on each individual trial. Show that for a given k this likelihood function is maximized by

$$\bar{p} = \frac{1}{k} .$$

14. Repeat the preceding problem, but with k the number of trials from beginning to the jth success. Show that this time the likelihood function is maximized by

$$\bar{p} = \frac{j}{k} .$$

15. Consider an n-element sample from a uniformly distributed population with $0 \le x \le \beta$. Show that twice the sample mean is an unbiased estimator of the unknown upper limit β, if the lower limit is known to be zero, i.e.,

$$E(2\bar{X}) = \beta .$$

a) Show that the mean square deviation of this estimator is

$$E(2\bar{X} - \beta)^2 = \frac{\beta^2}{3n} .$$

b) What can we conclude concerning the usefulness of this estimator compared with that given by Eq. (36)?

16. Consider a uniformly distributed random variable X, $\alpha \leq x \leq \beta$, where neither the upper nor the lower limits are known. Show that for an n-element sample the maximum likelihood estimator for the lower limit is the smallest element. Show that this smallest element has the pdf

$$f(x_m) = \frac{n(\beta - x_m)^{n-1}}{(\beta - \alpha)^n}.$$

Use this result to show that

$$E(X_m) = \frac{n\alpha}{n + 1} + \frac{\beta}{n + 1},$$

$$E(X_m - \alpha)^2 = \frac{2(\beta - \alpha)^2}{(n + 1)(n + 2)}.$$

17. Consider Example 5 of Section 6.3, with α known to have the particular value α_0. Show that

$$y = \frac{n + 1}{n} x_M - \frac{\alpha_0}{n}$$

is now an unbiased estimator of the upper limit, β. Show that

$$E(Y - \beta)^2 = \frac{(\beta - \alpha)^2}{n(n + 2)}.$$

18. Consider the signal transmission problem of Example 1 of this section, and let the same signal be transmitted a second time with the second received signal being denoted by z_2 and the first received signal by z_1. Using the a priori input pdf given in Eq. (1), compute the a posteriori pdf for x and show that the maximum a posteriori estimate for x is

$$x_0 = \frac{z_1 + z_2}{2 + \dfrac{\sigma_y^2}{\sigma_z^2}}.$$

6.4 BAYES ESTIMATION

In Sections 6.2 and 6.3 the computed a posteriori probability has been employed to determine the maximum a posteriori estimate of the value for some unknown parameter. In the following discussion we will use a posteriori probabilities in the computation of the values of Bayes estimators. It will be seen that, in general, the Bayes estimate is not equal to the maximum a posteriori estimate.

The reader should recall from Section 5.6 that if we have two random variables X and Y, with an assumed relation, generally nonlinear, of the form

$$Y = \phi(X), \tag{1}$$

then the functional form for $\phi(X)$ which minimizes the expectation of the square deviation (a measure of the extent to which Eq. (1) is not satisfied),

$$E[Y - \phi(X)]^2 , \tag{2}$$

is given by

$$\phi(X) = E(Y|X) . \tag{3}$$

This function is frequently called the Bayes estimate of Y given some particular value of X. We illustrate the application of this procedure with the following examples. These examples are not really sampling problems, but rather probability problems.

Example 1. Consider the problem of Example 1, Section 6.2, and let the random variable X take on the values 1, 2, or 3, according to whether the selected urn is I, II, or III, respectively. We can then use the a posteriori probabilities given in Eq. (1) of Section 6.2 to compute the a posteriori expectation, or Bayes estimate, of X.

We may write

$$E(X|r) = \sum_{k=1}^{3} k \Pr\{X = k|r\} = \tfrac{17}{9} . \tag{4}$$

The reader should recall that the maximum a posteriori probability estimate for X, computed in Example 1 of Section 6.2 was $X = 2$, which is close to, but not equal to, the Bayes estimate of X.

Example 2. Consider a transmitted signal which has an a priori pdf

$$f_0(x) = \mu\, e^{-\mu x}\, U(x). \tag{5}$$

The signal is sent through a channel which adds a noise y having pdf

$$h(y) = \nu\, e^{-\nu y}\, U(y), \qquad 0 < \mu < \nu. \tag{6}$$

If we denote the received signal by $Z = X + Y$, then the conditional pdf for Z, given x, is

$$g_0(z|x) = h(z - x) = \nu\, e^{-(z-x)\nu}\, U(z - x). \tag{7}$$

The marginal pdf for z is easily computed:

$$f_1(z) = \int g_0(z|x)\, f_0(x)\, dx$$

$$= \mu\nu\, e^{-z\nu} \int_0^z e^{-x(\mu - \nu)}\, dx$$

$$= \frac{e^{-z\mu} - e^{-z\nu}}{\dfrac{1}{\mu} - \dfrac{1}{\nu}} . \tag{8}$$

This result can be used to compute the a posteriori pdf

$$g_1(x|z) = \frac{g_0(z|x) f_0(x)}{f_1(x)}$$

$$= \frac{(\nu - \mu) e^{-zv - x(\mu - \nu)}}{e^{-z\mu} - e^{-zv}}, \qquad 0 \le x \le z. \qquad (9)$$

Using this pdf we can compute the a posteriori expectation of X (or Bayes estimate), as

$$E(X|z) = \int_0^z g_1(x|z)x \, dx$$

$$= \frac{z}{1 - e^{-z(\nu - \mu)}} - \frac{1}{\nu - \mu}. \qquad (10)$$

It is interesting to compare this result with the "maximum a posteriori probability density estimate." It is easily seen that since $\mu < \nu$, the pdf $g_1(x|z)$ will increase with increasing x. Now z is the largest possible value of x (recall that the noise y can never be negative), so $g_1(x|z)$ will be maximized for $x = z$. Since this estimate represents the extreme limit, we would expect that $E(X|z) < z$ which is easily seen, from Eq. (10), to be true. It is particularly interesting to compare these results in the limit $\mu \to \nu$.

For μ close to ν, we see that the dependence of $g_1(x|z)$ on x becomes very weak and in the limit

$$\lim_{\mu \to \nu} g_1(x|z) = \frac{1}{z}.$$

This implies that the maximum a posteriori probability estimate could be anything in the range $0 \le x \le z$. The Bayes estimate, in this limit, is found by taking the limiting form of Eq. (10)

$$\lim_{\mu \to \nu} E(X|z) = \frac{z}{2}.$$

We have given two examples in which the Bayes estimate differs from the maximum a posteriori probability estimate. The reader can easily verify that the two estimators will be identical whenever the a posteriori pdf is symmetric, about a single peak, in the unknown variable x. The reader should verify that the a posteriori pdf in Example 1 of Section 6.3 has just such a symmetry, so that the Bayes and maximum a posteriori probability estimators would be identical.

PROBLEMS

1. Consider a transmitted signal which has a pdf $f_0(x) = 2x$, $0 \le x \le 1$, sent through a channel. It adds the random variable Y which happens to be $U(0, 1)$ distributed. Let the received signal be $Z = X + Y$, and

a) compute $f_1(z)$,

b) compute $g_1(x|z)$,

c) show that the Bayes estimate for x is

$$E(X|z) = \frac{2}{3} z \qquad \text{for} \qquad z \leq 1,$$

$$= \frac{2}{3z} (z^2 - z + 1) \qquad \text{for} \qquad z \geq 1.$$

d) Show that the maximum likelihood estimate for x would be

$$\hat{x} = z \qquad \text{for} \qquad z \leq 1,$$

$$= 1 \qquad \text{for} \qquad z \geq 1.$$

2. Consider a pair of random variables, X, Y, distributed bivariate normal $N(\mu_1, \mu_2, \sigma_1^2, \sigma_2^2, \rho)$. Show that the Bayes estimate of Y for given X is

$$E(Y|x) = \mu_2 + \frac{\rho \sigma_2}{\sigma_1} (x - \mu_1).$$

3. Consider the trinomial distribution characterized by the joint ff

$$f_{k_1, k_2} = \frac{n!}{k_1! \, k_2! \, (n - k_1 - k_2)!} \, p_1^{k_1} p_2^{k_2} (1 - p_1 - p_2)^{n - k_1 - k_2}.$$

Show that the marginal ff's for k_1 and k_2 are just $B(p_1, n)$ and $B(p_2, n)$, respectively, so that

$$E(k_1) = np_1, \qquad E(k_2) = np_2,$$

$$\text{var}(k_1) = np_1(1 - p_1), \qquad \text{var}(k_2) = np_2(1 - p_2).$$

Show that the conditional ff

$$f_{k_2|k_1} = \binom{n - k_1}{k_2} \left(\frac{p_2}{1 - p_1} \right)^{k_2} \left(\frac{1 - p_1 - p_2}{1 - p_1} \right)^{n - k_1 - k_2},$$

so that the Bayes estimate of k_2 given k_1 is

$$E(k_2|k_1) = (n - k_1) \left(\frac{p_2}{1 - p_1} \right).$$

4. Consider Problem 1 of Section 6.2, and use the a posteriori probabilities computed there to compute the Bayes estimate of the urn number actually selected.

6.5 SIMPLE REGRESSION

The simplest type of estimator for Y based on some observed X is the linear relation

$$\hat{Y} = \alpha X + \beta. \tag{1}$$

This equation arises naturally as the Bayes estimate when X and Y are joint normally distributed,

$$N(\nu_x, \nu_y, \sigma_x^2, \sigma_y^2, \rho_{xy}).$$

In Section 4.6 we saw that, for such a distribution,

$$E(Y|X) = \alpha X + \beta, \tag{2}$$

where

$$\alpha = \sigma_y \rho_{xy}/\sigma_x, \tag{3}$$

$$\beta = \nu_y - \nu_x \sigma_y \rho_{xy}/\sigma_x. \tag{4}$$

In most practical situations we do not know the parameters of the joint distribution of X and Y. This means that before we can use a relation such as Eq. (1) for predicting or estimating Y when X is given, we must first estimate α and β.

To estimate α and β we sample from the X, Y population in such a way that each of the n sample elements is a pair x_i, y_i. Since X and Y are joint normally distributed, the joint pdf for a sample pair can be written (see Section 4.6)

$$f(x_i, y_i) = f(y_i|x_i)f(x_i), \tag{5}$$

or

$$f(x_i, y_i) = \frac{1}{\sqrt{2\pi}\sigma_y \sqrt{1 - \rho_{xy}^2}} \exp\left[-\frac{(y_i - \alpha x_i - \beta)^2}{2\sigma_y^2(1 - \rho_{xy}^2)}\right]$$

$$\times \frac{1}{\sqrt{2\pi}\sigma_x} \exp\left[-\frac{(x_i - \nu_x)^2}{2\sigma_x^2}\right], \tag{6}$$

where α and β are given by Eqs. (3) and (4). With this expression, the joint pdf for the entire sample can be written

$$\prod_{i=1}^{n} f(x_i, y_i) = (2\pi\sigma_x\sigma_y \sqrt{1 - \rho_{xy}^2})^{-n} \exp\left[-\sum_{i=1}^{n} \frac{(x_i - \nu_x)^2}{2\sigma_x^2}\right]$$

$$\times \exp\left[-\sum_{i=1}^{n} \frac{(y_i - \alpha x_i - \beta)^2}{2\sigma_y^2(1 - \rho_{xy}^2)}\right]. \tag{7}$$

Now this joint pdf can be viewed as a pdf for the sample elements, conditioned on the particular values of α and β. This conditioned pdf can in turn be interpreted as a likelihood function, so that the most likely values of α and β are those which maximize Eq. (7). All of the α and β dependence of Eq. (7) is contained in the last factor on the right-hand side, so we use it as the modified likelihood function

$$L' = \exp\left[-\frac{\sum_{i=1}^{n}(y_i - \alpha x_i - \beta)^2}{2\sigma_y^2(1 - \rho_{xy}^2)}\right]. \tag{8}$$

It is easily seen that L' will be maximized by the values of α and β which minimize the sum of the square deviations

$$d^2 = \sum_{i=1}^{n} (y_i - \alpha x_i - \beta)^2. \tag{9}$$

This expression can be viewed as the particular sample value of the sample statistic

$$D^2 = \sum_{i=1}^{n} (Y_i - \alpha X_i - \beta)^2. \tag{10}$$

The reader should note that both Eqs. (9) and (10) are quite different from the expectation of the mean square deviation given in Eq. (2) of Section 6.4.

In order to put Eq. (9) in a convenient form, we add and subtract $\bar{y} - \alpha \bar{x}$ inside the parentheses to get

$$d^2 = \sum_{i=1}^{n} [(y_i - \bar{y}) - \alpha(x_i - \bar{x}) + (\bar{y} - \alpha\bar{x} - \beta)]^2. \tag{11}$$

Expanding the square of the trinomial on the right side of Eq. (11), we obtain

$$d^2 = \sum_{i=1}^{n} (y_i - \bar{y})^2 + \alpha^2 \sum_{i=1}^{n} (x_i - \bar{x})^2 + n(\bar{y} - \alpha\bar{x} - \beta)^2$$

$$- 2\alpha \sum_{i=1}^{n} (y_i - \bar{y})(x_i - \bar{x}) + 2(\bar{y} - \alpha\bar{x} - \beta) \sum_{i=1}^{n} (y_i - \bar{y})$$

$$- 2\alpha(\bar{y} - \alpha\bar{x} - \beta) \sum_{i=1}^{n} (x_i - \bar{x}). \tag{12}$$

Recalling the definition of $\bar{x}$ and $\bar{y}$, we have

$$\sum_{i=1}^{n} (x_i - \bar{x}) = 0 = \sum_{i=1}^{n} (y_i - \bar{y}) \tag{13}$$

so the last two terms of Eq. (12) are zero. If we use the notation

$$(n - 1)s_y^2 = \sum_{i=1}^{n} (y_i - \bar{y})^2 ,$$

$$(n - 1)s_x^2 = \sum_{i=1}^{n} (x_i - \bar{x})^2 ,$$

$$(n - 1)v_{xy} = \sum_{i=1}^{n} (x_i - \bar{x})(y_i - \bar{y})$$

(which is the natural notation for particular sample values of the sample statistics S_x, S_y, and V_{xy}, defined in the previous chapter), then Eq. (12) can be rewritten as

$$\frac{d^2}{n - 1} = s_y^2 + \alpha^2 s_x^2 + \frac{n}{n - 1} (\bar{y} - \alpha\bar{x} - \beta)^2 - 2\alpha\, v_{xy}. \tag{14}$$

To find the values of α and β which minimize this expression, we compute the partial derivatives of d^2 with respect to α and β, and set each of the resulting expressions equal to zero. Thus,

$$\frac{1}{n-1} \frac{\partial(d^2)}{\partial\alpha} = 2\alpha_m s_x^2 - \frac{2\bar{x}n}{n-1} (\bar{y} - \alpha_m \bar{x} - \beta) - 2v_{xy} = 0 , \tag{15a}$$

$$\frac{1}{(n-1)} \frac{\partial(d^2)}{\partial\beta} = - \frac{n}{n-1} (\bar{y} - \alpha_m \bar{x} - \beta_m) = 0 . \tag{15b}$$

Equation (15b) implies that the second term of Eq. (15a) must be identically zero, and the remaining terms in Eq. (15a) do not contain β. Therefore, Eq. (15a) yields the unique solution for α_m

$$\alpha_m = v_{xy}/s_x^2 . \tag{16}$$

If we substitute this expression into Eq. (15b) we obtain the unique solution for β_m:

$$\beta_m = \bar{y} - \bar{x} \frac{v_{xy}}{s_x^2} . \tag{17}$$

The reader should compare the results of this discussion with those found (in our discussion of continuous probability) for the values of α and β which minimize the expectation of the sum of the square deviations:

$$D^2 = \sum_{i=1}^{n} (Y_i - \alpha X_i - \beta)^2 . \tag{18}$$

In that discussion we found that the appropriate expressions had the same form as Eqs. (16) and (17), except that instead of the particular sample values $\bar{x}$, $\bar{y}$, s_x^2, s_y^2, v_{xy}, we used the expectations of the corresponding sample statistics, which could be expressed in terms of the actual population parameters, $E(X) = \mu_x$, $E(Y) = \mu_y$, $E(s_x^2) = \sigma_x^2$, etc. These analogies are conveniently summarized in Table 1.

Table 1

COMPARISON OF LEAST SQUARES AND MINIMUM EXPECTED
DEVIATION PROCEDURES

	Present procedure (least squares)	Probability procedure (minimum expected deviation)
Quantity minimized	$\sum_{i=1}^{n} (y_i - \alpha x_i - \beta)^2$	$\sum_{i=1}^{n} (Y_i - \alpha X_i - \beta)^2$
Minimizing α	$\dfrac{v_{xy}}{s_x^2}$	$\dfrac{\sigma_x \sigma_y \rho_{xy}}{\sigma_x^2}$
Minimizing β	$\bar{y} - \dfrac{\bar{x} v_{xy}}{s_x^2}$	$\mu_y - \dfrac{\mu_x \sigma_x \sigma_y \rho_{xy}}{\sigma_x^2}$

The correspondence described in this table enables us to prescribe sample statistics which serve as estimators for the true population values of the parameters α and β. We merely replace the particular sample values used in Eqs. (16) and (17) by the corresponding sample statistics whose expected values are given by the population parameters used in the last column of Table 1.

$$\hat{\alpha} = \frac{V_{xy}}{S_x^2} , \tag{19}$$

$$\hat{\beta} = \bar{Y} - \bar{X} \frac{V_{xy}}{S_x^2} , \tag{20}$$

where $\hat{\alpha}$ and $\hat{\beta}$ are now random variables and are called the linear least square estimators of α and β.

The reader should note that although V_{xy} is an unbiased estimator of $\sigma_x \sigma_y \rho_{xy}$, and S_x^2 is an unbiased estimator of σ_x^2, $E(\hat{\alpha})$ is not generally equal to $\sigma_x \sigma_y \rho_{xy}/\sigma_x^2$. Therefore, $\hat{\alpha}$ and $\hat{\beta}$ are generally biased estimators of the corresponding minimum expected deviation quantities shown in the last column of Table 1. They can, however, be shown to be consistent estimators for these quantities. As a related difficulty we see that although the particular sample values of $\hat{\alpha}$ and $\hat{\beta}$ will always minimize d^2 of Eq. (10), $\hat{\alpha}$ and $\hat{\beta}$ may not be the sample statistics which minimize $E(\hat{\alpha} - \alpha)^2$ and $E(\hat{\beta} - \beta)^2$. Nevertheless, these least squares estimators are widely used because the procedure is reasonably accurate for many cases and it is easy to apply in a systematic manner. A typical application is illustrated by the following example.

Example 1. Consider a 10-element sample from a joint population. The values of the random variables are given in Table 2. For these values we can easily compute the particular values of the sample statistics

$$\bar{x} = 3.9 ,$$

$$\bar{y} = 7.1 .$$

Table 2

VALUES OF THE JOINT RANDOM VARIABLES X AND Y
FOR A PARTICULAR 10-ELEMENT SAMPLE

i	1	2	3	4	5	6	7	8	9	10
x_i	4	5	3	2	5	2	6	4	3	5
y_i	8	8	6	7	8	5	9	8	5	7

$$s_x^2 = \frac{1}{9} \sum_{i=1}^{10} (x_i - \bar{x})^2 = 1.88$$

$$s_y^2 = 1.88$$

$$v_{xy} = \frac{1}{9} \sum_{i=1}^{10} (x_i - \bar{x})(y_i - \bar{y}) = 1.46$$

The estimate of the linear relation between X and Y, which gives the minimum square deviation, is then

$$Y = 0.78\ X + 4.1. \tag{21}$$

This linear relation is frequently called the regression line of Y on X, and α and β are called the regression coefficients. If we are only interested in this regression line, then we need not compute s_y^2, since it does not appear in either Eq. (16) or Eq. (17). Furthermore, we do not need to compute the factor $(n - 1)^{-1}$ in s_x^2 or v_{xy}, because only the ratio of these two quantities is used in Eqs. (16) and (17), so that the identical factors of $(n - 1)^{-1}$ cancel.

The reader should carefully note the distinction between the least squares fitting procedure described in this section, and the minimization of expected square deviation discussed in Sections 4.6 and 6.4 and summarized in Table 1 of this section. In the minimization of the expected square deviation, we pretended that we knew the actual values of the population parameters. We showed that if the parameters α and β were set equal to the appropriate expressions involving these population parameters, then the expectation of the square of the deviation, $E(Y - \alpha X - \beta)^2$, would be minimized with respect to α and β. However, we must usually sample in order to estimate the values of the population parameters such as $\mu_x, \mu_y, \sigma_x, \sigma_y, \rho_{xy}$. Since we are usually unsure of the values of the population parameters, we cannot find the values of α and β which minimize the expectation of the square deviation, $E(Y - \alpha X - \beta)^2$. The best we can do is minimize the particular sample value of the square derivation, or the sum of the squares given by Eq. (9).

In this sense the "minimum expectation of square deviation" procedure can serve as a justification of the least squares procedure, since it connects this least squares procedure with certain parameters of the distribution of the actual population from which the sample is taken.

It is possible to characterize the assumed linear relation between Y and X in a different manner by interchanging the roles of Y and X in the preceding analysis so that we obtain a regression line of X on Y:

$$\hat{X} = \alpha'\ Y + \beta' \tag{22}$$

where the least squares estimators for α' and β' are of the same form as those given by Eq. (19) and (20), except that the roles of x and y are interchanged.

$$\hat{\alpha}' = \frac{V_{xy}}{S_y^2}, \tag{23}$$

$$\hat{\beta}' = \bar{X} - \frac{\bar{Y} V_{xy}}{S_y^2}. \tag{24}$$

The student will find it instructive to derive these estimators (see Problem 2 at the end of this section).

If the regression line gives the true relation between X and Y, then we would expect both X on Y line, and Y on X line, to give the same geometric line. To compare these two regression lines, we rewrite Eq. (22) by subtracting β' from each side and dividing each side by α'.

Thus,

$$Y = \frac{X}{\alpha'} - \frac{\beta'}{\alpha'}.$$

Now, this equation will represent the same straight line as given by Eq. (1) only when

$$\alpha' = \frac{1}{\alpha}, \qquad \beta' = -\beta\alpha'. \tag{25}$$

The reader can easily verify that this will only occur when $v_{xy} = \pm s_x s_y$. Under these circumstances we would estimate the correlation coefficient $\rho_{xy} = \pm 1$. Unless such a complete correlation is found in the sample, the regression lines will be different. This difference serves as some crude measure of the accuracy of the least squares procedure for estimating the regression coefficients. We can also distinguish between Eqs. (1) and (22) by noting that the former provides an estimate of Y given X, while the latter provides an estimate of X given Y.

The least squares procedure can be easily extended to the estimation of the coefficients in a nonlinear relation, as shown in the following example.

Example 2. Consider the random variables Y and X with the assumed relation

$$Y = \gamma X^2 + \alpha X + \beta. \tag{26}$$

We must find the values of the parameters α, β, γ which minimize the sum of the square deviations

$$d^2 = \sum_{i=1}^{n} (y_i - \gamma x_i^2 - \alpha x_i - \beta)^2. \tag{27}$$

To put this expression in the appropriate form for minimizing, we add and subtract $\bar{y} - \gamma\overline{x^2} - \alpha\bar{x}$, where we have defined

$$\overline{x^2} = \frac{1}{n} \sum_{i=1}^{n} x_i^2. \tag{28}$$

With these substitutions we can express Eq. (27) in the form analogous to Eq. (11):

$$d^2 = \sum_{i=1}^{n} [(y_i - \bar{y}) - \gamma(x_i^2 - \overline{x^2}) - \alpha(x_i - \bar{x}) + (\bar{y} - \gamma\overline{x^2} - \alpha\bar{x} - \beta)]^2.$$

If we expand the square and eliminate the terms linear in $y_i - \bar{y}$, $x_i^2 - \overline{x^2}$, $x_i - \bar{x}$ by performing the sums over i to get zero, recalling the definitions of $\bar{x}$, $\bar{y}$, $\overline{x^2}$ and the procedure used in Eq. (13), we obtain

$$d^2 = \sum_{i=1}^{n} (y_i - \bar{y})^2 + \gamma^2 \sum_{i=1}^{n} (x_i^2 - \bar{x^2})^2 + \alpha^2 \sum_{i=1}^{n} (x_i - \bar{x})^2$$

$$+ n(\bar{y} - \gamma\bar{x^2} - \alpha\bar{x} - \beta)^2 - 2\gamma \sum_{i=1}^{n} (y_i - \bar{y})(x_i^2 - \bar{x^2})$$

$$- 2\alpha \sum_{i=1}^{n} (y_i - \bar{y})(x_i - \bar{x}) + 2\alpha\gamma \sum_{i=1}^{n} (x_i^2 - \bar{x^2})(x_i - \bar{x}). \qquad (29)$$

To find the values of α, β, γ which minimize this expression, we compute the partial derivatives of d^2 with respect to α, β, γ, and set these three expressions equal to zero, i.e.,

$$0 = \frac{1}{(n-1)} \frac{\partial(d^2)}{\partial\gamma}$$

$$= 2\gamma\sigma_{x^2}^2 - \frac{2\bar{x^2}n}{n-1}(\bar{y} - \bar{x^2}\gamma - \alpha\bar{x} - \beta) - 2v_{x^2,\,y} + 2\alpha v_{x^2,\,x}, \qquad (30a)$$

$$0 = \frac{1}{(n-1)} \frac{\partial(d^2)}{\partial\alpha}$$

$$= 2\alpha\sigma_x^2 - \frac{2n\bar{x}}{n-1}(\bar{y} - \gamma\bar{x^2} - \alpha\bar{x} - \beta) - 2v_{x,\,y} + 2\gamma v_{x^2}\,x, \qquad (30b)$$

$$0 = \frac{\partial(d^2)}{\partial\beta} = n(\bar{y} - \gamma\bar{x^2} - \alpha\bar{x} - \beta), \qquad (30c)$$

where we have introduced the simplifying notations

$$\sigma_{x^2}^2 = \frac{1}{n-1} \sum_{i=1}^{n} (x_i^2 - \overline{x^2})^2,$$

$$v_{x^2,\,y} = \frac{1}{n-1} \sum_{i=1}^{n} (x_i^2 - \overline{x^2})(y_i - \bar{y}),$$

$$v_{x^2,\,x} = \frac{1}{n-1} \sum_{i=1}^{n} (x_i^2 - \overline{x^2})(x_i - \bar{x}),$$

and used $\sigma_x^2 = s_x^2$ for consistency. If we use Eq. (30c) in Eqs. (30a) and (30b), we obtain the two simultaneous equations for α and γ:

$$\gamma\sigma_{x^2}^2 + \alpha v_{x^2,\,x} = v_{x^2,\,y}, \qquad (31a)$$

$$\gamma v_{x^2,\,x} + \alpha\sigma_x^2 = v_{x,\,y}. \qquad (31b)$$

These linear inhomogeneous equations can be solved simultaneously for α and γ to obtain the minimizing values

$$\alpha_m = \frac{(\sigma_{x^2}^2 \, v_{x, \, y} - v_{x^2, \, y} \, v_{x^2, \, x})}{\Delta},$$

$$\gamma_m = \frac{(\sigma_x^2 \, v_{x^2, \, y} - v_{x^2, \, x} \, v_{x, \, y})}{\Delta},$$

(32)

where Δ is the determinant of the homogeneous system,

$$\Delta = \sigma_{x^2}^2 \, \sigma_x^2 - v_{x^2, \, x}^2.$$

(33)

The expressions for α_m and γ_m can now be used in Eq. (30c) to determine β_m. The reader should note that if $n \leq 2$, we will have $\Delta = 0$ regardless of the value of the sample elements. This is a manifestation of the requirement that the number of elements in the sample (or number of data points) be at least as large as the number of parameters to be determined in the procedure.

PROBLEMS

1. Consider the 12-element sample, from a jointly distributed population, given by the following table.

i	1	2	3	4	5	6	7	8	9	10	11	12
x_i	1	2	2	3	4	5	6	6	8	8	10	10
y_i	3.2	1.8	2.6	5.2	4.3	6	6	3.8	4.4	6.7	8	9.2

Compute $\bar{x}$, $\bar{y}$, v_{xy}, and s_x^2 for this sample. Show that the regression line of Y upon X is $Y = 0.59 \, X + 1.9$.

2. Let the regression line of X upon Y be of the form $X = \alpha' Y + \beta'$. Derive β' by the following steps:

   a) Express the sum of the square derivations in a form analogous to Eq. (11) of Section 6.5.

   b) Expand and simplify to obtain the form analogous to Eq. (14) of Section 6.5.

   c) Compute the partial derivatives with respect to α' and β' and set these expressions equal to zero to obtain the least squares estimates of α' and β' given by Eqs. (23) and (24).

3. Compute the regression lines of X upon Y for (a) the sample elements given in Table 2 of Section 6.5, and (b) the sample elements given in Problem 1 above.

4. Show that Eqs. (25) will only be satisfied for $v_{xy} = s_x s_y$, where we use the least squares estimates for α, β, α', β'.

5. Consider the 13-element sample given in the following table:

i	1	2	3	4	5	6	7	8	9	10	11	12	13
x_i	0	1	1	2	2	2.5	3	3	4	4	4.5	5	5
y_i	1.5	0.7	2.2	3.8	3	5.1	4.7	7.8	7.9	10.3	12.2	12.3	11.5

a) Assume a quadratic relation of the form $Y = \gamma X^2 + \alpha X + \beta$ and compute the sample values of $\bar{x}$, $\bar{y}$, s_x^2, σ_{x2}^2, $v_{x,y}$, $v_{x^2,x}$, $v_{x^2,y}$.

b) Show that the regression quadratic is

$$Y = 0.35X^2 + 0.58X + 1.15 .$$

6. Consider a measuring process in which the error is $N(0, \sigma_i^2)$ distributed for the ith measurement. Let there be n measurements $\{x_i\}$ of the true value t of some parameter. Assume that the σ_i are known.

a) Show that the pdf for the $\{x_i\}$ given t is

$$f(x_1, x_2, \ldots, x_n | t) = (2\pi)^{-n/2} \exp\left[-\frac{1}{2} \sum_{i=1}^{n} \frac{(x_i - t)^2}{\sigma_i^2} \right] \prod_{i=1}^{n} \sigma_i^{-1} .$$

b) Assume that the estimator for t is of the form

$$\hat{T} = \sum_{i=1}^{n} a_i x_i, \qquad \text{where} \qquad \sum_{i=1}^{n} a_i = 1 .$$

Use the Lagrange multiplier method to show that the maximum likelihood values for the a_i are

$$\hat{a}_i = \frac{1}{\sigma_i^2} \left(\sum_{i=1}^{n} \frac{1}{\sigma_i^2} \right)^{-1} .$$

6.6 MULTI-DIMENSIONAL LINEAR REGRESSION

Consider a variable y which is assumed to depend linearly on the two variables x_1 and x_2 according to the relation

$$y = \lambda_0 + \lambda_1 x_1 + \lambda_2 x_2 , \tag{1}$$

where the parameters λ_0, λ_1, and λ_2 are unknown and must be estimated from sample data. The relation specified by Eq. (1) is presumed to be strictly deterministic, but the process of measuring the sample values of y is presumed to be corrupted by noise.

These assumptions may seem restrictive by comparison with the general bivariate normal assumptions of the previous section. However, the following simple example serves to show that the two formulations are really equivalent. Let y be a measure of an individual's suffering from respiratory infections, let x_1 be a measure of the number of cigarettes he smokes, and let x_2 be a measure of the time he spends breathing a polluted urban atmosphere. We know that an individual's health will depend on many other factors, so we cannot expect to find a set of universal parameters, λ_0, λ_1, λ_2, which will make Eq. (1) strictly true for all individuals. The effect of these other factors could be represented by some noise term, z, added to the right side of Eq. (1).

If we represent the extraneous factors (or noise) for the ith individual (or sample element) by z_i, Eq. (1) is replaced by the n individual (n-element sample) equations

$$z_i = y_i - \lambda_0 - \lambda_1 x_{1i} - \lambda_2 x_{2i}, \qquad 1 \leq i \leq n. \tag{2}$$

We assume that the z_i are joint normally distributed with zero mean and with covariance matrix V, so that $V_{ij} = \text{cov}(Z_i, Z_j)$. For mathematical convenience, the $\{y_i\}$, $\{x_{1i}\}$, $\{x_{2i}\}$, and $\{z_i\}$ are represented in the vector notation

$$\mathbf{y} = \begin{pmatrix} y_1 \\ y_2 \\ \vdots \\ y_n \end{pmatrix}, \text{ etc.}$$

The joint normal pdf for the z_i can be written

$$f(z_1, z_2, \ldots, z_n) = (\sqrt{2\pi})^{-n} |V|^{-1/2} \exp\{-\tfrac{1}{2} \mathbf{z}^T V^{-1} \mathbf{z}\}. \tag{3}$$

This pdf can also be viewed as a conditional pdf for the $\{y_i\}$ by simply substituting Eq. (2) for the $\{z_i\}$. To simplify the notation, we define the matrix

$$A = \begin{pmatrix} 1 & x_{11} & x_{21} \\ 1 & x_{12} & x_{22} \\ 1 & x_{13} & x_{23} \\ & \vdots & \\ 1 & x_{1n} & x_{2n} \end{pmatrix}, \tag{4}$$

so that we can write the vector form of Eq. (2) as

$$\mathbf{z} = \mathbf{y} - A\boldsymbol{\lambda}, \tag{5}$$

where the parameter vector is

$$\boldsymbol{\lambda} = \begin{pmatrix} \lambda_0 \\ \lambda_1 \\ \lambda_2 \end{pmatrix}.$$

With these substitutions the pdf defined by Eq. (3) can be viewed as a conditional pdf for the $\{y_i\}$ given the parameter vector $\boldsymbol{\lambda}$ and the matrix A:

$$f(\mathbf{y}) = (\sqrt{2\pi})^{-n} |V|^{-1/2} \exp\{-\tfrac{1}{2}(\mathbf{y} - \boldsymbol{\lambda}A)^T V^{-1} (\mathbf{y} - \boldsymbol{\lambda}A)\}. \tag{6}$$

This conditional pdf can, in turn, be interpreted as a likelihood function to be maximized in terms of the components of the parameter vector $\boldsymbol{\lambda}$. The only $\boldsymbol{\lambda}$ dependence of Eq. (6) is contained in the quadratic form of the exponent,

$$Q = (\mathbf{y} - A\boldsymbol{\lambda})^T V^{-1}(\mathbf{y} - A\boldsymbol{\lambda}). \tag{7}$$

In our discussion of the n-variable distribution, we showed that the general quadratic form $\boldsymbol{\mu}^T V^{-1} \boldsymbol{\mu}$ was positive definite, so $Q > 0$. This conclusion shows that the likelihood function will be maximized by those values of the components of the parameter vector $\boldsymbol{\lambda}$ which minimize Q. In most applications V^{-1} is diagonal (the diagonal matrix elements are frequently identical), so Q is actually a sum of square deviations (divided by the appropriate weighting variance). For this reason, the present parameter determination procedure is frequently called the method of weighted least squares.

The derivation thus far has been based on the three dimensional linear relation of the form given by Eq. (1). However, since all of the significant relations for our procedure can be written in vector-matrix notation, the treatment can easily be extended to m dimensions by simply using an m dimensional parameter vector,

$$\boldsymbol{\lambda} = \begin{pmatrix} \lambda_0 \\ \lambda_1 \\ \vdots \\ \lambda_{m-1} \end{pmatrix}, \tag{8}$$

and an m column matrix

$$\mathsf{A} = \begin{pmatrix} 1 & x_{1,1} & x_{2,1} & \cdots & x_{m-1,1} \\ 1 & x_{1,2} & x_{2,2} & \cdots & x_{m-1,2} \\ & & \vdots & & \\ 1 & x_{1,n} & x_{2,n} & \cdots & x_{m-1,n} \end{pmatrix}. \tag{9}$$

The reader should note that the order of subscripts in the elements of A, the $x_{i,j}$, is interchanged from the usual notation. In other words, $A_{ij} = x_{j-1,i}$, with $x_{0,i} = 1$ for all i.

To best understand the minimization of Q, in an elementary way, we write Eq. (7) in component notation

$$Q = \sum_{i,j,\nu,\mu} (y_i - A_{i\nu}\lambda_\nu)(V^{-1})_{ij}(y_j - A_{j\mu}\lambda_\mu). \tag{10}$$

Differentiating with respect to some particular λ_k yields,

$$\frac{\partial Q}{\partial \lambda_k} = -\sum_{i,j,\mu} A_{ik}(V^{-1})_{ij}(y_j - A_{j\mu}\lambda_\mu) - \sum_{i,j,\nu}(y_i - A_{i\nu}\lambda_\nu)(V^{-1})_{ij}A_{jk}. \tag{11}$$

In order to combine these two summations we interchange the labels i and j in the second sum and also replace the label ν by μ. Eq. (11) can then be rewritten as

$$\frac{\partial Q}{\partial \lambda_k} = -\sum_{i,j,\mu} A_{ik}[(V^{-1})_{ij} + (V^{-1})_{ji}](y_j - A_{j\mu}\lambda_\mu). \tag{12}$$

Since the covariance matrix V is symmetric, its inverse must be symmetric, so that $(V^{-1})_{ij} = (V^{-1})_{ji}$. With this simplification, the m equations of the form

$$\frac{\partial Q}{\partial \lambda_k} = 0$$

can be combined into the single vector equation, with $\hat{\lambda}$ being the value of $\boldsymbol{\lambda}$ which minimizes Q. Thus,

$$\mathsf{A}^T V^{-1}(\mathbf{y} - \mathsf{A}\hat{\lambda}) = 0. \tag{13}$$

Of course, we could have changed indices in the first term of Eq. (11) and combined it with the second term. Following the above procedure and setting the m equations

$$\frac{\partial Q}{\partial \lambda_k} = 0$$

would have simply yielded the transpose of Eq. (13). The two procedures are equivalent, since we have the same m linear equations, whether we consider a certain vector equation or its transpose.

The solution of Eq. (13) for the estimator $\hat{\lambda}$ can be most conveniently written in terms of the square $m \times m$ matrix

$$J = A^T V^{-1} A. \tag{14}$$

If J is nonsingular, we can simply multiply Eq. (13) by J^{-1} and obtain

$$J^{-1} A^T V^{-1} y = \hat{\lambda}. \tag{15}$$

Example 1. Using Eq. (15) to rederive the simple linear regression results of the previous section, we take

$$\lambda = \begin{pmatrix} \lambda_0 \\ \lambda_1 \end{pmatrix} = \begin{pmatrix} \beta \\ \alpha \end{pmatrix}, \qquad A = \begin{pmatrix} 1 & x_1 \\ 1 & x_2 \\ 1 & x_3 \\ 1 & x_4 \\ \vdots & \\ 1 & x_n \end{pmatrix}, \qquad V = I,$$

$$J = A^T A = \begin{pmatrix} n & \sum\limits_{i=1}^{n} x_i \\ \sum\limits_{i=1}^{n} x_i & \sum\limits_{i=1}^{n} x_i^2 \end{pmatrix} \tag{16}$$

We can easily compute

$$\det J = n \sum_{i=1}^{n} x_i^2 - \left(\sum_{i=1}^{n} x_i \right)^2$$

$$= n \sum_{i=1}^{n} x_i^2 - n^2 \bar{x}^2 = n \sum_{i=1}^{n} (x_i - \bar{x})^2, \tag{17}$$

$$J^{-1} = \begin{pmatrix} \dfrac{1}{n} \sum\limits_{i=1}^{n} x^2 & -\bar{x} \\ -\bar{x} & 1 \end{pmatrix} \dfrac{1}{\sum\limits_{i=1}^{n} (x_i - \bar{x})^2}, \tag{18}$$

$$A^T \mathbf{y} = \begin{pmatrix} \sum_{i=1}^{n} y_i \\ \sum_{i=1}^{n} x_i y_i \end{pmatrix} = \begin{pmatrix} n\bar{y} \\ \sum_{i=1}^{n} x_i y_i \end{pmatrix},$$

(19)

$$\hat{\lambda} = J^{-1} A^T \mathbf{y} = \begin{pmatrix} \bar{y} \sum_{i=1}^{n} x^2 - \bar{x} \sum_{i=1}^{n} x_i y_i \\ -n\bar{x}\bar{y} + \sum_{i=1}^{n} x_i y_i \end{pmatrix} \frac{1}{\sum_{i=1}^{n} (x_i - \bar{x})^2}.$$

Now this vector can be simplified by noting that

$$\sum_{i=1}^{n} x_i^2 = \sum_{i=1}^{n} (x_i - \bar{x})^2 + n\bar{x}^2,$$

$$\sum_{i=1}^{n} x_i y_i = \sum_{i=1}^{n} (x_i - \bar{x})(y_i - \bar{y}) + n\bar{x}\bar{y},$$

so that the first component of $\hat{\lambda}$ can be written

$$\frac{\bar{y}\left[\sum_{i=1}^{n}(x_i - \bar{x})^2 + n\bar{x}^2\right] - \bar{x}\left[\sum_{i=1}^{n}(x_i - \bar{x})(y_i - \bar{y}) + n\bar{x}\bar{y}\right]}{\sum_{i=1}^{n}(x_i - \bar{x})^2}$$

$$= \bar{y} - \frac{\bar{x}\sum(x_i - \bar{x})(y_i - \bar{y})}{\sum(x_i - \bar{x})^2} = \bar{y} - \frac{\bar{x}\,v_{xy}}{s_x^2}.$$

(20)

The second component of $\hat{\lambda}$ can be similarly simplified so that

$$\hat{\lambda} = \begin{pmatrix} \bar{y} - \dfrac{\bar{x}\,v_{xy}}{s_x^2} \\ \dfrac{v_{xy}}{s_x^2} \end{pmatrix}.$$

The reader will immediately recognize this as the result obtained by the elementary methods of the previous section.

For higher dimensional problems $(m > 2)$, the details of this procedure become rather complicated, but some simplification can be obtained by expressing the expectation of Y in terms of the variables $x_1 - \bar{x}_1$, $x_2 - \bar{x}_2$, etc., which have zero mean

$$\left(\bar{x}_1 = \frac{1}{n}\sum_{i=1}^{n} x_{1i}, \text{ etc.}\right).$$

In terms of these variables, we have

$$E(Y|x_{1i} - \bar{x}_1, x_{2i} - \bar{x}_2, \ldots, x_{m-1,i} - \bar{x}_{m-1}) = \sum_{j=1}^{m} \beta_j (x_{ji} - \bar{x}_j) + \beta_0. \quad (21)$$

If we define the analog of the A matrix

$$B = \begin{pmatrix} 1 & x_{11} - \bar{x}_1 & x_{21} - \bar{x}_2 & x_{m-1,1} - \bar{x}_{m-1} \\ 1 & x_{12} - \bar{x}_1 & x_{22} - \bar{x}_2 \ldots x_{m-1,2} - \bar{x}_{m-1} \\ 1 & x_{13} - \bar{x}_1 & x_{23} - \bar{x}_2 & x_{m-1,3} - x_{m-1} \\ & & \vdots \\ 1 & x_{1n} - \bar{x}_1 & x_{2n} - \bar{x}_2 \ldots x_{m-1,n} - \bar{x}_{m-1} \end{pmatrix} \quad (22)$$

the analog of Eq. (5) can be written as

$$z = y - B\beta. \quad (23)$$

By the same procedure that had been employed to derive the estimator $\hat{\lambda}$ in Eq. (15) we can easily find the maximum likelihood estimate

$$\hat{\beta} = K^{-1}B^T V^{-1} y, \quad (24)$$

where $K = B^T V^{-1} B$. The similarity between Eqs. (15) and (24) is, obviously, to be expected.

Example 2. Consider the three dimensional case, and let $V = I$, with an n-element sample. For this case let

$$B = \begin{pmatrix} 1 & x_{11} - \bar{x}_1 & x_{21} - \bar{x}_2 \\ 1 & x_{12} - \bar{x}_1 & x_{22} - \bar{x}_2 \\ & \vdots \\ 1 & x_{1n} - \bar{x}_1 & x_{2n} - \bar{x}_2 \end{pmatrix}, \quad (25)$$

which leads to

$$K = B^T B$$

$$= \begin{pmatrix} n & 0 & 0 \\ 0 & \sum_{i=1}^{n}(x_{1i} - \bar{x}_1)^2 & \sum_{i=1}^{n}(x_{1i} - \bar{x}_1)(x_{2i} - \bar{x}_2) \\ 0 & \sum_{i=1}^{n}(x_{1i} - \bar{x}_1)(x_{2i} - \bar{x}_2) & \sum_{i=1}^{n}(x_{2i} - \bar{x}_2)^2 \end{pmatrix}. \quad (26)$$

It is now easy to compute

$$\det(K) = n\left\{ \left[\sum_{i=1}^{n}(x_{1i} - \bar{x}_1)^2\right]\left[\sum_{i=1}^{n}(x_{2i} - \bar{x}_2)^2\right] \right.$$

$$\left. - \left[\sum_{i=1}^{n}(x_{1i} - \bar{x}_1)(x_{2i} - \bar{x}_2)\right]^2 \right\} = n\Delta \quad (27)$$

and

$$K^{-1} = \frac{1}{\Delta} \begin{pmatrix} \dfrac{\Delta}{n} & 0 & 0 \\ 0 & \sum_{i=1}^{n} (x_{2i} - \bar{x}_2)^2 & -\sum_{i=1}^{n} (x_{1i} - \bar{x}_1)(x_{2i} - \bar{x}_2) \\ 0 & -\sum_{i=1}^{n} (x_{1i} - \bar{x}_1)(x_{2i} - \bar{x}_2) & \sum_{i=1}^{n} (x_{1i} - \bar{x}_1)^2 \end{pmatrix}. \tag{28}$$

These results lead to Eq. (29):

$$\hat{\beta} = K^{-1}B^{T}\,y = \begin{pmatrix} \bar{y} \\ \dfrac{1}{\Delta}\left\{\left[\sum_{i=1}^{n} y_i(x_{1i} - \bar{x}_1)\right]\sum_{i=1}^{n}(x_{2i}-\bar{x}_2)^2 \right. \\ \left. -\left[\sum_{i=1}^{n} y_i(x_{2i}-\bar{x}_2)\right]\left[\sum_{i=1}^{n}(x_{1i}-\bar{x}_1)(x_{2i}-\bar{x}_2)\right]\right\} \\ \dfrac{1}{\Delta}\left\{-\left[\sum_{i=1}^{n} y_i(x_{1i}-\bar{x}_1)\right]\left[\sum_{i=1}^{n}(x_{1i}-\bar{x}_1)(x_{2i}-\bar{x}_2)\right] \right. \\ \left. +\left[\sum_{i=1}^{n}(x_{1i}-\bar{x}_1)^2\right]\left[\sum_{i=1}^{n} y_i(x_{2i}-\bar{x}_2)\right]\right\} \end{pmatrix}. \tag{29}$$

Equation (29) can be simplified if we note that

$$\sum_{i=1}^{n} y_i(x_{ji} - \bar{x}_j) = \sum_{i=1}^{n} (y_i - \bar{y})(x_{ji} - \bar{x}_j) = (n-1)v_{y,x_j},$$

and, therefore,

$$\beta = \begin{pmatrix} \bar{y} \\ \dfrac{v_{y,x_1} s_{x_2}^2 - v_{y,x_2} v_{x_1,x_2}}{s_{x_1}^2 s_{x_2}^2 - v_{x_1,x_2}^2} \\ \dfrac{v_{y,x_2} s_{x_1}^2 - v_{y,x_1} v_{x_1,x_2}}{s_{x_1}^2 s_{x_2}^2 - v_{x_1,x_2}^2} \end{pmatrix}. \tag{30}$$

In this section we have derived expressions for the estimators $\hat{\lambda}$ and $\hat{\beta}$ in terms of the covariance matrix V of the noise on the individual measurements. In the two examples, $V = I$ has been specified for simplicity. The reader should verify that taking $V = \sigma^2 I$ for any real σ would yield the same answer, since the σ^2 would cancel in either Eq. (15) or (24).

In the following section we will compute the variances of $\hat{\lambda}$ or $\hat{\beta}$ viewed as random variables. For such computations a knowledge of σ^2 is required, or else it must be estimated from the data by the method to be described in the succeeding section.

6.7 VARIANCE OF REGRESSION PARAMETERS

In the preceding two sections we computed the maximum likelihood estimates of regression parameters. In order to specify the usefulness, or validity, of these estimates, we must determine their variances when they are viewed as random variables. For this purpose we define the random variable

$$\tilde{\beta} = K^{-1}B^T V^{-1}Y, \tag{1}$$

where Y is a random variable whose components are the n individual sample elements with particular values y_i. (We have resorted to the special notation $\tilde{\beta}$ for the random variable so that both the parameter (β) and the random variable whose particular sample value is the estimator for the parameter will use the same basic symbol. In this manner every step of the calculation exhibits the parameter being estimated.)

(The reader may wish to think of $\tilde{\beta}$ as analogous to an upper case Roman letter representing a random variable.)

The randomness of Y arises from the randomness of Z according to the relation

$$Z = Y - B\beta \tag{2}$$

where β is a vector whose components are true values of the unknown parameters. Since the mean of the noise fluctuation, Z, is zero, the Expectation of Eq. (2) gives

$$E(Y) = B\beta . \tag{3}$$

Now the expectation of Eq. (1) is

$$E(\tilde{\beta}) = K^{-1} B^T V^{-1} E(Y)$$

which is easily seen to be satisfied by

$$E(Y) = BE(\tilde{\beta}) . \tag{4}$$

Eqs. (3) and (4) together imply that

$$\beta = E(\tilde{\beta}) \tag{5}$$

which shows that $\tilde{\beta}$ is an unbiased estimator of the true parameter vector β, as would be expected.

    To find the covariance matrix for the random variables $\tilde{\beta}$, we write the deviations from the mean

$$\tilde{\beta} - E(\tilde{\beta}) = K^{-1}B^T V^{-1}[Y - E(Y)], \tag{6}$$

from which we can easily compute

$$[\tilde{\beta} - E(\tilde{\beta})] [\tilde{\beta} - E(\tilde{\beta})]^T = K^{-1}B^T V^{-1}[Y - E(Y)] [Y - E(Y)]^T V^{-1}BK^{-1} . \tag{7}$$

Now the expectation of the left side of this equation is the covariance matrix C whose elements are $(C)_{ij} = \text{cov}(\beta_i, \beta_j)$. Taking the expectation of Eq. (7) and using the relation

$$E\{[Y - E(Y)] [Y - E(Y)]^T\} = E(ZZ^T) = V, \tag{8}$$

we obtain

$$C = K^{-1}B^T V^{-1} V V^{-1} B K^{-1} = K^{-1}. \tag{9}$$

Unfortunately, this elegant relationship is of little value unless we know the statistics of the noise, as represented by the covariance matrix V, so that K can be computed. In most practical situations, the noise arises from our ignorance, so we seldom have a detailed knowledge of its statistics. Under such circumstances it is usually assumed that the Z_i are independent and identically $N(0, \sigma^2)$ distributed so that

$$V = \sigma^2 I, \tag{10}$$

where σ^2 is unknown. This simplification permits the construction of an estimator for the unknown σ^2 based upon the sample data.

We first consider the quadratic form

$$Q = \frac{1}{\sigma^2} Z^T Z = \frac{1}{\sigma^2} [Y - E(Y)]^T [Y - E(Y)]. \tag{11}$$

Since the n components of Z are assumed to be independent and $N(0, \sigma^2)$ distributed, Q must be chi-square distributed with n degrees of freedom. We cannot use $\sigma^2 Q$ as an estimator for σ^2 because $E(Y)$ cannot be determined precisely from sample data. We can only determine the particular sample value of $B\tilde{\beta}$. Therefore, we rewrite Q in a form containing this computable parameter by adding and subtracting $B\tilde{\beta}$:

$$Q = \frac{1}{\sigma^2} \{Y - B\tilde{\beta} + B[\tilde{\beta} - E(\tilde{\beta})]\}^T \{Y - B\tilde{\beta} + B[\tilde{\beta} - E(\tilde{\beta})]\} \tag{12}$$

where we have also used Eq. (4) to re-express $E(Y)$ as $BE(\tilde{\beta})$. Expanding the product, we can rewrite Eq. (12) as

$$Q = \frac{1}{\sigma^2} (Y - B\tilde{\beta})^T (Y - B\tilde{\beta}) + \frac{1}{\sigma^2} [\tilde{\beta} - E(\tilde{\beta})]^T B^T B[\tilde{\beta} - E(\tilde{\beta})]$$

$$+ \frac{1}{\sigma^2} (Y - B\tilde{\beta})^T B[\tilde{\beta} - E(\tilde{\beta})] + \frac{1}{\sigma^2} [\tilde{\beta} - E(\tilde{\beta})]^T B^T (Y - B\tilde{\beta}). \tag{13}$$

This expression can be simplified by noting that for the simplified form of V given in Eq. (10), the multiplication of Eq. (1) by $K(= B^T B \sigma^{-2})$ yields

$$B^T B\tilde{\beta} = B^T Y. \tag{14}$$

This result implies directly that the last term of Eq. (13) must be zero. The transpose of Eq. (14) implies that the third term of Eq. (13) must also be zero, leaving the relation

$$Q = \frac{1}{\sigma^2} (Y - B\tilde{\beta})^T (Y - B\tilde{\beta}) + \frac{1}{\sigma^2} [\tilde{\beta} - E(\tilde{\beta})]^T B^T B[\tilde{\beta} - E(\tilde{\beta})]. \tag{15}$$

Now, according to Eq. (7), $K^{-1}(= (B^T B)^{-1} \sigma^2)$ is the covariance matrix for the estimated parameters $\tilde{\beta}$. Since there are m independent components of $\tilde{\beta}$, the last term of Eq. (15) is a quadratic form of the same nature as described in Eqs. (1) and (2) of Section 4.9. In that section it was shown that such a quadratic form is chi-square distributed with m degrees of freedom, whenever the m independent components of $\tilde{\beta}$ are joint normally distributed.

Using the rotation matrix procedures described in Section 5.10, it can be shown that the two expressions on the right-hand side of Eq. (15) are independent. Since Q has n degrees of freedom and the second term on the right-hand side has m degrees of freedom, the first term must also be chi-square distributed, with $n - m$ degrees of freedom. Therefore it is reasonable to take the random variable

$$\tilde{\sigma}^2 = (Y - B\tilde{\beta})^T (Y - B\tilde{\beta}) \left(\frac{1}{n - m} \right) \tag{16}$$

to be the estimator for the unknown parameter σ^2. Since $\tilde{\beta}$ is a function of Y, according to Eq. (1), this estimator can be computed from the known sample values of Y and B. The following example will illustrate the application of this estimator.

Example 1. Consider the regression line of Example 1 of Section 6.5. For simplicity the line will be written

$$y = 0.78(x - \bar{x}) + 7.1 = \hat{\beta}_1(x - \bar{x}) + \hat{\beta}_0 .$$

To find the variances of β_0 and β_1 we use the data from the sample and compute

$$(B^T B)^{-1} = \begin{pmatrix} \frac{1}{n} & 0 \\ 0 & \frac{1}{(n-1)\, s_x^2} \end{pmatrix} = \begin{pmatrix} \frac{1}{10} & 0 \\ 0 & \frac{1}{(9)(1.88)} \end{pmatrix} .$$

The particular sample value of the estimator $\tilde{\sigma}^2$ is

$$\tilde{\sigma}^2 = \frac{1}{10 - 2} \sum_{i=1}^{10} [y_i - \beta_0 - \beta_1(x_i - \bar{x})]^2 = \frac{10 - 1}{10 - 2} [s_y^2 + \beta_1^2 s_x^2 - 2\beta_1 v_{xy}] = .84$$

We can then use this estimated value of σ^2 in Eq. (9) to compute the variances

$$\text{var}(\beta_0) = \frac{\sigma^2}{n} = 0.084 ,$$

$$\text{var}(\beta_1) = \frac{\sigma^2}{(n - 1)s_x^2} = 0.05 .$$

A useful result of this example is the fact that the two estimated parameters in a simple ($m = 2$) linear regression are independent. For general m, an examination of the form K^{-1} shows that $\tilde{\beta}_0$ is always independent of the other estimators, but there is generally a dependence among the other $\tilde{\beta}_i$'s (see Problem 1).

In this section we have derived the estimator $\tilde{\sigma}^2$ for the variance of the noise random variable $Z_i = Y_i - E(Y_i)$. This estimate of variance was then used to compute the covariance matrix of the estimated parameters $\tilde{\beta}$. In the next chapter we will make further use of $\tilde{\sigma}^2$ itself. The particular sample value $(n-1)\,\tilde{\sigma}^2$ is frequently called the residual sum of squares.

PROBLEMS

1. Consider the three dimensional linear regression of Example 2 of Section 6.6. Use the results of that example to show that β_0 must be independent of β_1 and β_2, but that $\tilde{\beta}_1$ and $\tilde{\beta}_2$ will generally be dependent.

2. Compute the covariance matrix for the regression parameters α, β in Example 1 of Section 6.5.

3. Let x_1 be the average number of cigarettes smoked per day, and t be the age in years. Data given in "The Health Consequences of Smoking", PHS publication 1696, can be adapted into the following table of death rates y due to coronary heart disease per 100,000 men of each category:

x_1 \ t	50	60	70
5	195	594	1374
15	297	830	1577
30	390	912	1701
45	502	1101	1955

Since death rate varies exponentially with age, approximately doubling every 10 years for men of middle age and beyond, it is convenient to define the second variable $x_2 = \exp(0.0693t)$.

a) Estimate the parameters of the regression line

$$y = \beta_0 + \beta_1\,(x_1 - \bar{x}_1) + \beta_2(x_2 - \bar{x}_2)\,.$$

b) Estimate the standard deviations of the parameters β_0, β_1, β_2.

BIBLIOGRAPHY

1. H. Cramer, *Mathematical Methods of Statistics*, Princeton University Press, Princeton, 1961. A well written, rigorous treatment.

2. D. A. S. Fraser, *Statistics—An Introduction*, John Wiley & Sons, New York, 1958. An elementary text with a particularly good treatment of transformation of random variables and regression analysis.

3. P. G. HOEL, *Introduction to Mathematical Statistics*, John Wiley & Sons, New York, 1962. A good elementary text.

4. A. M. MOOD and F. A. GRABILL, *Introduction to the Theory of Statistics*, 2nd ed., McGraw-Hill Book Company, New York, 1963. A good discussion of regression analysis.

5. S. S. WILKS, *Mathematical Statistics*, John Wiley & Sons, New York, 1962. This advanced text contains a very comprehensive treatment of the whole subject.

CHAPTER 7

PARAMETRIC INTERVAL ESTIMATION

7.1 INTRODUCTION

Most statistical experiments have many possible outcomes, and the probability associated with any one of them is generally quite small. It is usually more convenient to associate a probability with a range of possible values for the random variable than with a single value. In the preceding chapter we derived a number of estimates of the most probable, or most likely, values of certain parameters. These estimators were random variables, and in most cases were continuous. The probability associated with these most probable or most likely point estimates was nil.

Under these circumstances, it is generally not meaningful to specify the probability that a certain random variable (parameter estimator) be precisely equal to the estimated parameter. It is, however, quite convenient to specify the probability that a random *interval* include the estimated parameter. The reader should be familiar with this probability interval concept from the specification of tolerances in all aspects of technological activity. The measuring instruments in a general laboratory have a large probability of falling within some level of agreement with those kept at the National Bureau of Standards, but have zero probability of giving precisely the same measurement. We don't expect an airplane to depart or arrive *precisely* on time, but we expect that there is a large probability of arrival or departure within a certain interval of the scheduled time.

In this chapter we will describe some of the more frequently used procedures for estimating intervals having specified probabilities for containing some particular parameter of a distribution. Such estimated intervals will be called *confidence intervals*. These procedures are quite simple, but it will be useful to begin with some introductory discussions of probabilities associated with intervals when the distributions are known.

Most statistical analyses assume samples from a normally distributed population. This assumption is based on the generality of the normal distribution and on the central limit theorem which implies that all distributions will appear to tend to normality for large samples. A few examples of interval estimates for other distributions will be given for illustrative purposes.

The commonly used confidence interval procedures, discussed in Sections 7.3 through 7.7, are conveniently summarized in Table 1 of Section 7.8.

7.2 PROBABILITY INTERVALS

Let the random variable X be normally distributed with mean ν_1 and variance σ^2. Let us ask for the probability that some particular sample element will fall within an interval of length $2x_0$ centered about ν_1. In mathematical language we want $\Pr\{|X - \nu_1| \le x_0\}$. It will be most convenient to express answers in terms of the tabulated cumulative distribution function (CDF) of the $N(0, 1)$ distribution, so we note that the statement $|X - \nu_1| \le x_0$ is equivalent to $|X - \nu_1|/\sigma \le x_0/\sigma$. Since the random variable $(X - \nu_1)/\sigma$ is $N(0, 1)$ distributed we have

$$\Pr\{|X - \nu_1| \le x_0\} = \Pr\left\{\frac{|X - \nu_1|}{\sigma} \le \frac{x_0}{\sigma}\right\} = \frac{1}{\sqrt{2\pi}} \int_{-x_0/\sigma}^{x_0/\sigma} \exp\left(-\frac{t^2}{2}\right) dt. \quad (1)$$

The CDF of the $N(0, 1)$ distribution is

$$F(u) = \frac{1}{\sqrt{2\pi}} \int_{-\infty}^{u} \exp\left(-\frac{t^2}{2}\right) dt. \quad (2)$$

This function can only be integrated numerically, so a convenient tabulation for positive values of u is provided in Table 1 of Appendix B. Since $F(\infty) = 1$, and the $N(0, 1)$ pdf is symmetric about 0,

$$F(-u) = 1 - F(u). \quad (3)$$

Using Eqs. (2) and (3) we can express Eq. (1) in terms of the normal distribution function

$$\Pr\{|X - \nu_1| \le x_0\} = F\left(\frac{x_0}{\sigma}\right) - F\left(-\frac{x_0}{\sigma}\right) = 2F\left(\frac{x_0}{\sigma}\right) - 1. \quad (4)$$

To facilitate comparisons, interval lengths are usually expressed in terms of the standard deviation. If we let

$$x_0 = u\sigma, \quad (5)$$

then Eq. (4) can be written as

$$\Pr\{|X - \nu_1| \le u\sigma\} = -1 + 2F(u). \quad (6)$$

This type of problem can be stated from a somewhat different point of view. We can ask for the length of the interval which should be taken, centered about the mean, so that the probability that a randomly sampled element will fall within that interval is some specified value, say $p_0 \le 1$. In mathematical terms, we wish to find a number x_0 such that

$$\Pr\{|X - \nu_1| \le x_0\} = p_0. \quad (7)$$

The length of the desired interval centered about the mean $X = \nu_1$ will then be $2x_0$. The solution to this problem can be expressed in terms of the tabulated $N(0, 1)$ CDF by writing $x_0 = u\sigma$,

$$\Pr\{|X - \nu_1| \le x_0\} = \Pr\{|(X - \nu_1)/\sigma| \le u\} = -1 + 2F(u). \quad (8)$$

Substituting this result into Eq. (7), we see that the desired value of $u = x_0/\sigma$ is the solution to the equation

$$-1 + 2F(u) = p_0. \tag{9}$$

The solution of this equation, utilizing the tabulated values of $F(u)$, is illustrated in the following example.

Example 1. If we wish to have a 0.95 probability of a randomly sampled value of X falling within an interval, centered about the mean of a Gaussian distribution with variance $\sigma^2 = 4$, how long must that interval be?

The solution is found by determining u from Eq. (9) with $p_0 = 0.95$; that is, u must satisfy $F(u) = 0.975$. From the tabulated values of the integral $F(u)$, we see that $F(u) = 0.975$ for $u = 1.96$. The desired interval length is then simply

$$2x_0 = 2u\sigma = 2(1.96)\,(2) = 7.84. \tag{10}$$

This interval is shown in Fig. 1, and the probability 0.95 is equal to the area between the interval limits, shown shaded.

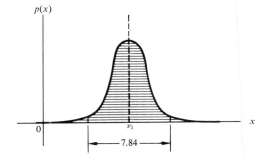

Figure 7.1

A typical practical situation leading to this type of problem arises with the specification of tolerances. Consider the manufacture of a certain chemical. During the manufacturing process, several reagents are mixed and several reactions take place. These reactions are statistical in nature, so that there is a nonzero probability that the chemical composition will be something other than the desired value.

The probability distribution of possible values is frequently conveniently characterized by a Gaussian pdf. The user of this chemical will be mainly interested in the range of composition which the chemical is likely to have. If the user defines "likely" as "having a better than 1% probability," then he will be interested in an interval about the mean of such a length that only 1% of the samples will fall outside the interval. This problem is stated mathematically in the following example.

Example 2. How many standard deviation units on each side of the mean must an interval extend so that there is less than a 1% probability that a randomly chosen element will fall outside that interval? In other words, what value of u will satisfy the equation

$$\Pr\{|X - v_1| \geq \sigma u\} = p_1 , \tag{11}$$

where $p_1 = 0.01$ for this particular example? Now,

$$\Pr\{|X - v_1| \geq \sigma u\} = 1 - \Pr\{|X - v_1| \leq \sigma u\} . \tag{12}$$

However, using the value of $\Pr\{|X - v_1| \leq \sigma u\}$, given in Eq. (6), this expression can be rewritten as

$$\begin{aligned}\Pr\{|X - v_1| \geq u\sigma\} &= 1 - [2F(u) - 1] \\ &= 2[1 - F(u)] . \end{aligned} \tag{13}$$

Substituting Eq. (13) into (11) gives the specific relation

$$2[1 - F(u)] = p_1 . \tag{14}$$

For the present problem, $p_1 = 0.01$, so the tabulated values of the $N(0, 1)$ CDF give

$$u = 2.576 .$$

At this point it is worthwhile to recall that the theme of this chapter is the use of statistical samples for estimating parameters of distributions. The present section is somewhat incongruous, because it only considers interval estimation from completely known distributions. This discussion was included only to familiarize the reader with certain properties of tabulated distribution functions and to reexamine some properties already familiar from the treatment of continuous probability.

Having explored these properties with the examples of this section, we now proceed to discuss their application to confidence interval estimation. We can summarize these properties in the following equations:

a) $\Pr\{X - v_1 \leq u\sigma\} = F(u) ,$

b) $\Pr\{X - v_1 \geq u\sigma\} = 1 - F(u) ,$

c) $\Pr\{|X - v_1| \leq u\sigma\} = 2F(u) - 1 ,$ (15)

d) $\Pr\{|X - v_1| \geq u\sigma\} = 2[1 - F(u)] ,$

where X is a $N(v_1, \sigma^2)$ random variable, and $F(u)$ is the CDF for a $N(0, 1)$ distribution.

PROBLEMS

1. Let the random variable X be $N(2, 2^2)$ distributed. Use the tables of normal distribution to find

a) $\Pr\{0 \leq X \leq 4\}$.

b) u such that $\Pr\{|X - 2| < u\} = 0.90$.
c) u such that $\Pr\{X > u\} = 0.90$.
d) u such that $\Pr\{X < u\} = 0.90$.

2. Repeat the above problem with X as $N(0, 2^2)$ distributed.

3. Let X be $N(1, 1)$ distributed. Find the following;

a) $\Pr\{0 \le X \le 2\}$.
b) u such that $\Pr\{|X - 2| < u\} = 0.90$.
c) u such that $\Pr\{X > u\} = 0.90$.
d) u such that $\Pr\{X < u\} = 0.90$.

7.3 CONFIDENCE INTERVALS FOR THE
MEAN OF A DISTRIBUTION WITH KNOWN VARIANCE

Consider an n element sample from an $N(v_1, \sigma_0^2)$ population. The sample mean $\bar{X}$ will be $N(v_1, \sigma_0^2/n)$. According to Eq. (15c) of Section 7.2 we can specify a p_0 probability interval of length $2u\sigma_0/\sqrt{n}$ such that

$$\Pr\{|\bar{X} - v_1| \le u\sigma_0/\sqrt{n}\} = 2F(u) - 1 = p_0 . \tag{1}$$

This equation specifies a range of values of $\bar{X}$, ($|\bar{X} - v_1| \le u\sigma_0/\sqrt{n}$), which can be rewritten without the absolute value markers as the double inequality

$$-\frac{u\sigma_0}{\sqrt{n}} \le -\bar{X} + v_1 \le u\sigma_0/\sqrt{n} . \tag{2}$$

Adding $\bar{X}$ to all three parts of this inequality preserves the direction of both inequality signs and changes the inequality into

$$\bar{X} - \frac{u\sigma_0}{\sqrt{n}} \le v_1 \le \bar{X} + \frac{u\sigma_0}{\sqrt{n}} . \tag{3}$$

We can view Eq. (3) as specifying an interval of length $2u\sigma_0/\sqrt{n}$ centered about the random variable $\bar{X}$. Since the location of this interval is specified by a random variable, it is called a random interval.

Now, our n element sample specified a particular value of $\bar{X}$ denoted by $\bar{x}$. This particular value, $\bar{x}$, in turn specifies a particular location for the random interval defined by Eq. (3). According to Eq. (1), $\bar{x}$ is expected to fall within $u\sigma_0/\sqrt{n}$ of the true mean in a fraction, $2F(u) - 1$, of the samples out of the ensemble of all possible samples. This means that in the fraction $2F(u) - 1$ of the possible ensemble of samples, the particular interval specified by $\bar{x}$ according to Eq. (3) will include the true mean of the population, v_1.

This random interval is called a confidence interval, and is defined, for a $N(v_1, \sigma_0^2)$ random population in the following manner. For an n element sample from an $N(v_1, \sigma_0^2)$, where σ_0^2 is known and v_1 is unknown, the p_0 confidence interval for the mean v_1 is specified by the inequality

$$\bar{x} - \frac{u\sigma_0}{\sqrt{n}} \le v_1 \le \bar{x} + \frac{u\sigma_0}{\sqrt{n}} , \tag{4}$$

where u is determined from the equation

$$p_0 = \frac{1}{\sqrt{2\pi}} \int_{-u}^{+u} \exp\left(-\frac{t^2}{2}\right) dt = 2F(u) - 1 .$$
(5)

This interval is frequently referred to as the $100p_0\%$ confidence interval. This derivation procedure is illustrated by the following example.

Example 1. Consider a sample of 10 elements for which

$$\bar{x} = \frac{1}{10} \sum_{i=1}^{10} x_i = 5$$
(6)

from a normally distributed population with unknown mean and variance $\sigma_0^2 = 4$. What is the 95% confidence interval for the true population mean? Since $p_0 = 0.95$ is given, we use Eq. (5) and the appropriate table to compute

$$u = 1.96 .$$
(7)

Substituting this value of u, together with the given σ_0^2, $\bar{x}$, and n, into Eq. (4), we obtain the 95% confidence interval for the true population mean ν_1:

$$3.76 \leq \nu_1 \leq 6.24 .$$
(8)

The reader should note that we would not be justified in saying that the probability of ν_1 falling in the interval specified by Eq. (8) is 0.95. The confidence interval is not an a posteriori probability notion, but only a simple and widely used procedure which can be applied with great generality since it does not require any restrictive a priori probability assumptions concerning the unknown parameter. The price we must pay for this generality of applicability is that we can only say the following: The probability that a $100p_0\%$ confidence interval specified by a sample value of the sample mean will actually include the true mean, is p_0. We cannot say that the probability that the *particular* interval determined by a single sample (such as given by Eq. (8)) includes the true mean, is p_0. (We could make such an a posteriori probability statement only if we assumed a uniform a priori distribution for the unknown parameter, ν_1.)

The reader may find the concept of confidence interval somewhat obscured by the inability to express the length parameter u as a simple function of p_0. The following example of a two element sample from a uniform distribution provides a relation between p_0 and u which is more transparent than Eq. (5).

Example 2. Consider a two element sample from a uniform, $\mathcal{U}(\alpha, 1 + \alpha)$, distribution of length one and unknown mean, $\alpha + \frac{1}{2}$. Use the sample mean to construct the p confidence interval for α.

If we denote the sample mean by

$$\bar{X} = \frac{X_1 + X_2}{2} ,$$

the pdf for $\bar{X}$ can be found from the techniques of Section 4.4 to be the triangular pdf

$$f(\bar{x}) = 4(\bar{x} - \alpha), \qquad \alpha \le \bar{x} \le \tfrac{1}{2} + \alpha,$$

$$f(\bar{x}) = 4(1 + \alpha - \bar{x}), \qquad \alpha + \tfrac{1}{2} \le \bar{x} \le 1 + \alpha.$$

With these forms for the pdf we can easily compute the probability that $\bar{X}$ will fall within an interval of length $2v$ centered at $\alpha + \tfrac{1}{2}$:

$$\Pr\{\alpha + \tfrac{1}{2} - v \le \bar{X} \le \alpha + \tfrac{1}{2} + v\} = \int_{\alpha + \frac{1}{2} - v}^{\alpha + \frac{1}{2} + v} f(\bar{x})d\bar{x} = 4v - 4v^2 . \qquad (9)$$

The inequality in this equation can be re-expressed by subtracting $\alpha + \tfrac{1}{2} + \bar{X}$ from each of the three terms to get

$$- \bar{X} - v \le - (\alpha + \tfrac{1}{2}) \le - \bar{X} + v .$$

To express this inequality in standard form we multiply each term by -1, thereby reversing the direction of all the inequality signs to obtain

$$\bar{X} + v \ge \alpha + \tfrac{1}{2} \ge \bar{X} - v . \qquad (10)$$

This inequality can be viewed as specifying a random interval of length $2v$ centered about $\bar{X}$. Using Eq. (10) for the inequality in Eq. (9) we can write the general confidence interval statement

$$\Pr\{\bar{X} + v \ge \alpha + \tfrac{1}{2} \ge \bar{X} - v\} = 4v - 4v^2 = p . \qquad (11)$$

This equation can be solved for v in terms of p, the confidence level,

$$v = \frac{1 - \sqrt{1 - p}}{2} , \qquad (12)$$

where we have, naturally, chosen the v between 0 and $\tfrac{1}{2}$. If we substitute Eq. (12) into Eq. (10) we can replace Eq. (11) by the much simpler confidence interval statement that the level p confidence interval is specified by the inequality

$$\bar{X} + \frac{1 - \sqrt{1 - p}}{2} \ge \alpha + \tfrac{1}{2} \ge \bar{X} - \frac{1 - \sqrt{1 - p}}{2} . \qquad (13)$$

This inequality specifies the confidence interval in terms of a simple function of p itself, with the obscuring intermediary v entirely eliminated from the description.

In the present section we have given an interpretation of a confidence interval as the random interval which has a specified probability of including the desired parameter. The procedure for computing this interval estimate is mathematically equivalent to the computation of a range of values, for the unknown parameter, which would allow the actually observed value of the point estimation to fall within the specified probability interval. In other words, the confidence interval specified by Eqs. (4) and (5) could be interpreted as the range of values for v_1, which would allow the actually observed value $\bar{x}$ to fall within the p_0 probability interval appropriately centered about v_1. In the following sections we will use this interpretation.

PROBLEMS

1. Let the observed value of $\bar{X}$ be 12 for a particular 16 element sample. If it is known that the original population is $N(\mu, 4^2)$, what is the 95% confidence interval for μ?

2. In the previous problem, what is the 90% confidence interval for μ?

3. In Problem 1, what is the 99% confidence interval for μ?

4. We take a nine element sample from a population known to be $N(\mu, 6^2)$, and find the particular value $\bar{x} = 8$ for the sample mean. Find the following:
   a) The 95% confidence interval for μ.
   b) The 99% confidence interval for μ.
   c) The 99.9% confidence interval for μ.

The following problems provide excellent illustrations of the random interval concept. They utilize order statistics type estimators which will be developed further in the following chapter.

5. Consider a two element sample from a population uniformly distributed on the line [0, 1]. Let the random variable X be the smaller of the two, and the random variable Y be the larger. Show that:
   a) The joint pdf for x and y is $f(x, y) = 2, \; 0 \le x \le y \le 1$.
   b) The probability that the random interval between Y and X includes the mean of the original population ($\frac{1}{2}$) is $\frac{1}{2}$.
   c) The expected length of the interval $Y - X$ is $E(Y - X) = \frac{1}{3}$.

6. Consider a two element sample from a negative exponential distributed population (pdf $f(u) = \lambda e^{-\lambda u}$). Let the random variable X be the smaller of the two, and let the random variable Y be the larger. Show that:
   a) The marginal pdf for x is

$$f(x) = 2\lambda e^{-2\lambda x}.$$

   b) The conditional pdf for y given x is

$$g(y|x) = \lambda e^{-\lambda(y-x)}.$$

   c) The probability that the random interval between Y and X includes the mean, $1/\lambda$, is $2e^{-2}$.
   d) Why would you expect the answer in part (c) to be less than the corresponding result in the previous problem?

7.4 CONFIDENCE INTERVALS FOR THE VARIANCE OF A GAUSSIAN DISTRIBUTION WITH KNOWN MEAN

The maximum likelihood estimate of the variance of a Gaussian population, when the mean of the population is known to be v_1, is found from an n-element sample according to the recipe $\sigma^2 = \theta_m = y/n$ (refer to Eq. (20) of Section 6.3,) where y is the particular sample value of the random variable

$$Y = \sum_{i=1}^{n} (X_i - v_1)^2 . \tag{1}$$

Since the random variable Y plays an important role in the maximum likelihood estimate of σ^2, it is worthwhile to examine the properties of its tolerance intervals in the hope of finding behavior suitable for the estimation of confidence intervals for σ^2.

We begin by acting as if σ^2 were known and recall, from Section 4.8, that the random variable Y/σ^2 is chi-square distributed with n degrees of freedom.

The pdf for the chi-square distribution is not symmetric with respect to its maximum, so it is not desirable to center our probability interval for Y about the peak of its pdf, $Y_m/\sigma^2 = n$. We center the probability interval for the chi-square distribution by requiring that the probability of the random variable falling outside the interval on *one side*, is the same as the probability that it will fall outside the interval on the *other side*. In mathematical terms, we require that the probability interval for Y/σ^2 be defined by $u_1 \le Y/\sigma^2 \le u_2$, such that

$$\Pr\{Y/\sigma^2 \le u_1\} = \Pr\{Y/\sigma^2 \ge u_2\} . \tag{2}$$

We compute these probabilities from the tabulated values of the chi-square CDF,

$$\Pr\{Y/\sigma^2 \le u\} = \int_0^u \frac{z^{(n/2)-1} e^{(-z/2)} dz}{\Gamma(n/2) 2^{(n/2)}} = C_n(u) , \tag{3}$$

where the value of $C_n(u)$ for any positive u and integral n can be found from Table 2 of Appendix B at the end of the volume. We can now describe a tolerance interval of level p_0 by the equation

$$\Pr\{u_1 \le Y/\sigma^2 \le u_2\} = p_0 , \tag{4}$$

with the additional centering condition

$$\Pr\{Y/\sigma^2 \le u_1\} = \Pr\{Y/\sigma^2 \ge u_2\} . \tag{5}$$

Using the CDF defined in Eq. (3) we can rewrite these equations to obtain

$$C_n(u_2) - C_n(u_1) = p_0 , \tag{6}$$

$$C_n(u_1) = 1 - C_n(u_2) . \tag{7}$$

The simultaneous solutions of these two equations give

$$C_n(u_2) = \tfrac{1}{2}(p_0 + 1),\qquad(8)$$

$$C_n(u_1) = \tfrac{1}{2}(1 - p_0),\qquad(9)$$

where $C_n(u)$ is defined by Eq. (3) and tabulated in Table 2 of Appendix B. For any value of p_0 between 0 and 1, and any integral value of n, the appropriate values of u_1 and u_2 can be found from the table. This procedure is illustrated by the following example.

Example 1. Consider a 10 element sample from an $N(1,4)$ distribution. What is the appropriately centered interval such that there is a 0.95 probability of the random variable

$$\frac{Y}{4} = \frac{Y}{\sigma^2} = \frac{1}{4}\sum_{i=1}^{10}(X_i - 1)^2 \qquad(10)$$

falling between the upper and lower limits?

The upper and lower limits are found from Eqs. (8) and (9), respectively, with $p_0 = 0.95$ and $n = 10$. From Table 2 of Appendix B we find that

$$u_2 = 20.5,\qquad u_1 = 3.25,\qquad(11)$$

so Eq. (4) gives the 0.95 probability interval

$$3.25 \le \frac{Y}{4} \le 20.5.\qquad(12)$$

This interval is indicated in Figure 2, and the 0.95 probability is equal to the shaded area. Note that the excess area under the curve on the right side is equal to the excess area on the left side.

If σ^2 is not known and we have some particular value y of the random variable Y for an n element sample, then the confidence interval for σ^2 can be determined

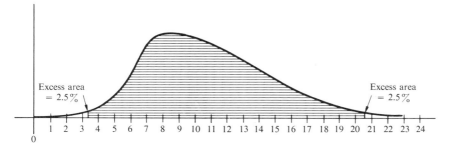

Fig. 7.2. 0.95 probability interval for a chi-square distribution with 10 degrees of freedom.

by the probability interval for Y. To find the confidence interval of level p_0, we simply ask for the range of σ^2 which will allow the p_0 probability interval to include the particular value y of the random variable Y. This requirement can be expressed mathematically by asking for the range of values for σ^2 which will satisfy Eqs. (12) and (13), with Y replaced by the particular sample value y.

If σ^2 is at the upper limit of this range, then y/σ^2 will have its lowest possible value, and this will be determined by the lower limit of the inequality in Eq. (4). In mathematical language, the upper limit of the confidence interval will be

$$u_1 \le \frac{y}{\sigma^2} \quad \text{or} \quad \sigma^2 \le \frac{y}{u_1}. \tag{13}$$

In a similar manner, the lower limit of the confidence range for σ^2 is found from the upper limit of the inequality in Eq. (4):

$$u_2 \ge \frac{y}{\sigma^2} \quad \text{or} \quad \sigma^2 \ge \frac{y}{u_2}. \tag{14}$$

The simultaneous requirements of Eqs. (13) and (14) can be expressed by the double inequality

$$\frac{y}{u_2} \le \sigma^2 \le \frac{y}{u_1}. \tag{15}$$

These results can be summarized by stating that the p_0 confidence interval for σ^2 is given by the double inequality (15), where u_1 and u_2 satisfy Eqs. (8) and (9), and where y is the value of the random variable Y, defined by Eq. (3), for some particular n element sample. (Note that this is frequently called the $100p_0\%$ confidence interval, so that the interval is described by a percentage of 100 rather than a fraction of 1.)

Example 2. Consider a 10 element sample from a normal distribution with unknown variance but known mean. If the values of x_i are such that

$$y = \sum_{i=1}^{10} (x_i - v_1)^2 = 2, \tag{16}$$

what is the 0.95 confidence interval for σ^2? From Example 1 we know that the solutions to Eqs. (8) and (9) for $p_0 = 0.95$, $n = 10$, are $u_1 = 3.25$, $u_2 = 20.5$. The 0.95 confidence interval can then be found by substituting the values for u_1, u_2, and y into Eq. (16), obtaining

$$\frac{2}{20.5} \le \sigma^2 \le \frac{2}{3.25}. \tag{17}$$

7.5 CONFIDENCE INTERVALS FOR THE VARIANCE
OF A GAUSSIAN DISTRIBUTION WITH UNKNOWN MEAN

From Eq. (28) of Section 6.3, we know that the maximum likelihood estimate of the variance of a Gaussian distributed random variable X with unknown mean is given by the recipe

$$\sigma^2 = \theta_m = \frac{z}{n-1},\tag{1}$$

where z is the value, for the particular n-element sample, of the random variable

$$Z = \sum_{i=1}^{n} (X_i - \bar{X})^2,\tag{2}$$

in which

$$\bar{X} = \frac{1}{n} \sum_{i=1}^{n} X_i.$$

In Section 5.10 it was shown that for a known σ^2, the random variable Z/σ^2 is chi-square distributed with $n-1$ degrees of freedom. Therefore, the results of the previous section show that the p_0 probability interval for the random variable Z/σ^2 is

$$u_1 \le \frac{Z}{\sigma^2} \le u_2,\tag{3}$$

where u_1 and u_2 are the solutions to the equations

$$C_{n-1}(u_1) = \tfrac{1}{2}(1 - p_0),\tag{4}$$

$$C_{n-1}(u_2) = \tfrac{1}{2}(1 + p_0).\tag{5}$$

As would be expected, Eqs. (4) and (5) are similar to Eqs. (8) and (9) of Section 7.4, with $n-1$ instead of n degrees of freedom.

Example 1. Consider the 10 random variables, X_i, $1 \le i \le 10$, with identical normal distributions having unknown mean and variance of 2. What is the appropriately centered interval such that the random variable

$$Z = \sum_{i=1}^{10} (X_i - \bar{X})^2,$$

with

$$\bar{X} = \frac{1}{10} \sum_{i=1}^{10} X_i,$$

has a 0.90 probability of falling within the endpoints? Since $Z/\sigma^2 = Z/2$ is chi-square distributed, there will be a 0.90 probability that $Z/2$ will fall in the interval

$$u_1 \le \frac{Z}{2} \le u_2\tag{6}$$

if u_1 and u_2 satisfy the equations

$$C_9(u_1) = \tfrac{1}{2}(1 - 0.9) = \tfrac{0.1}{2} = 0.05,$$
$$C_9(u_2) = \tfrac{1}{2}(1 + 0.9) = 0.95. \tag{7}$$

The tabulated values of the chi-square distribution function give the solutions to the equations $u_1 = 3.33$, $u_2 = 16.9$, so that the 0.90 probability interval for Z is

$$6.66 \le Z \le 33.8. \tag{8}$$

If we now consider a particular n element sample from a Gaussian distribution with unknown mean and variance, then we can compute the p_0 confidence interval for σ^2 by finding the range of values for σ^2 which would have permitted the particular sample value z of the random variable Z to lie within the p_0 probability interval. The sample value z will lie within the p_0 probability interval when

$$u_1 \le \frac{z}{\sigma^2} \le u_2, \tag{9}$$

where u_1 and u_2 are the solutions to Eqs. (4) and (5). Now the largest possible value of σ^2 will be that which gives the smallest possible value of z/σ^2, or

$$\sigma^2 \le \frac{z}{u_1}. \tag{10}$$

Similarly, the lower bound on the confidence interval for σ^2 will be found from the upper inequality of Eq. (9), i.e.,

$$\sigma^2 \ge \frac{z}{u_2}. \tag{11}$$

These upper and low bounds can then be combined into the double inequality

$$\frac{z}{u_2} \le \sigma^2 \le \frac{z}{u_1}, \tag{12}$$

where u_1 and u_2 are the solutions of Eq. (28).

Example 2. Consider a 10 element sample from a normal distribution with unknown mean and variance. If we find the particular sample value of Z to be

$$z = \sum_{i=1}^{10} (x_i - \bar{x})^2 = 20,$$

what is the 0.90 confidence interval for σ^2?

The appropriate confidence interval is given by Eq. (12), with $z = 20$ and u_1 and u_2 already determined in Example 1 to be $u_1 = 3.33$ and $u_2 = 16.9$ for the solutions to Eqs. (4) and (5), with $p_0 = 0.90$.

Substituting these quantities into Eq. (12) gives the 0.90 confidence interval

$$\frac{20}{16.9} \le \sigma^2 \le \frac{20}{3.33}. \tag{13}$$

PROBLEMS

1. Consider the sample obtained in Example 1 of Section 6.5. Assume that the elements come from a Gaussian population with unknown mean and unknown variance. Find the 90% confidence intervals for:
   a) σ_x^2
   b) σ_y^2

2. Repeat the previous problem for 99% confidence intervals.
   a) σ_x^2
   b) σ_y^2

3. Consider a 10-element sample obtained from a Gaussian distribution with unknown mean and variance, and suppose that

$$\sum_{i=1}^{10} (x_i - \bar{x})^2 = 2.5 .$$

Find u such that, for this distribution, $\Pr\{\sigma^2 \leq u\} = 0.95$.

7.6 CONFIDENCE INTERVALS FOR THE MEAN OF A GAUSSIAN DISTRIBUTION WITH BOTH MEAN AND VARIANCE UNKNOWN

Consider a sequence of n random variables X_i, $1 \leq i \leq n$ with identical normal distributions $N(v_1, \sigma^2)$. The random variable $\bar{X} - v_1$, where

$$\bar{X} = \frac{1}{n} \sum_{i=1}^{n} X_i , \tag{1}$$

is then $N(0, \sigma^2/n)$ distributed. From our knowledge of the distribution of $\bar{X} - v_1$, we can compute a probability interval for $\bar{X} - v_1$ in terms of the variance σ^2/n. If σ^2 is unknown, then this probability interval will be of unknown length, and, consequently, of little value. We can, however, construct a random variable which contains the unknown v_1 but not the unknown σ^2.

From Section 4.10 we know that dividing an $N(0, 1)$ distributed random variable by the square root of a chi-square distributed variable, divided by the number of degrees of freedom, we obtain a Student distributed variable. Now, from above, the variable $(\bar{X} - v_1)\sqrt{n}/\sigma$ is $N(0, 1)$ distributed, and we recall that $(n - 1)S^2/\sigma^2$, where

$$(n - 1)S^2 = \sum_{i=1}^{n} (X_i - \bar{X})^2 \tag{2}$$

is chi-square distributed with $n - 1$ degrees of freedom. Therefore, the random variable defined by the ratio

$$T = \frac{(\bar{X} - v_1)\sqrt{n}/\sigma}{S/\sigma} = \frac{(\bar{X} - v_1)\sqrt{n}}{S} \tag{3}$$

will be Student distributed with $n - 1$ degrees of freedom. The probability interval for the random variable T is centered about $T = 0$, since $E(T) = 0$, and the pdf for T is symmetric about $t = 0$. The probability interval of level p_0 is then specified by

$$\Pr\{|T| \leq \tau\} = p_0 , \tag{4}$$

where the probability is computed from the Student CDF, defined by

$$G_{n-1}(\tau) = \Pr\{T \leq \tau\}$$

$$= \frac{\Gamma\left(\dfrac{n}{2}\right)}{\sqrt{\pi(n-1)}\,\Gamma\left(\dfrac{n-1}{2}\right)} \int_{-\infty}^{\tau} \frac{dx}{\left(1 + \dfrac{x^2}{n-1}\right)^{n/2}} . \tag{5}$$

(The reader should note that this is the CDF for the Student distribution with $n - 1$ degrees of freedom. We use this form as an example because whenever we have a Student distribution in connection with the sum of n random variables, or with an n element sample, the Student distribution will have $n - 1$ degrees of freedom.) The values of $G_m(\tau)$ are found from tables such as Table 3 of Appendix B, at the end of this volume.

With the definition of the Student CDF given by Eq. (5), we have

$$\Pr\{|T| \leq \tau\} = \Pr\{T \leq \tau\} - \Pr\{T \leq -\tau\}$$

$$= G_{n-1}(\tau) - G_{n-1}(-\tau) . \tag{6}$$

Since the pdf for the Student distribution is symmetric $G_n(-\tau) = 1 - G_n(\tau)$, so

$$\Pr\{|T| \leq \tau\} = 2G_{n-1}(\tau) - 1 . \tag{7}$$

When this result is substituted into Eq. (4) we get the p_0 probability interval for T, determined by the inequality

$$|T| \leq \tau \qquad \text{or} \qquad -\tau \leq T \leq \tau , \tag{8}$$

where τ is the solution to

$$2G_{n-1}(\tau) - 1 = p_0 , \tag{9}$$

where $G_{n-1}(\tau)$ is defined by Eq. (5).

Example 1. Consider a sequence of 10 random variables X_i, $1 \leq i \leq 10$, identically normally distributed, with mean $\nu_1 = 2$ and an unknown variance. Determine 0.95 probability interval for the random variable

$$T = \frac{(\bar{X} - 2)\sqrt{10}}{S} . \tag{10}$$

The desired probability interval is given by Eq. (8), where τ is the solution of Eq. (9), with $p_0 = 0.95$ and $n = 10$. From the tabulated values of the CDF, defined by Eq. (5), we find the appropriate solution to (9):

$$\tau = 2.262 .\tag{11}$$

Substituting this value of τ into (8) gives the appropriate probability interval.

If the mean and variance of a normal distribution are unknown, then the mean can be estimated from an n element sample of this distribution. The p_0 confidence interval for this estimation is determined by the range of values of v_1 which will permit the particular sample value of the random variable T, t, to be within the p_0 probability interval of T. In other words, if 2τ is the length of the p_0 probability interval, as determined from Eq. (9), then the p_0 confidence interval for τ is the range of values which will satisfy the inequality

$$-\tau \leq t \leq \tau ,\tag{12}$$

where the particular value

$$t = \frac{(\bar{x} - v_1)\sqrt{n}}{s}\tag{13}$$

is determined solely from the values of the sample elements. If we substitute this expression for t into Eq. (12), multiplying each term by $s/\sqrt{n}$ and adding $-\bar{x}$ to each side, we obtain

$$-\frac{\tau s}{\sqrt{n}} - \bar{x} \leq -v_1 \leq \frac{\tau s}{\sqrt{n}} - \bar{x} .\tag{14}$$

Multiplying all terms of this inequality by -1 reverses the direction of the inequality signs and gives

$$\frac{\tau s}{\sqrt{n}} + \bar{x} \geq v_1 \geq \bar{x} - \frac{\tau s}{\sqrt{n}} .\tag{15}$$

This is the p_0 confidence interval for v_1, using an n element sample to compute $\bar{x}$ and s^2, where τ is the solution of Eq. (9).

Example 2. Consider a 10 element sample from a population with normal distribution but unknown mean and variance. If the sample elements are such that the computed values are

$$\bar{x} = \frac{1}{10} \sum_{i=1}^{10} x_i = 5 ,$$

$$s^2 = \frac{1}{9} \sum_{i=1}^{10} (x_i - \bar{x})^2 = 9 ,$$

what is the 0.95 confidence interval for the mean of the distribution? The confidence interval is determined by Eq. (15). Substituting the above values of $\bar{x}$ and s, using $n = 10$, and recalling from Example 1 that the solution to Eq. (9) is

$\tau = 2.262$ with $p_0 = 0.95$ and $n = 10$, Eq. (15) becomes the confidence interval

$$\frac{(2.262)\,(3)}{\sqrt{10}} + 5 \geq \nu_1 \geq 5 - \frac{(2.262)\,(3)}{\sqrt{10}}. \tag{16}$$

PROBLEMS

1. Consider the sample obtained in Example 1 of Section 6.5, and assume that the original populations were Gaussian. Find the 90% confidence interval for:

   a) μ_x
   b) μ_y

2. Find the 99.9% confidence intervals for the above problem.

   a) μ_x
   b) μ_y

3. In many situations we are interested in comparing the means of two samples from what may or may not be two different populations. Let $\bar{X}_1$ and S_1^2 be the sample mean and variance of the first sample (consisting of n_1 elements) and $\bar{X}_2$ and S_2^2 be the corresponding sample statistics for the second sample (consisting of n_2 elements). We assume that the first sample is taken from an $N(\mu_1, \sigma^2)$ population, while the second sample is taken from an $N(\mu_2, \sigma^2)$ population where μ_1, μ_2, σ are unknown. (Note that we are assuming that the two populations have the same variance.)

   a) Use the fact that

   $$\bar{X}_1 - \mu_1 \quad \text{is} \quad N\left(0, \frac{\sigma^2}{n_1}\right),$$

   $$\bar{X}_2 - \mu_2 \quad \text{is} \quad N\left(0, \frac{\sigma^2}{n_2}\right),$$

   to show that

   $$\bar{X}_1 - \mu_1 - (\bar{X}_2 - \mu_2) \quad \text{is} \quad N\left(0, \frac{\sigma^2}{n_1} + \frac{\sigma^2}{n_2}\right).$$

   b) Show that the random variable

   $$\frac{(n_1 - 1)S_1^2 + (n_2 - 1)S_2^2}{\sigma^2}$$

   is chi-square distributed with $n_1 + n_2 - 2$ degrees of freedom.

   c) Use the above results to show that the random variable

   $$\frac{\bar{X}_1 - \bar{X}_2 - \mu_1 + \mu_2}{\sqrt{\frac{1}{n_1} + \frac{1}{n_2}}\left[\frac{(n_1 - 1)S_1^2 + (n_2 - 1)S_2^2}{n_1 + n_2 - 2}\right]^{1/2}}$$

   is Student distributed with $n_1 + n_2 - 2$ degrees of freedom.

4. Consider one n element sample with mean $\bar{X}_1$, variance S_1^2 and ith element, X_{1i}, taken from an $N(\mu_1, \sigma_1^2)$ population. Consider another n element sample with X_2, S_2^2, and X_{2i} taken from an $N(\mu_2, \sigma_2^2)$ population.

a) Show that

$$\frac{(\bar{X}_1 - \bar{X}_2 - \mu_1 + \mu_2)\sqrt{n}}{\sqrt{\sigma_1^2 + \sigma_2^2}}$$

is $N(0, 1)$ distributed.

b) Show that $X_{1i} - \bar{X}_1$ is $N\left(0, \sigma_1^2 \left(\frac{n-1}{n}\right)\right)$ and $X_{2i} - \bar{X}_2$ is $N\left(0, \sigma_2^2\left(\frac{n-1}{n}\right)\right)$ for all i. Then use this result to show that

$$\frac{X_{1i} - \bar{X}_1 + \bar{X}_2 - X_{2i}}{\frac{n-1}{n}(\sigma_1^2 + \sigma_2^2)^{1/2}}$$

is $N(0, 1)$ distributed.

c) Use the result of part (b) to show that

$$(\sigma_1^2 + \sigma_2^2)^{-1} \sum_{i=1}^{n} [(X_{1i} - \bar{X}_1) - (X_{2i} - \bar{X}_2)]^2$$

is chi-square distributed with $n - 1$ degrees of freedom.

d) Use the above results to show that

$$\frac{[\bar{X}_1 - \bar{X}_2 - (\mu_1 - \mu_2)]\sqrt{n}}{[S_1^2 + S_2^2 - 2R\, S_1\, S_2]^{1/2}}$$

is Student distributed with $n - 1$ degrees of freedom, where R is the sample correlation coefficient random variable

$$R = \frac{1}{(n-1)S_1\, S_2} \sum_{i=1}^{n} (X_{1i} - \bar{X}_1)\,(X_{2i} - \bar{X}_2)\,.$$

7.7 CONFIDENCE INTERVALS FOR THE RATIO OF VARIANCE OF TWO SAMPLES FROM A GAUSSIAN POPULATION

Consider one sequence of n_1 random variables X_i, $1 \le i \le n_1$, identically $N(\mu_1, \sigma_1^2)$ distributed, and another sequence of n_2 random variables Y_i, $1 \le i \le n_2$, identically $N(\mu_2, \sigma_2^2)$ distributed. The random variables

$$S_1^2 \frac{(n_1 - 1)}{\sigma_1^2} \quad \text{and} \quad S_2^2 \frac{(n_2 - 1)}{\sigma_2^2}\,,$$

where

$$S_1^2 = \frac{1}{n_1 - 1} \sum_{i=1}^{n_1} (X_i - \bar{X})^2,$$

$$S_2^2 = \frac{1}{n_2 - 1} \sum_{i=1}^{n_2} (Y_i - \bar{Y})^2,$$

(1)

will be chi-square distributed with $n_1 - 1$ and $n_2 - 1$ degrees of freedom, respectively. In Section 4.10 on continuous probability we found that a random variable defined by the ratio of two chi-square distributed variables and divided by the ratio of the respective degrees of freedom of the distributions will be Snedecor F distributed with the respective degrees of freedom. Therefore we can say that the random variable

$$F = \frac{(n_1 - 1)(S_1^2/\sigma_1^2)}{(n_2 - 1)(S_2^2/\sigma_2^2)}\left(\frac{n_2 - 1}{n_1 - 1}\right) = \left(\frac{S_1\sigma_2}{S_2\sigma_1}\right)^2 \tag{2}$$

is F distributed with $n_1 - 1$ and $n_2 - 1$ degrees of freedom. The probability that this random variable will lie within a specified interval can be expressed in terms of the CDF's for the F distribution as

$$\Pr\{u_1 \le F \le u_2\} = \mathscr{F}_{n_1-1,\, n_2-1}(u_2) - \mathscr{F}_{n_1-1,\, n_2-1}(u_1), \tag{3}$$

where

$$\Pr\{F \le u\} = \mathscr{F}_{m,\, n}(u) = \int_0^u \frac{\Gamma\left(\dfrac{m+n}{2}\right) m^{m/2}\, n^{n/2}\, x^{(m-2)/2}}{\Gamma\left(\dfrac{m}{2}\right)\Gamma\left(\dfrac{n}{2}\right)(n + mx)^{(n+m)/2}}\, dx. \tag{4}$$

(The reader should note that the first subscript denotes the number of degrees of freedom in the numerator of the definition for F, while the second subscript denotes the number of degrees of freedom in the denominator.)

Since the pdf for F is not symmetric, we impose the centering condition $P\{F \le u_1\} = P\{F \ge u_2\}$ on the confidence interval, determined by

$$\Pr\{u_1 \le F \le u_2\} = p_0. \tag{5}$$

In terms of the CDF's the centering condition becomes

$$\mathscr{F}_{n_1-1,\, n_2-1}(u_1) = 1 - \mathscr{F}_{n_1-1,\, n_2-1}(u_2), \tag{6}$$

and the interval, determined by Eq. (5), becomes

$$\mathscr{F}_{n_1-1,\, n_2-1}(u_2) - \mathscr{F}_{n_1-1,\, n_2-1}(u_1) = p_0. \tag{7}$$

The simultaneous solution of Eqs. (6) and (7) is

$$\mathscr{F}_{n_1-1,\, n_2-1}(u_2) = \tfrac{1}{2}(1 + p_0),$$
$$\mathscr{F}_{n_1-1,\, n_2-1}(u_1) = \tfrac{1}{2}(1 - p_0), \tag{8}$$

where $\mathscr{F}$ is defined in Eq. (4).

For reasons of economy, the $\mathscr{F}$ distribution tables, such as Table 4 of Appendix B, include only those values of $\mathscr{F}$ close to one. Values of $\mathscr{F}$ close to zero can be determined from the tabulated values by transforming the CDF in the following manner.

Noting that $\mathscr{F}_{m,n}(\infty) = 1$, we can subtract Eq. (4) from the equation $1 = \mathscr{F}_{m,n}(\infty)$ to get

$$1 - \mathscr{F}_{m,n}(u) = \int_u^\infty \frac{\Gamma\left(\dfrac{m+n}{2}\right) m^{m/2} \, n^{n/2} \, x^{(m-2)/2}}{\Gamma\left(\dfrac{m}{2}\right) \Gamma\left(\dfrac{n}{2}\right) (n + mx)^{(m+n)/2}} \, dx. \tag{9}$$

We now change the variable of integration $x \to 1/y$ with $dx \to -dy/y^2$, so the integral in Eq. (9) becomes

$$-\int_{1/u}^0 \frac{\Gamma\left(\dfrac{m+n}{2}\right) m^{m/2} \, n^{n/2} \, y^{1-(m/2)}}{\Gamma\left(\dfrac{m}{2}\right) \Gamma\left(\dfrac{n}{2}\right) \left(n + \dfrac{m}{y}\right)^{(m+n)/2}} \, \frac{dy}{y^2}. \tag{10}$$

Next we change the sign of the integral by interchanging the upper and lower limits of integration. If we also multiply both numerator and denominator of the integral by $y^{(m+n)/2}$, the expression (10) becomes

$$\int_0^{1/u} \frac{\Gamma\left(\dfrac{m+n}{2}\right) m^{m/2} \, n^{n/2} \, y^{(n/2)-1} \, dy}{\Gamma\left(\dfrac{m}{2}\right) \Gamma\left(\dfrac{n}{2}\right) (ny + m)^{(n+m)/2}}. \tag{11}$$

Comparing this integral with the definition in Eq. (4) we see that Eq. (11) is simply

$$\mathscr{F}_{n,m}(1/u). \tag{12}$$

Substitution into Eq. (9) yields

$$1 - \mathscr{F}_{m,n}(u) = \mathscr{F}_{n,m}(1/u). \tag{13}$$

Equation (13) can be used to find the arguments which give small values of $\mathscr{F}_{m,n}$.

Example 1. Find the value of u which satisfies the equation

$$\mathscr{F}_{10,5}(u) = 0.025. \tag{14}$$

If we set $m = 10$, $n = 5$ in Eq. (13), and if we substitute Eq. (14) into the left-hand side of Eq. (13), we get

$$0.975 = \mathscr{F}_{5,10}(1/u). \tag{15}$$

Noting that 5 is now the number of degrees of freedom in the numerator, we can find the value of $1/u$ which satisfies this equation from the tables, $1/u = 4.24$. The solution to Eq. (14) is then

$$u = \tfrac{1}{4.24} = 0.236. \tag{16}$$

Example 2. Consider one sequence of 11 random variables X_i, $1 \le i \le 11$, normally distributed and with identical mean and variance. Consider another sequence of six random variables Y_i, $1 \le i \le 6$, identically normally distributed. Then assume that the ratio of the variance of the X_i distribution to the variance of the Y_i distribution is known to be $\sigma_1^2/\sigma_2^2 = 4$. What is the 0.95 probability interval for the random variable S_1^2/S_2^2, where S_1^2 and S_2^2 are defined in Eq. (1)?

To find the probability interval for S_1^2/S_2^2 we must first find the probability interval for the related random variable F defined in Eq. (2). This tolerance interval is defined by Eq. (5), where u_1 and u_2 are the solutions to Eq. (8), with $n_1 = 11$, $n_2 = 6$, and $p_0 = 0.95$. The solution to $\mathscr{F}_{10, 5}(u_2) = 0.975$ is, from the table

$$u_2 = 6.62. \tag{17}$$

From Example 1, the solution of $\mathscr{F}_{10, 5}(u_1) = 0.025$ is found to be

$$u_1 = 0.236. \tag{18}$$

Therefore, the 0.95 probability interval for F is

$$0.236 \le F \le 6.62. \tag{19}$$

Since $F = (S_1\sigma_2/S_2\sigma_1)^2$, the 0.95 tolerance interval for S_1^2/S_2^2 is found by multiplying the above inequality by σ_1^2/σ_2^2, which is defined to be equal to 4 in the present problem. The resulting probability interval for S_1^2/S_2^2 is then

$$0.944 \le S_1^2/S_2^2 \le 26.5. \tag{20}$$

Consider two normally distributed populations with unknown mean and variance. If we sample n_1 elements from the first population and n_2 elements from the second population, then the particular sample value of the random variable S_1^2/S_2^2 serves as an estimate of the ratio of the variances of the two populations. The p_0 confidence interval for this ratio is then the range of values of σ_1^2/σ_2^2 which will permit the particular sample value, $f = (s_1\sigma_2/s_2\sigma_1)^2$, to lie within the p_0 tolerance interval for the random variable F, defined by Eqs. (5) and (8). In mathematical language, σ_1^2/σ_2^2 must satisfy the double inequality

$$u_1 \le \left(\frac{s_1\sigma_2}{s_2\sigma_1}\right)^2 \le u_2. \tag{21}$$

Multiplying all three members of this inequality by s_2^2/s_1^2 gives the confidence interval for σ_2^2/σ_1^2

$$u_1 \frac{s_2^2}{s_1^2} \le \frac{\sigma_2^2}{\sigma_1^2} \le u_2 \frac{s_2^2}{s_1^2}. \tag{22}$$

Using the fact that the general inequality $a \le b$ is equivalent to $a^{-1} \ge b^{-1}$, we can obtain the confidence interval for σ_1^2/σ_2^2 by taking reciprocals of each term in Eq. (22), thereby reversing the order of the inequality signs to give

$$\frac{s_1^2}{(s_2^2 u_1)} \ge \frac{\sigma_1^2}{\sigma_2^2} \ge \frac{s_1^2}{(s_2^2 u_2)}. \tag{23}$$

Example 3. Assume that an experiment is performed with a quick and sloppy technique obtaining 16 samples such that

$$s_1^2 = \frac{1}{15} \sum_{i=1}^{16} (x_i - \bar{x})^2 = 25 . \tag{24}$$

This would seem to indicate a rather large variance and the procedure may be poor. Assume that the procedure is then refined to be more accurate, but now takes longer and is more costly. Therefore only eight samples are obtained, and from them

$$s_2^2 = \frac{1}{7} \sum_{i=1}^{8} (x_i - \bar{x})^2 = 5 \tag{25}$$

is computed. This seems to indicate that the new procedure yields a smaller variance which we wish to verify by computing the 0.95 confidence interval for σ_2^2/σ_1^2.

The extent of this confidence interval will indicate the decrease in variance which is provided by the second experiment. The 0.95 confidence interval for σ_2^2/σ_1^2 is now determined from Eq. (22) with

$$\frac{s_2^2}{s_1^2} = \frac{5}{25} = 0.2 ,$$

where u_1 and u_2 are found from the solution of Eq. (8), with $p_0 = 0.95$ and $n_1 = 16$, $n_2 = 8$. From the table, the solution to

$$\mathscr{F}_{15, 7} (u_2) = 0.025 \tag{26}$$

is found to be $u_2 = 4.57$. Equation (26) can be rewritten with the assistance of Eq. (13):

$$\mathscr{F}_{7, 15}\!\left(\frac{1}{u_1}\right) = 0.975 . \tag{27}$$

The solution to this equation is, from the table,

$$\frac{1}{u_1} = 3.29 \quad \text{or} \quad u_1 = 0.304 . \tag{28}$$

Substituting all these quantities into Eq. (22) gives the 0.95 confidence interval

$$0.068 \leq \frac{\sigma_2^2}{\sigma_1^2} \leq 0.915 . \tag{29}$$

If we were only interested in the minimum probable improvement effected by the change in experimental procedure we could say, with 97.5% confidence, that $\sigma_2^2/\sigma_1^2 \leq 0.915$, since we would not really care about the possible values of σ_2^2/σ_1^2 which would fall below the lower limit of this confidence interval. In this case we would not have to compute the lower limit u_1 of the confidence interval. This is an example of the reasoning involved in one-tail testing, to be discussed in greater detail in Chapter 9.

PROBLEMS

1. Use the conditions of Example 1, Section 6.5, and compute the 95% confidence interval for the difference between the means.

2. In Example 1 of Section 6.5 compute the 90% confidence interval for σ_x^2/σ_y^2.

3. With the conditions of the same example, compute the 99% confidence interval for σ_x^2/σ_y^2.

4. Show that if $F_{l,k}$ is $\mathscr{F}$ distributed with l degrees of freedom in the numerator and k degrees of freedom in the denominator, then $\sqrt{F_{1,k}}$ is Student distributed with k degrees of freedom.

7.8 SUMMARY OF CONFIDENCE INTERVAL DEFINITIONS FOR NORMAL DISTRIBUTIONS

The results of the preceding discussions on confidence intervals are summarized in Table 1. The first column gives the parameter estimated, followed by the number of the section in which the typical problem is discussed. The third column lists the sample statistics used for estimating the confidence interval. The fourth column gives the distribution of the random variable whose particular sample value gives the sample statistic of the third column. The fifth column gives the confidence interval in terms of the appropriate sample statistics and whatever parameters are given. The sixth column gives the CDF equations which determine the end points of the confidence interval. The last column gives the definition of the appropriate CDF.

7.9 JOINT PROBABILITY REGIONS FOR MULTIVARIATE DISTRIBUTIONS

In many problems one is concerned with joint distributions of random variables. The new degrees of freedom, introduced by additional random variables, can be characterized in many different ways. To illustrate one common and simple method we consider the independent random variable X_1, which is $N(\nu_1, \sigma_1^2)$ distributed, and X_2, which is $N(\nu_2, \sigma_2^2)$ distributed. According to the definition given in Section 4.8, Eq. (1), the sum of the squares of two $N(0, 1)$ random variables

$$Y_2 = \frac{(X_1 - \nu_1)^2}{\sigma_1^2} + \frac{(X_2 - \nu_2)^2}{\sigma_2^2} \tag{1}$$

Table 1

TABLE OF BASIC CONFIDENCE INTERVALS OF LEVEL p_0
(Assuming sample elements from a normally distributed population)

Desired Parameter	Given Parameter	Sample Statistic	Distribution of Variable	Confidence Interval	Defining Equations	Definition of CDF
ν_1 7.3	σ	$\dfrac{(\bar{X}-\nu_1)\sqrt{n}}{\sigma}$, $\bar{X}=\dfrac{1}{n}\sum_{i=1}^n X_i$	Gaussian with zero mean and unit variance	$\bar{x}-\dfrac{u\sigma}{\sqrt{n}}\le \nu_1 \le \bar{x}+\dfrac{u\sigma}{\sqrt{n}}$	$F(u)=\tfrac{1}{2}(1+p_0)$	$F(u)=\dfrac{1}{\sqrt{2\pi}}\displaystyle\int_{-\infty}^u e^{-x^2/2}\,dx$
σ^2 7.4	ν_1	$\dfrac{Y}{\sigma^2}$, $Y=\sum_{i=1}^n (X_i-\nu_1)^2$	Chi-square with n degrees of freedom	$\dfrac{y}{u_2}\le \sigma^2 \le \dfrac{y}{u_1}$	$C_n(u_2)=\tfrac{1}{2}(1+p_0)$ $C_n(u_1)=\tfrac{1}{2}(1-p_0)$	$C_n(u)=\displaystyle\int_0^u \dfrac{x^{(n-2)/2}\,e^{-x/2}}{2^{n/2}\,\Gamma\!\left(\frac{n}{2}\right)}\,dx$
σ^2 7.5	None	$\dfrac{(n-1)S^2}{\sigma^2}$, $S^2=\dfrac{\sum_{i=1}^n (X_i-\bar{X})^2}{n-1}$	Chi-square with $n-1$ degrees of freedom	Let $z=(n-1)s^2$ $\dfrac{z}{u_2}\le \sigma^2 \le \dfrac{z}{u_1}$	$C_{n-1}(u_2)=\tfrac{1}{2}(1+p_0)$ $C_{n-1}(u_1)=\tfrac{1}{2}(1-p_0)$	Same as above
ν_1 7.6	None	$\dfrac{(\bar{X}-\nu_1)\sqrt{n}}{S}$	Student with $n-1$ degrees of freedom	$\bar{x}-\dfrac{us}{\sqrt{n}}\le \nu_1 \le \bar{x}+\dfrac{us}{\sqrt{n}}$	$G_{n-1}(u)=\tfrac{1}{2}(1+p_0)$	$G_{n-1}(u)=$ $\dfrac{\Gamma\!\left(\frac{n}{2}\right)}{\sqrt{\pi(n-1)}\,\Gamma\!\left(\frac{n-1}{2}\right)}\displaystyle\int_{-\infty}^u \dfrac{dx}{\left(1+\frac{x^2}{n-1}\right)^{n/2}}$
$\dfrac{\sigma_2^2}{\sigma_1^2}$ 7.7	None	$\left(\dfrac{S_1\sigma_2}{S_2\sigma_1}\right)^2$, $S_1^2=\dfrac{\sum_{i=1}^{n_1}(X_i-\bar{X})^2}{n_1-1}$ $S_2^2=\dfrac{\sum_{i=1}^{n_2}(Y_i-\bar{Y})^2}{n_2-1}$	F with n_1-1 degrees of freedom in the numerator and n_2-1 degrees of freedom in the denominator	$\dfrac{u_1 s_2^2}{s_1^2}\le \left(\dfrac{\sigma_2}{\sigma_1}\right)^2 \le \dfrac{u_2 s_2^2}{s_1^2}$	$\mathscr{F}_{n_1-1,n_2-1}(u_2)=\tfrac{1}{2}(1+p_0)$ $\mathscr{F}_{n_1-1,n_2-1}(u_1)=\tfrac{1}{2}(1-p_0)$ Since $\mathscr{F}_{n_1-1,n_2-1}(u_1)=$ $1-\mathscr{F}_{n_2-1,n_1-1}(u_2)$ The equation for u_1 can be rewritten as $\mathscr{F}_{n_2-1,n_1-1}(1/u_1)=\tfrac{1}{2}(1+p_0)$.	$\mathscr{F}_{m,n}(u)=$ $\displaystyle\int_0^u \dfrac{\Gamma\!\left(\frac{m+n}{2}\right)m^{m/2}\,n^{n/2}\,x^{(m-2)/2}}{\Gamma\!\left(\frac{m}{2}\right)\Gamma\!\left(\frac{n}{2}\right)(n+mx)^{(m+n)/2}}\,dx$

is chi-square distributed with two degrees of freedom. It follows that

$$\Pr\{Y_2 \le u\} = \int_0^u \frac{e^{-z/2}}{2} \, dz = C_2(u) \, , \tag{2}$$

where the chi-square CDF with n degrees of freedom, $C_n(u)$ is tabulated in Appendix B. Of course, the integral in Eq. (2) can be evaluated analytically, as can any chi-square CDF with an even number of degrees of freedom. The result is easily seen to be

$$\Pr\{Y_2 \le u\} = 1 - e^{-u/2} \, . \tag{3}$$

The condition $Y_2 \le u$ implies that X_1 and X_2 must fall *within* the ellipse

$$\frac{(X_1 - \nu_1)^2}{\sigma_1^2} + \frac{(X_2 - \nu_2)^2}{\sigma_2^2} = u \, . \tag{4}$$

The ellipse specified by this equation could be called the p_0 probability ellipse, where

$$p_0 = \Pr\{Y_2 \le u\} = 1 - e^{-u/2} = C_2(u) \, . \tag{5}$$

Since the analytic relation between p_0 and u is quite simple, we can solve Eq. (5) for u in terms of p_0 and substitute into Eq. (4) to get the p_0 probability region of (X_1, X_2) specified by

$$\frac{(X_1 - \nu_1)^2}{\sigma_1^2} + \frac{(X_2 - \nu_2)^2}{\sigma_2^2} \le - 2 \ln(1 - p_0) \tag{6}$$

(for X_1, X_2 independent). The elliptical region is illustrated in Figure 3.

In many cases the joint variables are not independent. To illustrate the effect of dependence on the probability ellipse, we consider the random variables

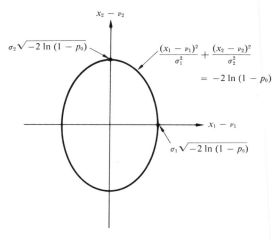

Fig. 7.3. p_0 probability ellipse for two independent Gaussian random variables ($\sigma_2 > \sigma_1$).

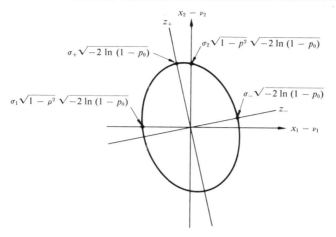

Fig. 7.4. p_0 probability ellipse for dependent jointly distributed variables.

X_1, X_2 which are joint normally distributed, $N(\nu_1, \sigma_1^2, \nu_2, \sigma_2^2, \rho)$. From Eq. (15) of Section 4.9, the joint pdf for X_1 and X_2 is

$$f(x_1, x_2) = \frac{1}{2\pi \sigma_1 \sigma_2 \sqrt{1 - \rho^2}} e^{-Q/2}, \tag{7}$$

where

$$Q = \frac{1}{1 - \rho^2}\left[\frac{(x_1 - \nu_1)^2}{\sigma_1^2} - \frac{2\rho(x_1 - \nu_1)(x_2 - \nu_2)}{\sigma_1 \sigma_2} + \frac{(x_2 - \nu_2)^2}{\sigma_2^2}\right]. \tag{8}$$

We showed in Section 4.9 that this quadratic form could be diagonalized by a rotation in the x_1, x_2 plane. Since this diagonal form is the sum of squares of two $N(0, 1)$ random variables, it must be chi-square distributed with two degrees of freedom. If the diagonalized form of Q is chi-square distributed, then Q itself must be chi-square distributed. Therefore we can use the derivation of Eq. (6) to show that the p_0 probability region for the two random variables X_1, X_2 is specified by

$$\frac{1}{1 - \rho^2}\left[\frac{(x_1 - \nu_1)^2}{\sigma_1^2} - \frac{2\rho(x_1 - \nu_1)(x_2 - \nu_2)}{\sigma_1 \sigma_2} + \frac{(x_2 - \nu_2)^2}{\sigma_2^2}\right] \leq -2\ln(1 - p_0). \tag{9}$$

A typical boundary ellipse for the region specified by Eq. (9) is shown in Figure 4. The axes of the ellipse are rotated from the coordinate axes by the same rotation matrix which diagonalizes the matrix

$$A = \frac{1}{1 - \rho^2}\begin{pmatrix} \dfrac{1}{\sigma_1^2} & -\dfrac{\rho}{\sigma_1 \sigma_2} \\[3mm] -\dfrac{\rho}{\sigma_1 \sigma_2} & \dfrac{1}{\sigma_2^2} \end{pmatrix}, \tag{10}$$

which is of the quadratic form

$$Q = (\mathbf{x} - \mathbf{v})^T A(\mathbf{x} - \mathbf{v}) . \tag{11}$$

Equation (11) is just the vector-matrix form of Eq. (8).

The reader can easily verify that the eigenvalues of A are

$$\sigma_{\pm}^{-2} = \left[\frac{\sigma_1^2 + \sigma_2^2}{2} \pm \tfrac{1}{2}\sqrt{(\sigma_1^2 - \sigma_2^2)^2 + 4\rho^2\sigma_1^2\sigma_2^2} \right]^{-2} \tag{12}$$

and the diagonal form of A is

$$D = R^T A R = \begin{pmatrix} \dfrac{1}{\sigma_+^2} & 0 \\ 0 & \dfrac{1}{\sigma_-^2} \end{pmatrix} . \tag{13}$$

The rotation matrix R is composed of the eigenvectors of A,

$$R = \begin{pmatrix} \dfrac{1}{\alpha} & -\dfrac{\beta}{\alpha} \\ \dfrac{\beta}{\alpha} & \dfrac{1}{\alpha} \end{pmatrix} , \tag{14}$$

where

$$\beta = \frac{\sigma_1\sigma_2}{\rho} \left[\frac{1}{\sigma_2^2} - \frac{1}{\sigma_1^2} + \sqrt{\left(\frac{1}{\sigma_1^2} - \frac{1}{\sigma_2^2}\right)^2 + \frac{4\rho^2}{\sigma_1^2\sigma_2^2}} \right] \tag{15}$$

(for $\sigma_2 > \sigma_1$), and the normalizing factor

$$\alpha = \sqrt{1 + \beta^2}. \tag{16}$$

The independent random variables in the rotated coordinate system are the components of

$$\mathbf{z} = \begin{pmatrix} z_+ \\ z_- \end{pmatrix} = R^T(\mathbf{x} - \mathbf{v}) \tag{17}$$

and the angle of rotation is

$$\theta = \arctan \beta. \tag{18}$$

In terms of the rotated coordinates, the ellipse equation is

$$-2 \ln (1 - p_0) = \mathbf{z}^T D\mathbf{z} = \frac{z_+^2}{\sigma_+^2} + \frac{z_-^2}{\sigma_-^2} . \tag{19}$$

Of course, the region specified by Eq. (19) is the same as that specified by Eq. (9). This can be easily verified by substituting z_+, z_-, as determined by Eq. (17), and σ_+, σ_-, as given in Eq. (12), into Eq. (19) to obtain the equality part of Eq. (9).

This procedure can be extended to more than two jointly distributed random variables. For an n-variate normal distribution with covariance matrix A^{-1}, the quadratic form

$$Q = (\mathbf{x} - \mathbf{v})^T A(\mathbf{x} - \mathbf{v}) \tag{20}$$

is chi-square distributed with n degrees of freedom, so the p_0 probability region is the interior of the n-dimensional ellipsoid specified by

$$(\mathbf{x} - \mathbf{v})^T A(\mathbf{x} - \mathbf{v}) = u_0, \tag{21}$$

where

$$C_n(u_0) = p_0 \tag{22}$$

and $C_n(u)$ is the chi-square CDF for n degrees of freedom, and is found from tables such as the one given in Appendix B. The probability for a randomly chosen n-tuple $\{x_1, x_2, \ldots, x_n\}$ to fall within the n-dimensional ellipsoid, specified by Eq. (21), is p_0.

PROBLEMS

1. Consider a bi-variate normal distribution with $v_1 = v_2 = 0, \sigma_1 = 1, \sigma_2 = 2, \rho = \sqrt{7}/4$.
   a) Find the equation for $p_0 = 0.95$ probability ellipse.
   b) Find the eigenvalues of the A matrix.
   c) Find the eigenvectors of A.
2. Derive Eqs. (12), (13), and (14) by diagonalizing the general A matrix given in Eq. (10).

7.10 CONFIDENCE REGIONS FOR REGRESSION PARAMETERS

Just as we developed the notion of a confidence interval for an estimated parameter from the notion of a probability interval, so can we develop confidence regions for jointly estimated parameters from the notion of the joint probability region. For the general linear regression problem discussed in Section 6.6, we would like to estimate the joint confidence region for the components of the parameter vector β or λ. The following discussion shows the method of estimating the confidence ellipsoid for the components of β, based on the assumption that the noise contributions at each data point are independent and identically distributed, so that the noise covariance matrix

$$V = \sigma I. \tag{1}$$

In Section 6.7 we showed that if the noise was normally distributed, the estimators for β could be viewed as joint, normally distributed random variables, $\tilde{\beta}$, with means $E(\tilde{\beta})$ and covariance matrix

$$K^{-1} = (B^T V^{-1} B)^{-1} = \sigma^2 (B^T B)^{-1}. \tag{2}$$

Now the discussion of Section 6.7 (particularly that following Eq. (15)) showed that if $\tilde{\beta}$ is an m-dimensional vector, the random variable

$$U_m = [\tilde{\beta} - E(\tilde{\beta})]^T \, \mathsf{K}[\tilde{\beta} - E(\tilde{\beta})]$$

$$= \frac{1}{\sigma^2} [\tilde{\beta} - E(\tilde{\beta})]^T \, \mathsf{B}^T \mathsf{B}[\tilde{\beta} - E(\tilde{\beta})] \qquad (3)$$

is chi-square distributed with m degrees of freedom. This relation could provide an estimate of the confidence region for the parameters $E(\tilde{\beta}) = \beta$, if σ^2 were known. However, since σ^2 is seldom known, we recall the estimator defined in Eq. (16) of Section 6.7 and define the random variable

$$Z_{n-m} = (n - m)\frac{\tilde{\sigma}^2}{\sigma^2} = \frac{1}{\sigma^2}[\mathbf{Y} - \mathsf{B}\tilde{\beta}]^T\,[\mathbf{Y} - \mathsf{B}\tilde{\beta}], \qquad (4)$$

which was shown to be chi-square distributed with $n - m$ degrees of freedom for an n-element sample.

Since U_m is chi-square distributed with m degrees of freedom and Z_{n-m} is chi-square distributed with $n - m$ degrees of freedom, the random variable

$$F_{m,\,n-m} = \frac{\dfrac{U_m/m}{Z_{n-m}}}{(n-m)} = \frac{[\tilde{\beta} - E(\tilde{\beta})]^T\,\mathsf{B}^T\mathsf{B}[\tilde{\beta} - E(\tilde{\beta})]\,(n-m)}{(\mathbf{Y} - \mathsf{B}\tilde{\beta})^T\,(\mathbf{Y} - \mathsf{B}\tilde{\beta})m} \qquad (5)$$

is $\mathscr{F}$, Snedecor, distributed with $(m, n - m)$ degrees of freedom. This means that

$$\Pr\{F_{m,\,n-m} \le u\} = \mathscr{F}_{m,\,n-m}(u), \qquad (6)$$

where the Snedecor CDF $\mathscr{F}_{n,\,n}$ is defined in Eq. (4) of Section 7.7, and tabulated in Appendix B.

To find the p_0 confidence region for the parameters $E(\tilde{\beta}) = \beta$, we determine u_0 from the equation

$$\mathscr{F}_{m,\,n-m}(u_0) = p_0. \qquad (7)$$

We then specify the ellipsoid of values for $E(\tilde{\beta}) = \beta$, which permit the particular sample value of $F_{m,\,n-m}(= f_{m,\,n-m})$ to satisfy the inequality

$$u_0 \ge f_{m,\,n-m} = \frac{[\hat{\beta} - E(\tilde{\beta})]^T\,\mathsf{B}^T\mathsf{B}[\hat{\beta} - E(\tilde{\beta})]\,(n-m)}{(\mathbf{y} - \mathsf{B}\hat{\beta})^T\,(\mathbf{y} - \mathsf{B}\hat{\beta})m}, \qquad (8)$$

where the components of $\hat{\beta}$ are the particular sample values of $\tilde{\beta}$.

Since $\hat{\beta}$, $\mathbf{y}$, B, and u_0 are known, Eq. (8) specifies an ellipsoidal region of confidence for the components of $E(\tilde{\beta}) = \beta$. The following example illustrates how this general ellipsoid degenerates into an ellipse in the case of simple $m = 2$ linear regression.

Example 1. Consider the simple regression problem defined in Example 1, Section 6.5, and further discussed in Example 1, Section 6.7. Compute the 0.95 confidence ellipse for the simple regression parameters β_0, β_1.

For this case, Eq. (7) becomes

$$\mathscr{F}_{2,\,8}(u_0) = 0.95. \tag{9}$$

From the table in Appendix B we find the solution to this equation

$$u_0 = 4.46. \tag{10}$$

To use the ellipse equation, Eq. (8), we recall from the discussion of Example 1, Section 6.7, that

$$\hat{\beta} - E(\hat{\beta}) = \hat{\beta} - \beta = \begin{pmatrix} 7.10 - \beta_0 \\ 0.775 - \beta_1 \end{pmatrix},$$

$$\frac{(\mathbf{y} - \mathbf{B}\hat{\beta})^T\,(\mathbf{y} - \mathbf{B}\hat{\beta})}{n - m} = \hat{\sigma}^2 = 0.84,$$

$$\mathbf{B}^T\mathbf{B} = \begin{pmatrix} n & 0 \\ 0 & (n-1)s_x^2 \end{pmatrix} = \begin{pmatrix} 10 & 0 \\ 0 & 16.9 \end{pmatrix}.$$

Substituting these quantities into Eq. (8) gives the elliptical region bounded by the ellipse

$$4.46 = 5.95(\beta_0 - 7.10)^2 + 10.1(\beta_1 - 0.775)^2. \tag{11}$$

This 0.95 confidence region is the interior of the ellipse shown in Fig. 5. Since β_0 and β_1 are uncorrelated, the axes of the ellipse lie along the coordinate axes in this simple regression example.

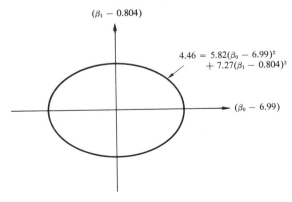

Fig. 7.5. Elliptical confidence region for simple regression.

BIBLIOGRAPHY

1. K. A. BROWNLEE, *Statistical Theory and Methodology in Science and Engineering*, 2nd ed., John Wiley & Sons, New York, 1965. A very comprehensive .discussion of regression analysis, although the multivariate case is rather complicated without the use of matrix algebra.

2. P. G. HOEL, *Introduction to Mathematical Statistics*, John Wiley & Sons, New York, 1962. An excellent elementary text.

3. S. S. WILKS, *Mathematical Statistics*, John Wiley & Sons, New York, 1962. This advanced text contains a comprehensive treatment of the whole subject.

4. M. G. KENDALL and A. STUART, *The Advanced Theory of Statistics*, Vol. II, 2nd ed., Hafner Publishing Company, New York, 1961. A comprehensive treatise covering the entire subject, including a discussion of fiducial intervals.

CHAPTER 8

ORDER STATISTICS AND NONPARAMETRIC METHODS

8.1 INTRODUCTION AND DEFINITIONS

In the previous chapters we were primarily concerned with using sampling information to provide estimates of certain important parameters of an underlying population distribution. In most of the previous cases we assumed the underlying population to be normally distributed, and in all cases we were interested in characterizing the distribution by a mean and variance.

In the present chapter we will characterize a distribution by the magnitudes of certain elements of an ordered sample taken from that distribution. In many cases we will not even be concerned with the distribution of the elements of the sample itself, but only in the distribution of elements in the ordered sample. In order to describe the situation more precisely we give the following definition of order statistic.

Let the random variables X_i, $1 \leq i \leq n$, be the n elements of a sample from a population. We will assume, for simplicity, that the distribution is continuous, so that we can describe the behavior of the sample elements in terms of pdf's.

According to our previous notation, we let x_i, $1 \leq i \leq n$, be the particular values assumed by the sample elements of a particular n element sample. Now let us order these n particular elements from smallest to largest, and let us call the ordered elements y_i, $1 \leq i \leq n$, so that we have $y_1 \leq y_2 \leq y_3 \leq \cdots \leq y_n$.

There is a unique mapping of the elements of the set $\{x_i\}$ into the elements of the set $\{y_i\}$. In other words, for each element of $\{x_i\}$ there is one, and only one element of $\{y_i\}$. (Some ambiguity could result if two or more of the elements of $\{x_i\}$ were equal. If the distribution is continuous, however, the probability of such an occurrence is zero.) Note that the inverse mapping from $\{y_i\}$ to $\{x_i\}$ is not unique because the n ordered elements of $\{y_i\}$ can be permuted to form $n!$ different sets $\{x_i\}$. This feature will be illustrated in the example below.

We may define the random variables Y_i, $1 \leq i \leq n$, to be the random variables which assume the particular values $\{y_i\}$ for a particular sample. For example, Y_1 is defined to be the random variable whose value, y_1, is determined by the smallest element of the particular sample $\{x_i\}$. Similarly, the value of Y_n will be the largest element of the particular sample. The random variable $Y_n - Y_1$ is called the sample range, since all the other sample elements fall within this interval.

The reader should note that all the Y_i are sample statistics. Since the Y_i form an ordered set, they are also called order statistics. We frequently use the following names for some of these:

a) $Y_{(n+1)/2}$ is called the sample median. This order statistic is not necessarily the median of the distribution, although we will show below that it is the maximum likelihood estimate of the population median. It is evident from this definition that there can only be a median if n is odd.

b) Y_k is generally called the kth order statistic, or the location of the kth quantile.

Example 1. Consider a four element sample from a population which is presumed to be continuously distributed. Let the particular values of the sample elements be $x_1 = 1.3$, $x_2 = 0.5$, $x_3 = 4.1$, $x_4 = 2.3$. If we order these four numbers we get the particular values of the order statistics $y_1 = 0.5$, $y_2 = 1.3$, $y_3 = 2.3$, $y_4 = 4.1$. Note that the four numbers in $\{x_i\}$ uniquely specify the ordered set $\{y_i\}$.

Now there are 4! permutations of the elements of the ordered set $\{y_i\}$. One of these permutations corresponds to the original sample elements $\{x_i\}$. The other 23 permutations (including one which is the set $\{y_i\}$ itself) correspond to the other possible orders in which the same four elements could have been picked. This discussion is nothing more than a formal way of stating that the ordered set $\{y_i\}$ depends only on which elements were chosen, not on the order in which they were chosen. In general, each $\{y_i\}$ corresponds to $n!$ possible original sets $\{x_i\}$.

8.2 PROBABILITY DISTRIBUTIONS OF ORDER STATISTICS

1. *Joint pdf for all Elements of the Sample.* If the sample elements are taken at random from a continuous distribution so that the X_i will be independent variables, then the joint pdf will be

$$f(x_1) f(x_2) \cdots f(x_n) , \tag{1}$$

where $f(x_i)$ is the pdf for the original population from which the sample is taken. The problem now is to transform this joint pdf into one for the $\{y_i\}$. The general transformation techniques were discussed in Section 4.7, but a simpler special procedure is appropriate to the present problem. To see the intuitive basis for this transformation procedure we illustrate with a four element sample.

Consider the range of values for the X_i over which we have $X_2 < X_1 < X_4 < X_3$. Under these circumstances we can establish the connection between the sample statistics and the order statistics directly as

$$Y_1 = X_2, \qquad Y_2 = X_1, \qquad Y_3 = X_4, \qquad Y_4 = X_3 \tag{2}$$

for

$$X_2 < X_1 < X_4 < X_3 . \tag{3}$$

For this range of values, the joint pdf for $\{Y_i\}$ is then

$$f(y_2) f(y_1) f(y_4) f(y_3) . \tag{4}$$

In this expression we have preserved the order of Eq. (1) for the f factors in order to further emphasize the direct connection between the $\{X_i\}$ and the $\{Y_i\}$.

Now consider the range of values

$$X_1 < X_2 < X_4 < X_3 \,. \tag{5}$$

Over this range, Y_3 and Y_4 are the same as in Eq. (2), but

$$Y_1 = x_1, \qquad Y_2 = x_2 \,. \tag{6}$$

In other words, the X_i's corresponding to Y_1 and Y_2 are interchanged. All values which X_1 can assume, while still satisfying Eq. (5), are the same as the values which X_2 could assume and still satisfy Eq. (3).

The same relationship holds between X_2 in Eq. (5) and X_1 in Eq. (3). Therefore, Y_1 and Y_2 have the same range of values for both the conditions of (3) and (5). We can conclude that for the ranges of sample statistics specified by Eq. (3) and (5), the pdf for the sample statistics is

$$2 f(y_1) f(y_2) f(y_3) f(y_4) \,, \tag{7}$$

where the factor of 2 appears because we have associated the range of y_i values, $y_1 \leq y_2 \leq y_3 \leq y_4$, with two different ranges for the x_i values. (This is possible since the mapping from $\{y_i\}$ to $\{x_i\}$ is not single valued.) In other words, when we integrate over all the y_i values, we will be integrating over two different sets of $\{x_i\}$ values simultaneously.

Now we know that there are $4! = 24$ different inequalities of the form of Eq. (3). Each of these inequalities specifies a range of values of the $\{x_i\}$. In other words, each of these $4!$ possible orderings specifies a range of values for the four $\{x_i\}$ and each of these $4!$ ranges maps into the same range, $Y_1 \leq Y_2 \leq Y_3 \leq Y_4$ of values for the $\{Y_i\}$. We therefore conclude that in general, when we integrate the four y_i over their range of values, $y_1 \leq y_2 \leq y_3 \leq y_4$, we will be simultaneously integrating over $4!$ ranges of values for the particular values, x_i, of the sample statistics. This conclusion can be summarized by the statement that the sum of the Jacobians (used to describe general transformations in Section 4.7) of the transformation from the $\{x_i\}$ to the $\{y_i\}$ is $4!$.

These arguments can easily be extended to n element samples in which case the Jacobian of the transformation from the $\{x_i\}$ to the $\{y_i\}$ is $n!$. We conclude, therefore, that the pdf for the order statistics of an n element sample from a continuous random variable with pdf $f(x)$ is

$$n! \, f(y_1) f(y_2) f(y_3) f(y_4) \cdots f(y_n) \,, \tag{8}$$

where $a \leq y_1 \leq y_2 \leq y_3 \cdots \leq y_n \leq b$, and $a \leq X \leq b$ is the range of the original population.

The reader should verify that integration of this pdf over the ranges of possible values for the y_i will give 1, so that the pdf is properly normalized. (See Problem 1 at the end of this section.)

Example 1. Let $f(x) = 2x$, $0 \le x \le 1$ be the pdf for a population. The pdf for the order statistics of a four element sample from this population is

$$g(y_1, y_2, y_3, y_4) = 4! \, 2^4 \, y_1 \, y_2 \, y_3 \, y_4 , \tag{9}$$

where

$$0 \le y_1 \le y_2 \le y_3 \le y_4 \le 1 .$$

The reader can easily verify that

$$\int_0^1 dy_4 \int_0^{y_4} dy_3 \int_0^{y_3} dy_2 \int_0^{y_2} dy_1 \, g(y_1, y_2, y_3, y_4) = 1 . \tag{10}$$

2. Distribution of Y_n (Largest Element of Sample). In examining properties of the sample extremes (Y_1 and Y_n) it is easiest to begin with the CDF for Y_n. Since all $X_i \le Y_n$, we write

$$\Pr\{Y_n \le y_n\} = \Pr\{X_1, X_2, \ldots, X_n \le y_n\} . \tag{11}$$

Since the X_i are independent of each other, the expression on the right side of this equation can be written as the product of n CDF's, so that the CDF for Y_n becomes

$$\Pr\{Y_n \le y_n\} = \prod_{i=1}^{n} \Pr\{X_i \le y_n\} = [F(y_n)]^n , \tag{12}$$

where $F(y)$ is the CDF for the original population. We can obtain the pdf for Y_n by simply differentiating this last equation with respect to y_n:

$$g_n(y_n) = \frac{d}{dy_n} \Pr\{Y_n \le y_n\}$$

$$= n f(y_n) \, [F(y_n)]^{n-1} . \tag{13}$$

The reader should recall, from the discussion of continuous probability, that we can also obtain this marginal pdf by integrating the joint pdf given in Eq. (8) over all possible values of the $n - 1$ variables $y_1, y_2, \ldots, y_{n-1}$, namely $a \le y_1 \le y_2 \le \cdots \le y_n$. The reader should verify that this procedure leads also to Eq. (13), see Problem 1, part c, at the end of this section.

Example 2. Consider a four element sample from the population used in Example 1. The pdf for Y_4 is easily seen to be

$$g_4(y_4) = 8 \, y_4^7 . \tag{14}$$

As would be expected intuitively, this pdf is heavily weighted to emphasize large values of y_4.

3. Distribution of Y_1 (Smallest Element of Sample). We begin again with the CDF and note that

$$\Pr\{Y_1 \le y_1\} = 1 - \Pr\{Y_1 \ge y_1\}$$

$$= 1 - \Pr\{X_1, X_2, \ldots, X_n \ge y_1\} . \tag{15}$$

Again, invoking the independence of the X_i, we can express the product of n probabilities, so that the CDF for Y_1 becomes

$$\Pr\{Y_1 \le y_1\} = 1 - \prod_{i=1}^{n} \Pr\{X_i \ge y_1\} = 1 - [1 - F(y_1)]^n . \tag{16}$$

Differentiating this CDF gives the pdf

$$g_1(y_1) = n f(y_1) [1 - F(y_1)]^{n-1} . \tag{17}$$

The reader should note that $g_1(y_1)$ could also be obtained by integrating the joint pdf given in Eq. (8) over all possible values of all the variables y_i except y_1 (see Problem 2).

Example 3. Consider the sampling problem of Examples 1 and 2. The pdf for the smallest sample element is easily seen to be

$$g_1(y_1) = 8 y_1(1 - y_1^2)^3 , \tag{18}$$

and the CDF is

$$\Pr\{Y_1 \le y_1\} = 1 - (1 - y_1^2)^4 . \tag{19}$$

4. Distribution of an Intermediate Y_k (1 < k < n). In this general case it is simplest to use a general argument to obtain the pdf directly. This is done by noting that

$$\Pr\{y_k \le Y_k \le y_k + dy_k\} =$$

$$
\begin{aligned}
&= \Pr\{(k - 1) \ X_i && \text{satisfy} && a \le x_i \le y_k, \\
&\quad\quad \text{one } X_i && \text{satisfies} && y_k \le x_i \le y_k + dy_k, \\
&\quad (n - k) \ X_i && \text{satisfy} && y_k + dy_k \le x_i \le b\}.
\end{aligned}
\tag{20}
$$

Since the X_i are independent, the probability on the right side of this equation has a trinomial distribution. From the n elements x_i we choose $k - 1$ to satisfy $a \le x_i \le y_k$, we choose 1 of the x_i to satisfy $y_k \le x_i \le y_k + dy_k$, and the remaining $n - k$ of the X_i must satisfy $y_k + dy_k \le X_i \le b$. The number of ways to make these choices, recalling the discussion of the trinomial coefficient in discrete probability theory, is

$$\frac{n!}{(k - 1)! \, (1!) \, (n - k)!} .$$

The probability of the chosen $(k - 1)$ x_i's being less than y_k is $[F(y_k)]^{k-1}$. The probability of the chosen 1 being in the interval $y_k \le X_i \le y_k + dy_k$, for infinitesimal dy_k, is $f(y_k) \, dy_k$. The probability of the remaining $(n - k)$ x_i's being greater than $y_k + dy_k$, is $[1 - F(y_k + dy_k)]^{n-k} \approx [1 - F(y_k)]^{n-k}$. Therefore we have

$$
\begin{aligned}
\Pr\{y_k \le Y_k \le y_k + dy_k\} &= g_k(y_k)dy_k \\
&= \frac{n! f(y_k)[F(y_k)]^{k-1}[1 - F(y_k)]^{n-k}dy_k}{(n - k)! \, (k - 1)!} .
\end{aligned}
\tag{21}
$$

This equation implies that the marginal pdf for Y_k is

$$g_k(y_k) = n \binom{n-1}{k-1} f(y_k)[F(y_k)]^{k-1}[1 - F(y_k)]^{n-k} . \tag{22}$$

The reader should note that $g_1(y_1)$ and $g_n(y_n)$ are just special cases of this general result. The pdf of Eq. (22) could, of course, be derived by integrating the general pdf of Eq. (8); however, this requires considerably more effort, and would not be as illuminating (see Problem 3) as the procedure described above.

Example 4. Consider the population and sample of Examples 1, 2 and 3 above. The pdf for the second order statistic is

$$g_2(y_2) = 24y_2^3(1 - y_2^2)^2 . \tag{23}$$

The pdf for the third order statistic is, similarly,

$$g_3(y_3) = 24y_3^5(1 - y_3^2) . \tag{24}$$

The shift in emphasis from g_2 to g_3 is obvious.

Example 5. Compute $E(Y_k)$ for an n element sample from a $U(0,1)$ population. The pdf for y_k is determined by Eq. (22) using the $U(0, 1)$ CDF for x_i, $F(y_k) = y_k$, so that

$$g_k(y_k) = n\binom{n-1}{k-1}y_k^{k-1}(1 - y_k)^{n-k} . \tag{25}$$

With this pdf we can easily compute

$$E(Y_k) = \int_0^1 yg_k(y)dy = n\binom{n-1}{k-1}\int_0^1 y^k(1 - y)^{n-k}dy = \frac{k}{n + 1} , \tag{26}$$

where the last integral (beta integral, see Eq. (22) of Section 4.4) is easily evaluated by repeated integration by parts.

We complete this discussion of the elementary properties of Y_k by computing the CDF for Y_k. The derivation is considerably simplified by noting that the CDF for Y_k can be written as

$$\Pr\{Y_k \le y_k\} = \Pr\{\text{at least } k \text{ of the sample } x_i \text{ satisfy } X_i \le y_k\}$$

$$= \sum_{j=0}^{n-k} \Pr\{\text{exactly } k + j \text{ of the sample } x_i \text{ satisfy } X_i \le y_k\}. \tag{27}$$

If exactly $k + j$ of the sample elements x_i satisfy $X_i \le y_k$, then all the remaining $n - k - j$ sample elements must satisfy $X_i \ge y_k$. Under such circumstances

$$Y_{k+j} \le y_k \le Y_{k+j+1} , \tag{28}$$

so

$$\Pr\{\text{exactly } k + j \text{ of the } x_i \text{ satisfy } X_i \le y_k\} = \Pr\{Y_{k+j} \le y_k \le Y_{k+j+1}\}. \tag{29}$$

Now the occurrence of the double inequality of Eq. (28) is the same as having $k + j$ sample elements fall below y_k and $n - k - j$ elements fall above y_k. Since the probability of a single element falling below y_k is $F(y_k)$, the probability of the event specified by Eq. (28) is simply the binomial frequency function

$$\Pr\{Y_{k+j} \le y_k \le Y_{k+j+1}\} = \binom{n}{k+j} [F(y_k)]^{k+j}[1 - F(y_k)]^{n-k-j}. \tag{30}$$

Substituting this expression for Eq. (29) into Eq. (27) we obtain

$$\Pr\{Y_k \le y_k\} = \sum_{j=0}^{n-k} \binom{n}{k+j} [F(y_k)]^{k+j} [1 - F(y_k)]^{n-k-j}. \tag{31}$$

Of course, this CDF could be obtained by integrating the pdf given in Eq. (22). The procedure requires successive integration by parts to generate all terms of the series of Eq. (31) (see Problem 4). The reader should verify that $g_k(y_k)$ can also be obtained by differentiating $\Pr\{Y_k \le y_k\}$ with respect to y_k (see Problem 4, part d at end of the section).

Example 6. Using the same population and sample size as given in Examples 1 through 5, we easily find

$$\Pr\{Y_2 \le y_2\} = 6y_2^4(1 - y_2^2)^2 + 4y_2^6(1 - y_2^2) + y_2^8,$$
$$\Pr\{Y_3 \le y_3\} = 4y_3^6(1 - y_3^2) + y_3^8.$$

Note that the subscript on y is simply to assist the reader in remembering what the problem is about. The principal item to be remembered is this: Whatever the subscript, y is simply a particular number (between 0 and 1 in the present problem) and serves to define an upper bound on some particular order statistic. We are frequently interested in combining CDF's such that

$$\Pr\{Y_2 \le y \le Y_3\} = \Pr\{Y_2 \le y\} - \Pr\{Y_3 \le y\}$$
$$= 6y^4(1 - y^2)^2.$$

This can also be viewed as a simple example of the application of Eq. (27).

PROBLEMS

1. Consider the joint pdf, given by Eq. (8). (All Eq. numbers referred to in Problems 1–7 are from Section 8.2.)

   a) Show that the integral over y_1, $a \le y_1 \le y_2$ gives

   $$n!\, F(y_2)\, f(y_2)f(y_3) \cdots f(y_n) ,$$

   where $F(x)$ is the CDF for the original population, so that $F(a) = 0$ and $F(b) = 1$.

   b) Show that a subsequent integration over y_2, $a \le y_2 \le y_3$ yields

   $$\frac{n!}{2} [F(y_3)]^2 f(y_3) \cdots f(y_n) .$$

c) Show that similar successive integrations over ranges of the remaining variables $0 \le y_3 \le y_4 \le \cdots \le y_n \le b$, yields 1. Note that after integrating over all the variables except y_n, one obtains the pdf of Eq. (13).

2. Consider the joint pdf given in Eq. (8).

a) Show that the integral over y_n, $y_{n-1} \le y_n \le b$, gives

$$n! f(y_1) f(y_2) \cdots f(y_{n-1}) [1 - F(y_{n-2})]^2 .$$

b) Show that the integral over y_{n-1}, $y_{n-2} \le y_{n-1} \le b$, gives

$$\frac{n!}{2} f(y_1) f(y_2) \cdots f(y_{n-2}) [1 - F(y_{n-2})]^2 .$$

c) Show that the integral over the remaining variables, except y_1, gives the result shown in Eq. (17).

3. Consider the joint pdf given in Eq. (8).

a) Show that the integral over the $k - 1$ variables, $y_1, y_2, \cdots, y_{k-1}$, over the ranges

$$a \le y_1 \le y_2 \le \cdots \le y_k \text{ gives}$$

$$\frac{n!}{(k - 1)!} [F(y_k)]^n f(y_k) f(y_{k+1}) \cdots f(y_n) .$$

b) Show that subsequent integration over the $n - k$ variables, $y_n, y_{n-1}, y_{n-2}, \ldots, y_{n-k}$, over the ranges $y_k \le y_{k+1} \le \cdots \le y_n$, gives the $g_k(y_k)$ shown in Eq. (22).

4. Consider the CDF defined by $\int_a^{y_k} g_k(y_k') \, dy_k'$.

a) Show that the change of variable $F(y) \to z$ will transform this integral to

$$\int_0^{z_k} n\binom{n-1}{k-1} z^{k-1} (1 - z)^{n-k} \, dz ,$$

where $z_k = F(y_k)$.

b) Show that integrating once by parts yields

$$\binom{n}{k} z_k^k (1 - z_k)^{n-k} + (k + 1) \binom{n}{k+1} \int_0^{z_k} z^k (1 - z)^{n-k-1} \, dz .$$

c) Show that repeated integration by parts leads to the CDF given in Eq. (31).

d) Show that the term by term differentiation of Eq. (31) leads to the pdf given by Eq. (22). Hint: Differentiating the $i = 0$ term of Eq. (31) gives two terms. The first is simply $g_k(y_k)$. The second will cancel with one of the two terms obtained from the differentiation of the $i = 1$ term of Eq. (31). Show that all the remaining terms also cancel in pairs.

5. Consider the sample median for a $2k + 1$ element sample from an $N(0, \sigma^2)$ population.

a) Show that the pdf for Y_{k+1} is

$$f(y_{k+1}) = \frac{(2k + 1)! \exp\left(-\dfrac{y_{k+1}^2}{2\sigma^2}\right)}{(k!)^2 (\sigma\sqrt{2\pi})^{2k+1}} \left[\int_{-\infty}^{y_{k+1}} \exp\left(-\frac{x^2}{2\sigma^2}\right) dx\right]^k \left[\int_{y_{k+1}}^{\infty} \exp\left(-\frac{x^2}{2\sigma^2}\right)\right]^k .$$

b) Show that this pdf is symmetric in y_{k+1}.

c) What conclusion can we draw concerning the value of $E(Y_{k+1})$?

d) What conclusion can we draw concerning the relation between the mean and the median for any symmetric distribution?

e) What conclusion can be drawn concerning the expected value of the sample median for any symmetric distribution?

6. Consider an n element sample from a $U(0, 1)$ distribution. Compute the following:

a) $E(Y_k^2)$.

b) var (Y_k).

7. Consider an n element sample from a uniform distribution with pdf

$$f(x) = \frac{1}{\theta_2} \quad \text{for} \quad \theta_1 - \tfrac{1}{2}\theta_2 \le x \le \theta_1 + \tfrac{1}{2}\theta_2.$$

Compute the following:

a) $E(Y_k)$.

b) var (Y_k).

8. Consider an n element sample from a negative exponential distribution with pdf

$$f(x) = \frac{1}{\lambda_2} \exp\left[-\frac{(x - \lambda_1)}{\lambda_2} \right] u(x - \lambda_1).$$

Compute the following:

a) $E(Y_1)$.

b) var (Y_1).

8.3 POPULATION QUANTILES AND ORDER STATISTICS

A family of population parameters which is frequently found to be useful is known as the *population quantiles*.

Consider a random variable X distributed according to the CDF $F(x)$. For any p such that $0 \le p \le 1$, the p quantile is defined as the value $\underline{x}_p$ which satisfies the equation

$$F(\underline{x}_p) = p. \tag{1}$$

In other words, $\underline{x}_p$ is the particular value of X such that the probability that x is smaller than $\underline{x}_p$ is equal to p. This notion is illustrated by the following example.

Example 1. Let the random variable X be distributed according to the CDF.

$$F(x) = x^2 \qquad 0 \le x \le 1. \tag{2}$$

Find the population median, $\underline{x}_{1/2}$, the upper quartile $\underline{x}_{3/4}$, and the lower quartile $\underline{x}_{1/4}$. The population median is determined by substituting the CDF of Eq. (2) into Eq. (1), with $p = \tfrac{1}{2}$

$$(\underline{x}_{1/2})^2 = \tfrac{1}{2}, \qquad \underline{x}_{1/2} = 1/\sqrt{2}.$$

Similarly, we can find the lower quartile

$$(\underline{x}_{1/4})^2 = \tfrac{1}{4}, \qquad \underline{x}_{1/4} = \tfrac{1}{2},$$

and the upper quartile

$$(\underline{x}_{3/4})^2 = 3/4, \qquad \underline{x}_{3/4} = \sqrt{3}/2.$$

Frequently this notion is expressed as a percentage by multiplying p by 100. With this terminology, Eq. (1) defines $\underline{x}_p$ as the $100p$ percentile.

In a typical problem we will not know the precise form of the CDF, so we take a sample from the population, using certain properties of the sample to estimate the values of population quantiles. To compute the maximum likelihood estimator for $\underline{x}_p$, we construct the likelihood function in a manner analogous to that used for the parametric estimators in the previous chapter.

We begin by pretending that we know the CDF, so we can use Eq. (21) or (22) of Section 8.2 to write

$$\Pr\{\underline{x}_p \leq Y_k \leq \underline{x}_p + d\underline{x}_p\} = n\binom{n-1}{k-1} [F(\underline{x}_p)]^{k-1}[1 - F(\underline{x}_p)]^{n-k} f(\underline{x}_p)\, d\underline{x}_p, \qquad (3)$$

where we have used the particular value $\underline{x}_p$, the p quantile of the actual population. From Eq. (1) we have

$$f(\underline{x}_p)\, d\underline{x}_p = dF(\underline{x}_p) = dp. \qquad (4)$$

Using this result and Eq. (1) we can replace $F(\underline{x}_p), f(\underline{x}_p)dp$ in Eq. (3) to obtain

$$\Pr\{\underline{x}_p \leq Y_k \leq \underline{x}_p + d\underline{x}_p\} = n\binom{n-1}{k-1} p^{k-1} (1 - p)^{n-k}\, dp. \qquad (5)$$

Equation (5) gives the probability that the kth order statistic of the n element sample will fall in the interval of length $d\underline{x}_p$ adjacent to $\underline{x}_p$, the p quantile of the population. It is most convenient to characterize the probability of Y_k falling close to $\underline{x}_p$ by the density

$$f(k|p) = \frac{\Pr\{\underline{x}_p \leq Y_k \leq \underline{x}_p + d\underline{x}_p\}}{dp} = n\binom{n-1}{k-1} p^{k-1} (1 - p)^{n-k}. \qquad (6)$$

If we know a particular n element sample value of Y_k but do not know $F(x)$, then it is frequently useful to view Eq. (6) as defining a likelihood function for p. (This is a natural assignment because Eq. (6) has the form of a conditional frequency function for the random variable k, given a particular value of p. It actually differs from a conditional ff only in the extra factor n. The reader should verify this by showing that the sum of Eq. (6) over k, from 1 to n, is simply n.) If we maximize this likelihood function with respect to p, we will determine the estimate of the order of the quantile corresponding to the particular sample value of the kth order statistics.

The value $\hat{p}$ which maximizes Eq. (6) is easily found, setting the derivative, with respect to p, equal to zero. Thus,

$$\hat{p} = \frac{k - 1}{n - 1}. \qquad (7)$$

(This result should also be evident intuitively.)

To summarize the discussion thus far, if we have an n element sample, then the maximum likelihood estimate of the order of the population quantile, whose value is equal to the particular sample value of Y_k (the kth order statistic), is $(k-1)/(n-1)$. The following simple example illustrates the application to a particular sample.

Example 2. Consider the five element sample with the particular values $x_1 = 3.2$, $x_2 = 3.7$, $x_3 = 1.2$, $x_4 = 5.1$, $x_5 = 4.0$. What are the values of the second, third, and fourth order statistics, and what is the maximum likelihood estimate of the order of the population quantiles which have these values?

Arranging the sample elements in order, we have

$$y_1 = 1.2, \qquad y_2 = 3.2, \qquad y_3 = 3.7, \qquad y_4 = 4.0, \qquad y_5 = 5.1.$$

The estimate of the order of the quantile which has $\underline{x}_p = y_2 = 3.2$ is

$$\hat{p} = \frac{2-1}{5-1} = \frac{1}{4}.$$

Similarly, the estimate of the order of the quantile which has $\underline{x}_p = y_3 = 3.7$ is $\hat{p} = \frac{1}{2}$, and the estimate of the order of the quantile whose value equals $y_4 = 4.0$, is $\hat{p} = \frac{3}{4}$.

In a typical problem we use the sample data to estimate the values of one or more quantiles of specified order. We determine this estimate by a slight variation of the above procedure.

For a given p we find the appropriate k from Eq. (7):

$$\hat{k} = p(n-1) + 1 . \tag{8}$$

The kth order statistic of the n element sample is then the estimator of the p quantile of the original population. This procedure is illustrated by the following example.

Example 3. Consider the sample with the order statistics

$$y_1 = 1.7, \qquad y_2 = 1.9, \qquad y_3 = 2.1, \qquad y_4 = 2.2,$$

$$y_5 = 2.8, \qquad y_6 = 2.9, \qquad y_7 = 3.0.$$

What is the maximum likelihood estimate of the actual population median?

$$\hat{k} = p(n-1) + 1 = (0.5)(6) + 1 = 4 .$$

Therefore, $y_4 = 2.2$ is the maximum likelihood estimate of the population median.

The reader should note that we can apply this procedure without any knowledge of the form of the CDF of the population. However, the estimator will in general be biased, and the extent of the bias cannot be determined and removed unless we know the precise form of the distribution. The following example demonstrates this difficulty.

Example 4. Consider a three element sample from a population having the pdf $f(x) = 2x$ for $0 \leq x \leq 1$. We can easily compute the pdf for the sample median

$$g_2(y_2) = 6(y_2^2)\,(2y_2)\,(1 - y_2^2)\,,$$

so that

$$E(Y_2) = \int_0^1 g_2(y_2)y_2 \, dy_2 = \tfrac{24}{35} = 0.686\,. \tag{9}$$

The actual value of the population median was found in Example 1 to be

$$\underline{x}_{1/2} = \frac{1}{\sqrt{2}} = 0.707\,. \tag{10}$$

By comparing Eqs. (9) and (10) it can easily be seen that Y_2 is a biased estimator for $\underline{x}_{1/2}$.

In the following section we will show that this estimator is consistent, and that the biasedness becomes negligible for large samples. The reader should verify that this is true for the distribution used in the above example.

PROBLEMS

1. Show that for a uniformly distributed population, the sample median is an unbiased estimator of the population median, regardless of the sample size.

2. Consider a sample from a population with pdf, $f(x) = 2x$, $0 \leq x \leq 1$.
   a) Show that for a five element sample, the expectation of the sample median is

$$E(Y_3) = \frac{(6)\,(8)\,(10)}{(7)\,(9)\,(11)}\,.$$

   This is closer to the $\underline{x}_{1/2}$ than the value computed for the three element sample of Example 4 of this section.
   b) Show that for an n element sample, with n odd,

$$E(Y_{(n+1)/2}) = \frac{(n + 1)\,(n + 3)\,(n + 5)\,\cdots\,(2n)}{(n + 2)\,(n + 4)\,(n + 6)\,\cdots\,(2n + 1)}\,,$$

   which approaches $1/\sqrt{2}$ as $n \to \infty$.

3. Discuss the biasedness of the kth order statistic of an n element sample as an estimator of the $(k - 1)/(n - 1)$ population quantile.

8.4 ASYMPTOTIC DISTRIBUTIONS OF ORDER STATISTICS IN LARGE SAMPLES

For large samples the probability of large deviations of Y_k from its most probable value will be small. Under such circumstances we can approximate the pdf for Y_k by a Taylor series expansion about the value y_{km} which maximizes the pdf for Y_k.

To determine the maximizing value y_{km}, we differentiate the pdf defined by Eq. (22) of Section 8.2 and set this derivative equal to zero. The resulting equation is, after cancelling common factors,

$$f'(y_{km})F(y_{km})[1 - F(y_{km})] + f^2(y_{km})(k - 1)[1 - F(y_{km})]$$
$$- f^2(y_{km})(n - k)F(y_{km}) = 0 . \tag{1}$$

As $n - k$ and k become large, the second and third terms of this equation become quite large, while the first term remains unaffected. For large $n - k$ and k we can, therefore, neglect the first term of Eq. (1), provided that the first derivative, $f'(y_{km})$, is bounded. Making this assumption of boundedness of $f'(y_{km})$, we can neglect the first term and cancel the common factor $f^2(y_{km})$ from the remaining terms so that Eq. (1) can be solved for

$$F(y_{km}) = \frac{k - 1}{n - 1} . \tag{2}$$

(As would be expected, this is the same result as the maximum likelihood estimator of the order of the population quantile corresponding to the value of the kth order statistic, given in Eq. (7) of Section 8.3.) The integral involved in computing the CDF, $F(y_{km})$, can seldom be performed analytically, but this is not a serious problem since Eq. (2) can generally be solved numerically with the aid of tabulated values for the common types of CDF's.

To expand $g_k(y_k)$ about y_{km} we consider the first few terms of the Taylor expansions for

$$f(y_k) \approx f(y_{km}) + f'(y_{km})\,(y_k - y_{km}) + \tfrac{1}{2}f''(y_{km})\,(y_k - y_{km})^2, \tag{3}$$

$$F(y_k) \approx F(y_{km}) + f(y_{km})\,(y_k - y_{km}) + \tfrac{1}{2}f'(y_{km})\,(y_k - y_{km})^2. \tag{4}$$

In order to use these approximations we assume that the deviations $y_k - y_{km}$ will be small, and so we make the simplifying transformation

$$y_k - y_{km} = \frac{z}{f(y_{km})\sqrt{n}} . \tag{5}$$

We will assume that values of z much larger than 1 will reduce the pdf $g_k(y_k)$ to a negligible value. This assumption will be verified by the final asymptotic form of $g_k(y_k)$. Under this assumption the expansions of Eqs. (3) and (4) are correct to order $1/n$.

Writing Eqs. (3) and (4) in terms of z, and substituting the result into the definition of $g_k(y_k)$ given in Eq. (22) of Section 8.2, we obtain

$$\frac{g_k(y_k)}{n\binom{n-1}{k-1}} \approx \left[f + \frac{zf'}{f\sqrt{n}} + \frac{z^2 f''}{2fn} \right] \left[F + \frac{z}{\sqrt{n}} + \frac{f'z^2}{2nf^2} \right]^{k-1} \left[1 - F - \frac{z}{\sqrt{n}} - \frac{z^2 f'}{2nf^2} \right]^{n-k},$$
(6)

where the functions f, f', f'', F are evaluated at the y_{km} determined from Eq. (2). The first factor on the right side of Eq. (6) does not have a large exponent, so the terms of order $1/\sqrt{n}$ and $1/n$ in this factor will be negligible for large n. To simplify the remaining two factors we use the natural notation

$$p = F, \qquad q = 1 - F,$$
(7)

so that

$$k - 1 = (n - 1)p, \qquad n - k = (n - 1)q.$$
(8)

Using this notation we factor p^{k-1} out of the second factor and q^{n-k} out of the third factor, so that Eq. (6) can be rewritten as

$$\frac{g_k(y_k)}{n\binom{n-1}{k-1}} \approx f p^{k-1} q^{n-k} \left[\left(1 + \frac{z}{p\sqrt{n}} + \frac{f'z^2}{2pnf^2} \right)^p \left(1 - \frac{z}{q\sqrt{n}} - \frac{z^2 f'}{2nqf^2} \right)^q \right]^{n-1},$$
(9)

where we have also factored out the $n - 1$ from the exponents of the second and third factors. Expanding each of the factors inside the brackets in Eq. (9) to order $1/n$, we have

$$\frac{g_k(y_k)}{n\binom{n-1}{k-1}} \approx f p^{k-1} q^{n-k} \left[\left(1 + \frac{pz}{p\sqrt{n}} + \frac{f'z^2 p}{2pnf^2} + \frac{p(p-1)z^2}{2p^2 n} \right) \right.$$
$$\left. \left(1 - \frac{qz}{q\sqrt{n}} - \frac{qz^2 f'}{2nqf^2} + \frac{q(q-1)z^2}{2q^2 n} \right) \right]^{n-1}.$$
(10)

We take the product of the two factors in the brackets and retain terms to order $1/n$, and after combining terms of like powers of z, we get

$$\frac{g_k(y_k)}{n\binom{n-1}{k-1}} = f p^{k-1} q^{n-k} \left(1 - \frac{z^2}{2npq} \right)^{n-1}.$$
(11)

To simplify this expression further we use Stirling's approximation for the factorials and divide numerator and denominator by $(n - 1)^n$ to obtain

$$g_k(y_k) \approx \frac{\sqrt{n} \left(\frac{n}{n-1} \right)^n p^{k-1} q^{n-k} f \left(1 - \frac{z^2}{2npq} \right)^{n-1}}{\sqrt{2\pi} \left(\frac{k-1}{n-1} \right)^{k-1/2} \left(\frac{n-k}{n-1} \right)^{n-k+1/2} e}.$$
(12)

Using Eq. (8) for $k - 1$ and $n - k$, this expression further simplifies to

$$g_k(y_k) \approx f \sqrt{\frac{n}{2\pi pq}} \left(\frac{n}{n-1} \right)^n e^{-1} \left(1 - \frac{z^2}{2npq} \right)^{n-1}.$$
(13)

For large n, the factors raised to the nth power become exponentials, so Eq. (13) further simplifies to

$$g_k(y_k) \approx f \sqrt{\frac{n}{2\pi pq}} \exp\left(-\frac{z^2}{2pq} \right).$$ (14)

It is easily seen that this pdf drops off very rapidly for large values of z^2, so our original assumption underlying the transformation of Eq. (5) has proved consistent. Using Eq. (5) to re-express the answer in terms of y_k, we obtain the asymptotic form

$$g_k(y_k) \approx f \sqrt{\frac{n}{2\pi pq}} \exp\left[-\frac{(y_k - y_{km})^2 nf^2}{2pq} \right], \qquad \text{for} \qquad n, k, n - k \gg 1.$$ (15)

We therefore conclude that in the asymptotic limit, Y_k is $N(y_{km}, pq/f^2 n)$ distributed. We illustrate the application of this asymptotic approximation with the following example.

Example 1.   Consider a 101 element sample from a Cauchy distributed population with pdf

$$f(x) = \frac{1}{\pi(1 + x^2)}.$$ (16)

What is the pdf of the sample median?

The CDF for the above Cauchy pdf is easily seen to be

$$F(x) = \frac{1}{2} + \frac{2}{\pi} \arctan x.$$ (17)

For the sample median, $k = 51$ for $n = 101$, and Eq. (2) becomes

$$\frac{1}{2} = F(y_{km}) = \frac{1}{2} + \frac{2}{\pi} \arctan y_{km}, \qquad (k = 51),$$ (18)

which implies that for the sample median $y_{51, m} = 0$. From the pdf defined in Eq. (16),

$$f(y_{51, m}) = f(0) = 1/\pi.$$ (19)

Substituting into Eq. (15) gives the asymptotic pdf for Y_{51}

$$g_{51}(y_{51}) = \sqrt{\frac{404}{2\pi(\pi^2)}} \exp\left[-\frac{y_{51}^2(404)}{2\pi^2} \right].$$ (20)

The reader should note that this pdf for the sample median has a finite variance. This seems remarkable when we recall that the variance of a Cauchy distributed random variable is infinite.

If the population is symmetrically distributed about the mean, then the population mean and median will be identical. In this case it might be advantageous to use the sample *median* as an estimator of the population mean. This will certainly be the case if the population is Cauchy distributed, since the sample mean is not a consistent estimator of the population mean. The sample median may also be a more efficient estimator than the sample mean for other distributions in which both sample mean and median are consistent estimators. The following example illustrates such a situation.

Example 2. Consider an n element sample from a population with pdf

$$f(x) = \frac{4}{3\pi(1 + x^2)^3}.\tag{21}$$

Find the variance of the sample median and compare with the variance of the sample mean.

Without bothering to compute the CDF for this population we can simply note that the value of y_k which maximizes $g_k(y_k)$ is simply the true population quantile of order $(k - 1)/(n - 1)$. The true population median is 0, so

$$y_{[(n+1)/2],\, m} = 0.$$

(We could have saved some effort in the previous problem by this reasoning, but the extra algebra was illustrative.) Using this value in Eq. (21) and substituting the appropriate quantities into Eq. (15) we find that in the asymptotic limit, $Y_{(n+1)/2}$ is $N[0, (9\pi^2/64n)]$ distributed. On the other hand, the variance of the sample mean is

$$\operatorname{var}(\bar{X}) = \frac{1}{n}\int (x - \nu)^2 f(x)\, dx = \frac{1}{n}\int_{-\infty}^{+\infty} \frac{4x^2 dx}{3\pi(1 + x^2)^3} = \frac{2}{n}.$$

It is easily seen that

$$\operatorname{var}(\bar{X}) > \operatorname{var}[Y_{(n+1)/2}],$$

although the difference is not great.

Of course, we cannot use the sample median as an estimator of the population mean unless we know that the distribution of the random variable is symmetric. We cannot determine which estimator is more efficient unless we have some further information concerning the distribution. The previous example shows, however, that in cases where applicable, the use of the sample median can provide more accurate estimates. Whether or not the sample median is easier to compute depends on the type of sample and the procedure used. For most of the samples given in this book the sample median can be found by inspection, while the sample mean requires a laborious summation.

On the other hand, if a digital computer is to be used, it will be faster to simply sum all the elements to compute the sample mean, rather than completely order the sample, as would be required to compute the sample median.

PROBLEMS

1. Consider a 101 element sample from an $N(0, 1)$ population.

   a) What is the index k of the order statistic which estimates the lower limit of the upper quartile? (In other words, $p_k = \frac{3}{4}$.)

   b) What is the variance (in the large n approximation) of this order statistic?

2. Consider a population with the pdf

$$f(x) = \frac{2}{\pi(1 + x^2)^2}, \quad -\infty \le x \le +\infty.$$

   a) Compute the variance of the sample median for the large sample approximation.

   b) Compute the variance of the sample mean.

3. Consider a random variable X with pdf $f(x)$ and CDF $F(x)$. Define the random variable $U_k = F(Y_k)$ where Y_k is the kth order statistic of an n element sample. Show that in the asymptotic limit U_k has an $N(p_k, p_k q_k/n)$ distribution, where $p_k = 1 - q_k = (k - 1)/(n - 1)$.

4. Consider a 91 element sample from a population with pdf $f(x) = \lambda e^{-\lambda x}, 0 \le x \le \infty$.

   a) What is the order statistic which estimates the median?

   b) What is the value of $\underline{x}_{1/2}$?

   c) What is the variance of Y_{46}? (Use the large n approximation.)

8.5 JOINT DISTRIBUTIONS OF PAIRS OF ORDER STATISTICS

To compute the joint pdf, $h(y_i, y_j)$, for a pair of order statistics Y_i, Y_j (where $i < j$), we divide the range of values of the random variable into five segments:

Segment 1	$a \le x_i \le y_i$
Segment 2	$y_i \le x_i \le y_i + dy_i$
Segment 3	$y_i + dy_i \le x_i \le y_j$
Segment 4	$y_j \le x_i \le y_j + dy_j$
Segment 5	$y_j + dy_j \le x_i \le b$

We begin the computation of the probability $h(y_i, y_j)dy_i\,dy_j$ by simply counting the number of combinations which have the n, X_i, distributed so that $i - 1$ are in Segment 1, 1 is in Segment 2, $j - i - 1$ are in Segment 3, 1 is in Segment 4, and $n - j$ are in Segment 5. We then multiply the resulting combinatorial factors by

$$[F(y_i)]^{i-1} f(y_i)dy_i \, [F(y_j) - F(y_i)]^{j-i-1} f(y_j)dy_j \, [1 - F(y_j)]^{n-j},$$

which is the probability that a specified combination of the X_i will have the appropriate numbers falling in each of the five segments. (Note that we have taken the limit $dy_i, dy_j \to 0$ in the arguments of the CDF's. This procedure can be justified in exactly the same manner as the similar approximation had been in the derivation of Eq. (21) of Section 8.2.)

If we divide this product by $dy_i \, dy_j$, we obtain the joint pdf

$$h(y_i, y_j) = \frac{n! \, f(y_i) f(y_j)}{(i - 1)! \, (j - i - 1)! \, (n - j)!}$$

$$\times \, [F(y_i)]^{i-1} \, [F(y_j) - F(y_i)]^{j-i-1} \, [1 - F(y_j)]^{n-j}. \tag{1}$$

We have not bothered with cumbersome subscripts on $h(y_i, y_j)$ because the arguments y_i, y_j have subscripts which clearly indicate the particular order statistics under discussion.

Equation (1) could also be obtained by integrating the general pdf, given in Eq. (8) of Section 8.2, over all possible values of all the variables except y_i and y_j (see Problem 2).

Example 1. Compute the expected value of the sample range, for an n element sample from a population which is uniformly distributed over the range 0 to 1.

From Eq. (1) we compute the joint pdf for Y_1 and Y_n,

$$h(y_1, y_n) = n(n - 1) \, (y_n - y_1)^{n-2}. \tag{2}$$

Using this pdf, we can easily compute

$$E(Y_n - Y_1) = n(n - 1) \int_0^1 dy_n \int_0^{y_n} dy_1 (y_n - y_1)^{n-1}$$

$$= \frac{n - 1}{n + 1}. \tag{3}$$

The reader should note that for large n, this expected range tends to 1, the actual range of the population random variable.

It is worth pointing out that, while the sample elements, X_i, are independently distributed, the order statistics, Y_i, are generally not independent of each other. In fact we can compute the conditional pdf for one order statistic given another order statistic by simply dividing the joint pdf of Eq. (1) by the marginal pdf of Eq. (22) of Section 8.2. For $i < j$ we use this procedure to compute

$$\phi(y_j|y_i) = \frac{h(y_i, y_j)}{g_i(y_i)} = \frac{(n - i)! \, f(y_j)[F(y_j) - F(y_i)]^{j-i-1}[1 - F(y_j)]^{n-j}}{(j - i - 1)! \, (n - j)! \, [1 - F(y_i)]^{n-i}}, \tag{4}$$

and

$$\phi(y_i|y_j) = \frac{h(y_i, y_j)}{g_j(y_j)} = \frac{(j - 1)! \, f(y_i) \, [F(y_i)]^{i-1}[F(y_j) - F(y_i)]^{j-i-1}}{(i - 1)! \, (j - i - 1)! \, [F(y_j)]^{j-i}}. \tag{5}$$

These expressions look rather formidable, but for certain populations they can be considerably simplified. The following example of the negative exponential pdf illustrates the case which provides the greatest simplification.

Example 2. Compute the conditional pdf for the jth order statistic y_j, given the ith order statistic y_i $(i < j)$ for an n element sample from a negative exponential distribution with pdf.

$$f(x) = \frac{1}{\lambda_2} \exp\left[-\frac{(x - \lambda_1)}{\lambda_2} \right], \tag{6}$$

which implies a CDF

$$F(x) = 1 - \exp\left[-\frac{(x - \lambda_1)}{\lambda_z} \right]. \tag{7}$$

Using these expressions in Eq. (4), with the appropriate arguments y_i or y_j, we obtain

$$\phi(y_j|y_i) = (n - i)!\, \exp\left[-\frac{(y_j - \lambda_1)}{\lambda_2} \right]$$

$$\times \frac{\left[\exp\left(\frac{\lambda_1 - y_i}{\lambda_2}\right) - \exp\left(\frac{\lambda_1 - y_j}{\lambda_2}\right) \right]^{j-i-1} \exp\left[-\frac{(y_j - \lambda_1)(n - j)}{\lambda_2} \right]}{\lambda_2 (j - i + 1)!\, (n - j)!\, \exp\left[-\frac{(y_i - \lambda_1)(n - i)}{\lambda_2} \right]}. \tag{8}$$

Factoring $\exp[-(y_i - \theta)/\lambda]$ out of the expression in brackets (raised to the $j - i - 1$ power) we can simplify this expression to

$$\phi(y_j|y_i) = \frac{(n - i)!\left[1 - \exp\left(\frac{y_i - y_j}{\lambda_2}\right) \right]^{j-i-1} \exp\left[-\frac{(y_j - y_i)(n - i - 1)}{\lambda_2} \right]}{(j - i - 1)!\, (n - j)!}. \tag{9}$$

Since the variables y_i, y_j occur only in the difference $y_j - y_i$ we can say that for a negative exponential population, the combined order statistic $Y_j - Y_i$ is independent of Y_i. This property is used to compute cov (Y_j, Y_i), as is shown in Problem 8 below.

PROBLEMS

1. Compute the expected value of the range of a three element sample from a distribution with pdf $f(x) = 2x$, $0 \le x \le 1$. Why is this answer smaller than what we would obtain by using $n = 3$ in Eq. (3) of Section 8.5?

2. Consider the general joint pdf given in Eq. (8) of Section 8.2.

   a) Show that integration over the y_l having $1 \le l \le i - 1$ with the range of possible values $a \le y_1 \le y_2 \cdots \le y_i$ gives

$$\frac{n!}{(i - 1)!}\, [F(y_i)]^{i-1} f(y_i) f(y_{i+1}) \cdots f(y_n).$$

b) Show that the subsequent integration over the y_l having $i + 1 \leq l \leq j - 1$, with the range of possible values $y_i \leq y_{i+1} \leq y_{i+2} \cdots, \leq y_j$ gives

$$\frac{n! \, f(y_i)}{(i-1)! \, (j-i-1)!} [F(y_i)]^{i-1} [F(y_j) - F(y_i)]^{j-i-1} f(y_j) f(y_{j+1}) \cdots f(y_n).$$

c) Show that the subsequent integration over the y_l having $j + 1 \leq l \leq n$, with the range of possible values $y_j \leq y_{j+1} \leq \cdots \leq y_n \leq b$, gives the function $h(y_i, y_j)$ given in Eq. (1) of Section 8.5.

3. Consider an n element sample from a uniform distribution with

$$f(x) = \frac{1}{\theta_2} \quad \text{for} \quad \theta_1 - \tfrac{1}{2}\theta_2 \leq x \leq \theta_1 + \tfrac{1}{2}\theta_2 \,.$$

a) Multiply the joint pdf of Eq. (1) by $(y_j - y_i)^2$ and integrate over the appropriate values of y_i and y_j to show that (for $j > 1$)

$$E(Y_j - Y_i)^2 = \frac{(j - i)(j - i + 1)\,\theta_2^2}{(n + 1)(n + 2)} \,.$$

b) Use the result of part (a) to show that

$$E(Y_i Y_j) = \frac{i(j + 1)}{(n + 1)(n + 2)} \qquad \text{which in turn implies that}$$

$$\text{cov}(Y_j, \, Y_i) = \frac{i(n - j + 1)\theta_2^2}{(n + 1)^2 (n + 2)}.$$

4. Compute the joint pdf for three order statistics, Y_i, Y_j, Y_k $(k > j > i)$ and use the result to show that the conditional pdf for

a) Y_k given Y_i, Y_j is

$$\phi(y_k | y_i, y_j) = \frac{(n - j)! \, f(y_k) \, [F(y_k) - F(y_j)]^{k-j-1} [1 - F(y_k)]^{n-k}}{(k - j - 1)! \, (n - k)! \, [1 - F(y_j)]^{n-j}} \,,$$

b) Y_j given Y_i, Y_k is

$$\phi(y_j | y_i, y_k) = \frac{(k - i - 1)! \, f(y_j) \, [F(y_j) - F(y_i)]^{j-i-1} [F(y_k) - F(y_j)]^{k-j-1}}{(j - i - 1)! \, (k - j - 1)! \, [F(y_k) - F(y_i)]^{k-i-1}} \,.$$

c) Why is the answer in part (a) independent of y_i?

5. Consider the conditional pdf $\phi(y_{i+1}|y_i)$. Multiply by y_{i+1} and integrate over all values possible for y_{i+1} given y_i, to show that

$$E(Y_{i+1}|y_i) = y_i + \int_{y_i}^{\infty} \left[\frac{1 - F(z)}{1 - F(y_i)}\right]^{n-i} dz \,,$$

where for many distributions $F(z) = 1$ for z greater than some finite upper limit.

6. Consider an n element sample from a negative exponential distribution with pdf and CDF given by Eqs. (6) and (7).

a) Show that the conditional pdf of Y_k, given Y_{k-1}, is

$$\phi(y_k|y_{k-1}) = \frac{n - k + 1}{\lambda_2} \exp\left[- \frac{(y_k - y_{k-1})(n - k + 1)}{\lambda_2} \right].$$

b) Multiply this conditional pdf by y_k and integrate over y_k to show that

$$E(Y_k|y_{k-1}) = y_{k-1} + \frac{\lambda_2}{n - k + 1}.$$

c) Use the result of (b) to show that

$$E(Y_k) = E(Y_{k-1}) + \frac{\lambda_2}{n - k + 1}.$$

d) Compute $E(Y_1)$, using the pdf of Eq. (17), Section 8.2, and use it in the result of (c) to show that

$$E(Y_k) = \lambda_1 + \sum_{j=1}^{k} \frac{\lambda_2}{n - j + 1}.$$

7. Consider the sample of the previous problem and let $m_k = E(Y_k)$.

a) Show that for any distribution,

$$E(Y_j - m_j)^2 = E(Y_j - Y_{j-1})^2 - (m_j - m_{j-1})^2 + E[(Y_{j-1} - m_{j-1})^2]$$
$$+ 2E[(Y_j - Y_{j-1})(Y_{j-1} - m_{j-1})].$$

b) Show that for the negative exponential distribution,

$$E[(Y_j - Y_{j-1})(Y_{j-1} - m_{j-1})] = 0.$$

c) Simplify the pdf given in Eq. (9) for the case $i = j - 1$, and show that

$$E[(Y_j - Y_{j-1})^2] = \frac{2\lambda_2^2}{(n - j + 1)^2}.$$

d) Use the results of (a), (b) and (c) to show that

$$\text{var}(Y_j) = \text{var}(Y_{j-1}) + \frac{\lambda_2^2}{(n - j + 1)^2} = \lambda_2^2 \sum_{i=1}^{j} \frac{1}{(n - i + 1)^2},$$

$$\text{cov}(Y_i, Y_j) = \text{var}(Y_i) \quad \text{for} \quad i < j.$$

(See Problem 8 of Section 8.2.)

8. a) With the notation $m_k = E(Y_k)$ show that, in general,

$$\text{cov}(Y_j, Y_i) = E[(Y_j - m_j)(Y_i - m_i)] = E\{[(Y_j - Y_i) - (m_j - m_i)](Y_i - m_i)\}$$
$$+ E(Y_i - m_i)^2.$$

b) For cases in which $Y_j - Y_i$ is independent of Y_i (such as the negative exponential), show that the above expression reduces to

$$\text{cov}(Y_j, Y_i) = E[(Y_i - m_i)^2] = \text{var}(Y_i).$$

9. Consider a three element sample from a $U(\theta_1 - \theta_2/2, \theta_1 + \theta_2/2)$ distribution (pdf defined in Problem 3 above). Construct the linear least squares estimators for θ_1 and θ_2 by using the techniques of Section 6.6 to show that

$$\hat{\boldsymbol{\theta}} = \begin{pmatrix} \theta_1 \\ \theta_2 \end{pmatrix} = J^{-1} A^T V^{-1} y = \begin{bmatrix} \frac{1}{2}(y_1 + y_3) \\ 2(y_3 - y_1) \end{bmatrix}$$

where $y = \begin{pmatrix} y_1 \\ y_2 \\ y_3 \end{pmatrix}$ is the vector of order statistic values, and where V is the covariance

matrix of these order statistics, computed in Problem 3 above. Hint: Use the result of Problem 7, Section 8.2, to show that the matrix which relates the true values of θ_1, θ_2 to the expectations of the order statistics, $E(Y) = A\boldsymbol{\theta}$, is given by

$$A = \begin{pmatrix} 1 & -\frac{1}{4} \\ 1 & 0 \\ 1 & \frac{1}{4} \end{pmatrix}.$$

As the reader might suspect from the form of the estimator $\hat{\boldsymbol{\theta}}$, the least square linear estimators, based on the order statistics of an n element sample and assuming a uniform distribution, are

$$\hat{\theta}_1 = \frac{1}{2}(y_1 + y_n), \qquad \hat{\theta}_2 = \frac{n+1}{n-1}(y_n - y_1).$$

(For the general derivation see E. H. Loyd, "Least squares estimation of location and scale parameters using order statistics." *Biometrica*, Vol. 39 (1952), pp. 88–95.) These estimators are easily seen to be more efficient than the more frequently used sample mean and sample variance. Why do you think that this is so?

10. Consider a three element sample from a negative exponential distribution with mean λ_1, variance λ_2, and pdf defined in Problem 8 of Section 8.2. Show that the least squares linear estimator for λ_1, λ_2 is

$$\hat{\boldsymbol{\lambda}} = \begin{pmatrix} \hat{\lambda}_1 \\ \hat{\lambda}_2 \end{pmatrix} = J^{-1} A^T V^{-1} y = \begin{pmatrix} \dfrac{3y_1 - \bar{y}}{2} \\ \dfrac{3(\bar{y} - y_1)}{2} \end{pmatrix},$$

where $\bar{y}$ is the sample mean, and V is the covariance matrix computed with the results of Problem 7 above:

$$V = \begin{pmatrix} \frac{1}{9} & \frac{1}{9} & \frac{1}{9} \\ \frac{1}{9} & \frac{13}{36} & \frac{13}{36} \\ \frac{1}{9} & \frac{13}{36} & \frac{49}{36} \end{pmatrix}.$$

Hint: Use the result of Problem 8 in Section 8.2 to show that

$$A = \begin{pmatrix} 1 & \frac{1}{3} \\ 1 & \frac{1}{2} + \frac{1}{3} \\ 1 & 1 + \frac{1}{2} + \frac{1}{3} \end{pmatrix},$$

and then compute

$$J = A^T V^{-1} A = \begin{pmatrix} 9 & 3 \\ 3 & 3 \end{pmatrix}.$$

As the reader might suspect from the form of the estimator $\hat{\lambda}$, the linear least squares estimator, based on the order statistics of an n element sample, is

$$\hat{\lambda}_1 = \frac{n y_1 - \bar{y}}{n - 1}, \qquad \hat{\lambda}_2 = \frac{n(\bar{y} - y_1)}{n - 1}.$$

(For the general derivation, see A. E. Sarhan, "Estimation of mean and standard deviation by order statistics," *Ann. Math. Statist*, vol. 25 (1954), pp. 317–328.)

8.6 TOLERANCE INTERVALS

In the preceding sections of this chapter, we frequently had to rely upon some knowledge of the actual distribution of the population sampled in order to obtain specific practical results. In the remaining sections we will consider several types of questions which can be answered without any recourse to knowledge of the actual population distribution.

One such question is the probability that at least some fraction of the original population lies between two particular sample order statistics. To answer this question, we note that the fraction of the actual population lying between the two values y_i and y_j is $F(y_j) - F(y_i)$. Therefore we require the pdf for $u_{ij} = F(y_j) - F(y_i)$ to be viewed as a particular value of a random variable. Now Eq. (1) of Section 8.5 gives the pdf for y_i, y_j. To obtain the pdf for u_{ij}, we simply make the change of variable

$$F(y_j) - F(y_i) = u_{ij}, \qquad F(y_i) = v_i. \tag{1}$$

The Jacobian of the transformation from (v_i, u_{ij}) to (y_i, y_j) is easily seen to be $J = f(y_i) f(y_j)$. Dividing the pdf given in Eq. (1) of Section 8.5 by this Jacobian, and using Eq. (1) above to express the transformed pdf in terms of the new variables, we obtain the pdf for (v_i, u_{ij}):

$$f(u_{ij}, v_i) = \frac{n! \, v_i^{i-1} \, u_{ij}^{j-i-1} \, (1 - u_{ij} - v_i)^{n-j}}{(i - 1)! \, (j - i - 1)! \, (n - j)!}, \tag{2}$$

where the new variables have the ranges

$$0 \leq u_{ij} \leq 1 - v_j, \qquad 0 \leq v_i \leq 1. \tag{3}$$

These ranges are appropriate to integration over u_{ij} before integration over v_i. If we wish to compute the marginal pdf of u_{ij}, we integrate $f(u_{ij}, v_i)$ over the range of values of v_i:

$$0 \leq v_i \leq 1 - u_{ij}. \tag{4}$$

Integrating by parts once, we get

$$\int_0^{1-u_{ij}} f(u_{ij}, v_i)dv_i = \frac{du_{ij}\, n!\, u_{ij}^{j-i-1}}{(i-2)!\,(j-i-1)!\,(n-j+1)!}$$

$$\times \int_0^{1-u_{ij}} v_i^{i-2}\,(1-u_{ij}-v_i)^{n-j+1}\, dv_i. \tag{5}$$

Note that the integrated term has dropped out because it was zero at the two limits of the v_i integration. This will also happen on the subsequent integrations by parts, until the power of v_i in the integrand has been reduced to zero. Integration by parts a total of $i - 1$ times, with a final integration of the remaining integral, yields the marginal pdf for u_{ij}:

$$g(u_{ij}) = \frac{n!\, u_{ij}^{j-i-1}\,(1-u_{ij})^{n-j+i}}{(j-i-1)!\,(n-j+i)!}. \tag{6}$$

With this pdf for u_{ij} we can compute the probability that at least the fraction α of the original population lies between the ith and jth order statistics:

$$\Pr\{F(y_j) - F(y_i) \geq \alpha\} = \int_\alpha^1 g(u_{ij})\, du_{ij}. \tag{7}$$

For general i and j, the actual evaluation of this integral by parts may become rather tedious. There are some particular cases of interest which can be evaluated without too much difficulty, such as the following example.

Example 1. Compute the probability P that at least the fraction α of the actual population lies within the range of an n element sample.

Let $i = 1, j = n$ in Eq. (6), and substitute into Eq. (7), obtaining

$$P = \int_\alpha^1 g(u_{1n})du_{1n} = 1 - n\,\alpha^{n-1} + (n-1)\alpha^n. \tag{8}$$

The reader should note that this result is completely independent of the actual population distribution as long as it is continuous.

For $n \gg 1$ there will be a large probability that the sample range will cover a large fraction of the true population. In fact, for values of α not equal to 1, the P computed from Eq. (8) will approach 1 as $n \to \infty$. This means that for large samples it is virtually certain that the sample range will include at least a fraction α, for any α which is significantly less than 1, of the true population. To examine the behaviour of Eq. (8) for values of α close to 1 we let

$$\alpha = 1 - \frac{\lambda}{n}, \tag{9}$$

where λ is a constant. Substituting this expression into Eq. (8) we obtain the probability that the sample range will include at least the fraction $1 - (\lambda/n)$ of the true population

$$P = 1 - n\left(1 - \frac{\lambda}{n}\right)^{n-1} + (n-1)\left(1 - \frac{\lambda}{n}\right)^n = 1 - \lambda\left(1 - \frac{\lambda}{n}\right)^{n-1} - \left(1 - \frac{\lambda}{n}\right)^n. \tag{10}$$

This equation is exact, but it can be simplified by taking the limit for large n,

$$\text{Lim}_{n \to \infty} P = \text{Lim}_{n \to \infty} \Pr\left\{ F(y_n) - F(y_1) \geq 1 - \frac{\lambda}{n} \right\} = 1 - \lambda e^{-\lambda} - e^{-\lambda}. \tag{11}$$

The reader should note that the right side of this equation is independent of n. This justifies our use of λ as defined by Eq. (9). It also makes Eq. (11) much easier to use than the more general form of Eq. (8). Such an application is illustrated by the following example.

Example 2. How many elements must be taken in a sample in order to have a 0.975 probability that the sample range will include at least 95% of the actual population? The solution of Eq. (8) for n, with $P = 0.975$, $\alpha = 0.95$, would be quite an exercise in numerical gymnastics. We have a much easier time if we use Eq. (11), which becomes

$$P = 0.975 = 1 - \lambda e^{-\lambda} - e^{-\lambda}, \tag{12}$$

and determine n from Eq. (9):

$$\alpha = 0.95 = 1 - \frac{\lambda}{n}. \tag{13}$$

Equation (12) can be solved numerically for λ with the aid of a table of powers of e, or a table of values for the summed Poisson distribution, or with a log-log slide rule, to obtain

$$\lambda = 5.57. \tag{14}$$

Substituting this value into Eq. (13), we obtain

$$n = 111.4.$$

Since n must be an integer, we need 112 sample elements to have a 0.975 probability that the sample range will include at least 95% of the true population.

(The reader should remember, of course, that Eq. (11) is only correct to order $1/n$, as are any answers derived from it.)

PROBLEMS

1. What is the smallest sample which has a 95% probability that at least half of the actual population falls within the sample range?

2. Consider a five element sample. What is the probability that at least the fraction α falls between Y_2 and Y_4?

3. Consider an n element sample. What is the probability that at least the fraction α falls between Y_2 and Y_{n-1}?

4. What is the probability that at least 80% of the actual population lies within the range of a six element sample?

5. What is the approximate probability that the sample range of a 40 element sample will include at least 0.95 of the true population?

6. How many elements must be sampled in order to have a probability of 0.90 that the sample range will include at least 95% of the actual population?

7. Consider Eq. (7) for an n element sample and take $j = n - i + 1$.
   a) Integrate by parts $2i$ times and show that

   $$\Pr\{F(y_{n-i+1}) - F(y_i) \geq \alpha\} = 1 - \sum_{k=0}^{2i-1} \binom{n}{k} \alpha^{n-k}(1 - \alpha)^k.$$

   b) Use $\alpha = 1 - (\lambda/n)$ and show that as $n \to \infty$ while i remains finite,

   $$\lim_{n \to \infty} \Pr\left\{F(y_{n-i+1}) - F(y_i) \geq 1 - \frac{\lambda}{n}\right\} = 1 - e^{-\lambda} \sum_{k=0}^{2i-1} \frac{\lambda^k}{k!}. \tag{16}$$

   (Note that this is just a summed Poisson distribution.)

8. Use Eq. (16) to find the approximate number of sample elements required to have a 0.90 probability that at least 95% of the true population falls between the sample statistics Y_2 and Y_{n-2}.

9. Derive Eq. (6) from Eq. (2.22) applied to a uniform distribution.

8.7 CONFIDENCE INTERVALS FOR QUANTILES

Another question which we can answer without recourse to the details of the population distribution is "What is the probability that the interval between the ith and jth order statistics includes some particular true population quantile?" In other words, we wish to compute $\Pr\{Y_i \leq \underline{x}_p \leq Y_j\}$ for some particular quantile level p.

To express the desired probability in more familiar terms, we note that

$$\Pr\{\underline{x}_p \leq Y_i\} + \Pr\{Y_i \leq \underline{x}_p \leq Y_j\} = \Pr\{\underline{x}_p \leq Y_j\}, \tag{1}$$

which is simply the mathematical statement that if $\underline{x}_p$ is less than Y_j, it must be either less than Y_i or between Y_i and Y_j, and these two possibilities are mutually exclusive. Rearranging terms in Eq. (1) gives the desired probability:

$$\Pr\{Y_i \leq \underline{x}_p \leq Y_j\} = \Pr\{\underline{x}_p \leq Y_j\} - \Pr\{\underline{x}_p \leq Y_i\}$$
$$= \Pr\{Y_i \leq \underline{x}_p\} - \Pr\{Y_j \leq \underline{x}_p\}. \tag{2}$$

We may use Eq. (31) of Section 8.2 to determine the probabilities on the right side of this last equation. If we also use the definition of the p quantile, Eq. (1) of

Section 8.3, to avoid writing out the CDF's explicitly, we find the desired probability

$$\Pr\{Y_i \leq x_p \leq Y_j\} = \sum_{l=i}^{j-1} \binom{n}{l} p^l (1 - p)^{n-l}. \tag{3}$$

Note that this result is completely independent of the actual form of the population distribution and depends only on the level of the quantile p. If Eq. (3) contains an uncomfortably large number of terms, it may be easier to work directly with the form given in Eq. (2), as in the following illustration.

Example 1. What is the probability that the p quantile is contained within the range of an n element sample?

If we set $i = 1, j = n$ in Eq. (3), the resulting series will contain $n - 1$ terms. A simple glance at Eq. (2) gives us the clue that this series is really the $n - 1$ middle terms in the $n + 1$ term binomial theorem expansion of $[p + (1 - p)]^n$. The desired probability is then simply 1 minus the two end terms in this expansion:

$$\Pr\{Y_1 \leq x_p \leq Y_n\} = 1 - p^n - (1 - p)^n. \tag{4}$$

As would be expected, this expression is maximized for $p = \frac{1}{2}$.

PROBLEMS

1. What is the probability that the range of a four element sample will include the median?

2. How large a sample is required so that the probability of the range including the population median is at least 0.95?

3. Compute the probability that the interval Y_2 to Y_{n-1} of an n element sample will include the p population quantile.

4. How large a sample is required for the probability to exceed 0.95 that the interval Y_2 to Y_{n-1} will contain the population median?

5. Consider Eq. (3) of Section 8.7 for large n, i, j, such that $i = \alpha_1 n, j - 1 = \alpha_2 n$. Use Stirling's approximation to show that the summation in that equation can be approximated by the integral

$$\frac{\sqrt{n}}{\sqrt{2\pi pq}} \int_{\alpha_1}^{\alpha_2} \exp\left[-\frac{(x - p)^2 n}{2pq} \right] dx,$$

where $q = 1 - p$. Why do we expect the integrand in this expression to look like the pdf given in Eq. (10) of Section 8.4?

6. Use the result of the previous problem to determine the interval of order statistics which has at least a 0.95 probability of including the median of the actual population, when we have taken a 101 element sample.

BIBLIOGRAPHY

1. P. G. HOEL, *Introduction to Mathematical Statistics*, John Wiley & Sons, New York, 1962. A good elementary text.

2. A. E. SARHAN and B. G. GREENBERG, *Contributions to Order Statistics*, John Wiley & Sons, New York, 1962. An excellent compilation of the latest applications of order statistics.

3. S. S. WILKS, *Mathematical Statistics*, John Wiley & Sons, New York, 1962. A good discussion of the distribution properties of order statistics.

CHAPTER 9

HYPOTHESIS TESTING

9.1 INTRODUCTION AND GENERAL DEFINITIONS

Before undertaking an experiment, or test, to determine information on a population distribution, we should analyze the possible outcomes and predict the expected outcomes according to our discussion of discrete and continuous probability. When the experiment or test is actually performed, the data will be organized according to one or more of the sample statistics discussed in the previous three chapters. The final step is to take some action based on the outcome of the experiment. The numerous methods of weighing the various possible courses of action form the general subject of *decision theory*. Much of this subject is beyond the scope of this text, but the special topic of *hypothesis testing* contains many of the essential features. The particular examples of hypothesis testing given in the present chapter will provide many illustrations of typical practical applications of the probabilistic and statistical methods discussed in the previous chapters. The interested reader can further explore the details of hypothesis testing and decision theory through one of the excellent texts included in the bibliography at the end of this chapter.

The hypotheses of interest will be assumptions concerning population distributions. If the assumptions of the hypothesis completely specify the distribution, then the hypothesis is called *simple*. If the assumptions fail to specify the distribution completely, then the hypothesis is called *composite*. For example, the assumption that a distribution is $N(0, 1)$ is a simple hypothesis, while a hypothesis which does not assume a particular value for the population mean would be composite. We will generally be concerned with tests which are used to distinguish between a primary hypothesis and some alternative, or secondary, hypothesis. The primary hypothesis will always be simple, but the alternative may be either simple or composite.

In a typical test we will decide between the competing hypotheses according to the value of some sample statistic. Since the particular value of the sample statistic is determined by a process subject to random fluctuations, we will look for a decision criterion which shows the greatest likelihood of indicating the correct hypothesis. Now the primary hypothesis is either true or false, and we can decide to accept it or reject it on the basis of sample data. Therefore there are four possible decision combinations which can occur with respect to this primary hypothesis:

1. Correctly accept the primary hypothesis when it is true.
2. Correctly reject the primary hypothesis when it is false.
3. Incorrectly reject the primary hypothesis when it is actually true.
4. Incorrectly accept the primary hypothesis when it is actually false.

The first two combinations involve a correct choice, the third is known as type I error, and the fourth is known as type II error. Since the two hypotheses are mutually exclusive and exhaustive, the specification of the disposition of the primary hypothesis (according to one of the four combinations above) automatically specifies the disposition of the alternative, or secondary, hypothesis. For example, item 1 above implies that we also correctly reject the alternative hypothesis when it is false.

When the primary hypothesis is simple, the specification of the decision criterion permits the computation of the probability of type I error, which is frequently denoted by the symbol α. If the secondary hypothesis is also simple, the probability of type II error, denoted by β, is also computable. The computation of these errors is illustrated by the following example.

Example 1. Consider a random variable X from a normally distributed population with known variance σ^2. Let us further assume that we only know the mean to be either m_1 or m_2. Let us arbitrarily choose the mean m_1 to be the primary hypothesis which leaves the mean m_2 to be the alternative, or secondary, hypothesis. The pdf's for these two hypotheses are shown in Fig. 1. The most logical way to test the primary hypothesis is to actually sample the random variable a certain number of times, n, and then decide whether to accept or reject the primary hypothesis according to where the particular value of the sample mean occurs with respect to the two alternative pdf's.

Let us select a critical value, $\bar{x}_c$, for the decision criterion. If the sample value $\bar{x} > \bar{x}_c$, we will reject the hypothesis, and if the sample value $\bar{x} < \bar{x}_c$ we will accept the hypothesis. If the primary hypothesis is actually correct, but the sample value turns out to be $\bar{x} > \bar{x}_c$, we will reject the primary hypothesis and make a type I error. The probability of such an error is

$$\alpha = \Pr\{\bar{X} > \bar{X}_c\} = \frac{\sqrt{n}}{\sqrt{2\pi}\sigma} \int_{\bar{x}_c}^{\infty} \exp\left[-\frac{(\bar{x} - m_1)^2 n}{2\sigma^2}\right] d\bar{x} \qquad (1)$$

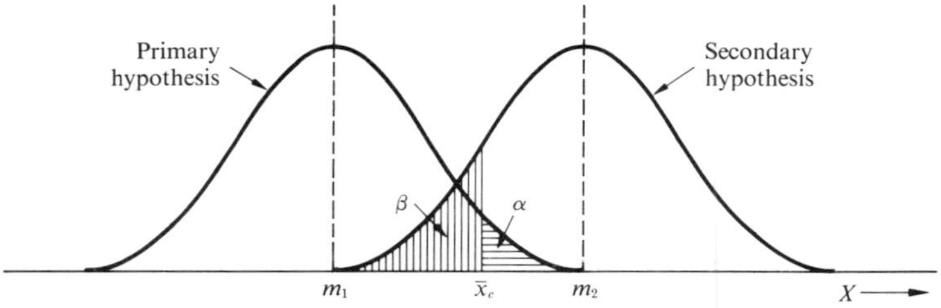

Fig. 9.1. Pdf's for primary and secondary hypotheses.

for an n element sample. The numerical value of α is equal to the area of the horizontally shaded region of Fig. 1. Equation (1) can be simplified by the transformation of the variable of integration $\bar{x} \to (z\sigma/\sqrt{n}) + m_1$, $d\bar{x} \to (\sigma dz/\sqrt{n})$, so that

$$\alpha = \frac{1}{\sqrt{2\pi}} \int_{(\bar{x}_c - m_1)\sqrt{n}/\sigma}^{\infty} \exp(-z^2/2)\, dz$$

$$= 1 - \frac{1}{\sqrt{2\pi}} \int_{-\infty}^{(\bar{x}_c - m_1)\sqrt{n}/\sigma} \exp(-z^2/2)\, dz$$

$$= 1 - F[(\bar{x}_c - m_1)\sqrt{n}/\sigma], \tag{2}$$

where $F[(\bar{x}_c - m_1)n/\sigma]$ is the well-known normal CDF. If the primary hypothesis is actually false, but the sample value is $\bar{x} < \bar{x}_c$, we will erroneously accept the primary hypothesis and commit a type II error. The probability of such an error is equal to the area of the vertically shaded region in Fig. 1.

$$\beta = \Pr\{\bar{X} < \bar{X}_c\} = \frac{\sqrt{n}}{\sqrt{2\pi}\sigma} \int_{-\infty}^{x_c} \exp\left[-\frac{(\bar{x} - m_2)^2 n}{2\sigma^2}\right] d\bar{x}. \tag{3}$$

The reader should note that Eq. (3) differs from Eq. (1) in two respects: (a) the regions of integration are complementary, and (b) the integrand in Eq. (1) is the pdf conditioned on a mean of m_1, while the integrand in Eq. (3) is the pdf conditioned on a mean of m_2. The reader should be able to identify both these observations directly from Fig. 1. The integral in Eq. (3) can be simplified by the transformation of variable $\bar{x} \to (z\sigma/\sqrt{n}) + m_2$, $d\bar{x} \to (dz)\sigma/\sqrt{n}$, so that Eq. (3) becomes

$$\beta = \frac{1}{\sqrt{2\pi}} \int_{-\infty}^{(\bar{x}_c - m_2)\sqrt{n}/\sigma} \exp(-z^2/2)\, dz = F\left(\frac{(\bar{x}_c - m_2)\sqrt{n}}{\sigma}\right). \tag{4}$$

In the above example we used the value $\bar{x}_c$ to divide the range of possible values of the random variable $\bar{X}$ into a region in which we accepted the primary hypothesis and a region in which we rejected the primary hypothesis and accepted the alternative hypothesis. This latter region, to the right of $\bar{x}_c$ in Fig. 1, is frequently called the *critical* region.

The probability of type I error, α, is frequently called the *significance level of the test*, because the probability of a chance fluctuation causing a value of X greater than $\bar{x}_c$, while the primary hypothesis is really true, is less than α. The probability $1 - \beta$, where β is the type II error probability, is called the *power of the test*, because it is the probability that the alternative hypothesis will be correctly accepted when true. The larger the probability of correctly accepting the alternative hypothesis, the more powerful the test will be. We therefore want to choose $\bar{x}_c$ to make β small. It is also desirable to have a small level of significance, α, so that there is little chance of a random fluctuation leading us to reject the primary hypothesis when it is true.

When the test is actually performed, some particular value of the sample statistic will result.   In describing the outcome of the test we will say that the primary hypothesis was accepted or rejected according to whether the particular value of the sample statistic fell outside or inside the critical region. It is frequently useful to provide a more complete description by giving some information which reflects the precise location in which the sample statistic fell.   Now, the critical region is chosen before the test is begun (otherwise we would not have an impartial test), so α and β are independent of the test outcome. It is useful to define the P level of the test to be the value which α would have if the critical value of the sample statistic had been chosen to be the particular value of the sample statistic which actually occurred. According to such a definition, the P level tells us the probability of observing a fluctuation greater than the one which actually occurred, under the condition that the primary hypothesis is correct. The use of this concept is illustrated by the following example.

Example 2. In Example 1, let $n = 9$, $\sigma = 3$, $m_1 = 2$, $m_2 = 5$, $\bar{x}_c = 4$. With these values we can use Eqs. (2) and (4) to compute

$$\alpha = 0.023 \, ,$$
$$\beta = 0.159 \, . \tag{5}$$

Suppose the actual sample turns out to have a mean $\bar{x} = 4.4$. The P level of this particular outcome is found from Eq. (2) by using the value 4.4 for $\bar{x}_c$, with all the other parameters the same as in the computation for α,

$$P = 0.008 \, . \tag{6}$$

This P value implies that although the general test is only significant at the 0.023 level, the actual outcome has such a violent disagreement with the primary hypothesis that the probability of a larger disagreement occurring by chance is only 0.008. In other words, the test is set up so that the probability of a fluctuation leading us to incorrectly reject the primary hypothesis will be only 0.023. However, the probability of the occurrence of a sample mean which represents a fluctuation greater than, or equal to, that represented by the mean of the *actual sample* will be equal to 0.008. Thus, for values of the sample statistic which lie in the critical region, the P level is simply the probability of the decision being incorrect.

   In this context it is helpful to express the definitions of type I and II probability in terms of the pdf's, conditioned on the primary and secondary hypotheses, $f(x|h_1)$ and $f(x|h_2)$ integrated over the critical region (R_c), of the random variable x and its complement ($\bar{R}_c$),

$$\alpha = \int_{R_c} f(x|h_1)dx \, , \tag{7}$$

$$\beta = \int_{\bar{R}_c} f(x|h_2)dx \, . \tag{8}$$

   In this section we have introduced the following notions, which will frequently be useful in subsequent discussions of examples of hypothesis testing:

1. Level of significance = type I error probability = α.
2. Power of test = $1 -$ type II error probability = $1 - \beta$.
3. The P level of a particular test outcome.
4. Simple and composite hypotheses.
5. Primary and secondary hypotheses.

The following sections describe some of the more frequently used, and interesting, tests. The selection is not meant to be complete in any way, and the interested reader can find extensive compilations in the excellent references listed at the end of the chapter.

PROBLEMS

1. Consider a random variable X having a distribution $N(2, 1)$ according to the primary hypothesis and $N(2\frac{3}{4}, 1)$ according to the alternative hypothesis. Suppose we attempt to decide between these hypotheses by taking a 16 element sample of the random variable and computing the particular value of the sample mean $\bar{x}$.

   a) What value should be chosen for $\bar{x}_c$ so that the level of significance $\alpha = 0.05$?
   b) For this value of $\bar{x}_c$, what is the power of the test?

2. Consider a random variable X having an $N(\xi_0, 1)$ distribution according to the primary hypothesis and an $N(\xi_1, 1)$ distribution according to the alternative hypothesis. If we wish to design a test in which we sample n elements of X and use the sample mean $\bar{X}$, such that $\alpha = 0.05$ and $\beta = 0.10$:

   a) What value must be used for $\bar{x}_c$?
   b) What is the minimum value of n such that α and β are less than 0.05 and 0.10, respectively?

3. Do Problem 2 for the case in which the alternative hypothesis is $N(\xi_1, 4)$ while all the other parameters remain unchanged.

4. Consider a primary hypothesis that the random variable X has pdf e^{-x} for $0 \le x < \infty$. Consider the alternative hypothesis that the pdf is $2e^{-2x}$.

   a) Determine x_c so that $\alpha = \beta$.
   b) What is the level of significance of an outcome which lies just to one side of this value of x_c?

9.2 COMPOSITE ALTERNATIVE HYPOTHESES

In the test situations discussed in the remainder of this chapter, the primary hypothesis will be simple but the secondary hypothesis will be composite. Since there is no way to compute probabilities conditioned on a composite hypothesis, it is not possible to compute a type II error probability β, which implies that there is no way to characterize the power of the test (its capacity to correctly accept the secondary hypothesis).

In the typical example of this sort, the primary hypothesis has a well defined pdf and the secondary hypothesis is either symmetrically or asymmetrically distributed with respect to the primary hypothesis. The following example of the computation of α illustrates the second of these two possibilities.

Example 1. A company produces distilled water and periodically samples the output to ensure that it is sufficiently free of contaminants. The primary hypothesis is that the processor is functioning normally and the contaminant concentration is Gaussian distributed about a mean of 10 parts per million with a standard deviation of 2 parts per million. (Note that this distribution gives a nonzero probability for a negative contaminant concentration, but the probability of such a deviation of 5σ, or more is less than 10^{-6}, so the error caused by this unrealistic part of the distribution is negligible.) The quality control department will only be concerned when the contaminant concentration becomes abnormally large, so it is natural to take the secondary hypothesis to simply imply that the mean impurity concentration is greater than 10 parts per million. Since the secondary hypothesis only permits concentrations greater than 10 parts per million we refer to it as being asymmetrically located with respect to the primary hypothesis. The problem is to select the critical region so that the type I error probability, or level of significance, is

$$\alpha = 0.01 .$$

According to the statement of the problem, the pdf for the primary hypothesis is of the $N(10, 4)$ form

$$f(x|h_1) = \frac{1}{2\sqrt{2\pi}} \exp\left[\frac{(x - 10)^2}{8}\right] , \tag{1}$$

where x is the contaminant concentration. Since this pdf is a decreasing function of x for $x > 10$, it is natural to choose the critical region so that it covers all values of x greater than some particular critical value x_c. In this manner we will reject the primary hypothesis whenever the impurity concentration is abnormally large. With the pdf given in Eq. (1), the type I error probability can be easily computed from the definition given in Eq. (7) of Section 9.1:

$$\alpha = F(\infty) - F\left(\frac{x_c - 10}{2}\right) = 1 - F\left(\frac{x_c - 10}{2}\right) , \tag{2}$$

where F is the CDF of the $N(0, 1)$ distribution. Setting $\alpha = 0.01$ in Eq. (2) gives

$$x_c = 14.64 . \tag{3}$$

Whenever the quality control department observes an impurity concentration greater than 14.64 parts per million it will reject the hypothesis that all is well and will take appropriate steps to locate and correct the source of the presumed malfunction. The critical region for this solution is shown in Fig. 2.

The reader should note that the critical region lies entirely on one side of the primary hypothesis mean. This feature results directly from the asymmetry of the location of the secondary hypothesis with respect to the primary hypothesis, whether the secondary hypothesis is simple or compound. Because of the appearance of the critical region shown in Fig. 2, this type of test is frequently called a one-sided, or one-tail, test. The reader will find it helpful to review Example 1 of Section 9.1 to verify that the one-sided test also arises for an asymmetrically located simple secondary hypothesis.

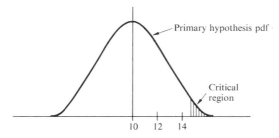

Fig. 9.2. Primary hypothesis and critical region for Example 1 (one-tail test).

When the secondary hypothesis is symmetrically located with respect to the primary hypothesis, there will, in general, be more than one critical region, as the following example illustrates.

Example 2. A certain alloy is supposed to consist of 65% iron and 35% nickel. The quality control department samples the process output in such a way that the nickel concentration is $N(0.35, 0.0025)$ distributed when everything is functioning normally, so this is the primary hypothesis. A large deviation in the nickel concentration, in either direction, will significantly affect the properties of the alloy and the quality control department must give the alarm whenever such a deviation occurs. It is, therefore, natural to take the completely general secondary hypothesis that the mean is not 0.35. Since values of the actual nickel concentration x are equally likely to be larger or smaller than 0.35, we say that the location of the secondary hypothesis is symmetric with respect to the primary hypothesis. The problem is to find the critical region such that the level of significance of the test is

$$\alpha = 0.02.$$

According to the conditions of the problem, the pdf of the concentration x for the primary hypothesis is of the form

$$f(x|h_1) = \frac{1}{0.05\sqrt{2\pi}} \exp\left[-(x - 0.35)^2/0.005\right]. \tag{4}$$

Since this pdf is a decreasing function of $|x - 0.35|$, it is natural to choose the critical region to cover all values of x such that $|x - 0.35| > c$ for some particular constant c. With this selection, a large deviation in the nickel concentration will cause the sample value of x to fall in the critical region, and the primary hypothesis will be rejected. The precise location of the critical region can be obtained by formally computing α from Eq. (7) of Section 9.1, using Eq. (4), with the critical region defined by the two inequalities

$$-\infty \leq x \leq 0.35 - (x_c - 0.35) \qquad \text{or} \qquad x_c < x < +\infty,$$

so that it is symmetric about $x = 0.35$,

$$\alpha = F\left(\frac{-x_c + 0.35}{0.05}\right) - F(-\infty) + F(\infty) - F\left(\frac{x_c - 0.35}{0.05}\right)$$

$$= F\left(\frac{-x_c + 0.35}{0.05}\right) + 1 - F\left(\frac{x_c - 0.35}{0.05}\right)$$

$$= 2\left[1 - F\left(\frac{x_c - 0.35}{0.05}\right)\right], \tag{5}$$

where we have taken $x_c > 0.35$. For $\alpha = 0.02$, the solution of Eq. (5) is

$$x_c = 0.466. \tag{6}$$

This is the lower bound of the upper critical region. The upper bound of the lower critical region is

$$0.35 - (x_c - 0.35) = 0.234. \tag{7}$$

The two critical regions are shown in Fig. 3.

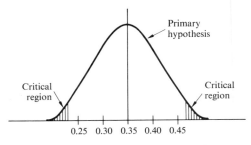

Fig. 9.3. Primary hypothesis pdf and critical regions for Example 2 (two-tail test).

The reader should note that the critical region lies on both sides of the mean of the primary hypothesis. For this reason the test is called a two-sided or two-tail test. This two-sided feature results from the symmetry of the secondary hypothesis, whether this hypothesis is composite or simple.

In many of the applications to be discussed in the following sections the primary hypotheses will be concerned with the identity of two populations from which two samples are drawn. Such a hypothesis is called a *null hypothesis*. Frequently such a problem will set up so that the mean of the distribution for the sample statistic of interest will be zero. For example, if two samples are assumed to be drawn from the same population, the expectation of the difference between the sample means will be zero.

PROBLEMS

1. Consider a particular sample of the process described in Example 2 of Section 9.2, and assume that the nickel concentration is found to be $x = 0.45$. This value does not fall within the critical region show in Fig. 3, but show that the two-tail P value is 0.045. What does this value suggest about the safety margin incorporated into the critical region?

2. Suppose we toss a coin 100 times and get 61 heads. Let the primary hypothesis be that the coin is fair. Assume that the number of trials is large enough so that we may consider the distribution to be normal. What is the P level of this test of the primary hypothesis against the alternative?

   a) The head side will appear more often.
   b) The coin is not fair.

3. Suppose we toss a coin 100 times to test the primary hypothesis that the coin is fair. What should be the critical number of heads in order to test the hypothesis at the 25% significance level, if:

   a) The alternative is more frequent heads.
   b) The alternative is an unfair coin.

9.3 THE ONE-SAMPLE t TEST

Consider a normally distributed population with unknown variance. Let the primary hypothesis be the null hypothesis that the mean has some particular value μ against the alternative hypothesis that the mean has some other value. To test this hypothesis we sample n elements from the population and compare the sample mean with μ. Since we do not know the true variance of the population we cannot make this comparison directly, as we did in the previous sections. In fact, it may appear as if our lack of specification of the population variance has left the primary hypothesis incompletely specified and composite.

However, we know from our discussion of continuous probability and parameter estimation that for an n element sample from a normally distributed population with mean μ, the sample statistic

$$T = \frac{\bar{X} - \mu}{\dfrac{S}{\sqrt{n}}},$$ (1)

is Student distributed with $n - 1$ degrees of freedom. Since the primary hypothesis is that the normal population has the mean μ, the pdf for t (the particular value of T) is the Student pdf

$$f(t|h_1) = \frac{\Gamma\left(\dfrac{n}{2}\right)}{\sqrt{\pi(n-1)}\ \Gamma\left(\dfrac{n-1}{2}\right)} \frac{1}{\left[1 + \dfrac{t^2}{n-1}\right]^{n/2}} . \tag{2}$$

For a given n this pdf is completely specified, and it can be used in Eq. (7) of Section 9.1 to compute the probability of a type I error. Since we are testing the null hypothesis that $t = 0$ against a completely general alternative, it is natural to take the critical regions to be symmetrically located with respect to $t = 0$. Since the pdf given in Eq. (2) is a decreasing function of t^2, it is natural to choose the critical region to be $t_c^2 \leq t^2 \leq \infty$. With this choice of critical region the type I error probability can be computed from Eq. (7) of Section 9.1:

$$\alpha = G_{n-1}(-t_c) - G_{n-1}(-\infty) + G_{n-1}(+\infty) - G_{n-1}(t_c)$$
$$= G_{n-1}(-t_c) + 1 - G_{n-1}(t_c)$$
$$= 2[1 - G_{n-1}(t_c)], \tag{3}$$

where $G_m(x)$ is the CDF for the Student distributed random variable x, with m degrees of freedom. (This simple type of result is expected from the symmetry of the Student distribution.) Using the values of the Student CDF given at the end of this volume, the value of t_c can be determined from Eq. (3) for given α and n. In this manner we can determine the critical region for the t-test of significance level α. In an actual test we would accept or reject the null hypothesis according to whether t^2 were less or greater than t_c^2. This procedure is illustrated by the following example.

Example 1. Consider a class of 16 students who take a standard examination. The general population is supposed to have a mean score of 5, so we take this as the null hypothesis. What value of t_c is required so that the test will have a significance level of $\alpha = 0.05$? If the actual sample scores turn out to be

$$5.3, \quad 11.3, \quad 8.7, \quad 7.8, \quad 10.8, \quad 3.6, \quad 6.7, \quad 7.3,$$
$$3.3, \quad 6.6, \quad 3.2, \quad 5.6, \quad 9.5, \quad 6.9, \quad 7.4, \quad 11.8,$$

do we accept or reject the null hypothesis at the $\alpha = 0.05$ significance level?
    Using Eq. (3) with $\alpha = 0.05$, $n = 16$, we can easily compute

$$t_c = 2.131 . \tag{4}$$

If the value of t for the particular class of 16 students turns out to be such that $t^2 > t_c^2$, then the null hypothesis must be rejected.

From the sample data given above we can easily compute the particular values of the sample statistics

$$\bar{x} = \frac{1}{16} \sum_{i=1}^{16} x_i = 7.24 \, ,$$

$$s^2 = \frac{1}{15} \sum_{i=1}^{16} (x_i - \bar{x})^2 = 7.33 \, ,$$

from which we can easily compute

$$t = \frac{\bar{x} - \mu}{(s/\sqrt{16})} = \frac{(4)\,(2.24)}{(7.33)^{1/2}} = 3.31 \, . \tag{5}$$

Since this value of $t > t_c$ we must reject the null hypothesis at the $\alpha = 0.05$ significance level for the two-tail test. In fact, by interpolating in the tables at the end of this volume, we can easily see that the probability of observing a fluctuation from the null hypothesis population mean greater than the $t = 3.31$ actually observed is

$$\Pr\{|T| \geq 3.31\} = \Pr\{T \leq -3.31\} + \Pr\{T \geq 3.31\}$$

$$= G_{15}(-3.31) + 1 - G_{15}(3.31)$$

$$= 2[1 - G_{15}(3.31)]$$

$$= 0.006 \, . \tag{6}$$

Thus the P value of the test is $P = 0.006$. This means that although we only started out to test at the 0.05 significance level, the actual sample value obtained gives us additional confidence in rejecting the null hypothesis.

PROBLEMS

1. Suppose a component being inspected is supposed to measure a certain length. For a particular sample of 16 items the deviations in length turn out to be

$$6.8, \quad 0.3, \quad -1.7, \quad 6.3, \quad 3.7, \quad 1.6, \quad -1.8, \quad 2.8,$$
$$0.6, \quad 5.8, \quad 4.5, \quad -1.4, \quad 1.9, \quad 1.7, \quad 2.4, \quad 2.3$$

Compute the two-tail P value for the test of the null hypothesis that the deviations are sampled from a normally distributed population with zero mean.

2. Compute the one-tail P value of the test of the null hypothesis against the alternative that the true population mean is greater than zero. Repeat this computation for the cases of the alternative mean being greater than 1, and greater than 4.

9.4 THE TWO-SAMPLE t TEST

Consider two samples, having n_1 and n_2 elements, which are assumed to be both taken from the same $N(\mu, \sigma^2)$ population. This is the null hypothesis which is to be tested against the general alternative that the two samples are not taken from the same $N(\mu, \sigma^2)$ population. This test can be performed by the following procedure without any particular assumptions concerning the values of μ and σ.

In Problem 3 of Section 7.6 we outlined the proof that two-sample statistic

$$T = \frac{\bar{X}_1 - \bar{X}_2 - (\mu_1 - \mu_2)}{\sqrt{\frac{1}{n_1} + \frac{1}{n_2}}\left[\frac{(n_1 - 1)S_1^2 + (n_2 - 1)S_2^2}{n_1 + n_2 - 2}\right]^{1/2}} \tag{1}$$

is Student distributed with $n_1 + n_2 - 2$ degrees of freedom. If we set $\mu_1 = \mu_2$, Eq. (1) becomes a statistic which depends only on the particular sample values. The pdf for this statistic is, then, the same as that given in Eq. (2) of Section 9.3, except that n is replaced by $n_1 + n_2 - 1$, since that pdf was for $n - 1$ degrees of freedom.

By the same argument followed in Eq. (2) of Section 9.3 we can also take the critical region to be $t_c^2 \le t^2 \le \infty$. We can then compute the significance level of the test, or the type I error probability,

$$\alpha = 2[1 - G_{n_1 + n_2 - 2}(t_c)], \tag{2}$$

which is just the same as Eq. (3) of Section 9.3, with the number of degrees of freedom $n - 1$ replaced by $n_1 + n_2 - 2$, the number of degrees of freedom in the present problem. For given α, n_1, n_2, Eq. (2) can be used to compute t_c, which bounds the critical region for t. We can then accept or reject the null hypothesis according to whether the particular two-sample value of t is such that $|t| < t_c$ or $|t| \ge t_c$. The following example illustrates the application of this procedure.

Example 1. Consider two different sections of the same subject, each section taught by a different teacher. The two classes are given an examination and the scores are compared to determine whether the two teachers have been effective to the same degree, assuming, of course, that the students are of the same caliber in both sections. Let there be eight students in Section 1 and ten students in Section 2. What is the critical region for the statistic T, defined by Eq. (1) with $\mu_1 = \mu_2$, such that the level of significance of the comparison will be $\alpha = 0.05$ on the two-tail test? If the scores in the two sections are as given in Table 1, should the null hypothesis be accepted or rejected at the $\alpha = 0.05$ significance level?

Table 1

TEST SCORES

Section 1	120	122	103	120	79	84	108	114	
Section 2	91	103	90	113	108	54	99	80	100	87

Using Eq. (2) with $n_1 + n_2 - 2 = 16$, $\alpha = 0.05$ we can determine

$$t_c = 2.120. \tag{3}$$

If the particular sample value of t happens to be greater in absolute value than $t_c = 2.120$, we will reject the null hypothesis at the 0.05 significance level.

Using the test scores given in Table 1 we can easily compute the particular sample values

$$\bar{x}_1 = 106, \qquad \bar{x}_2 = 92.5,$$
$$s_1^2 = 276, \qquad s_2^2 = 283.$$

With these particular values the particular value of t can be computed from Eq. (1) with $\mu_1 = \mu_2$,

$$t = 1.73. \tag{4}$$

Since this value of t is less than the $t_c = 2.120$, we will accept the null hypothesis that the students have received the same instruction.

We can utilize the comparison statistic t in a more precise manner by computing the probability of observing a fluctuation as great as the value $t = 1.73$ actually observed,

$$\Pr\{|T| \geq 1.73\} = 2[1 - G_{16}(1.73)] \approx 0.10. \tag{5}$$

This is the P value of the comparison test, and it tells us that not only is the agreement significant at the 0.05 level, but that under the null hypothesis a fluctuation in magnitude greater than the 1.73 actually observed has a 0.10 probability of occurring.

The reader should note that when the test yields acceptance of the primary hypothesis, the two-tail P value may be misleadingly optimistic, just as it was misleadingly pessimistic when the test yielded rejection. The reason for this is if a moderately large positive value of t leads us to question the null hypothesis, it certainly would not cause us to accept an alternative hypothesis with a negative value of t. Therefore, in weighing the significance of the particular t value actually observed, we should not include the probability of t values which are made less likely by the receipt of the sample information. In other words, once we have determined a particular sample value of t, we shift from the completely general secondary hypothesis to a secondary hypothesis which specifies the sign of t to agree with the sign of t observed in the actual sample.

PROBLEMS

1. Consider two lots of iron samples which have the melting points given by the following table.

Lot A	1493	1519	1518	1512	1512
	1514	1489	1508	1508	1494
Lot B	1509	1494	1512	1483	1507
	1491				

What is the one-tail P value for the test of the null hypothesis that both samples come from the same normal distribution?

2. The following table gives the weights of the contents of two samples of tomato cans, one sample being taken in the morning and the other in the afternoon.

Morning Sample	22.0	22.5	22.5	24.0	23.5
Afternoon Sample	22.5	19.5	22.5	22.0	21.0

What is the P value of the one-tail test of the null hypothesis that the weights always have the same normal distribution?

9.5 THE CHI-SQUARE TEST

Consider an experiment in which we have some idea of the underlying physical process involved to the extent that we would like to describe certain details of the outcome by a specific probability distribution. There are statistical fluctuations and noise which may cause the outcome to differ from the theoretical predictions of the specific probability distribution based on the basic underlying process. We are not generally concerned with the specific details of these statistical fluctuations. We are only interested in how they modify the outcomes of the experiments, and thereby confuse our attempt to evaluate our theoretical predictions based on knowledge and assumptions concerning the underlying physical process. The natural response to this dichotomy is to use some general model to describe the fluctuations from the theoretically predicted outcomes. In other words, the theory and assumptions concerning the underlying physical process form the primary hypothesis to be tested.

For the standard chi-square test we consider n experimental outcomes or events. For convenience, these outcomes are classified into k categories. Let the theory of the basic underlying process predict that the fraction p_i of the total number of outcomes will fall in the ith category. Let the number of outcomes, which fall in the ith category, be represented by the random variable N_i. In the absence of any better knowledge of the statistics of the fluctuation process, we assume that deviations of the numbers N_i from their expected values

$$E(N_i) = np_i \tag{1}$$

will be due to the random fluctuations inherent in a finite number, n, of elements sampled from a multinomial population. In mathematical language, the null hypothesis states that the N_i will be distributed according to the multinomial frequency function

$$\Pr\{N_1 = n_1, N_2 = n_2, \ldots, N_k = n_k\} = f_{n_1, n_2, n_3, \ldots, n_k} = \frac{n!}{\prod\limits_{i=1}^{k} n_i!} \prod_{i=1}^{k} p_i^{n_i}. \tag{2}$$

To find a convenient sample statistic to measure the deviation of the N_i from their expected values, we take the large sample, $n \gg 1$, approximation to this frequency function. For the following analysis it is convenient to define the deviation $x_i = n_i - np_i$, so that

$$\sum_{i=1}^{k} x_i = 0. \tag{3}$$

With Stirling's approximation, we write

$$n_i! \approx \sqrt{2\pi} \, n_i^{n_i + 1/2} \, e^{-n_i}$$

$$= \sqrt{2\pi} \, (np_i + x_i)^{np_i + x_i + 1/2} \, e^{-np_i - x_i}$$

$$= \sqrt{2\pi} \, n^{np_i + x_i + 1/2} \, p_i^{np_i + x_i + 1/2} \left(1 + \frac{x_i}{np_i}\right)^{np_i + x_i + 1/2} e^{-np_i - x_i}. \tag{4}$$

Substituting this expression for each of the factorials in Eq. (2) and simplifying, using

$$\sum_{i=1}^{k} p_i = 1, \qquad \sum_{i=1}^{k} x_i = 0,$$

we may write

$$f_{n_1, n_2, n_3, \ldots, n_k} \approx \frac{1}{(2\pi n)^{(k-1)/2}} \prod_{i=1}^{k} \frac{1}{\sqrt{p_i} \left(1 + \dfrac{x_i}{np_i}\right)^{np_i + x_i + 1/2}}. \tag{5}$$

To determine the behavior of

$$\Phi_i = \sqrt{p_i} \left(1 + \frac{x_i}{np_i}\right)^{np_i + x_i + 1/2} \tag{6}$$

for $n \gg 1$, we take the natural logarithm

$$\ln \Phi_i = (np_i + x_i + \tfrac{1}{2}) \ln \left(1 + \frac{x_i}{np_i}\right) + \tfrac{1}{2} \ln p_i. \tag{7}$$

Since $x_i \ll np_i$, this expression can be approximated to order x_i^2 by

$$\ln \Phi_i \approx (np_i + x_i + \tfrac{1}{2}) \left(\frac{x_i}{np_i} - \frac{x_i^2}{2n^2 p_i^2}\right) + \tfrac{1}{2} \ln p_i$$

$$\approx x_i + \frac{x_i^2}{2np_i} + \frac{x_i}{2np_i} - \frac{x_i^2}{2n^2 p_i^2} + \tfrac{1}{2} \ln p_i. \tag{8}$$

The effect of this expression is best seen by taking the logarithm of the product of the Φ_i, and using the fact that

$$\sum_{i=1}^{k} x_i = 0$$

to obtain

$$\ln \prod_{i=1}^{k} \frac{1}{\Phi_i} = - \sum_{i=1}^{k} \ln \Phi_i$$

$$= - \sum_{i=1}^{k} \frac{x_i^2}{2np_i} - \sum_{i=1}^{k} \frac{x_i}{2np_i} + \sum_{i=1}^{k} \frac{x_i^2}{2n^2 p_i^2} - \frac{1}{2} \sum_{i=1}^{k} \ln p_i . \tag{9}$$

By analogy with the large sample approximation to the binomial distribution, we expect that values of x_i^2 much larger than n would be very improbable [give very small values for the frequency function of Eq. (5)]. We will verify that this is true for the present multinomial case as well; therefore we accept it as true, and observe that the first and last term of Eq. (9) will most likely be of order k (not much larger than 1), while the second and third are of order $k/\sqrt{n}$ and k/n respectively. In the limit of $n \gg 1$ these second and third terms will, therefore, be much smaller than the first and last terms. With this approximation Eq. (9) becomes

$$\ln \prod_{i=1}^{k} \frac{1}{\Phi_i} \approx - \sum_{i=1}^{k} \frac{x_i^2}{2np_i} - \frac{1}{2} \sum_{i=1}^{k} \ln p_i . \tag{10}$$

Substituting this result into Eq. (5) and replacing x_i according to Eq. (3), we obtain

$$f_{n_1, n_2, n_3, \ldots, n_k} \approx \frac{1}{(2\pi n)^{(k-1)/2}} \exp \left[- \frac{1}{2} \sum_{i=1}^{k} \frac{(n_i - np_i)^2}{np_i} \right] \prod_{i=1}^{k} \frac{1}{\sqrt{p_i}} . \tag{11}$$

The reader will immediately note that the exponent of this function bears a striking resemblance to the sample statistic

$$(k - 1)S^2 = \sum_{i=1}^{k} \frac{(X_i - \bar{X})^2}{\sigma^2} \tag{12}$$

(and the frequency function of Eq. (11) resembles the pdf for $(k - 1)S^2$), which was shown in Chapter 1 to be chi-square distributed with $k - 1$ degrees of freedom. If the frequency function of Eq. (11) is transformed to a continuous pdf, arguments similar to those used to show that $(k - 1)S^2$ was chi-square distributed can be used to show that this exponent is also approximately chi-square distributed with $k - 1$ degrees of freedom. In fact, the chi-square distribution has been so intimately connected with this exponent that it is commonly denoted by

$$\chi^2 = \sum_{i=1}^{k} \frac{(n_i - np_i)^2}{np_i} . \tag{13}$$

Unfortunately, this notation does not indicate the number of degrees of freedom, but that should always be evident from the context of the problem.

The χ^2 defined by Eq. (13) forms a convenient measure of the deviation of the n element sample data away from the null hypothesis theoretically predicted values. Since we know that this sample statistic is approximately chi-square distributed with $k - 1$ degrees of freedom, we can determine the one-tail P value for a test which yields a particular value of χ^2,

$$P = 1 - C_{k-1}(\chi^2), \tag{14}$$

where C_{k-1} denotes the CDF of the chi-square distribution with $k - 1$ degrees of freedom. The general application of this procedure is illustrated by the following example.

Example 1. It is possible to determine the growth rate of bacteria by allowing them to use a nutrient containing a radioactive nucleus and then counting the decays from each bacteria after a certain time. Let us assume that we know the mean growth rate, the nucleus decay rate, and the observing time, so that we can predict a mean number of counts $\lambda = 1.1$ per bacterium. If the basic physical process is as described, then the actual number of counts per cell should follow a Poisson distribution with mean $\lambda = 1.1$. In other words, the probability of observing l counts should be

$$p_l = \frac{\lambda^l e^{-\lambda}}{l!} = \frac{(1.1)^l e^{-1.1}}{l!}. \tag{15}$$

If we examine 1000 bacteria, we expect that 1000 p_l of these will give l counts each. Let us assume that the actual number of cells in each count category are as shown in Table 2.

Table 2

OBSERVED AND THEORETICALLY PREDICTED
NUMBER OF CELLS IN EACH COUNT CATEGORY

l	0	1	2	3	4	5	6	7	8	9
No. cells observed	340	360	210	60	24	5	1	0	0	0
1000 p_l	332.9	366.2	201.4	73.8	20.3	4.5	0.8	0.1		

In order to be precise we truncate the distribution at the largest value of l which is represented by at least one cell, $l = 6$, which means that there are $k = 7$ categories. If we were to increase the number of categories much beyond this value, we would be extending the number of degrees of freedom of the chi-square distribution without increasing the risk of encountering a significant deviation. Since the size of the tolerance interval increases with increasing number of degrees of freedom, we could easily be fooled into believing that we have an unrealistically large tolerance interval. (This point is further developed in Problem 1.)

In order to perform this truncation properly, we round off by lumping all the cells with six or more counts into one category which has $1000p_{\geq 6} = 0.9$. We can now use Eq. (13) to compute

$$\chi^2 = \frac{(7.1)^2}{332.9} + \frac{(6.2)^2}{366.2} + \frac{(8.6)^2}{201.4} + \frac{(13.8)^2}{73.8} + \frac{(3.7)^2}{20.3} + \frac{(0.5)^2}{4.5} + \frac{(0.1)^2}{0.9} \quad (16)$$

$$\chi^2 = 3.88 .$$

Unfortunately, the chi-square table at the end of this volume is not finely enough partitioned to determine the P value which corresponds to this precise value of χ^2. Since the table only shows $C_6(3.45) = 0.50$ and $C_6(5.35) = 0.25$, we can only say that the P value for the particular sample of the present example is somewhat greater than 0.50. With such a large P value we would, certainly, not reject the null hypothesis.

PROBLEMS

1. Consider a Poisson distribution with mean λ.
   a) Show that if $\lambda/m < 1$, then
   $$\sum_{k=m}^{\infty} p_k < \frac{mp_m}{m - \lambda} .$$
   b) Show that if we attempt a chi-square test on an n element sample and observe no element with more than m events, we can truncate the chi-square series at m terms.
   c) Show that this procedure leads to approximately the same result obtained by lumping all the elements with m or more successes into one category.

2. Consider an experiment consisting of five trials of what is presumed to be a Bernoulli process, with unknown p. Suppose that the experiment is repeated 100 times with the following distribution of number of successes.

Number of Successes	Number of Occurrences
0	7
1	22
2	40
3	22
4	9
5	0
100	Experiments

   a) Compute the total number of successes observed experimentally and determine p, the probability of success on a single trial, so that this total number of successes will match the expected number of successes for 500 Bernoulli trials.

b) Compute the sample statistic χ^2 from the experimental data and the probabilities of k successes ($0 \leq k \leq 5$) out of five Bernoulli trials with $p = 0.4$, using five degrees of freedom.

c) What is the level of significance of the agreement between hypothesis and experiment?

3. Consider a problem solving experiment. The hypothesis is that an individual will select one of several possibilities at random, but only one of these will solve the problem. If an individual does not succeed on one trial he may try the same method again or he may select another possible solution. He will keep repeating the process until he finds the right answer. If this hypothesis is correct, then the number of trials to succeed will have a Pascal distribution, $f_k = pq^{k-1}$, with p being the probability of selecting the right solution on any given trial. In order to test this hypothesis, consider that a psychologist has 1000 individuals attempt the problem. He observes the following frequencies of number of trials required for success.

Number of Trials	Number of Individuals
1	898
2	94
3	7
4	1

a) Compute the mean number of trials required, and determine p to match this mean.

b) Compute $f_{\geq 4}$.

c) Compute χ^2 by lumping all the individuals requiring four or more trials into one category.

d) What is the level of significance of agreement between hypothesis and experiment?

9.6 RUN TESTS FOR RANDOMNESS

Suppose a pollster stood on a street corner asking passersby which of two candidates, A or B, they favored in an upcoming election. He might receive a sequence of responses like

$$\text{ABBBBAAAAAABBABBB}.$$

Such a result immediately suggests that the successive responses are not independent. Perhaps the passersby were arriving in groups of like political persuasion, or perhaps each respondent heard the choices of the previous few passersby and did not want to appear conspicuous by being different.

The data give us no clue as to the reason for the strong positive correlation between successive responses, but they do strongly suggest that these successive responses are not independent.

On the other hand, the pollster might obtain a sequence of responses like

$$\text{ABABAABABABBBABABB}.$$

Such a strong negative correlation between successive responses might be due to a strong desire to start a political argument, or a desire to favor the underdog, that is, the candidate not favored by the previous respondent (who was probably overheard). Still another possibility is that the respondents are motivated by a perverse desire to mess up the statistics of those "smart aleck pollsters who are always playing the public for a bunch of boobs." Again the data can tell us little about the underlying cause of this unusual negative correlation, but they do indicate that our sample is not representative of how the entire population will vote on election day.

As these two examples indicate, we would be wise to examine some indicators of the nature of the sample itself, rather than being solely concerned with what the sample can tell us about the actual population. One of the simplest measures of the nature of the sample data is the number of runs, particularly if the random variable is, or can be, arranged to appear two-valued. Both of the above samples have 17 elements, nine B's and eight A's. If we recall the definition of a run as a sequence of consecutive elements (which may be only one element long), then the first sample has six runs while the second sample has 14 runs.

To test a hypothesis of randomness we must determine the likelihood or probability of the occurrence of such a sequence. In Eq. (10) of Section 2.4 we found the number of sequences having m zeros and n ones arranged into $2k$ runs. Dividing this result by the total number of sequences having m zeros and n ones, we obtain the probability of observing $2k$ runs in such a sequence

$$p_{2k} = \frac{2\binom{m-1}{k-1}\binom{n-1}{k-1}}{\binom{n+m}{m}}. \tag{1}$$

A similar formula is obtained for an odd number of runs using the result of Problem 15 of Section 2.4. For $n, m, k \gg 1$, the use of Sterling's approximation shows that the maximum of Eq. (1) (or the analogous equation for an odd number of runs) occurs for

$$2k = \frac{2nm}{n+m}. \tag{2}$$

This is also the asymptotic limit for the expected number of runs found in Eq. (15) of Section (3.7).

In order to estimate the significance of a particular sample outcome we must determine the probability of observing run numbers deviating from the mode, as given by Eq. (2), by more than some specified amount. For this purpose we approximate Eq. (1) by a continuous pdf in terms of the deviation from the mode given by

$$z = \frac{2k - \dfrac{2nm}{n+m}}{\sqrt{n+m}}. \tag{3}$$

The reader should verify that with this change of variable the asymptotic limit of Eq. (1) becomes

$$\Pr\{z \le Z \le z + dz\} = \frac{1}{2\sqrt{2\pi}\ \sigma} \exp\left(-\frac{z^2}{2\sigma^2}\right) dz,\tag{4}$$

where

$$\sigma = \frac{2nm}{(n+m)^2}, \qquad dz = \frac{2}{\sqrt{n+m}}.$$

In the limit of large n, m, k, the analog for Eq. (1) with an odd number of runs goes into the same form as Eq. (4), so the pdf for the deviation of run number from the mode is simply the sum for odd and even cases:

$$f(z) = \frac{1}{\sqrt{2\pi}\ \sigma} \exp\left(-\frac{z^2}{2\sigma^2}\right).\tag{5}$$

Having found z to be normally distributed, we can compute the probabilities for observing the number of runs K to be farther from the mode (or mean) than some specified value k. This provides the estimate of the significance of a one-tail test of the hypothesis of randomness:

$$P = \Pr\{K \ge k\} = 1 - F\left[\left(k - \frac{nm}{n+m}\right)\frac{(n+m)^{3/2}}{2nm}\right] \qquad \text{for} \qquad k > \frac{nm}{n+m},\tag{6}$$

and

$$P = \Pr\{K \le k\} = F\left[\left(k - \frac{nm}{n+m}\right)\frac{(n+m)^{3/2}}{2nm}\right] \qquad \text{for} \qquad k < \frac{nm}{n+m},\tag{7}$$

where F is the normal CDF tabulated in Appendix B.

The following example illustrates the application of this criterion.

Example 1. Consider a manufacturer of air conditioners who wants to see whether the "keeping up with the Joneses" phenomenon holds to such an extent that a person's decision to purchase an air conditioner is seriously affected by whether his neighbor has one. One hundred consecutive houses along a street are sampled and it is found that 60 houses have air conditioners while 40 do not. The sequence of 60 successes and 40 failures is arranged so that there are 32 runs. What does this data indicate?

With this data we can easily compute the expected number of runs

$$E(K) = \frac{2nm}{n+m} = 48.\tag{8}$$

Since the number of runs in the sample, 32, is considerably less than this, the indication is that the variable of air-conditioner ownership is strongly correlated from one neighbor to the next. The one-tail P value for the null hypothesis that air-conditioner ownership is randomly distributed is obtained by substituting the numerical values of the present example into Eq. (7),

$$P = F\left(\frac{32 - 48}{4.8}\right) = 0.0004 . \tag{9}$$

The run test for randomness can also be applied to a sampling situation in which the random variable has more than two values, or is continuously distributed. The simplest procedure for such cases is to transform the values of the random variable into one of two values, depending on whether the particular sample element is above or below the sample median. Once the variable has been transformed in this manner, the run test can be applied as described above. This procedure is sometimes referred to as counting runs above and below the median and is illustrated by the following example.

Example 2. Consider a group of 30 students who sit at a long row of desks to take an examination. Assume that the test scores for the students, in their order of seating, are

$$65, 67, 70, 80, 58, 43, 51, 69, 65, 75, 85, 80, 53, 51, 61,$$

$$58, 56, 53, 59, 57, 65, 62, 70, 61, 65, 59, 40, 55, 45, 59.$$

Since there are 30 students in the sample, there is no actual sample median, but the reader can easily verify that the scores can be grouped into one of two categories according to whether the scores are above or below 60. If we let A represent a score above 60 and B a score below 60, the sample sequence of scores looks like this:

$$AAAABBBAAAAABBABBBBBAAAAABBBBB \tag{10}$$

This dividing score of 60 is convenient because there are an equal number of scores above and below, so that the mean and variance of the number of runs are

$$\mu = \frac{2nm}{n + m} = 15 ,$$

$$\sigma^2 = \frac{4n^2m^2}{(n + m)^3} = 7.5 . \tag{11}$$

The reader can easily verify, by counting, that the number of runs in the sequence of (10) above is equal to eight, which is considerably fewer than the expected (mean) number of 15. For the null hypothesis that the scores are distributed at random along the row of desks, the one-tail P value is, from Eq. (7)

$$P = \Pr\{K \le 8\} = F\left(\frac{8 - 15}{\sqrt{7.5}}\right) = 0.005 . \tag{12}$$

With a P value this low the teacher would be strongly inclined to reject the null hypothesis and will suspect collaboration.

PROBLEMS

1. In Eq. (1) of tnis section, let us define the parameters α and z such that $m = \alpha\,(n + m)$ $k = z\sqrt{n + m} + 2n\alpha$. Use Stirling's approximation to show that in the limit of large n, Eq. (1) becomes

$$\frac{1}{\sqrt{2\pi(n+m)}\sigma}\exp\left(-\frac{z^2}{2\sigma^2}\right), \qquad \text{where} \qquad \sigma = 2\alpha(1-\alpha).$$

Show that we get the same limit for an odd number of runs. Show that a difference of one unit in k transforms into $dz = (n + m)^{-1/2}$. Show that these results imply that a summation of Eq. (1), and the corresponding expression for an odd number of runs, over values of k is equivalent to an integration of the pdf given in Eq. (4) over the corresponding values of z.

2. Consider a line of 20 workers in a machine shop turning out identical parts at the following rates:

$$65,\ 67,\ 72,\ 71,\ 81,\ 79,\ 53,\ 55,\ 66,\ 73,$$

$$74,\ 77,\ 80,\ 69,\ 69,\ 80,\ 75,\ 74,\ 73,\ 58.$$

It is suspected that a worker's productivity may be strongly influenced by how hard his neighbor is working. What is the one-tail P value for the run test (for runs above and below the median rate) of the null hypothesis that the occurrences of rates above and below the median are completely random?

3. To determine whether people have a natural tendency to veer to the left or to right, and obstacle is placed in the middle of a walk. The experimenter notes the following sequence of pedestrians passing to the right and to the left of the obstacle.

$$\text{L L L R R R R L L L L L R L R R R R R L L L L L L}$$

The experimenter realizes afterwards that the pedestrians might have been influenced by the direction taken by the people in front of them. What is the one-tail P value for the run test of the null hypothesis that the passing directions were randomly selected from a binomially distributed population?

9.7 THE SIGN TEST FOR THE EQUALITY OF MEDIANS

Let us consider two samples having equal numbers of elements with each element of one sample having a natural pairing with one element of the other sample (a one-to-one pairing). For example, we could have 20 batches of ore which are to be assayed by two different methods for gold content. The content given by one method for each batch would form the elements of one sample and the contents obtained by the other assay process would form the elements of the other sample. Since the same batch would be subjected to both processes, there would be a natural pairing of the elements in the two samples.

Let the random variable for the ith element of one sample be x_i, and the corresponding element of the other sample y_i. If the two samples are drawn from the same population (e.g., the two assay procedures described above are equivalent), the x_i and y_i will be identically distributed. Under such circumstances

$$\Pr\{X_i > Y_i\} = \Pr\{Y_i > X_i\}. \tag{1}$$

If we define the random variable

$$Z_i = 1 \quad \text{for} \quad X_i > Y_i,$$
$$Z_i = 0 \quad \text{for} \quad Y_i > X_i, \tag{2}$$

and assume X_i and Y_i are continuous random variables, so that $\Pr\{X_i = Y_i\}$ is negligible, then Eq. (1) implies that

$$\Pr\{Z_i = 1\} = \Pr\{Z_i = 0\} = \tfrac{1}{2}. \tag{3}$$

Therefore, under the null hypothesis that the two samples are taken from identical populations, the random variable Z_i is binomially distributed. For n element samples, let

$$S = \sum_{i=1}^{n} Z_i, \tag{4}$$

so that

$$E(S) = n/2. \tag{5}$$

We would suspect the null hypothesis to be incorrect if the actual sample value of S turned out to be improbably far from this expected value. The usual convenient measure of this probability of deviation is the one-tail P value, computed in the present case as,

$$P = \Pr\{S \geq s\} \quad \text{if} \quad s > \frac{n}{2}, \tag{6}$$

while

$$P = \Pr\{S \leq s\} \quad \text{if} \quad s < \frac{n}{2}, \tag{7}$$

where the probabilities of interest are computed according to the usual formula for n Bernoulli trials

$$\Pr\{S \leq s\} = \sum_{k=0}^{s} \binom{n}{s} p^k q^{n-k} = \frac{1}{2^n} \sum_{k=0}^{s} \binom{n}{s}. \tag{8}$$

The reader should note that the sample value of s is actually just the number of positive signs in all n of the pairwise differences $x_i - y_i$. For this reason the above procedure is frequently called the sign test. The following example illustrates the application.

Example 1. Consider the problem of twenty batches of ore described above. Assume that the two types of assays produce the sample values as shown in Table 3. The last row of Table 3 shows that there are 16 positive signs in the set of the 20

Table 3

TWO DIFFERENT ASSAYS ON THE SAME ORE

i	1	2	3	4	5	6	7	8	9	10
Process x	2.30	2.03	2.51	1.99	2.20	2.11	2.34	1.93	2.15	1.98
Process y	2.01	2.02	2.31	1.95	2.11	2.07	2.10	3.00	1.98	1.91
Sign $(x_i - y_i)$	+	+	+	+	+	+	+	−	+	+

i	11	12	13	14	15	16	17	18	19	20
Process x	2.63	2.60	1.85	1.72	1.81	1.82	2.12	2.10	2.13	1.91
Process y	1.77	1.68	1.51	2.04	2.14	1.91	1.95	1.88	1.73	1.83
Sign $(x_i - y_i)$	+	+	+	−	−	−	+	+	+	+

pairwise differences $x_i - y_i$. From Eq. (6) we can compute the one-tail P value corresponding to these two samples

$$P = \sum_{k=16}^{20} \binom{20}{k} \frac{1}{2^{20}} = 0.0059 , \qquad (9)$$

using a table of summed binomial, or actually adding the five terms together.

The reader will note that the type of result obtained from this test, namely the indication of the rejection of the null hypothesis that two samples are drawn from the same population, is similar to that obtained with the t test described in Section 9.4. The present test is useful because it does not require the assumption of a normally distributed population as does the t test. It does, however, require that the two samples not only have the same number of elements, but also that there be a one-to-one pairing of elements between the two samples. The next procedure under discussion will eliminate these restrictions.

PROBLEM

Consider the data in the following table which describes the differences between the assays for a certain chemical in sixteen different samples of material when two different assay procedures are used on each sample.

.3	6.3	3.7	2.8	5.8	−1.4	1.7	2.3
−1.7	1.6	−1.8	0.6	4.5	1.9	2.4	6.8

What is the one-tail P value for the sign test of the null hypothesis that both assay procedures lead to the same determination of chemical content?

9.8 THE WILCOXON TWO-SAMPLE RANK TEST

The sign test required the two compared samples to have the same number of elements, enabling a pairwise one-to-one correspondence between samples. The Wilcoxon rank test takes a somewhat more sophisticated approach to the problem of comparison of two arbitrary samples. The procedure is as follows.

Let the two samples have n and $N - n$ elements. Pool the elements into one sample and order them so that each element of the pooled sample has a unique number, called its rank, between 1 and N, associated with it. Denote by X_i the order, or rank, of the ith element of the n elements from the first sample. (We could make a similar labeling for the elements from the second sample, but it would be unnecessary for the present analysis.) If the two samples have been originally drawn from the same population, the ranks should be randomly distributed between the two populations. In mathematical language, the X_i should be a random sampling of n out of N elements, without replacement.

If this statement is taken as the null hypothesis, the process is equivalent to sampling n balls, without replacement, from an urn containing N balls, numbered 1 through N. We, therefore, analyze this problem before completing the discussion of the general method.

One simple sample statistic, which is representative of this null hypothesis, is the sample mean

$$\bar{X} = \frac{1}{n} \sum_{i=1}^{n} X_i. \tag{1}$$

Using the result of Problem 5 of Section 3.7 and 3.8 we can compute

$$E(\bar{X}) = \frac{1}{n} \sum_{i=1}^{n} E(X_i) = \frac{N + 1}{2}, \tag{2}$$

$$\text{var}\,(\bar{X}) = \frac{(N + 1)\,(N - n)}{12n}. \tag{3}$$

Having determined the mean and variance of the sample mean $\bar{X}$, we can use the central limit theorem to infer that for sufficiently large samples $(n \gg 1)$, the random variable

$$U = \frac{\bar{X} - E(\bar{X})}{\sqrt{\text{var}\,(\bar{X})}} \tag{4}$$

is approximately $N(0, 1)$ distributed for values of X which are closer to $E(\bar{X})$ than to either limit, 1 or N.

Returning to the original problem of the comparisons of two samples, we can now establish the following test procedure.

1. Combine the two samples and label each element of the combined sample according to its rank.

2. Compute the particular value of $\bar{X}$, where $\bar{X}$ is defined by Eq. (1) to be the mean of the ranks of the elements from the first sample.
3. Use this particular value $\bar{x}$ in Eq. (4) to determine the particular sample value of U.
4. Compute the probability of observing a random fluctuation leading to a value of $|U|$ greater than, or equal to, the particular value obtained in step 3. This is the two-tail P value

$$P = \Pr\{|U| \geq u\} = 2[1 - F(u)], \tag{5}$$

where $F(u)$ is the normal CDF. Since the normal distribution is symmetric, the one-tail P value is obtained by simply dividing the two-tail result of Eq. (5) by 2.

The following example illustrates the application of this procedure.

Example 1. Consider the lifetimes for two lots of vacuum tubes shown in Table 4.

Table 4

LIFETIMES FOR TWO LOTS OF TUBES

Lot A	33, 34, 35, 36, 37, 37, 41, 44, 48, 57, 58, 62, 73, 79, 85, 90 $n_A = 16$
Lot B	38, 40, 65, 72, 74, 75, 88, 89, 95, 98, 102, 109 $n_B = 12$

The lifetimes from the two samples can be pooled together and ordered, as shown in Table 5.

From the x_i given in Table 5 we can easily compute the particular value of the sample mean

$$\bar{x} = \frac{1}{16} \sum_{i=1}^{16} x_i = 10.7. \tag{6}$$

Using $n = 16$, $N = 28$ in Eqs. (2) and (3) we can compute the expected values

$$E(\bar{X}) = \frac{N+1}{2} = 14.5, \tag{7}$$

$$\text{var}(\bar{X}) = 1.81. \tag{8}$$

Using Eqs. (8), (7), and (6) in Eq. (4), we obtain the particular value

$$u = \frac{10.7 - 14.5}{\sqrt{1.81}} = -2.83. \tag{9}$$

The one-tail P value, corresponding to this particular value of u, is

$$P = \Pr\{U \leq -2.83\} = 1 - F(2.83) = 0.0023. \tag{10}$$

Table 5
RANKS OF ELEMENTS OF TWO SAMPLES

Lifetime	Sample	Rank	x_i
33	A	1	1
34	A	2	2
35	A	3	3
36	A	4	4
37	A	5	5
37	A	6	6
38	B	7	
40	B	8	
41	A	9	9
44	A	10	10
48	A	11	11
57	A	12	12
58	A	13	13
62	A	14	14
65	B	15	
72	B	16	
73	A	17	17
74	B	18	
75	B	19	
79	A	20	20
85	A	21	21
88	B	22	
89	B	23	
90	A	24	24
95	B	25	
98	B	26	
102	B	27	
109	B	28	

PROBLEMS

1. Consider the data in the table below describing the lifetimes of electron tubes in samples from two lots.

Sample from Lot A	32, 34, 35, 37, 42, 43, 47, 58, 59, 62, 69, 71, 78, 84 $n_A = 14$
Sample from Lot B	39, 48, 54, 65, 70, 76, 87, 90, 111, 118, 126, 127 $n_B = 12$

What is the P value of the one-tail Wilcoxon rank test for the null hypothesis that both lots have the same lifetime distribution?

2. Adjustment for Ties:

If there are t elements of the pooled sample which have the same value, there will be a tie in rank among these t elements. The natural procedure is to assign each element the average rank which these elements would have if they were slightly separated. For example, the ordered sample

$$2.1, \quad 2.2, \quad 3.1, \quad 3.1, \quad 3.1, \quad 3.7, \quad 3.9$$

would have the ranks 1, 2, 4, 4, 4, 6, 7, since the average rank of the tied elements is 4.

a) Show that if the element of value y has rank x, the elements of values $y + \epsilon$, $y + 2\epsilon$, $y + 3\epsilon, \dots, y + (t - 1)\epsilon$ will have the sum of their ranks equal to t times the average rank. (Average rank $= x + (t - 1)/2$, independent of ϵ.)

b) Show that the difference between the sum of the squares of the separated ranks and the sum of the squares of the average ranks will be

$$\sum_{k=0}^{t-1} (x + k)^2 - t\left(x + \frac{t - 1}{2}\right)^2 = \frac{t(t^2 - 1)}{12}.$$

(*Hint:* Use the result of Problem 5, Section 3.8, to evaluate the sum of squares.)

c) Use the result of (b) above to show that the sum of squares of the ranks for N ordered elements, having a tie among t elements with each element of the tied group having an averaged rank, will be

$$\frac{N(N + 1)(2N + 1)}{6} - \frac{t(t^2 - 1)}{12}.$$

d) Use the above results to show that Eq. (3) of this section is replaced by the generalized form

$$\text{var}(\bar{X}) = \frac{N(N^2 - 1) - t(t^2 - 1)}{12Nn}\left[\frac{N - n}{N - 1}\right]. \tag{11}$$

e) Show that if there are k groups of ties, with t_i identical elements in group i, Eq. (11) is generalized to

$$\text{var}(\bar{X}) = \frac{N(N^2 - 1) - \sum_{i=1}^{k} t_i(t_i^2 - 1)}{12Nn}\left[\frac{N - n}{N - 1}\right]. \tag{12}$$

f) Would this correction be important for a 10 element ordered sample having one three-way tie?

3. Apply the Wilcoxon test to the data of Problem 1, Section 9.4.

a) Show that the adjustment for ties changes the variance by only 1%.

b) Show that the P value for the one-tail test is less than 0.10. Is the difference between the Student and Wilcoxon test significant?

4. Apply the Wilcoxon test to the data of Problem 2, Section 9.4.

   a) Show that the adjustment for ties changes the variance by over 6%.

   b) Show that the one-tail P value is 0.04. How much would this change if the correction for ties were neglected?

BIBLIOGRAPHY

1. K. A. BROWNLEE, *Statistical Theory and Methodology in Science and Engineering*, 2nd ed., John Wiley & Sons, New York, 1965. A compilation of many useful tests, with a large number of interesting, practical examples.

2. H. D. BRUNK, *An Introduction to Mathematical Statistics*, 2nd ed., Blaisdell Publishing Company, Waltham, 1965. A good introduction to the philosophy of hypothesis testing.

3. E. L. LEHMAN, *Testing Statistical Hypotheses*, John Wiley & Sons, New York, 1959. A complete discussion of the philosophy (and many techniques) of hypothesis testing.

4. S. S. WILKS, *Mathematical Statistics*, John Wiley & Sons, New York, 1962. A sophisticated general discussion of most of the techniques of the subject.

MATHEMATICAL PRELIMINARIES

A.1 SEQUENCES · DIFFERENCES

Let us consider a sequence of real or complex numbers

$$u_1, u_2, u_3, \ldots, u_n, \ldots \tag{1}$$

Here, u_n is the *nth term* of the sequence. If $u_n = f(n)$ for $n = 1, 2, \ldots$, we say that the sequence is *generated* by the function $f(n)$, and we often denote the sequence by $\{f(n)\}$. For example, the *n*th term of the sequence

$$1^2, 2^2, 3^2, \ldots, n^2, \ldots \tag{2}$$

is n^2. Hence the sequence is generated by n^2, and is denoted by $\{n^2\}$.

In Eq. (2), the *n*th term of the sequence is given explicitly in terms of n. On the other hand, the *Fibonacci* sequence is defined by the following rules: (a) the first two terms each equal 1, that is,

$$u_1 = u_2 = 1,$$

and (*b*) for $n > 2$, the *n*th term is the sum of the two preceding terms, i.e.,

$$u_n = u_{n-1} + u_{n-2}, \qquad n > 2$$

or, equivalently,

$$u_{n+2} = u_n + u_{n+1}, \qquad n = 1, 2, 3, \ldots \tag{3}$$

The rule (3) enables us to calculate any term of the sequence but does not give a definite expression for the *n*th term. Thus, since $u_1 = u_2 = 1$, we obtain

$$u_3 = 1 + 1 = 2, \qquad u_4 = 1 + 2 = 3,$$
$$u_5 = 2 + 3 = 5, \qquad u_6 = 3 + 5 = 8,$$

etc., yielding the sequence $1, 1, 2, 3, 5, 8, 13, \ldots$ In Example 4 we will determine u_n explicitly in terms of n.

Returning to the sequence (1), one can obtain a new sequence composed of first differences. Let

$$\Delta u_1 = u_2 - u_1,$$
$$\Delta u_2 = u_3 - u_2,$$
$$\Delta u_3 = u_4 - u_3, \tag{4}$$
$$\vdots$$
$$\Delta u_n = u_{n+1} - u_n.$$

The sequence of first differences,

$$\Delta u_1, \Delta u_2, \Delta u_3, \dots, \Delta u_n, \dots, \tag{5}$$

is analogous to the first derivative in the differential calculus. Recall that the first derivative is given by

$$Df(t) \equiv \lim_{h \to 0} \frac{f(t + h) - f(t)}{h}. \tag{6}$$

Similarly,

$$\Delta u_n \equiv u_{n+1} - u_n = \frac{f(n + h) - f(n)}{h}, \tag{7}$$

if $u_n = f(n)$ and $h = 1$.

Now, in the calculus, if $Df(t) \equiv 0$, then $f(t) \equiv$ constant. Does the analogous statement hold in the *difference calculus*, i.e., is it true that $u_n \equiv$ constant if $\Delta u_n \equiv 0$? The answer is in the affirmative, for in this case

$$\Delta u_1 = u_2 - u_1 = 0,$$

$$\Delta u_2 = u_3 - u_2 = 0,$$

$$\Delta u_3 = u_4 - u_3 = 0, \tag{8}$$

$$\vdots$$

$$\Delta u_{n-1} = u_n - u_{n-1} = 0.$$

A simple addition yields $u_n = u_1$ for all integers n.

We may look upon Δ as a *difference operator*. If $\{u_n\}$ and $\{v_n\}$ are any two sequences defined over the positive integers, then for any constants a, b (independent of n),

$$\Delta(au_n + bv_n) = (au_{n+1} + bv_{n+1}) - (au_n + bv_n)$$

$$= a(u_{n+1} - u_n) + b(v_{n+1} - v_n)$$

$$= a\Delta u_n + b\Delta v_n, \tag{9}$$

so that Δ is a linear operator. Let the reader deduce that

$$\left.\begin{array}{c} \Delta a = 0, \\ \text{(i.e. } \Delta u_n = 0 \text{ if } u_n = a \text{ (constant)),} \\ \Delta(u_n v_n) = u_n \Delta v_n + v_{n+1} \Delta u_n \\ = v_n \Delta u_n + u_{n+1} \Delta v_n. \end{array}\right\} \tag{10}$$

Second differences may be formed analogous to the second derivative. We define

$$\Delta^2 u_1 = \Delta(\Delta u_1) = \Delta u_2 - \Delta u_1 = (u_3 - u_2) - (u_2 - u_1) = u_3 - 2u_2 + u_1,$$

$$\Delta^2 u_2 = \Delta(\Delta u_2) = \Delta u_3 - \Delta u_2 = (u_4 - u_3) - (u_3 - u_2) = u_4 - 2u_3 + u_2,$$

$$\vdots$$

$$\Delta^2 u_n = \Delta(\Delta u_n) = \Delta u_{n+1} - \Delta u_n = (u_{n+2} - u_{n+1}) - (u_{n+1} - u_n),$$

$$= u_{n+2} - 2u_{n+1} + u_n,$$

$$\vdots \tag{11}$$

as the sequence of second differences. The third difference is obtained from

$$\Delta^3 u_n = \Delta(\Delta^2 u_n) = \Delta^2 u_{n+1} - \Delta^2 u_n$$

$$= (u_{n+3} - 2u_{n+2} + u_{n+1}) - (u_{n+2} - 2u_{n+1} + u_n)$$

$$= u_{n+3} - 3u_{n+2} + 3u_{n+1} - u_n. \tag{12}$$

At the moment we have

$$\Delta u_n = u_{n+1} - u_n,$$

$$\Delta^2 u_n = u_{n+2} - 2u_{n+1} + u_n, \tag{13}$$

$$\Delta^3 u_n = u_{n+3} - 3u_{n+2} + 3u_{n+1} - u_n.$$

We note that the coefficients in the above expressions are the coefficients which arise in the binomial expansions of $(x - y)$, $(x - y)^2$, $(x - y)^3$, respectively. One can prove that

$$\Delta^k u_n = u_{n+k} - \binom{k}{1} u_{n+k-1} + \binom{k}{2} u_{n+k-2} - \binom{k}{3} u_{n+k-3}$$

$$+ \cdots + (-1)^r \binom{k}{r} u_{n+k-r} + \cdots + (-1)^k u_n$$

$$= \sum_{r=0}^{k} (-1)^r \binom{k}{r} u_{n+k-r}, \tag{14}$$

with

$$\binom{k}{r} = \frac{k!}{r!\,(k - r)!}$$

called the binomial coefficients (see Section 2.4).

Example 1. Consider the sequence generated by $u_n = n^2$. Then

$$\Delta u_n = (n + 1)^2 - n^2 = 2n + 1,$$

$$\Delta^2 u_n = \Delta(2n + 1) = 2\Delta n + \Delta 1,$$

$$= 2\Delta n = 2[(n + 1) - n] = 2$$

$$\Delta^3 u_n = \Delta 2 = 0, \text{ etc.}$$

The following table exhibits these differences:

u_n	Δu_n	$\Delta^2 u_n$	$\Delta^3 u_n$
1			
4	3		
9	5	2	
16	7	2	0
25	9	2	0
.	.	.	.
.	.	.	.
.	.	.	.
n^2			
$(n + 1)^2$	$2n + 1$		
$(n + 2)^2$	$2n + 3$	2	
$(n + 3)^2$	$2n + 5$	2	0
.	.	.	.
.	.	.	.
.	.	.	.

Example 2. We are given a sequence $\{u_n\}$ such that $\Delta^2 u_n = 0$ for $n = 1, 2, 3, \ldots$. We wish to determine u_n as a function of n.

Solution. We have $u_{n+2} - 2u_{n+1} + u_n = 0$ for all integers n. Let $v_n = u_{n+1} - u_n$, so that $v_{n+1} = u_{n+2} - u_{n+1}$ and $v_{n+1} - v_n = 0$ for all n. Thus, $v_2 = v_1, v_3 = v_2 = v_1$, etc., so that $v_n = $ constant $= b$, for all n. Hence

$$v_1 = u_2 - u_1 = b,$$

$$v_2 = u_3 - u_2 = b,$$

$$\vdots$$

$$v_{n-1} = u_n - u_{n-1} = b.$$

Addition yields $u_n - u_1 = b(n - 1)$, so that $u_n = u_1 + b(n - 1) = a + bn$, with $a = u_1 - b, b = u_2 - u_1$. Hence the sequence is uniquely specified in terms of u_1 and u_2. Furthermore, u_n is linear in n. This is not a surprising result. In the calculus, if $d^2u/dt^2 = 0$, then $u = a + bt$. The integer n plays the same role in a discussion of sequences as does the real variable t in a discussion of continuous processes.

It can be shown that if a sequence $\{u_n\}$ has the property that $\Delta^k u_n = 0$ for all integers n, then

$$u_n = a_0 + a_1 n + a_2 n^2 + \cdots + a_{k-1} n^{k-1}, \qquad n = 1, 2, 3, \ldots, \qquad (15)$$

so that u_n is a polynomial in n of degree $\leq (k - 1)$.

Example 3. We wish to find the sum of the first n integers. Let

$$S_n = \sum_{k=1}^{n} k,$$

so that

$$S_{n+1} = \sum_{k=1}^{n+1} k$$

and $\Delta S_n = n + 1$. Thus $\Delta^2 S_n = 1$ and $\Delta^3 S_n = 0$, yielding S_n as a polynomial in n of degree two, say

$$S_n = a + bn + cn^2.$$

From $S_1 = 1$, $S_2 = 1 + 2 = 3$, $S_3 = 1 + 2 + 3 = 6$, we obtain

$$\begin{array}{l} a + b + c = 1 \\ a + 2b + 4c = 3 \\ a + 3b + 9c = 6 \end{array} \Rightarrow \begin{array}{l} b + 3c = 2 \\ b + 5c = 3 \end{array} \Rightarrow c = \tfrac{1}{2}, \quad b = \tfrac{1}{2}, \quad a = 0,$$

and

$$S_n = \tfrac{1}{2}n + \tfrac{1}{2}n^2 = \frac{n(n+1)}{2}. \tag{16}$$

There are simpler methods for obtaining this result. Note that

$$S_n = 1 + 2 + 3 + \cdots + (n-2) + (n-1) + n,$$
$$S_n = n + (n-1) + (n-2) + \cdots + 3 + 2 + 1.$$

Hence

$$2S_n = (n+1) + (n+1) + \cdots + (n+1) + (n+1) + (n+1)$$
$$= n(n+1),$$

yielding

$$S_n = \tfrac{1}{2}n(n+1).$$

We note also that $(k+1)^2 - k^2 \equiv 2k + 1$ for all k. Setting $k = 1, 2, 3, \ldots,$ n, yields

$$2^2 - 1^2 = 2\cdot 1 + 1,$$
$$3^2 - 2^2 = 2\cdot 2 + 1,$$
$$4^2 - 3^2 = 2\cdot 3 + 1,$$
$$\vdots$$
$$(n+1)^2 - n^2 = 2\cdot n + 1.$$

A simple addition yields

$$(n+1)^2 - 1 = 2\left(\sum_{k=1}^{n} k\right) + n,$$

so that

$$\sum_{1}^{n} k = \tfrac{1}{2}n(n+1).$$

Example 4. Returning to the Fibonacci sequence, we have

$$u_{n+2} - u_{n+1} - u_n = 0, \qquad n = 1, 2, 3, \ldots, \tag{17}$$

with $u_1 = u_2 = 1$.

Hence

$$(u_{n+2} - 2u_{n+1} + u_n) + (u_{n+1} - u_n) - u_n = 0,$$

$$\Delta^2 u_n + \Delta u_n - u_n = 0, \tag{18}$$

which is analogous to the differential equation

$$\frac{d^2 f}{dt^2} + \frac{df}{dt} - f = 0.$$

We recall that in the calculus a solution was obtained by setting $f = Ae^{rt}$, with A and r unknown constants. We may write

$$f(t) = A(e^r)^t = A\lambda^t.$$

For Eq. (18) we assume a solution of the form $u_n = A\lambda^n$, with A and λ unknown constants. Substituting into Eq. (17) yields

$$A\lambda^{n+2} - A\lambda^{n+1} - A\lambda^n = 0, \qquad n = 1, 2, 3 \ldots \tag{19}$$

$$A\lambda^n(\lambda^2 - \lambda - 1) = 0,$$

We are not interested in setting $A = 0$ or $\lambda = 0$ (which yield the trivial solution $u_n \equiv 0$). Hence $\lambda^2 - \lambda - 1 = 0$, yielding

$$\lambda_{1,\,2} = \frac{1 \pm \sqrt{5}}{2}. \tag{20}$$

Two solutions of Eq. (17) are

$$u_n^{(1)} = A\lambda_1^n = A\left(\frac{1 + \sqrt{5}}{2}\right)^n,$$

$$u_n^{(2)} = B\lambda_2^n = B\left(\frac{1 - \sqrt{5}}{2}\right)^n, \tag{21}$$

with A and B arbitrary constants. Since

$$u_{n+2}^{(1)} - u_{n+1}^{(1)} - u_n^{(1)} = 0, \qquad n = 1, 2, 3, \ldots,$$

$$u_{n+2}^{(2)} - u_{n+1}^{(2)} - u_n^{(2)} = 0,$$

it follows on addition that

$$(u_{n+2}^{(1)} + u_{n+2}^{(2)}) - (u_{n+1}^{(1)} + u_{n+1}^{(2)}) - (u_n^{(1)} + u_n^{(2)}) = 0 \qquad n = 1, 2, 3, \ldots,$$

so that

$$u_n = u_n^{(1)} + u_n^{(2)}$$

is also a solution of Eq. (17). Thus

$$u_n = A\left(\frac{1 + \sqrt{5}}{2}\right)^n + B\left(\frac{1 - \sqrt{5}}{2}\right)^n \tag{22}$$

satisfies Eq. (17).

Now we ask whether the two unknown constants can be determined from the initial conditions $u_1 = 1$, $u_2 = 1$. Of necessity

$$1 = A\lambda_1 + B\lambda_2, \tag{23}$$
$$1 = A\lambda_1^2 + B\lambda_2^2.$$

A unique solution for A and B will exist provided the determinant of the coefficients does not vanish,

$$\begin{vmatrix} \lambda_1 & \lambda_2 \\ \lambda_1^2 & \lambda_2^2 \end{vmatrix} \neq 0, \tag{24}$$

or equivalently, if $\lambda_1 \lambda_2 (\lambda_2 - \lambda_1) \neq 0$. From Eq. (20) we note that this condition is fulfilled. Solving for A and B yields

$$A = \frac{\begin{vmatrix} 1 & \lambda_2 \\ 1 & \lambda_2^2 \end{vmatrix}}{\lambda_1 \lambda_2(\lambda_2 - \lambda_1)} = \frac{\lambda_2 - 1}{\lambda_1(\lambda_2 - \lambda_1)} = \frac{\sqrt{5}}{5},$$

$$B = \frac{\begin{vmatrix} \lambda_1 & 1 \\ \lambda_1^2 & 1 \end{vmatrix}}{\lambda_1 \lambda_2(\lambda_2 - \lambda_1)} = \frac{1 - \lambda_1}{\lambda_2(\lambda_2 - \lambda_1)} = -\frac{\sqrt{5}}{5}.$$

Hence

$$u_n = \frac{\sqrt{5}}{5}\left[\left(\frac{1 + \sqrt{5}}{2}\right)^n - \left(\frac{1 - \sqrt{5}}{2}\right)^n\right], \tag{25}$$

$$n = 1, 2, 3, \ldots.$$

The solution given by Eq. (25) must be unique, since $u_1 = u_2 = 1$ and $u_{n+2} = u_n + u_{n+1}$ for $n = 1, 2, 3, \ldots.$

PROBLEMS

1. Show that
$$\Delta n^4 = 4n^3 + 6n^2 + 4n + 1,$$
$$\Delta^2 n^4 = 12n^2 + 24n + 14,$$
$$\Delta^3 n^4 = 24n + 36,$$
$$\Delta^4 n^4 = 24.$$

2. Show that $\sum_1^n k^2 = \frac{1}{6} n(n + 1)(2n + 1)$.

3. Show that $\sum_1^n k^3 = \frac{1}{4} n^2(n + 1)^2$.

4. Solve for u_n, given that $u_{n+1} = 2u_n$, $n = 1, 2, 3, \ldots$, with $u_1 = 1$.

5. Let $u_{n+1} u_n = 1$ for $n = 1, 2, 3, \ldots$ Given $u_1 = a \neq 0$, find u_n in terms of a.

6. If $\Delta^3 u_n = 0$, $n = 1, 2, 3, \ldots$, show that $u_n = a + bn + cn^2$.

7. From

$$u_2 = u_1 + (u_2 - u_1) = u_1 + \Delta u_1 = (1 + \Delta)u_1,$$

$$u_3 = u_1 + 2(u_2 - u_1) + u_3 - 2u_2 + u_1 = u_1 + 2\Delta u_1 + \Delta^2 u_1$$

$$= (1 + 2\Delta + \Delta^2)u_1 = (1 + \Delta)^2 u_1,$$

show by mathematical induction that $u_{n+1} = (1 + \Delta)^n u_1$, with $(1 + \Delta)^n$ the operator defined by

$$\sum_{k=0}^{n} \binom{n}{k} \Delta^k,$$

so that

$$(1 + \Delta)^n u_1 \equiv \sum_{k=0}^{n} \binom{n}{k} (\Delta^k u_1).$$

8. Consider two sequences $\{u_n\}$, $\{v_n\}$ such that $u_n \neq 0$, $v_n \neq 0$ for all n. Show that if $\left| \begin{smallmatrix} u_n & v_n \\ \Delta u_n & \Delta v_n \end{smallmatrix} \right| = 0$ for all n, then $v_n = (v_1/u_1) u_n$ for all n. Is the converse true?

A.2 LINEAR, CONSTANT-COEFFICIENT, HOMOGENEOUS DIFFERENCE EQUATIONS

Let D be the set of all integers $\geq d$ (an integer, not necessarily positive), and let u_n be a function of n, with n an element of D. An equation of the form

$$u_{n+k} + a_1 u_{n+k-1} + a_2 u_{n+k-2} + \cdots + a_k u_n = 0, \tag{1}$$

with n a member of D, $a_k \neq 0$, and $a_1, a_2, \ldots, a_k$, constants, is called a linear, constant-coefficient, homogeneous difference equation of order k. We note that k is the difference between the largest and the smallest subscripts which occur in Eq. (1). The following difference equations are of this type.

$$u_{n+2} + u_{n+1} - 2u_n = 0, \qquad n = 1, 2, 3, \ldots,$$

$$u_{n+1} + u_n - 2u_{n-1} = 0, \qquad n = 1, 2, 3, \ldots, \tag{2}$$

$$u_{n-3} - 4u_{n-5} + u_{n-8} = 0, \qquad n = -2, -1, 0, 1, 2, \ldots$$

The difference equation

$$y_{n+2} - 2ny_{n+1} + (n + 1)^2 y_n = 0, \qquad n = 0, 1, 2, \ldots, \tag{3}$$

is linear and homogeneous, but has nonconstant coefficients. An example of a nonlinear difference equation is

$$w_n w_{n+1} - 2w_n^2 + w_{n-1} = 0, \qquad n = 1, 2, 3, \ldots \tag{4}$$

Now let v_n and w_n be any two solutions of Eq. (1). We have

$$v_{n+k} + a_1 v_{n+k-1} + \cdots + a_k v_n = 0, \qquad (n \in D).* \qquad (5)$$
$$w_{n+k} + a_1 w_{n+k-1} + \cdots + a_k w_n = 0,$$

A simple addition yields

$$(v_{n+k} + w_{n+k}) + a_1(v_{n+k-1} + w_{n+k-1}) + \cdots + a_k(v_n + w_n) = 0, \qquad (6)$$

so that $u_n = v_n + w_n$ also satisfies Eq. (1).

We have proved the following *Theorem*. The sum of any number of solutions of a linear, constant-coefficient, homogeneous difference equation is also a solution of that equation.

The reader should be aware that only the linearity and homogeneity properties were required to prove this result, so that the theorem applies also to *nonconstant-coefficient*, linear, homogeneous difference equations. To solve Eq. (1) we assume a solution of the form

$$u_n = A\lambda^n, \qquad (7)$$

with A and λ unknown constants. Substituting into Eq. (1) yields

$$A\lambda^n(\lambda^k + a_1\lambda^{k-1} + \cdots + a_k) = 0. \qquad (8)$$

If A or λ is zero, then $u_n \equiv 0$, $n \in D$, which is a trivial solution. For nontrivial solutions, A is arbitrary and λ must satisfy the characteristic equation

$$\lambda^k + a_1\lambda^{k-1} + \cdots + a_k = 0. \qquad (9)$$

Equation (9) is a polynomial in λ of degree k, the order of the difference equation. The roots of this equation are called the eigenvalues associated with the difference equation. None of these roots vanish, since $a_k \neq 0$.

We assume, for the moment, that the eigenvalues $\lambda_1, \lambda_2, \ldots, \lambda_k$ are distinct. From our previous theorem, we note that

$$u_n = A_1\lambda_1^n + A_2\lambda_2^n + \cdots + A_k\lambda_k^n \qquad (10)$$

is a solution of Eq. (1).

Let us suppose that D is the set of positive integers and that $u_1, u_2, \ldots, u_k$ are specified numbers (initial conditions). The constants $A_1, A_2, \ldots, A_k$ must satisfy the following equations:

$$A_1\lambda_1 + A_2\lambda_2 + \ldots + A_k\lambda_k = u_1,$$
$$A_1\lambda_1^2 + A_2\lambda_2^2 + \ldots + A_k\lambda_k^2 = u_2, \qquad (11)$$
$$\vdots$$
$$A_1\lambda_1^k + A_2\lambda_2^k + \ldots + A_k\lambda_k^k = u_k.$$

---

* $n \in D$ means that n is an element of the set D.

For distinct roots the determinant of the coefficients, namely

$$
\begin{vmatrix}
\lambda_1 & \lambda_2 & \lambda_3 & \cdots & \lambda_k \\
\lambda_1^2 & \lambda_2^2 & \lambda_3^2 & \cdots & \lambda_k^2 \\
 & & \vdots & & \\
\lambda_1^k & \lambda_2^k & \lambda_3^k & \cdots & \lambda_k^k
\end{vmatrix}, \tag{12}
$$

can be shown to be different from zero. Thus one can solve Eq. (11) for unique $A_1, A_2, \ldots, A_k$. When the values of $A_1, A_2, \ldots, A_k$ are substituted into Eq. (10) one obtains the unique solution of Eq. (1) subject to the initial specified values $u_1, u_2, \ldots, u_k$.

Let us note that u_{k+1} is uniquely determined in terms of $u_1, u_2, \ldots, u_k$, see Eq. (1). It follows that u_{k+2} is uniquely determined from $u_1, u_2, \ldots, u_k$, etc.

Example 1. Solve $f_{n+2} - 3f_{n+1} + 2f_n = 0$, $n = 1, 2, 3, \ldots$, such that $f_1 = 0$, $f_2 = 1$.

Solution. The characteristic equation is $\lambda^2 - 3\lambda + 2 = 0$, yielding the eigenvalues $\lambda_1 = 1$, $\lambda_2 = 2$. Hence

$$f_n = A \cdot 1^n + B \cdot 2^n = A + B2^n.$$

From the initial conditions we have $A + 2B = 0$, $A + 4B = 1$, so that $A = -1$, $B = \frac{1}{2}$, and $f_n = 2^{n-1} - 1$, $n \geq 1$.

Example 2. Solve

$$u_{n+3} - 2u_{n+2} - 5u_{n+1} + 6u_n = 0, \, n \geq 1,$$

subject to the initial conditions $u_1 = 0$, $u_2 = 1$, $u_3 = 0$.

Solution. The characteristic equation is $\lambda^3 - 2\lambda^2 - 5\lambda + 6 = 0$, or $(\lambda - 1)(\lambda + 2)(\lambda - 3) = 0$, so that $u_n = A \cdot 1^n + B(-2)^n + C3^n$. From the initial conditions we have

$$
\begin{aligned}
A - 2B + 3C &= 0 \\
A + 4B + 9C &= 1 \\
A - 8B + 27C &= 0
\end{aligned}
\Rightarrow
\begin{aligned}
B + C &= \tfrac{1}{6} \\
2B - 3C &= \tfrac{1}{6}
\end{aligned}
\Rightarrow
\begin{aligned}
B &= \tfrac{2}{15} \\
C &= \tfrac{1}{30},
\end{aligned}
$$

and $A = \frac{1}{6}$, so that

$$u_n = \tfrac{1}{6} + \tfrac{2}{15}(-2)^n + \tfrac{1}{30}3^n, \quad n \geq 1.$$

Let us consider next the situation for which the characteristic equation has multiple roots. Consider, for example, the difference equation

$$u_{n+2} - 4u_{n+1} + 4u_n = 0, \qquad n = 1, 2, 3, \ldots, \tag{13}$$

whose characteristic equation is $\lambda^2 - 4\lambda + 4 = 0$, yielding $\lambda_1 = \lambda_2 = 2$. The two solutions $A2^n$ and $B2^n$ are such that their sum is $(A + B)2^n = C2^n$, yielding only one arbitrary constant. To find another solution of Eq. (13) let

$$u_n = A_n 2^n, \qquad n \geq 1, \tag{14}$$

with A_n an unknown function of n. This corresponds to the variation of parameter method used in finding solutions of differential equations. Thus A_n satisfies

$$A_{n+2}2^{n+2} - 4A_{n+1}2^{n+1} + 4A_n 2^n = 0,$$
$$A_{n+2} - 2A_{n+1} + A_n = 0,$$
(15)

for $n \geq 1$. We recognize that $\Delta^2 A_n \equiv 0$, so that $A_n = an + b$, with a and b arbitrary constants. The general solution of Eq. (13) is

$$u_n = (a + bn)2^n.$$
(16)

The term $bn2^n$ is a secular term which has its analog in the solution of linear differential equations whose characteristic equations have multiple roots. If, in this example, $u_1 = 2$, $u_2 = -4$, then $2(a + b) = 2$, $4(a + 2b) = -4$, so that $a = 3$, $b = -2$, and $u_n = (3 - 2n)2^n$.

It can be shown that if λ_1 is a root of multiplicity m, then

$$u_n = (a_0 + a_1 n + a_2 n^2 + \cdots + a_{m-1}n^{m-1})\lambda_1^n$$
(17)

is a solution of the difference equation, with $a_0, a_1, a_2, \ldots, a_{m-1}$ arbitrary constants.

Example 3. If a linear, homogeneous difference equation has the characteristic equation $(\lambda - 3)^2 (\lambda + 2)^3 = 0$, then

$$u_n = (a + bn)3^n + (c + dn + en^2)(-2)^n$$

is the general solution.

PROBLEMS

1. Solve for u_n such that $u_{n+2} - 5u_{n+1} + 6u_n = 0$, $n \geq 1$, with $u_1 = 0$, $u_2 = -3$.

2. Solve for u_n such that $u_{n+2} - 3u_{n+1} + u_n = 0$, $n \geq 0$, with $u_0 = 1$, $u_\infty = \lim_{n \to \infty} u_n = 0$.

3. Find a general solution of
$$u_{n+3} - u_{n+2} - 8u_{n+1} + 12u_n = 0, \qquad n \geq 1.$$

4. By the variation of parameter method show that the general solution of
$$u_{n+3} - 6u_{n+2} + 12u_{n+1} - 8u_n = 0, \qquad n \geq 1$$
is $u_n = (a + bn + cn^2)2^n$.

5. Solve for u_n such that $u_{n+2} - 2u_{n+1} + u_n = 0$, $n \geq 0$, with $u_0 = 1$, $u_z = 0$, z a positive integer.

6. Solve for u_n, v_n, given that $u_n = v_{n-1}$, $v_n = u_{n-1}$, for $n \geq 0$, with $u_0 = 1$, $v_0 = 0$. [*Hint:* $u_{n+1} = v_n = u_{n-1}$.]

7. Let $u_{n+1} - u_n = 1/n$ for $n \geq 1$. From $u_2 - u_1 = 1, u_3 - u_2 = \frac{1}{2}, u_4 - u_3 = \frac{1}{3}$, etc., show that

$$u_n = u_1 + \left(1 + \frac{1}{2} + \frac{1}{3} + \cdots + \frac{1}{n-1}\right) \text{ for } n \geq 2.$$

A.3 FORCING FUNCTIONS ·
INHOMOGENEOUS DIFFERENCE EQUATIONS

Let us consider the linear inhomogeneous difference equation

$$u_{n+k} + a_1 u_{n+k-1} + \cdots + a_k u_n = f(n), \qquad n = 1, 2, 3, \ldots, \tag{1}$$

with $a_k \neq 0$. This difference equation is a simple extension of the homogeneous difference equation of Eq. (1), Section A.2. The given term, $f(n)$, is called the *forcing* or *driving* function.

Now let v_n be a general solution of the homogeneous equation, and let w_n be any solution of the inhomogeneous equation. Thus

$$
\begin{aligned}
v_{n+k} + a_1 v_{n+k-1} + \cdots + a_k v_n &= 0, \\
w_{n+k} + a_1 w_{n+k-1} + \cdots + a_k w_n &= f(n), \qquad n \geq 1.
\end{aligned}
\tag{2}
$$

A simple addition yields

$$(v_{n+k} + w_{n+k}) + a_1(v_{n+k-1} + w_{n+k-1}) + \cdots + a_k(v_n + w_n) = f(n) \tag{3}$$

for $n \geq 1$, so that $u_n = v_n + w_n$ is also a solution of the inhomogeneous equation.

To find a particular solution of the inhomogeneous equation requires special techniques. Two such methods, namely the method of undetermined coefficients and the variation of parameter method, will be illustrated below.

Example 1. Solve the inhomogeneous equation

$$u_{n+2} - 5u_{n+1} + 6u_n = 1 + n, \qquad n = 1, 2, 3, \ldots, \tag{4}$$

such that $u_1 = 1, u_2 = -1$.

Solution. The homogeneous equation is $v_{n+2} - 5v_{n+1} + 6v_n = 0$ whose characteristic equation is $\lambda^2 - 5\lambda + 6 = 0$, yielding $\lambda = 2, 3$. Thus $v_n = A2^n + B3^n$ is the general solution of the homogeneous equation with A and B arbitrary constants.

To find a particular solution we note that $f(n) = 1 + n$ is linear in n. Thus we try a particular solution of the form $w_n = a + bn$, with a and b undetermined constants. Substituting into $w_{n+2} - 5w_{n+1} + 6w_n = 1 + n$ yields

$$a + b(n + 2) - 5[a + b(n + 1)] + 6(a + bn) = 1 + n,$$

$$(a + 2b - 5a - 5b + 6a) + (b - 5b + 6b)n = 1 + n, \qquad n \geq 1,$$

$$(2a - 3b) + 2bn = 1 + n.$$

This equation will hold for all $n \geq 1$ provided $2a - 3b = 1$, $2b = 1$, yielding $a = \frac{5}{4}$, $b = \frac{1}{2}$. The general solution of Eq. (4) is

$$u_n = A2^n + B3^n + \tfrac{5}{4} + \tfrac{1}{2}n. \tag{5}$$

From $u_1 = 1$, $u_2 = -1$ we obtain $2A + 3B + \frac{7}{4} = 1$, $4A + 9B + \frac{9}{4} = -1$, so that $A = \frac{1}{2}$, $B = -\frac{7}{12}$. Hence

$$u_n = 2^{n-1} - \tfrac{7}{12}3^n + \tfrac{5}{4} + \tfrac{1}{2}n. \tag{6}$$

Example 2. Solve $p_n - \frac{1}{4}p_{n-1} = \frac{1}{4}$, $n = 2, 3, 4, \ldots$, with $p_1 = \frac{1}{2}$.

Solution. The solution of the homogeneous equation is $p_n = A(\frac{1}{4})^n$. Since the forcing function, $f(n) \equiv \frac{1}{4}$, is a constant, we assume a particular solution of the form $p_n = a \equiv$ constant for all n. Substituting into $p_n - \frac{1}{4}p_{n-1} = \frac{1}{4}$ yields $a - \frac{1}{4}a = \frac{1}{4}$, so that $a = \frac{1}{3}$. Hence $p_n = A(\frac{1}{4})^n + \frac{1}{3}$ is the general solution of the inhomogeneous equation. From $p_1 = \frac{1}{2}$ we have $\frac{1}{2} = \frac{1}{4}A + \frac{1}{3}$, yielding $p_n = \frac{2}{3}(\frac{1}{4})^n + \frac{1}{3}$.

Example 3. Find a general solution of

$$\mu_{n+2} - 2\mu_{n+1} + \mu_n = -2, \qquad n \geq 1.$$

Solution. The homogeneous equation $\mu_{n+2} - 2\mu_{n+1} + \mu_n = 0$ has the solution $\mu_n = A + Bn$, since $\lambda = 1$ is a double root of the characteristic equation $\lambda^2 - 2\lambda + 1 = 0$. Since the forcing function is a constant independent of n, we might be tempted to look for a particular solution of the form $\mu_n = a =$ constant. But $\mu_n \equiv a$ is a solution of the homogeneous equation, $(A = a, B = 0)$. Similarly, $\mu_n = bn$ is a solution of the homogeneous equation, $(A = 0, B = b)$. Let us assume that $\mu_n = cn^2$ is a particular solution (a quadratic in n), with c an unknown constant. Substituting into $\mu_{n+2} - 2\mu_{n+1} + \mu_n = -2$ yields

$$c(n + 2)^2 - 2c(n + 1)^2 + cn^2 = -2,$$
$$4c - 2c = -2,$$
$$c = -1,$$

and the general solution is

$$\mu_n = A + Bn - n^2, \qquad n \geq 1.$$

The astute reader may have recognized that $\Delta^2\mu_n = -2$, so that $\mu_n = A + Bn - n^2$, since $\Delta^2 n^2 = +2$. Note that the general solution of $d^2u/dt^2 = -2$ is

$$u = A + Bt - t^2.$$

Example 4. Find the general solution of the second order inhomogeneous equation

$$u_{n+2} - u_{n+1} - u_n = 2^n, \qquad n = 1, 2, 3, \ldots$$

Solution. The homogeneous equation produces the characteristic equation $\lambda^2 - \lambda - 1 = 0$, yielding the two eigenvalues $\lambda_{1, 2} = \frac{1}{2}(1 \pm \sqrt{5})$. To find a particular solution of the inhomogeneous equation, we assume a solution of the same form as the forcing function. Let $u_n = a2^n$, so that $a2^{n+2} - a2^{n+1} - a2^n = 2^n$, yielding $a = 1$. Thus the general solution is

$$u_n = A\left(\frac{1 + \sqrt{5}}{2}\right)^n + B\left(\frac{1 - \sqrt{5}}{2}\right)^n + 2^n, \qquad n \geq 1,$$

with A and B arbitrary constants.

Example 5. Find the general solution of $u_{n+1} - 2u_n = 2^n$, $n \geq 1$.

Solution. The solution of the homogeneous equation is $u_n = A2^n$, which is of the same form as the forcing function. Hence we try $u_n = an2^n$ as the form of a particular solution. Substituting into $u_{n+1} - 2u_n = 2^n$ yields $a(n + 1)2^{n+1} - 2an2^n = 2^n$, so that $2a = 1$, and $u_n = A2^n + n2^{n-1}$ is the general solution.

One may obtain a particular solution by the variation of parameter method. Since $u_n = A2^n$ is a solution of the homogeneous equation, we look for a solution of the inhomogeneous equation of the form $u_n = A_n2^n$, with A_n an unknown function of n. Thus $A_{n+1}2^{n+1} - 2A_n2^n = 2^n$ yields $A_{n+1} - A_n = \frac{1}{2}$, or $\Delta A_n = \frac{1}{2}$. Hence $A_n = n/2$, and $u_n = \frac{1}{2}n2^n$ is a particular solution as noted above. The constant A above is obtained from $u_1 = 2A + 1$. We can also solve for u_n by an iteration process. Thus $u_{n+1} = 2u_n + 2^n$ yields

$$u_2 = 2u_1 + 2 = 2^2A + 4,$$
$$u_3 = 2u_2 + 4 = 2^3A + 12 = 2^3A + 3\cdot2^{3-1},$$
$$u_4 = 2u_3 + 8 = 2^4A + 32 = 2^4A + 4\cdot2^{4-1},$$
$$u_5 = 2u_4 + 16 = 2^5A + 80 = 2^5A + 5\cdot2^{5-1}, \qquad \text{etc.}$$

One then conjectures that $u_n = 2^nA + n2^{n-1}$. It is a simple matter to show that $u_{n+1} - 2u_n \equiv 2^n$ for all values of A.

PROBLEMS

In the following problems the domain of n is the set of positive integers.

1. $u_{n+1} + 3u_n = 2 - n$, $u_1 = 0$.
2. $u_{n+2} + 2u_{n+1} + u_n = 3n + 1$, $u_1 = 1, u_2 = 0$.
3. $u_{n+1} + 2u_n = 2n - 3^n$, $u_1 = 1$.
4. $u_{n+1} + 4u_n = 2(-4)^n$, $u_1 = 0$.
5. $u_{n+2} - 2u_{n+1} + u_n = 1 - 2n$, $u_1 = u_2 = 1$.
6. $u_{n+1} - 2u_n = 7n + 6n^2$, $u_1 = 0$.
7. Let $u_n = n/(n + 1)$, $n = 1, 2, 3, \ldots$ Show that

$$u_{n+1} - u_n = \frac{1}{(n + 1)(n + 2)}.$$

Then deduce that

$$\frac{n}{n+1} = \frac{1}{1\cdot 2} + \frac{1}{2\cdot 3} + \cdots + \frac{1}{n(n+1)}.$$

What is the value of

$$\sum_{k=1}^{\infty} \frac{1}{k(k+1)} \ ?$$

A.4 ELEMENTARY EXAMPLES · SOLUTIONS OF DIFFERENCE EQUATIONS · THE GAMMA FUNCTION

Example 1. Consider the infinite sequence of meshes (1Ω resistors) (Fig. 1).

Figure A.1

For the loop containing i_n, $n \geq 1$, we have

$$3i_n - i_{n-1} - i_{n+1} = 0,$$

whose characteristic equation is $\lambda^2 - 3\lambda + 1 = 0$, so that

$$i_n = A\left(\frac{3 - \sqrt{5}}{2}\right)^n + B\left(\frac{3 + \sqrt{5}}{2}\right)^n, \qquad n \geq 1.$$

We must have $B \equiv 0$, for otherwise i_n would increase beyond bound as $n \to \infty$. Hence

$$i_n = A\left(\frac{3 - \sqrt{5}}{2}\right)^n, \qquad n \geq 1.$$

For the loop containing i_0 we have $3i_0 - i_1 = E$. Since A is arbitrary we can choose $i_0 = A$.
Hence

$$3A - A\left(\frac{3 - \sqrt{5}}{2}\right) = E,$$

$$A = \frac{2E}{3 + \sqrt{5}},$$

and

$$i_n = \frac{2E}{3 + \sqrt{5}}\left(\frac{3 - \sqrt{5}}{2}\right)^n, \qquad n = 0, 1, 2, 3, \ldots$$

Example 2. Let $P_o = L$ be the amount of a loan, and suppose N payments of A units per payment are made to pay off the loan at an interest rate of $r\%$ per payment. For example, a 6% loan with monthly installments yields $r = 0.06/12 = 0.005$.

Let P_n be the principal owed just after the nth payment, $n = 0, 1, 2, \ldots, N$. For the next period an amount rP_n is due the lender. The next payment, A, covers this interest and also reduces the principal by an amount $P_n - P_{n+1}$. Thus

$$A = rP_n + P_n - P_{n+1},$$
$$P_{n+1} - (1 + r)P_n = -A,$$

(1)

whose general solution is

$$P_n = B(1 + r)^n + \frac{A}{r}.$$

From $P_0 = L$, $P_N = 0$, we have

$$L = B + \frac{A}{r}, \qquad 0 = B(1 + r)^N + \frac{A}{r},$$

yielding

$$A = \frac{rL(1 + r)^N}{(1 + r)^N - 1}$$

(2)

as the payment per period.

For example, a $10,000 loan at 6% for 10 years yields monthly payments given by

$$A = \frac{(0.005)\, 10{,}000\, (1.005)^{120}}{(1.005)^{120} - 1} \approx \$111.00.$$

Example 3. *Towers of Hanoi.* Consider a peg containing n discs graduated in size, the largest disc at the bottom of the peg. Two empty pegs are available for transferring the discs, but no disc can be placed on top of a smaller disc. We wish to determine the minimum number of moves which are required to transfer the discs to a new peg.

Solution. Let u_n be the required minimum number of moves. Before the largest disc can be transferred to a new peg the $n - 1$ smaller discs must be transferred to a new peg, requiring u_{n-1} moves. The largest disc is now transferred to the third peg, and the process is repeated (u_{n-1} further moves are now necessary to place the smaller discs on top of the largest disc). Hence $u_n = u_{n-1} + 1 + u_{n-1}$, $u_n - 2u_{n-1} = 1$, yielding $u_n = A2^n - 1$. Since $u_1 = 1$ we have $u_n = 2^n - 1$ as the required number of moves. To transfer 30 discs requires more than 10^9 moves.

Example 4. The following difference equation arises in queuing theory.

$$(n + 1)p_{n+1} - (\alpha + n)p_n + \alpha p_{n-1} = 0, \qquad n = 0, 1, 2, \ldots,$$

(3)

with $p_{-1} = 0$, and α a constant. This difference equation is linear and homogeneous, but it has nonconstant coefficients. The generating function

$$F(s) = \sum_{n=0}^{\infty} p_n s^n \tag{4}$$

is a useful tool for solving the above difference equation. Quite formally, we have

$$F'(s) = \sum_{0}^{\infty} n p_n s^{n-1},$$

$$sF'(s) = \sum_{0}^{\infty} n p_n s^n. \tag{5}$$

Multiplying Eq. (3) by s^{n+1} and summing on n yields

$$\sum_{0}^{\infty} (n + 1) p_{n+1} s^{n+1} - \alpha s \sum_{0}^{\infty} p_n s^n - s \sum_{0}^{\infty} n p_n s^n + \alpha s^2 \sum_{0}^{\infty} p_{n-1} s^{n-1} = 0,$$

so that

$$sF'(s) - \alpha sF(s) - s^2 F'(s) + \alpha s^2 F(s) = 0,$$

$$\frac{F'(s)}{F(s)} = \alpha, \qquad s \neq 1, \tag{6}$$

by making use of Eq. (5). Thus

$$F(s) = Ae^{\alpha s} = p_0 e^{\alpha s} = p_0 \sum_{0}^{\infty} \frac{\alpha^n}{n!} s^n, \tag{7}$$

since $F(0) = p_0$. The coefficient of s^n, namely $p_0(\alpha^n/n!)$, is p_n, so that

$$p_n = p_0 \frac{\alpha^n}{n!}, \qquad n = 0, 1, 2, 3, \ldots \tag{8}$$

The reader can verify directly that p_n satisfies Eq. (3).

Example 5. *The gamma, or factorial, function.* The difference equation

$$\Gamma(n + 1) = n\Gamma(n), \qquad n = 1, 2, 3, \ldots, \tag{9}$$

with $\Gamma(1) = 1$, yields recursively,

$$\Gamma(2) = 1\Gamma(1) = 1!,$$
$$\Gamma(3) = 2\Gamma(2) = 2 \cdot 1 = 2!,$$
$$\Gamma(4) = 3\Gamma(3) = 3 \cdot 2! = 3!,$$

and so on, so that $\Gamma(n + 1) = n!$ for all positive integers n. Let us determine an integral representation for $\Gamma(n)$. We assume that

$$\Gamma(n) = \int_{-\infty}^{\infty} e^{-ns} F(s) \, ds, \tag{10}$$

with $F(s)$ an unknown function. Then

$$n\Gamma(n) = \int_{-\infty}^{\infty} n\, e^{-ns} F(s)\, ds$$

$$= \int_{-\infty}^{\infty} -\frac{d}{ds}(e^{-ns}) F(s)\, ds$$

$$= -F(s)\, e^{-ns} \Big|_{-\infty}^{\infty} + \int_{-\infty}^{\infty} e^{-ns} F'(s)\, ds$$

$$= \int_{-\infty}^{\infty} e^{-ns} F'(s)\, ds, \tag{11}$$

provided

$$\lim_{s \to \pm\infty} F(s)\, e^{-ns} = 0.$$

Since

$$\Gamma(n+1) = \int_{-\infty}^{\infty} e^{-s}\, e^{-ns} F(s)\, ds,$$

we have

$$\int_{-\infty}^{\infty} e^{-ns} [e^{-s} F(s) - F'(s)]\, ds = 0 \tag{12}$$

from $\Gamma(n+1) - n\Gamma(n) = 0$. Equation (12) is satisfied for all integers n if

$$e^{-s} F(s) - F'(s) = 0,$$

$$\frac{dF}{F} = e^{-s}\, ds, \tag{13}$$

$$F(s) = A \exp(-e^{-s}).$$

We note that

$$\lim_{s \to \pm\infty} F(s)\, e^{-ns} = 0.$$

Hence

$$\Gamma(n) = A \int_{-\infty}^{\infty} e^{-ns} \exp(-e^{-s})\, ds. \tag{14}$$

Let $e^{-s} = w$, so that

$$\Gamma(n) = A \int_{0}^{\infty} w^{n-1}\, e^{-w}\, dw. \tag{15}$$

From $\Gamma(1) = 1$ we have

$$A \int_{0}^{\infty} e^{-w}\, dw = A = 1.$$

The gamma function is defined by

$$\Gamma(z) = \int_{0}^{\infty} w^{z-1}\, e^{-w}\, dw \tag{16}$$

for $Re\ z > 0$.

Let the reader show that $\Gamma(n + 1) = n\Gamma(n)$ on integrating Eq. (16) by parts. The study of the gamma function belongs properly to the domain of functions of a complex variable. It will also play an important role in the study of the chi-square random variable of statistics.

Stirling has shown that

$$n! \approx \sqrt{2\pi n}\left(\frac{n}{e}\right)^n, \qquad n \gg 1, \tag{17}$$

in the sense that

$$\lim_{n \to \infty} \frac{n!}{\sqrt{2\pi n}\left(\dfrac{n}{e}\right)^n} = 1 .$$

To evaluate the integral

$$\int_0^\infty x^n e^{-sx}\, dx ,$$

we let $sx = y$, $sdx = dy$, so that

$$\int_0^\infty x^n e^{-sx}\, dx = \frac{1}{s^{n+1}} \int_0^\infty y^{n+1-1} e^{-y}\, dy$$

$$= \frac{\Gamma(n + 1)}{s^{n+1}} = \frac{n!}{s^{n+1}} \tag{18}$$

for any non-negative integer n.

PROBLEMS

1. In the following network (1Ω resistors, Fig. 2) show that

$$i_n = \frac{E}{1 + \sqrt{3}}\,(2 - \sqrt{3})^n .$$

2. For $n \gg 1$ show that $\ln(n!) \approx n \ln n$.

3. Let

$$f_{n+1} = \frac{1}{n + 1} f(n), \qquad n = 0, 1, 2, 3, \dots ,$$

with $f(0) = 1$. By means of the generating function

$$F(s) = \sum_0^\infty f_n s^n ,$$

show that $f_n = 1/n!$.

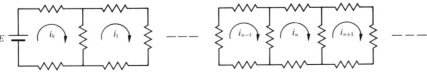

Figure A.2

4. Referring to Example 2 of Section A.4, suppose that the payments per period decrease with n, such that $A_n = \beta(N - n)$. Show that

$$\beta = \frac{r^2(1 + r)^N L}{1 + (Nr - 1)(1 + r)^N} \, .$$

5. If, in Example 3 of Section 1.4, four pegs are available, show that $u_n \leq 2^{n-1} + 1$, with u_n the minimum number of moves required to transfer the discs to a new peg. Can you find an explicit form for u_n?

A.5 THE SUMMATION CONVENTION

In dealing with linear equations, matrices, and general systems involving many unknowns, it is expedient to adapt the summation convention first introduced by A. Einstein. Let us consider first the set of linear equations

$$a_1 x + b_1 y + c_1 z = d_1 ,$$
$$a_2 x + b_2 y + c_2 z = d_2 , \qquad (1)$$
$$a_3 x + b_3 y + c_3 z = d_3 .$$

We will find it convenient to set $x = x^1$, $y = x^2$, $z = x^3$. The superscripts do *not* denote powers, but are simply a means for distinguishing between the three quantities x, y, z. Thus the single letter x and a set of superscripts $1, 2, 3, \ldots, n$ yields a set of n different quantities

$$x^1, x^2, x^3, \ldots, x^n . \qquad (2)$$

Now the coefficients of x, y, z in Eq. (1) may be expressed by the square array

$$\begin{bmatrix} a_1 & b_1 & c_1 \\ a_2 & b_2 & c_2 \\ a_3 & b_3 & c_3 \end{bmatrix} . \qquad (3)$$

We note that this square array has three rows and three columns. Let a_j^i be the element in the ith row and jth column, $i, j, = 1, 2, 3$, so that $a_1 = a_1^1$, $b_1 = a_2^1$, etc. The square array now assumes the form

$$\begin{bmatrix} a_1^1 & a_2^1 & a_3^1 \\ a_1^2 & a_2^2 & a_3^2 \\ a_1^3 & a_2^3 & a_3^3 \end{bmatrix} . \qquad (4)$$

Furthermore, the linear equations above now become

$$a_1^1 x^1 + a_2^1 x^2 + a_3^1 x^3 = d^1 ,$$
$$a_1^2 x^1 + a_2^2 x^2 + a_3^2 x^3 = d^2 , \qquad (5)$$
$$a_1^3 x^1 + a_2^3 x^2 + a_3^3 x^3 = d^3 ,$$

with $d^1 = d_1$, $d^2 = d_2$, $d^3 = d_3$. By the familiar summation notation of mathematics these equations become

$$\sum_{\alpha=1}^{3} a_\alpha^1 x^\alpha = d^1, \qquad \sum_{\alpha=1}^{3} a_\alpha^2 x^\alpha = d^2, \qquad \sum_{\alpha=1}^{3} a_\alpha^3 x^\alpha = d^3, \tag{6}$$

or simply

$$\sum_{\alpha=1}^{3} a_\alpha^i x^\alpha = d^i, \qquad i = 1, 2, 3. \tag{7}$$

Thus the system of equations

$$\sum_{\alpha=1}^{n} a_\alpha^i x^\alpha = d^i, \qquad i = 1, 2, \ldots, n, \tag{8}$$

represents n linear equations involving $x^1, x^2, \ldots, x^n$. A. Einstein noticed that it was superfluous to carry along the $\sum$ sign of Eq. (8). We rewrite this system as

$$a_\alpha^i x^\alpha = d^i, \qquad i = 1, 2, \ldots, n, \tag{9}$$

provided it is understood that whenever an index occurs exactly twice in an expression (once as a superscript and once as a subscript) a summation is indicated for this index over its full range of definition. Notice above that α occurs as a subscript in a_α^i and as a superscript in x^α.

The index of summation is called a dummy index, since the final result (a summation) is independent of the symbol that is used for the index of summation. Thus for three dimensions

$$a_\alpha^1 x^\alpha = a_1^1 x^1 + a_2^1 x^2 + a_3^1 x^3,$$

$$a_\beta^1 x^\beta = a_1^1 x^1 + a_2^1 x^2 + a_3^1 x^3, \tag{10}$$

$$a_r^1 x^r = a_1^1 x^1 + a_2^1 x^2 + a_3^1 x^3.$$

The index of summation is analogous to the integration variable of the integral calculus. Note that

$$\int_a^b f(x)\, dx = \int_a^b f(t)\, dt = \int_a^b f(\alpha)\, d\alpha. \tag{11}$$

Example 1. Let **A** be a vector in a three-dimensional Euclidean space having the components (A_1, A_2, A_3) in rectangular coordinates, and denote the components of a similar vector **B** by (B^1, B^2, B^3). Then

$$A_\alpha B^\alpha \equiv A_1 B^1 + A_2 B^2 + A_3 B^3$$

defines the scalar or dot product of these two vectors, i.e., $\mathbf{A} \cdot \mathbf{B} = A_\alpha B^\alpha$. The same result applies to n-dimensional vectors with α summed from one to n.

Example 2. Let y^1 be a differentiable function of three variables x^1, x^2, x^3. From the calculus we have

$$dy^1 = \frac{\partial y^1}{\partial x^1} dx^1 + \frac{\partial y^1}{\partial x^2} dx^2 + \frac{\partial y^1}{\partial x^3} dx^3$$

$$= \sum_{\alpha=1}^{3} \frac{\partial y^1}{\partial x^\alpha} dx^\alpha$$

$$= \frac{\partial y^1}{\partial x^\alpha} dx^\alpha . \tag{12}$$

In general, if we have $y^i = y^i(x^1, x^2, \ldots, x^n)$, $i = 1, 2, \ldots, n$ as a set of transformations from an $(x^1, x^2, \ldots, x^n)$ coordinate system to a $(y^1, y^2, \ldots, y^n)$ coordinate system, then

$$dy^i = \frac{\partial y^i}{\partial x^\alpha} dx^\alpha , \tag{13}$$

provided the partial derivatives exist. We will have more to say about coordinate transformations subsequently.

Example 3. The linear system of differential equations,

$$\frac{dx^1}{dt} = a_1^1 x^1 + a_2^1 x^2 + a_3^1 x^3 ,$$

$$\frac{dx^2}{dt} = a_1^2 x^1 + a_2^2 x^2 + a_3^2 x^3 ,$$

$$\frac{dx^3}{dt} = a_1^3 x^1 + a_2^3 x^2 + a_3^3 x^3 ,$$

may be expressed by

$$\frac{dx^i}{dt} = a_\alpha^i x^\alpha, \qquad i = 1, 2, 3 .$$

Example 4. Let us consider the quantity $Q = a_{\alpha\beta} x^\alpha x^\beta$ (called a quadratic form) for a three-dimensional space. Since the index α occurs both as a subscript and a superscript, we must sum on α from 1 to 3. This yields

$$Q = a_{1\beta} x^1 x^\beta + a_{2\beta} x^2 x^\beta + a_{3\beta} x^3 x^\beta .$$

Now each term of Q above is such that β is both a subscript and a superscript. Summing on β from 1 to 3 as prescribed by our summation convention yields the quadratic form

$$Q = a_{11} x^1 x^1 + a_{12} x^1 x^2 + a_{13} x^1 x^3$$

$$+ a_{21} x^2 x^1 + a_{22} x^2 x^2 + a_{23} x^2 x^3$$

$$+ a_{31} x^3 x^1 + a_{32} x^3 x^2 + a_{33} x^3 x^3. \tag{14}$$

In terms of $x^1 = x$, $x^2 = y$, $x^3 = z$, Q becomes

$$Q = ax^2 + by^2 + cz^2 + 2dxy + 2eyz + 2fzx.$$

with $a = a_{11}$, $b = a_{22}$, $c = a_{33}$, $2d = a_{12} + a_{21}$, etc. The most general quadratic form in n variables is $Q = a_{\alpha\beta}x^\alpha x^\beta$, discussed in Section A. 9.

Example 5. We define ϵ^{ij}, $i, j = 1, 2$ as follows: Let $\epsilon^{11} = \epsilon^{22} = 0$, $\epsilon^{12} = +1$, $\epsilon^{21} = -1$. Now we consider the expression

$$\Delta = \epsilon^{ij}a_i^1 a_j^2$$

$$= \epsilon^{11}a_1^1 a_1^2 + \epsilon^{12}a_1^1 a_2^2 + \epsilon^{21}a_2^1 a_1^2 + \epsilon^{22}a_2^1 a_2^2$$

$$= a_1^1 a_2^2 - a_2^1 a_1^2.$$

The reader will recall from algebra that

$$\Delta = \epsilon^{ij}a_i^1 a_j^2 = \begin{vmatrix} a_1^1 & a_2^1 \\ a_1^2 & a_2^2 \end{vmatrix}$$

represents a second-order determinant.

Example 6. We define ϵ^{ijk}, $i, j, k = 1, 2, 3$ as follows: If two or more of the superscripts are the same, the numerical value of ϵ^{ijk} is zero. Thus $\epsilon^{131} = \epsilon^{222} = \epsilon^{323} = 0$, etc. If the i, j, k are all different (there are six cases, since there are $3! = 6$ permutations of the integers 1, 2, 3), the numerical value of ϵ^{ijk} is to be $+1$ or -1, according to whether it takes an even or odd number of permutations to rearrange ijk into the natural order 123.

Let us look at the arrangement 321. Interchanging 3 and 2 yields 231, then interchanging 1 and 3 yields 213, and interchanging 2 and 1 yields the natural order 123. Three (an odd number) interchanges were necessary, so that $\epsilon^{321} = -1$. Considering all cases yields

$$\epsilon^{123} = \epsilon^{312} = \epsilon^{231} = +1,$$

$$\epsilon^{213} = \epsilon^{321} = \epsilon^{132} = -1. \tag{15}$$

Now let **A** be a vector with components (A_1, A_2, A_3) and let **B** be a vector with components (B_1, B_2, B_3). Let us consider the three numbers C^1, C^2, C^3 defined by

$$C^i = \epsilon^{ijk}A_j B_k, \qquad i = 1, 2, 3. \tag{16}$$

We obtain (from the summation convention)

$$C^1 = \epsilon^{1jk}A_j B_k$$

$$= \epsilon^{123}A_2 B_3 + \epsilon^{132}A_3 B_2$$

$$= A_2 B_3 - A_3 B_2,$$

by virtue of the definition of ϵ^{ijk}. Similarly,

$$C^2 = \epsilon^{2jk} A_j B_k = A_3 B_1 - A_1 B_3,$$
$$C^3 = \epsilon^{3jk} A_j B_k = A_1 B_2 - A_2 B_1.$$

The new vector $\mathbf{C}$ with components (C^1, C^2, C^3) is precisely the vector, or cross, product of elementary vector analysis. Recall that

$$\mathbf{C} = \begin{vmatrix} \mathbf{i} & \mathbf{j} & \mathbf{k} \\ A_1 & A_2 & A_3 \\ B_1 & B_2 & B_3 \end{vmatrix}$$
$$= (A_2 B_3 - A_3 B_2)\mathbf{i} + (A_3 B_1 - A_1 B_3)\mathbf{j}$$
$$+ (A_1 B_2 - A_2 B_1)\mathbf{k}.$$

Example 7. *The Kronecker delta.* In mathematics quite often a function of two indices, say i and j, assumes the value $+1$ if $i = j$ and zero if $i \neq j$. For example, consider n independent variables $x^1, x^2, \ldots, x^n$, yielding

$$\frac{\partial x^1}{\partial x^1} = \frac{\partial x^2}{\partial x^2} = \cdots = \frac{\partial x^n}{\partial x^n} = 1,$$

$$\frac{\partial x^1}{\partial x^2} = 0, \qquad \frac{\partial x^2}{\partial x^5} = 0, \qquad \text{etc.,}$$

so that $\partial x^i / \partial x^j = \delta^i_j$, where the symbol δ^i_j is called the Kronecker delta [after the famous German mathematician L. Kronecker (1823–1891)] defined by

$$\delta^i_j = \begin{cases} 1 & \text{for} & i = j, \\ 0 & \text{for} & i \neq j. \end{cases} \tag{17}$$

In particular,

$$\delta^\alpha_\alpha = \delta^1_1 + \delta^2_2 + \cdots + \delta^n_n = n$$

for an n dimensional space. Furthermore we note that

$$\delta^i_\alpha a^\alpha = \delta^i_1 a^1 + \delta^i_2 a^2 + \cdots + \delta^i_i a^i + \cdots + \delta^i_n a^n = a^i \tag{18}$$

for $i = 1, 2, \ldots, n$. It is important to note that every term in the sum $\delta^i_\alpha a^\alpha$ is zero except the term (no sum on i)

$$\delta^i_i a^i = 1 \cdot a^i = a^i.$$

Returning to the quadratic form $Q = a_{\alpha\beta} x^\alpha x^\beta$ let us assume that Q vanishes identically for all values of the independent variables $x^1, x^2, \ldots, x^n$. Then

$$\frac{\partial Q}{\partial x^i} = a_{\alpha\beta} x^\alpha \frac{\partial x^\beta}{\partial x^i} + a_{\alpha\beta} x^\beta \frac{\partial x^\alpha}{\partial x^i}$$
$$= a_{\alpha\beta} x^\alpha \delta^\beta_i + a_{\alpha\beta} x^\beta \delta^\alpha_i$$
$$= a_{\alpha i} x^\alpha + a_{i\beta} x^\beta \equiv 0$$

for all values of i. Now, differentiating with respect to x^j, with j arbitrary, yields

$$\frac{\partial^2 Q}{\partial x^j \partial x^i} = a_{\alpha i}\frac{\partial x^\alpha}{\partial x^j} + a_{i\beta}\frac{\partial x^\beta}{\partial x^j}$$

$$= a_{\alpha i}\delta_j^\alpha + a_{i\beta}\delta_j^\beta$$

$$= a_{ji} + a_{ij} \equiv 0$$

for all i, j. Hence $a_{ij} + a_{ji} = 0$ or $a_{ij} = -a_{ji}$ for all values of $i, j = 1, 2, \ldots, n$. Conversely, let $a_{ij} = -a_{ji}$ for $i, j = 1, 2, \ldots, n$, and let the reader show that $a_{\alpha\beta}x^\alpha x^\beta \equiv 0$ for all values of $x^1, x^2, \ldots, x^n$. This is a very useful result.

Example 8. In Euclidean geometry the line element is

$$(ds)^2 = (dx)^2 + (dy)^2 + (dz)^2,$$

using Cartesian coordinates (three-dimensional space). Riemann considered the more general line element given by

$$ds^2 = g_{\alpha\beta}(x)\, dx^\alpha dx^\beta, \qquad g_{\alpha\beta} = g_{\beta\alpha} \qquad (19)$$

for an n dimensional space, with $g_{\alpha\beta}$ a function of the space coordinates $x^1, x^2, \ldots, x^n$. The study of such spaces involving the above line element, or metric, leads to a discussion of Riemannian geometry, formulated in the 19th century. Einstein's general theory of relativity (1915) deals precisely with a 4-dimensional Riemannian geometry whose coordinates are (x, y, z, ct).

Under a coordinate transformation

$$x^1 = x^1(\bar{x}^1, \bar{x}^2, \ldots, \bar{x}^n),$$

$$x^2 = x^2(\bar{x}^1, \bar{x}^2, \ldots, \bar{x}^n), \qquad (20)$$

$$\vdots$$

$$x^n = x^n(\bar{x}^1, \bar{x}^2, \ldots, \bar{x}^n),$$

or, in simplified notation, $x^i = x^i(\bar{x})$, $i = 1, 2, \ldots, n$, we have

$$dx^\alpha = \frac{\partial x^\alpha}{\partial \bar{x}^j}\, d\bar{x}^j, \qquad dx^\beta = \frac{\partial x^\beta}{\partial \bar{x}^k}\, d\bar{x}^k,$$

so that ds^2 becomes

$$ds^2 = g_{\alpha\beta}(x)\frac{\partial x^\alpha}{\partial \bar{x}^j}\cdot\frac{\partial x^\beta}{\partial \bar{x}^k}\, d\bar{x}^j\, d\bar{x}^k$$

$$= \bar{g}_{jk}(\bar{x})d\bar{x}^j\, d\bar{x}^k, \qquad (21)$$

which again is a quadratic form in the differentials. Thus

$$\bar{g}_{jk}(\bar{x}) = g_{\alpha\beta}(x)\frac{\partial x^\alpha}{\partial \bar{x}^j}\cdot\frac{\partial x^\beta}{\partial \bar{x}^k} \qquad (22)$$

for $j, k = 1, 2, \ldots, n$. This is the fundamental relationship between the components of the metric tensor, $\{g_{\alpha\beta}(x)\}$, in the x-coordinate system and the metric tensor, $\{\bar{g}_{jk}(\bar{x})\}$, in the $\bar{x}$-coordinate system.

Example 9. Under a coordinate transformation , $y^i = y^i(x^1, x^2, \ldots, x^n)$, $i = 1, 2, \ldots, n$, we have

$$dy^i = \frac{\partial y^i}{\partial x^\alpha} dx^\alpha ,$$

$$\frac{\partial y^i}{\partial y^j} = \frac{\partial y^i}{\partial x^\alpha} \frac{\partial x^\alpha}{\partial y^j} \equiv \delta_j^i ,$$

(23)

provided the partial derivatives exist and that $x^1, x^2, \ldots, x^n$ can be solved uniquely in terms of $y^1, y^2, \ldots, y^n$.

Equation (23) is of fundamental importance in manipulating equations involving partial derivatives. For example, if

$$\bar{A}^i(\bar{x}) = A^\alpha(x) \frac{\partial \bar{x}^i}{\partial x^\alpha}, \qquad i = 1, 2, \ldots, n ,$$

then

$$\bar{A}^i(\bar{x}) \frac{\partial x^j}{\partial \bar{x}^i} = A^\alpha(x) \frac{\partial \bar{x}^i}{\partial x^\alpha} \frac{\partial x^j}{\partial \bar{x}^i}$$

$$= A^\alpha(x) \frac{\partial x^j}{\partial \bar{x}^i} \frac{\partial \bar{x}^i}{\partial x^\alpha}$$

$$= A^\alpha(x) \frac{\partial x^j}{\partial x^\alpha} = A^\alpha(x) \, \delta_\alpha^j = A^j(x) \tag{24}$$

for $j = 1, 2, \ldots, n$, so that

$$A^j(x) = \bar{A}^\alpha(\bar{x}) \frac{\partial x^j}{\partial \bar{x}^\alpha} ,$$

and we have determined $A^1, A^2, \ldots, A^n$ as linear functions of $\bar{A}^1, \bar{A}^2, \ldots, \bar{A}^n$.

Example 10. In Fig. 3 two lines intersect at the point O. Lines are projected from any point P (not necessarily in the plane of the two lines) to these lines yielding the projected distances x and y. The point Q is obtained by moving a distance Δx parallel to the x axis, yielding a change in y of an amount Δy.

It follows that $\Delta y / \Delta x = \cos \theta$, so that

$$\lim_{\Delta x \to 0} \frac{\Delta y}{\Delta x} = \frac{\partial y}{\partial x} = \cos \theta = \cos (y, x) ,$$

with $\cos (y, x)$ the cosine of the angle between the y and x axis. Now consider two Cartesian coordinate systems with a common origin (Fig. 4).

If a point P is described by the x^1–x^2–x^3 coordinate system, its components are designated by (x^1, x^2, x^3). Similarly, the same point P is described by the coordinates (y^1, y^2, y^3). Now we have seen that

$$\frac{\partial y^i}{\partial x^\alpha} = \cos(y^i, x^\alpha), \qquad i, \alpha = 1, 2, 3$$

$$= a^i_\alpha. \tag{25}$$

Since

$$dy^i = \frac{\partial y^i}{\partial x^\alpha} dx^\alpha = a^i_\alpha dx^\alpha,$$

it follows from a simple integration that

$$y^i = a^i_\alpha x^\alpha, \qquad i = 1, 2, 3 \tag{26}$$

is the coordinate transformation between two Cartesian coordinate systems. Such a transformation is called an orthogonal transformation.

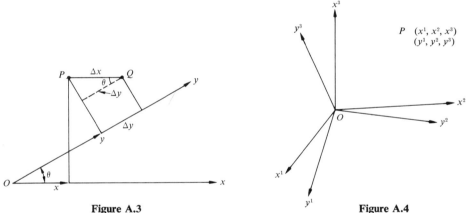

Figure A.3   Figure A.4

We may imagine, for example, that the 0–y^1–y^2–y^3 coordinate system is fixed in space, whereas the 0–x^1–x^2–x^3 coordinate system is fixed to a rigid body (gyroscope), which has a fixed point at 0. Then the direction cosines a^i_α are functions of time,

$$a^i_\alpha = a^i_\alpha(t), \qquad i, \alpha = 1, 2, 3.$$

PROBLEMS

1. If $y^i = a^i_\alpha x^\alpha$, $z^i = b^i_\beta y^\beta$ for an n-dimensional space, show that $z^i = b^i_\beta a^\beta_\alpha x^\alpha = c^i_\alpha x^\alpha$ with $c^i_\alpha = b^i_\beta a^\beta_\alpha$.

2. Referring to the orthogonal transformation $y^i = a^i_\alpha x^\alpha$ of Eq. (26), explain why

$$\sum_{i=1}^{3} a^i_\alpha a^i_\beta = \delta_{\alpha\beta} ,$$

with $\delta_{\alpha\beta} = 0$ if $\alpha \neq \beta$, $\delta_{\alpha\beta} = 1$ otherwise.

3. Show that

$$\delta^\alpha_\beta \frac{\partial y^i}{\partial x^\alpha} \frac{\partial x^\beta}{\partial y^j} = \delta^i_j .$$

4. Given $a_{ijk} x^i x^j x^k \equiv 0$ for all values of $x^1, x^2, \ldots, x^n$, $a_{ijk} \equiv$ constants, show that

$$a_{ijk} + a_{kij} + a_{jki} + a_{jik} + a_{kji} + a_{ikj} = 0$$

for all i, j, k.

5. If $a_{\alpha\beta} \equiv - a_{\alpha\beta}$ for all $\alpha, \beta = 1, 2, \ldots, n$, show that $a_{rs} x^r x^s \equiv 0$ for all $x^1, x^2, \ldots, x^n$.

6. Given

$$\bar{A}_i(\bar{x}) = A_\alpha(x) \frac{\partial x^\alpha}{\partial \bar{x}^i}$$

for an n-dimensional space, show that

$$A_i(x) = \bar{A}_\alpha(\bar{x}) \frac{\partial \bar{x}^\alpha}{\partial x^i} .$$

7. Show that $\epsilon^{ijk} = - \epsilon^{jik}$ for all $i, j, k = 1, 2, 3$.

8. Referring to Eq. (16), show that $A_i C^i = 0$, so that $\mathbf{A} \cdot (\mathbf{A} \times \mathbf{B}) = 0$.

9. Show that the triple scalar product in elementary vector analysis can be expressed as

$$\mathbf{A} \cdot (\mathbf{B} \times \mathbf{C}) \equiv \epsilon^{ijk} A_i B_j C_k .$$

10. Let $ds^2 = (dx)^2 + (dy)^2 + (dz)^2$, and consider the spherical coordinate transformation $x = r \sin \theta \cos \phi$, $y = r \sin \theta \sin \phi$, $z = r \cos \theta$. Let $x = x^1, y = x^2, z = x^3, r = \bar{x}^1$, $\theta = \bar{x}^2$, $\phi = \bar{x}^3$. Apply Eq. (22) and show that $\bar{g}_{11} = 1$, $\bar{g}_{22} = r^2$, $\bar{g}_{33} = r^2 \sin^2 \theta$, $\bar{g}_{jk} = 0$ otherwise, so that

$$ds^2 = (dr)^2 + r^2 (d\theta)^2 + r^2 \sin^2 \theta (d\phi)^2$$

in spherical coordinates.

A.6 DETERMINANTS

The solution of Eq. (5) of Section A.5 for x^1, x^2, x^3 leads one to consider the square array of Eq. (4) of that section. The determinant of this square array is, by definition,

$$\Delta = \begin{vmatrix} a^1_1 & a^1_2 & a^1_3 \\ a^2_1 & a^2_2 & a^2_3 \\ a^3_1 & a^3_2 & a^3_3 \end{vmatrix}$$

$$= \epsilon^{ijk} a^1_i a^2_j a^3_k , \tag{1}$$

where the ϵ^{ijk}, i, j, $k = 1$, 2, 3 have been defined in Example 6 of Section A.5. We repeat that the 27 values of ϵ^{ijk} are defined by $\epsilon^{ijk} = 0$ if at least two of the indices are the same: $\epsilon^{ijk} = +1$ if i, j, k are all different and an even number of permutations are required to bring ijk into the natural order 123, $\epsilon^{ijk} = -1$ if an odd number of permutations are required to bring ijk into the natural order 123. The astute reader may recognize that

$$\epsilon^{ijk} = \tfrac{1}{2}(i - j)(j - k)(k - i). \tag{2}$$

It should be clear that $\epsilon^{ijk} = -\epsilon^{jik}$, etc., since if two or more indices are the same, both terms are zero, and if the indices are all different, an additional permutation takes ijk into jik. Expanding $\epsilon^{ijk} a_i^1 a_j^2 a_k^3$ yields

$$\Delta = (a_1^1 a_2^2 a_3^3 + a_3^1 a_1^2 a_2^3 + a_2^1 a_3^2 a_1^3)$$

$$- (a_2^1 a_1^2 a_3^3 + a_3^1 a_2^2 a_1^3 + a_1^1 a_3^2 a_2^3). \tag{3}$$

If we define ϵ_{ijk} in exactly the same manner as ϵ^{ijk}, let the reader show that

$$\Delta = \epsilon^{ijk} a_i^1 a_j^2 a_k^3 = \epsilon_{ijk} a_1^i a_2^j a_3^k. \tag{4}$$

The generalization of the second and third order determinants to nth order determinants is simple (the order of a determinant is simply the number of rows or columns comprising the square array of elements). We have

$$|a_j^i| = \begin{vmatrix} a_1^1 & a_2^1 & \cdots & a_n^1 \\ a_1^2 & a_2^2 & \cdots & a_n^2 \\ \vdots & & & \\ a_1^n & a_2^n & \cdots & a_n^n \end{vmatrix}$$

$$= \epsilon^{\alpha_1 \alpha_2 \cdots \alpha_n} a_{\alpha_1}^1 a_{\alpha_2}^2 \cdots a_{\alpha_n}^n$$

$$= \epsilon_{\alpha_1 \alpha_2 \cdots \alpha_n} a_1^{\alpha_1} a_2^{\alpha_2} \cdots a_n^{\alpha_n}, \tag{5}$$

with $\epsilon^{\alpha_1 \alpha_2 \cdots \alpha_n}$ zero if at least two of the indices are the same. If α_1, α_2, $\ldots$, α_n are all different, the value of $\epsilon^{\alpha_1 \alpha_2 \cdots \alpha_n}$ is $+1$ if an even number of permutations are required to bring $\alpha_1 \alpha_2 \cdots \alpha_n$ into the natural order $1\ 2\ 3\ \cdots\ n$, $\epsilon^{\alpha_1 \alpha_2 \cdots \alpha_n} = -1$ otherwise. It must be emphasized that the indices range from 1 to n.

To facilitate writing, we will deal with third-order determinants, but it will be clear to the reader that any theorem so derived will apply to determinants of any finite order. The upper case ϵ's of Eq. (4) are used to prove theorems concerning the rows of a determinant, and the lower case ϵ's of Eq. (4) are used to prove the corresponding theorems regarding the columns of a determinant.

Let us interchange the first and third row of the determinant of Eq. (1) and obtain a new determinant, namely

$$\Delta' = \begin{vmatrix} a_1^3 & a_2^3 & a_3^3 \\ a_1^2 & a_2^2 & a_3^2 \\ a_1^1 & a_2^1 & a_3^1 \end{vmatrix}$$

$$= \epsilon^{ijk} a_i^3 a_j^2 a_k^1$$

$$= \epsilon^{ijk} a_k^1 a_j^2 a_i^3 = \epsilon^{\alpha j \beta} a_\beta^1 a_j^2 a_\alpha^3$$

$$= \epsilon^{kji} a_i^1 a_j^2 a_k^3 .$$

Since

$$\epsilon^{kji} = - \epsilon^{kij} = \epsilon^{ikj} = - \epsilon^{ijk} ,$$

it follows that

$$\Delta' = - \epsilon^{ijk} a_i^1 a_j^2 a_k^3 = - \Delta .$$

Thus we have proved the

Theorem. Interchanging two rows (or columns) of a determinant changes the sign of the determinant.

Had we chosen

$$\Delta = \epsilon_{ijk} a_1^i a_2^j a_3^k ,$$

we would have obtained the corresponding theorem for columns. As an immediate corollary it follows that if two rows (or columns) of a determinant are the same, including the order of the elements, the value of the determinant is zero, since $\Delta = - \Delta$ for this case.

If we replace the elements of the first row of Δ by la_1^1, la_2^1, la_3^1, we observe that

$$\Delta'' = \begin{vmatrix} la_1^1 & la_2^1 & la_3^1 \\ a_1^2 & a_2^2 & a_3^2 \\ a_1^3 & a_2^3 & a_3^3 \end{vmatrix}$$

$$= \epsilon^{ijk} (la_i^1) a_j^2 a_k^3 = l \epsilon^{ijk} a_i^1 a_j^2 a_k^3$$

$$= l \Delta ,$$

yielding the

Theorem. If a row (or column) of a determinant is multiplied by a factor l, the value of the determinant is multiplied by l.

Let us now investigate the determinant

$$\Delta''' = \begin{vmatrix} a_1^1 + la_1^3 & a_2^1 + la_2^3 & a_3^1 + la_3^3 \\ a_1^2 & a_2^2 & a_3^2 \\ a_1^3 & a_2^3 & a_3^3 \end{vmatrix} ,$$

so that

$$\Delta''' = \epsilon^{ijk}(a_i^1 + la_i^3)\, a_j^2\, a_k^3$$
$$= \epsilon^{ijk}\, a_i^1\, a_j^2\, a_k^3 + l\epsilon^{ijk}\, a_i^3\, a_j^2\, a_k^3$$
$$= \epsilon^{ijk}\, a_i^1\, a_j^2\, a_k^3 = \Delta,$$

since

$$\epsilon^{ijk}\, a_i^3\, a_j^2\, a_k^3 = 0$$

from our corollary above, recalling that $e^{ijk}\, a_i^3\, a_j^2\, a_k^3$ is a determinant whose first and third rows contain identical elements. Thus we have the following

Theorem. The value of a determinant remains unchanged if, to the elements of any row (or column) is added a scalar multiple of the corresponding elements of another row (or column).

It follows from Eq. (3) that if the elements below the main diagonal vanish (that is, $a_j^i = 0$ for $i > j$), then $\Delta = a_1^1\, a_2^2\, a_3^3$. Hence we have the

Theorem. If the elements below (or above) the principal diagonal vanish, the value of the determinant is the product of the terms along the principal diagonal.

The theorems above are valuable aids in evaluating a determinant.

Example 1. Evaluate

$$\Delta = \begin{vmatrix} 1 & 0 & -3 & 2 \\ 6 & 3 & 0 & 3 \\ -1 & 2 & 1 & 0 \\ 0 & 1 & -2 & 3 \end{vmatrix} = 3 \begin{vmatrix} 1 & 0 & -3 & 2 \\ 2 & 1 & 0 & 1 \\ -1 & 2 & 1 & 0 \\ 0 & 1 & -2 & 3 \end{vmatrix}$$

$$= 3 \begin{vmatrix} 1 & 0 & -3 & 2 \\ 0 & 1 & 6 & -3 \\ -1 & 2 & 1 & 0 \\ 0 & 1 & -2 & 3 \end{vmatrix} = 3 \begin{vmatrix} 1 & 0 & -3 & 2 \\ 0 & 1 & 6 & -3 \\ 0 & 2 & -2 & 2 \\ 0 & 1 & -2 & 3 \end{vmatrix}$$

$$= 6 \begin{vmatrix} 1 & 0 & -3 & 2 \\ 0 & 1 & 6 & -3 \\ 0 & 1 & -1 & 1 \\ 0 & 1 & -2 & 3 \end{vmatrix} = 6 \begin{vmatrix} 1 & 0 & -3 & 2 \\ 0 & 1 & 6 & -3 \\ 0 & 0 & -7 & 4 \\ 0 & 1 & -2 & 3 \end{vmatrix}$$

$$= 6 \begin{vmatrix} 1 & 0 & -3 & 2 \\ 0 & 1 & 6 & -3 \\ 0 & 0 & -7 & 4 \\ 0 & 0 & -8 & 6 \end{vmatrix} = 42 \begin{vmatrix} 1 & 0 & -3 & 2 \\ 0 & 1 & 6 & -3 \\ 0 & 0 & -1 & \frac{4}{7} \\ 0 & 0 & -8 & 6 \end{vmatrix}$$

$$= 42 \begin{vmatrix} 1 & 0 & -3 & 2 \\ 0 & 1 & 6 & -3 \\ 0 & 0 & -1 & \frac{4}{7} \\ 0 & 0 & 0 & \frac{10}{7} \end{vmatrix} = -42 \cdot \tfrac{10}{7} = -60.$$

The final result is obtained as follows: (a) factor 3 from row two; (b) multiply row one by (-2) and add to row two; (c) add row one to row three; (d) factor 2 from row three; (e) subtract row two from row three; (f) subtract row two from row four; (g) factor 7 from row three; (h) multiply row three by 8 and subtract from row four; (i) with zeros below the main diagonal the final answer is evident.

We now expand a determinant in terms of its *cofactors*. We sum first the index i and obtain

$$\Delta = |a_\beta^\alpha| = \epsilon^{ijk} a_i^1 a_j^2 a_k^3$$
$$= a_1^1 (\epsilon^{1jk} a_j^2 a_k^3) + a_2^1 (\epsilon^{2jk} a_j^2 a_k^3)$$
$$+ a_3^1 (\epsilon^{3jk} a_j^2 a_k^3)$$
$$= a_1^1 A_1^1 + a_2^1 A_1^2 + a_3^1 A_1^3 = a_\alpha^1 A_1^\alpha, \tag{6}$$

with

$$A_1^1 = \epsilon^{1jk} a_j^2 a_k^3 = \epsilon^{123} a_2^2 a_3^3 + \epsilon^{132} a_3^2 a_2^3$$
$$= a_2^2 a_3^3 - a_3^2 a_2^3 = \begin{vmatrix} a_2^2 & a_3^2 \\ a_2^3 & a_3^3 \end{vmatrix}.$$

$$A_1^2 = \epsilon^{2jk} a_j^2 a_k^3 = \epsilon^{213} a_1^2 a_3^3 + \epsilon^{231} a_3^2 a_1^3$$
$$= -[a_1^2 a_3^3 - a_3^2 a_1^3] = (-1)^{1+2} \begin{vmatrix} a_1^2 & a_3^2 \\ a_1^3 & a_3^3 \end{vmatrix}.$$

$$A_1^3 = \epsilon^{3jk} a_j^2 a_k^3 = \epsilon^{312} a_1^2 a_2^3 + \epsilon^{321} a_2^2 a_1^3$$
$$= a_1^2 a_2^3 - a_2^2 a_1^3 = \begin{vmatrix} a_1^2 & a_2^2 \\ a_1^3 & a_2^3 \end{vmatrix}.$$

The elements A_1^1, A_1^2, A_1^3 are the cofactors of the elements a_1^1, a_2^1, a_3^1, respectively. Now the minor M_1^1 of a_1^1 is, by definition, the new determinant obtained by removing the row and column containing a_1^1, see Eq. (1). We note that $A_1^1 = M^1$. The minor of a_2^1 is M_1^2, and we note that $A_1^2 = -M_1^2$, while $A_1^3 = M_1^3$. In general, the determinant obtained by deleting the rth row and sth column of the array $[a_\beta^\alpha]$ is called the minor, M_r^s, of the element a_s^r, and the cofactor of a_s^r is

$$A_r^s = (-1)^{r+s} M_r^s.$$

Equation (6) is the expansion of Δ in terms of the cofactors of the first row. Had we expanded Δ by summing first on the index j, we would have obtained the expansion of Δ in terms of the cofactors of the second row, etc. Thus

$$\Delta = a_\alpha^1 A_1^\alpha = a_\alpha^2 A_2^\alpha = a_\alpha^3 A_3^\alpha$$
$$= a_1^\alpha A_\alpha^1 = a_2^\alpha A_\alpha^2 = a_3^\alpha A_\alpha^3, \tag{7}$$

with $a_1^\alpha A_\alpha^1$ the expansion of Δ in terms of the cofactors of the first column, etc.

Now let us see what happens if we multiply the elements of the second row by the corresponding cofactors of the first row, and sum these products. We obtain

$$\bar{\Delta} = a_\alpha^2 A_1^\alpha$$

$$= a_1^2 A_1^1 + a_2^2 A_1^2 + a_3^2 A_1^3$$

$$= a_1^2 \epsilon^{1\,jk} a_j^2 a_k^3 + a_2^2 \epsilon^{2\,jk} a_j^2 a_k^3 + a_3^2 \epsilon^{3\,jk} a_j^2 a_k^3$$

$$= \epsilon^{ijk} a_i^2 a_j^2 a_k^3 \equiv 0,$$

since the first two rows of $\bar{\Delta}$ are the same. In general, $a_\alpha^i A_j^\alpha = 0$ if $i \neq j$, and $a_j^\alpha A_\alpha^i = 0$ if $i \neq j$. This result, along with (7), can be expressed by

$$a_\alpha^i A_j^\alpha = |a|\, \delta_j^i,$$
$$a_j^\alpha A_\alpha^i = |a|\, \delta_j^i,$$
(8)

and is of significant importance in dealing with linear equations.

Example 2. The following determinant is evaluated by expanding in terms of the cofactors (or minors) of the first row

$$\begin{vmatrix} 2 & 3 & -1 \\ -1 & 0 & 4 \\ 3 & 1 & -2 \end{vmatrix} = 2 \begin{vmatrix} 0 & 4 \\ 1 & -2 \end{vmatrix} - 3 \begin{vmatrix} -1 & 4 \\ 3 & -2 \end{vmatrix} + (-1) \begin{vmatrix} -1 & 0 \\ 3 & 1 \end{vmatrix}$$

$$= 2(-4) - 3(2 - 12) - (-1) = 23.$$

Cramer's rule. The linear system $a_\alpha^i x^\alpha = b^i$, $i = 1, 2, \ldots, n$, can be solved for the unknowns $x^1, x^2, \ldots, x^n$, provided $|a_\beta^\alpha| \neq 0$, by virtue of Eq. (8). We multiply each equation, $a_\alpha^i x^\alpha = b^i$, by A_i^j and sum on the index i, obtaining

$$A_i^j a_\alpha^i x^\alpha = b^i A_i^j,$$

$$\delta_\alpha^j |a|\, x^\alpha = b^i A_i^j,$$

$$|a|\, x^j = b^i A_i^j,$$
(9)

$$x^j = \frac{b^i A_i^j}{|a|}, \qquad |a| \neq 0,$$

for $j = 1, 2, \ldots, n$. Since A_i^j is the cofactor of a_j^i, we note that $b^i A_i^j$ is a determinant obtained by replacing the elements of the jth column of $[a_j^i]$ by the elements b^i, $i = 1, 2, \ldots, n$, (expanding a determinant using the cofactors of the jth column). The result above is called Cramer's rule, and is well known to students of algebra.

Example 3. For the system of linear equations

$$x + y + 3z = 12,$$

$$2x - y + z = 3,$$

$$4x + y - 2z = 0,$$

we have

$$|a^\alpha_\beta| = \begin{vmatrix} 1 & 1 & 3 \\ 2 & -1 & 1 \\ 4 & 1 & -2 \end{vmatrix} = 27 \neq 0,$$

so that

$$x = \frac{1}{27} \begin{vmatrix} 12 & 1 & 3 \\ 3 & -1 & 1 \\ 0 & 1 & -2 \end{vmatrix} = \frac{27}{27} = 1,$$

$$y = \frac{1}{27} \begin{vmatrix} 1 & 12 & 3 \\ 2 & 3 & 1 \\ 4 & 0 & -2 \end{vmatrix} = \frac{54}{27} = 2,$$

$$z = \frac{1}{27} \begin{vmatrix} 1 & 1 & 12 \\ 2 & -1 & 3 \\ 4 & 1 & 0 \end{vmatrix} = \frac{81}{27} = 3.$$

Returning to $|a| = \epsilon^{ijk} a^1_i a^2_j a^3_k$, let us assume that the elements a^i_j are differentiable functions of a variable t, $a^i_j = a^i_j(t)$. Then

$$\frac{d|a|}{dt} = \epsilon^{ijk} \frac{da^1_i}{dt} a^2_j a^3_k + \epsilon^{ijk} a^1_i \frac{da^2_j}{dt} a^3_k + \epsilon^{ijk} a^1_i a^2_j \frac{da^3_k}{dt}, \tag{10}$$

from the calculus. We note that $d|a|/dt$ is the sum of three determinants, each obtained by differentiating the elements of the first, second, and third rows, respectively, of the original determinant, $|a| = |a^i_j|$. For example, if

$$|a| = \begin{vmatrix} t & e^t & 1 \\ \sin t & -3 & 0 \\ 1 & -1 & 1 \end{vmatrix},$$

then

$$\frac{d|a|}{dt} = \begin{vmatrix} 1 & e^t & 0 \\ \sin t & -3 & 0 \\ 1 & -1 & 1 \end{vmatrix} + \begin{vmatrix} t & e^t & 1 \\ \cos t & 0 & 0 \\ 1 & -1 & 1 \end{vmatrix}$$

$$= -[3 + \cos t + e^t(\sin t + \cos t)],$$

since the elements of the third row are constants.

An expansion of the three determinants of Eq. (10) in terms of the cofactors of the first, second, and third rows, respectively, shows that $d|a|/dt$ is simply the derivative of each element multiplied by its cofactor, summed over all elements. This fact may be noted by examining

$$\frac{d|a|}{dt} = \begin{vmatrix} \dfrac{da^1_1}{dt} & \dfrac{da^1_2}{dt} & \dfrac{da^1_3}{dt} \\ a^2_1 & a^2_2 & a^2_3 \\ a^3_1 & a^3_2 & a^3_3 \end{vmatrix} + \begin{vmatrix} a^1_1 & a^1_2 & a^1_3 \\ \dfrac{da^2_1}{dt} & \dfrac{da^2_2}{dt} & \dfrac{da^2_3}{dt} \\ a^3_1 & a^3_2 & a^3_3 \end{vmatrix} + \begin{vmatrix} a^1_1 & a^1_2 & a^1_3 \\ a^2_1 & a^2_2 & a^2_3 \\ \dfrac{da^3_1}{dt} & \dfrac{da^3_2}{dt} & \dfrac{da^3_3}{dt} \end{vmatrix}$$

Thus we obtain

$$\frac{d|a|}{dt} = A^\alpha_\beta \frac{da^\beta_\alpha}{dt}.$$ (11)

Example 4. Let y^i_j, $i, j = 1, 2, \ldots, n$ satisfy the following system of equations.

$$\frac{dy^i_j}{dt} = a^i_\alpha(t)y^\alpha_j.$$ (12)

Now let Y^j_i be the cofactor of y^i_j, $i, j = 1, 2, \ldots, n$. Then

$$Y^j_i \frac{dy^i_j}{dt} = a^i_\alpha(t)y^\alpha_j Y^j_i,$$

$$\frac{d}{dt}|y| = a^i_\alpha(t)|y|\,\delta^\alpha_i = a^\alpha_\alpha(t)|y|,$$ (13)

whose solution is

$$|y^i_j(t)| = |y^i_j(t = 0)| \exp \left[\int^t_0 a^\alpha_\alpha(\tau)d\tau \right].$$

If, in particular, $a^\alpha_\alpha(t) \equiv 0$, then $|y^i_j| = \text{constant} = |y^i_j|_{t=0}$. This result is most useful in trajectory analysis. Let x^i, $i = 1, 2, \ldots, n$ satisfy a system of equations

$$\frac{dx^i}{dt} = f^i(x, t)$$ (14)

subject to the initial conditions $x^i(t = 0) = x^i_0$. Under suitable restrictions the solutions of Eq. (14) exist, with $x^i = x^i(t; x^1_0, x^2_0, \ldots, x^n_0)$. Now we may be interested in what happens to these solutions if the initial conditions are varied. Let

$$y^i_j = \frac{\partial x^i}{\partial x^j_0} \qquad \text{with} \qquad y^i_j(t = 0) = \delta^i_j.$$

From Eq. (14) we have

$$\frac{\partial}{\partial x^j_0}\left(\frac{dx^i}{dt}\right) = \frac{d}{dt}\left(\frac{\partial x^i}{\partial x^j_0}\right) = \frac{\partial f^i}{\partial x^\alpha}\frac{\partial x^\alpha}{\partial x^j_0},$$

$$\frac{dy^i_j}{dt} = \frac{\partial f^i(x, t)}{\partial x^\alpha}\,y^\alpha_j = a^i_\alpha(t)y^\alpha_j .$$ (15)

From our previous analysis with

$$|y^i_j|_{t=0} = |\delta^i_j| = 1 ,$$

we obtain

$$|y^i_j(t)| = \exp\left[\int^t_0 a^\alpha_\alpha(\tau)d\tau\right] = \exp\left(\int^t_0 \frac{\partial f^\alpha}{\partial x^\alpha}d\tau\right).$$ (16)

For example, the system $\dot{x} = y$, $\dot{y} = -x$, has the solution $x = x_0 \cos t + y_0 \sin t$, $y = -x_0 \sin t + y_0 \cos t$, so that

$$\frac{\partial x}{\partial x_0} = \cos t, \qquad \frac{\partial x}{\partial y_0} = \sin t,$$

$$\frac{\partial y}{\partial x_0} = -\sin t, \qquad \frac{\partial y}{\partial y_0} = \cos t.$$

Thus

$$|y_j^i| = \begin{vmatrix} \cos t & \sin t \\ -\sin t & \cos t \end{vmatrix} \equiv 1.$$

We note that $f^1 = y$, $f^2 = x$, so that

$$\frac{\partial f^1}{\partial x} + \frac{\partial f^2}{\partial y} = 0$$

and

$$\exp\left(\int_0^t \frac{\partial f^\alpha}{\partial x^\alpha} d\tau\right) = e^0 = 1.$$

We conclude this section with a discussion of the multiplication of two determinants of the same order. First we investigate the sum

$$S^{\alpha\beta\gamma} = \epsilon^{ijk} a_i^\alpha a_j^\beta a_k^\gamma.$$

If α, β, γ assume the values 1, 2, 3 respectively, then $S^{123} = |a|$. If α, β, γ assume the values 1, 2, 3, but not respectively, then $S^{\alpha\beta\gamma} = \pm |a|$ depending on whether it requires an even or odd number of permutations to permute $\alpha\beta\gamma$ into the natural order 1 2 3, since this is equivalent to interchanging the rows of $|a_j^i|$ an even or odd number of times. In all other cases $S^{\alpha\beta\gamma} = 0$, since at least two rows will be the same. From the very definition of $\epsilon^{\alpha\beta\gamma}$ we obtain

$$S^{\alpha\beta\gamma} = \epsilon^{ijk} a_i^\alpha a_j^\beta a_k^\gamma = |a| \epsilon^{\alpha\beta\gamma},$$

$$S_{\alpha\beta\gamma} = \epsilon_{ijk} a_\alpha^i a_\beta^j a_\gamma^k = |a| \epsilon_{\alpha\beta\gamma}. \tag{17}$$

Multiplying the second part of Eq. (17) by $b_1^\alpha b_2^\beta b_3^\gamma$ and summing over α, β, γ yields

$$\epsilon_{ijk} (a_\alpha^i b_1^\alpha)(a_\beta^j b_2^\beta)(a_\gamma^k b_3^\gamma) = |a| \epsilon_{\alpha\beta\gamma} b_1^\alpha b_2^\beta b_3^\gamma,$$

$$\epsilon_{ijk} c_1^i c_2^j c_3^k = |a| |b|, \tag{18}$$

$$|c| = |a| |b|,$$

with

$$c_1^i = a_\alpha^i b_1^\alpha, \qquad c_2^j = a_\beta^j b_2^\beta, \qquad c_3^k = a_\gamma^k b_3^\gamma,$$

so that

$$c_j^i = a_\alpha^i b_j^\alpha \qquad \text{for} \qquad i, j = 1, 2, 3.$$

Thus the elements of $|c_j^i|$ are obtained by multiplying the elements of the ith row of $|a_j^i|$ by the corresponding elements in the jth column of $|b_j^i|$ and summing. For example,

$$\begin{vmatrix} a & b \\ c & d \end{vmatrix} \cdot \begin{vmatrix} \alpha & \beta \\ \gamma & \delta \end{vmatrix} = \begin{vmatrix} a\alpha + b\gamma & a\beta + b\delta \\ c\alpha + d\gamma & c\beta + d\delta \end{vmatrix}.$$

As a simple check we note that

$$|a_j^i| \; |\delta_j^i| = |a_\alpha^i \, \delta_j^\alpha| = |a_j^i|,$$

which is a valid equation, since $|\delta_j^i| = 1$.

Let the reader verify that

$$\begin{vmatrix} 2 & 0 & -1 \\ -1 & 2 & 0 \\ 3 & 1 & 1 \end{vmatrix} \cdot \begin{vmatrix} -2 & 0 & 0 \\ 1 & 1 & -3 \\ 0 & -1 & 1 \end{vmatrix} = \begin{vmatrix} -4 & 1 & -1 \\ 4 & 2 & -6 \\ -5 & 0 & -2 \end{vmatrix},$$

$$11 \cdot 4 = 44.$$

PROBLEMS

1. Evaluate

$$\begin{vmatrix} 2 & -1 & 3 & 5 \\ 1 & 0 & 4 & 2 \\ 0 & -1 & 5 & 0 \\ 1 & 2 & 3 & 4 \end{vmatrix}.$$

2. Show that

$$\begin{vmatrix} 1 & 1 & 1 \\ a & b & c \\ bc & ca & ab \end{vmatrix} = (a - b)(b - c)(c - a).$$

3. Show that $F(0) = 0$, $F'(0) = 0$ if

$$F(t) = \begin{vmatrix} a^2 + t & ab & ac \\ ab & b^2 + t & bc \\ ac & bc & c^2 + t \end{vmatrix}.$$

4. Show that

$$\Delta = \begin{vmatrix} \lambda_1 & \lambda_2 & \lambda_3 \\ \lambda_1^2 & \lambda_2^2 & \lambda_3 \\ \lambda_1^3 & \lambda_2^3 & \lambda_3^3 \end{vmatrix} = \lambda_1 \lambda_2 \lambda_3 (\lambda_1 - \lambda_2)(\lambda_2 - \lambda_3)(\lambda_3 - \lambda_1).$$

Under what condition is $\Delta \neq 0$? Can you generalize this result?

5. From $a_\alpha^i A_j^\alpha = |a| \, \delta_j^i$, show that $|A_j^i| = |a_j^i|^{n-1}$. Verify this result for a general determinant of order 2.

6. Solve for x, y, z, u:

$$x + y + z + u = 2,$$
$$2x - y + z - 3u = 5,$$
$$x + 2y - 2z + u = -5,$$
$$y - z + 2u = -5.$$

7. The system $x + y = 3$, $2x + 2y = 5$, with $|a_j^i| = 0$, has no solution. How many solutions does the system $x + y = 3$, $2x + 2y = 6$ have? Exhibit the solutions.

8. From

$$\frac{\partial y^i}{\partial x^\alpha} \frac{\partial x^\alpha}{\partial y^j} = \delta_j^i,$$

show that

$$\begin{vmatrix} \dfrac{\partial y^1}{\partial x^1} & \dfrac{\partial y^1}{\partial x^2} & \cdots & \dfrac{\partial y^1}{\partial x^n} \\ & & \vdots & \\ \dfrac{\partial y^n}{\partial x^1} & \dfrac{\partial y^n}{\partial x^2} & \cdots & \dfrac{\partial y^n}{\partial x^n} \end{vmatrix} \cdot \begin{vmatrix} \dfrac{\partial x^1}{\partial y^1} & \dfrac{\partial x^1}{\partial y^2} & \cdots & \dfrac{\partial x^1}{\partial y^n} \\ & & \vdots & \\ \dfrac{\partial x^n}{\partial y^1} & \dfrac{\partial x^n}{\partial y^2} & \cdots & \dfrac{\partial x^n}{\partial y^n} \end{vmatrix} = 1.$$

9. Show that

$$\begin{vmatrix} 1 & 1 & 1 \\ 1 & w & w^2 \\ 1 & w^2 & w^4 \end{vmatrix} = w(w + 1)(w - 1)^3.$$

10. Evaluate

$$\Delta = \begin{vmatrix} 1 & 2 & 3 & 4 \\ 2 & 3 & 4 & 1 \\ 3 & 4 & 1 & 2 \\ 4 & 1 & 2 & 3 \end{vmatrix}.$$

11. Show that

$$\begin{vmatrix} b_1 + c_1 & c_1 + a_1 & a_1 + b_1 \\ b_2 + c_2 & c_2 + a_2 & a_2 + b_2 \\ b_3 + c_3 & c_3 + a_3 & a_3 + b_3 \end{vmatrix} = 2 \begin{vmatrix} a_1 & b_1 & c_1 \\ a_2 & b_2 & c_2 \\ a_3 & b_3 & c_3 \end{vmatrix}.$$

12. Given $y^i = y^i(x^1, x^2, \ldots, x^n)$ for $i = 1, 2, \ldots, n$ show that

$$\frac{\partial}{\partial x^k} \begin{vmatrix} \dfrac{\partial y^i}{\partial x^j} \end{vmatrix} = \begin{vmatrix} \dfrac{\partial y^i}{\partial x^j} \end{vmatrix} \frac{\partial x^\alpha}{\partial y^\beta} \frac{\partial^2 y^\beta}{\partial x^k \partial x^\alpha}.$$

13. Given

$$\bar{g}_{ij} = g_{\alpha\beta} \frac{\partial x^\alpha}{\partial y^i} \frac{\partial x^\beta}{\partial y^j}, \qquad g_{\alpha\beta} = g_{\beta\alpha},$$

show that $\bar{g}_{ij} = \bar{g}_{ji}$. Then show that

$$|\bar{g}| = |g| \left| \frac{\partial x}{\partial y} \right|^2.$$

A.7 LINEAR HOMOGENEOUS EQUATIONS

Let us examine the single linear homogeneous equation $x - 3y + 2z = 0$. An obvious solution is $x = y = z = 0$, called the trivial solution, It is apparent that an infinite number of nontrivial solutions exist, since we need only let $y = \lambda$, $z = \mu$, so that $x = 3\lambda - 2\mu$ for $-\infty < \lambda < \infty$, $-\infty < \mu < \infty$.

Let us now consider the following system of linear equations

$$x + 3y - 4z = 0,$$
$$2x - y + z = 0. \tag{1}$$

Multiplying the first equation by -2 and adding to the second equation yields $-7y + 9z = 0$, so that if $z = 7\lambda$ then $y = 9\lambda$, which yields $x = \lambda$. The most general solution of the system of Eq. (1) is $x = \lambda$, $y = 9\lambda$, $z = 7\lambda$, with $-\infty < \lambda < \infty$. The special case $\lambda = 0$ yields the trivial solution $x = y = z = 0$.

In dealing with a system of linear homogeneous equations one can multiply any equation by a scalar without changing the system. Moreover, one can multiply any equation by a scalar and add the resulting equation to any other equation without changing the system. These operations are reversible if the scalar is different from zero. Hence the solution to the final system (if it exists) will also be a solution of the initial system. In these operations only the coefficients of the unknowns play a role. Hence one need only manipulate the elements of the coefficient matrix (undefined as yet).

Example 1. We examine the system of four linear equations in five unknowns:

$$x - y + 2z + 3u + 3v = 0,$$
$$2x + y - z + u + 4v = 0,$$
$$-3x + 2y + 4z + u = 0,$$
$$4y + 4z + 2v = 0. \tag{2}$$

The matrix of the coefficients is

$$\begin{bmatrix} 1 & -1 & 2 & 3 & 3 \\ 2 & 1 & -1 & 1 & 4 \\ -3 & 2 & 4 & 1 & 0 \\ 0 & 4 & 4 & 0 & 2 \end{bmatrix}. \tag{3}$$

Multiplying row one by -2 and adding to row two, then multiplying row one by 3 and adding to row three, yields

$$\begin{bmatrix} 1 & -1 & 2 & 3 & 3 \\ 0 & 3 & -5 & -5 & -2 \\ 0 & -1 & 10 & 10 & 9 \\ 0 & 4 & 4 & 0 & 2 \end{bmatrix}. \tag{4}$$

Interchanging the second and third rows yields

$$\begin{bmatrix} 1 & -1 & 2 & 3 & 3 \\ 0 & -1 & 10 & 10 & 9 \\ 0 & 3 & -5 & -5 & -2 \\ 0 & 4 & 4 & 0 & 2 \end{bmatrix}.$$

Multiplying the second row by 3 and adding to the third row, and then multiplying the second row by 4 and adding to the fourth row, yields

$$\begin{bmatrix} 1 & -1 & 2 & 3 & 3 \\ 0 & -1 & 10 & 10 & 9 \\ 0 & 0 & 25 & 25 & 25 \\ 0 & 0 & 44 & 40 & 38 \end{bmatrix},$$

or, equivalently

$$\begin{bmatrix} 1 & -1 & 2 & 3 & 3 \\ 0 & -1 & 10 & 10 & 9 \\ 0 & 0 & 1 & 1 & 1 \\ 0 & 0 & 22 & 20 & 19 \end{bmatrix} \approx \begin{bmatrix} 1 & -1 & 2 & 3 & 3 \\ 0 & -1 & 10 & 10 & 9 \\ 0 & 0 & 1 & 1 & 1 \\ 0 & 0 & 0 & -2 & -3 \end{bmatrix}. \tag{5}$$

Our task is finished once zeros are obtained below the main diagonal as shown above. System (2) now may be written as

$$\begin{aligned} x - y + 2z + 3u + 3v &= 0, \\ -y + 10z + 10u + 9v &= 0, \\ z + u + v &= 0, \\ -2u - 3v &= 0. \end{aligned} \tag{6}$$

Starting with the last equation we let $v = 2\lambda$, so that $u = -3\lambda$. From the next equation we obtain $z = -(u + v) = \lambda$, then $y = 10z + 10u + 9v = -2\lambda$, and $x = y - 2z - 3u - 3v = -\lambda$, so that

$$\begin{aligned} x &= -\lambda, \\ y &= -2\lambda, \\ z &= \lambda, \quad -\infty < \lambda < \infty, \\ u &= -3\lambda, \\ v &= 2\lambda \end{aligned}$$

is the most general solution of the system of Eq. (2). It should be noted that the system of Eq. (2) could be solved by transposing the terms involving v to the right-hand side yielding four inhomogeneous equations for x, y, z, u which can be solved by Cramer's rule. Thus x, y, z, u can be solved in terms of $v = 2\lambda$.

It should be clear that if there are more unknowns than equations, one can obtain zeros below the main diagonal, yielding nontrivial solutions. Thus we have:

Theorem. A system of n linear homogeneous equations in m unknowns always possesses nontrivial solutions for $m > n$.

Now let us look at the interesting case $n = m$, $a_\alpha^i x^\alpha = 0$, $i = 1, 2, \ldots, n$, with $x^1, x^2, \ldots, x^n$ the unknowns. If $|a_j^i| \neq 0$, it follows from Cramer's rule that there is only one solution, the trivial solution $x^1 = x^2 = \cdots = x^n = 0$.

Let us assume that $|a_j^i| = 0$. By obtaining zeros below the main diagonal we obtain an equivalent system of equations, $b_\alpha^i x^\alpha = 0$ with $|b_j^i| = 0$. Let the reader explain this! Thus

$$\begin{vmatrix} b_1^1 & b_2^1 & & \cdots & b_n^1 \\ 0 & b_2^2 & & \cdots & b_n^2 \\ 0 & 0 & b_3^3 & \cdots & b_n^3 \\ & & \vdots & & \\ 0 & 0 & \cdots & 0 & b_n^n \end{vmatrix} = 0, \tag{7}$$

which implies that at least one of the elements $b_1^1, b_2^2, \ldots, b_n^n$ must vanish. If $b_n^n = 0$, our system, which is reduced to n unknowns and at most $(n - 1)$ equations, has a nontrivial solution.

If $b_n^n \neq 0$ and $b_{n-1}^{n-1} = 0$, then $x^n = 0$. The next to last equation disappears by virtue of the fact that $b_{n-1}^{n-1} = 0$ and $x^n = 0$. Hence we are now interested in a system involving $(n - 1)$ unknowns and at most $(n - 2)$ equations, so again we have nontrivial solutions. Continuing, we see that the vanishing of at least one element along the main diagonal implies the existence of nontrivial solutions. Thus we have the important

Theorem. A necessary and sufficient condition that a system of n linear homogeneous equations in n unknowns possess a nontrivial solution is that the determinant of the coefficients vanish.

Example 2. The determinant of the coefficients of the system

$$\begin{aligned} x - y + z &= 0, \\ 2x + 3y - z &= 0, \\ 4x + y + z &= 0, \end{aligned}$$

vanishes. The coefficient matrix

$$\begin{bmatrix} 1 & -1 & 1 \\ 2 & 3 & -1 \\ 4 & 1 & 1 \end{bmatrix}$$

can be shown to be equivalent to the matrices

$$\begin{bmatrix} 1 & -1 & 1 \\ 0 & 5 & -3 \\ 0 & 5 & -3 \end{bmatrix} \sim \begin{bmatrix} 1 & -1 & 1 \\ 0 & 5 & -3 \\ 0 & 0 & 0 \end{bmatrix},$$

so that $x - y + z = 0$, $5y - 3z = 0$. Let $z = 5\lambda$, which yields $y = 3\lambda$, $x = -2\lambda$, $-\infty < \lambda < \infty$.

Example 3. Consider the three lines in the x-y plane given by

$$a_1 x + b_1 y + c_1 = 0,$$
$$a_2 x + b_2 y + c_2 = 0, \tag{8}$$
$$a_3 x + b_3 y + c_3 = 0,$$

or equivalently

$$a_1 x + b_1 y + c_1 z = 0,$$
$$a_2 x + b_2 y + c_2 z = 0, \tag{9}$$
$$a_3 x + b_3 y + c_3 z = 0,$$

with $z = 1$. Now if the three lines intersect at a point $P(x_0, y_0)$, then the system of Eq. (9) must have a nontrivial solution $(x_0, y_0, z = 1)$. From our previous theorem a necessary condition for the existence of such a solution is

$$\begin{vmatrix} a_1 & b_1 & c_1 \\ a_2 & b_2 & c_2 \\ a_3 & b_3 & c_3 \end{vmatrix} = 0. \tag{10}$$

Conversely, if condition (10) holds, then the system of (9) has a nontrivial solution, say (x_0, y_0, z_0). If $z_0 \neq 0$, then we can find a λ such that $\lambda z_0 = 1$, so that $x_1 = \lambda x_0$, $y_1 = \lambda y_0$ will satisfy the system of Eq. (8).

Example 4. *Sylvester's dialytic method.* Consider the pair of equations

$$ax + b = 0 \qquad a \neq 0,$$
$$cx^2 + dx + e = 0 \qquad c \neq 0. \tag{11}$$

If there is a value of x which satisfies both equations, then $x = -b/a$, which yields

$$c\left(-\frac{b}{a}\right)^2 + d\left(-\frac{b}{a}\right) + e = 0,$$
$$cb^2 - abd + ea^2 = 0, \tag{12}$$

as a condition which must be satisfied by the constants a, b, c, d, e. Now let us obtain an additional equation by multiplying the first part of Eq. (11) by x, and obtain an equation which, together with Eqs. (11), gives the system

$$0x^2 + ax + b \cdot 1 = 0,$$
$$cx^2 + dx + e \cdot 1 = 0, \tag{13}$$
$$ax^2 + bx + 0 \cdot 1 = 0.$$

Looking on the system of (13) as three homogeneous equations in the unknowns

x^2, x, $z = 1$, a necessary condition for the existence of a nontrivial solution (since $z = 1 \neq 0$), is

$$\begin{vmatrix} 0 & a & b \\ c & d & e \\ a & b & 0 \end{vmatrix} = 0, \qquad (14)$$

which yields the result of (12). This method is due to the famous English mathematician J. J. Sylvester, 1814–1897.

The system of vectors

$$\mathbf{X}_r = \begin{bmatrix} x_r^1 \\ x_r^2 \\ \vdots \\ x_r^n \end{bmatrix} \qquad r = 1, 2, \ldots, m, \qquad (15)$$

is said to be linearly dependent if there exist scalars $\lambda^1, \lambda^2, \ldots, \lambda^m$, not all zero, such that

$$\lambda^\alpha \mathbf{X}_\alpha = \begin{bmatrix} 0 \\ 0 \\ \vdots \\ 0 \end{bmatrix}, \qquad (16)$$

or, equivalently, if $x_\alpha^i \lambda^\alpha = 0$, $i = 1, 2, \ldots, n$ has nontrivial solutions. This always occurs if $m > n$. Thus we have the following.

Theorem. Any m vectors in an n-dimensional space are linearly dependent if $m > n$.

Let us consider the n vectors $X_1, X_2, \ldots, X_n$, with components given by $(x_1^1, x_1^2, \ldots, x_1^n)$, $(x_2^1, x_2^2, \ldots, x_2^n)$, $\ldots$, $(x_n^1, x_n^2, \ldots, x_n^n)$ respectively. Now assume that the determinant of the components is different from zero, i.e., $|x_j^i| \neq 0$. The vectors are said to be linearly independent. Now let Y be an arbitrary vector with components $(y^1, y^2, \ldots, y^n)$. We show that Y can be expressed linearly in terms of $X_1, X_2, \ldots, X_n$, i.e., there exist scalars $\lambda^1, \lambda^2, \ldots, \lambda^n$ such that $Y = X_\alpha \lambda^\alpha$, or equivalently

$$y^i = x_\alpha^i \lambda^\alpha.$$

Since $|x_j^i| \neq 0$, it follows from Cramer's rule that one can solve for $\lambda^1, \lambda^2, \ldots, \lambda^n$. We say that the n linearly independent vectors $X_1, X_2, \ldots, X_n$ span the n dimensional space and form a basis for this space.

PROBLEMS

1. Solve for x, y, z, u:

$$\begin{aligned} x + 2y - z + u &= 0, \\ 2x - y + z - u &= 0, \\ 3x + 4y - z &= 0. \end{aligned}$$

2. Solve the system

$$x + 2y - z - 3u = 0,$$
$$2x - y + z + 4u = 0.$$

3. Solve the system

$$2x + y - z + u = 0,$$
$$x - y - z + u = 0,$$
$$x - 4y - 2z + 2u = 0,$$
$$5x + y - 3z + 3u = 0.$$

4. Determine λ so that the following system will have nontrivial solutions, and determine the solutions.

$$\lambda x = 4x + y,$$
$$\lambda y = -2x + y.$$

5. Show that if $a_\alpha^i x_1^\alpha = 0$ and $a_\alpha^i x_2^\alpha = 0$, then $y^\alpha = \lambda x_1^\alpha + \mu x_2^\alpha$ satisfies $a_\alpha^i y^\alpha = 0$, $i = 1$, $2, \ldots, m$; $\alpha = 1, 2, \ldots, n$ for arbitrary constants λ, μ.

6. Determine a necessary condition that the four planes

$$a_1 x + a_2 y + a_3 z + a_4 = 0,$$
$$b_1 x + b_2 y + b_3 z + b_4 = 0,$$
$$c_1 x + c_2 y + c_3 z + c_4 = 0,$$
$$d_1 x + d_2 y + d_3 z + d_4 = 0$$

intersect in at least one point (x_0, y_0, z_0).

7. Consider the family of circles $x^2 + y^2 + ax + by + c = 0$, with a, b, c arbitrary. Show that a necessary condition for a circle to pass through the four points $P_1(x_1, y_1)$, $P_2(x_2, y_2)$, $P_3(x_3, y_3)$, $P_4(x_4, y_4)$, is that

$$\begin{vmatrix} x_1^2 + y_1^2 & x_1 & y_1 & 1 \\ x_2^2 + y_2^2 & x_2 & y_2 & 1 \\ x_3^2 + y_3^2 & x_3 & y_3 & 1 \\ x_4^2 + y_4^2 & x_4 & y_4 & 1 \end{vmatrix} = 0.$$

8. Show that a necessary condition for $x^2 + ax + b = 0$ and $x^3 + cx^2 + dx + e = 0$ to have a common root is

$$\begin{vmatrix} 1 & a & b & 0 & 0 \\ 0 & 1 & a & b & 0 \\ 0 & 0 & 1 & a & b \\ 1 & c & d & e & 0 \\ 0 & 1 & c & d & e \end{vmatrix} = 0.$$

A.8 MATRICES

A matrix is defined as a rectangular array of elements (usually the elements are real or complex numbers). A calculus of matrices is developed by defining addition of matrices, multiplication of matrices, multiplication of a matrix by a scalar (real or complex number), differentiation of matrices, etc., in such a way that matrices become highly applicable to the fields of mathematics, physics, and engineering. A matrix A may be denoted as follows:

$$A = \begin{bmatrix} a_1^1 & a_2^1 & \cdots & a_n^1 \\ a_1^2 & a_2^2 & \cdots & a_n^2 \\ & & \vdots & \\ a_1^m & a_2^m & \cdots & a_n^m \end{bmatrix} = [a_j^i], \quad \begin{matrix} i = 1, 2, \ldots, m. \\ j = 1, 2, \ldots, n. \end{matrix} \tag{1}$$

If a matrix A is composed of m rows and n columns it is said to be of *order m by n*, written $m \times n$. The element a_s^r is that element* which belongs to the rth row and sth column of A. If $m = n$, we say that A is a square matrix of order n. A square matrix of order one is called a scalar. An $n \times 1$ matrix is called a vector for the space of n dimensions, and its elements are called the components of the vector. A vector may also be expressed as a row matrix $(1 \times n)$.

We now list a few examples of matrices. Let $A: (A_1, A_2, A_3, A_4)$ and $B: (B_1, B_2, B_3, B_4)$ be two four-dimensional vectors. We consider the set of numbers

$$C_{ij} = A_i B_j - A_j B_i, \quad i, j = 1, 2, 3, 4,$$

with C_{ij} the element in the ith row and jth column of the matrix C.
Thus

$$C = \begin{bmatrix} 0 & A_1 B_2 - A_2 B_1 & A_1 B_3 - A_3 B_1 & A_1 B_4 - A_4 B_1 \\ A_2 B_1 - A_1 B_2 & 0 & A_2 B_3 - A_3 B_2 & A_2 B_4 - A_4 B_2 \\ A_3 B_1 - A_3 B_1 & A_3 B_2 - A_2 B_3 & 0 & A_3 B_4 - A_4 B_3 \\ A_4 B_1 - A_1 B_4 & A_4 B_2 - A_2 B_4 & A_4 B_3 - A_3 B_4 & 0 \end{bmatrix}. \tag{2}$$

The matrix C is said to be the cross product of the vectors $\mathbf{A}$ and $\mathbf{B}$. We note that $C_{ij} = -C_{ji}$.

Next consider a deformable body such that $u_i(x^1, x^2, x^3)$, $i = 1, 2, 3$, is the vector displacement of a point P in that body from its equilibrium position, using rectangular coordinates $(x = x^1, y = x^2, z = x^3)$. Then

$$du_i = \frac{\partial u_i}{\partial x^j} dx^j$$

$$= \frac{1}{2}\left(\frac{\partial u_i}{\partial x^j} + \frac{\partial u_j}{\partial x^i}\right) dx^j + \frac{1}{2}\left(\frac{\partial u_i}{\partial x^j} - \frac{\partial u_j}{\partial x^i}\right) dx^j. \tag{3}$$

---

* The element in the rth row and sth column can also be designated by the element a_{rs}.

The nine numbers

$$\frac{1}{2}\left(\frac{\partial u_i}{\partial x^j} + \frac{\partial u_j}{\partial x^i}\right), \qquad i, j = 1, 2, 3,$$

are said to be the components of the strain matrix (or strain tensor) U, written

$$U = \begin{bmatrix} \dfrac{\partial u_1}{\partial x^1} & \dfrac{1}{2}\left(\dfrac{\partial u_1}{\partial x^2} + \dfrac{\partial u_2}{\partial x^1}\right) & \dfrac{1}{2}\left(\dfrac{\partial u_1}{\partial x^3} + \dfrac{\partial u_3}{\partial x^1}\right) \\[3mm] \dfrac{1}{2}\left(\dfrac{\partial u_2}{\partial x^1} + \dfrac{\partial u_1}{\partial x^2}\right) & \dfrac{\partial u_2}{\partial x^2} & \dfrac{1}{2}\left(\dfrac{\partial u_2}{\partial x^3} + \dfrac{\partial u_3}{\partial x^2}\right) \\[3mm] \dfrac{1}{2}\left(\dfrac{\partial u_3}{\partial x^1} + \dfrac{\partial u_1}{\partial x^3}\right) & \dfrac{1}{2}\left(\dfrac{\partial u_3}{\partial x^2} + \dfrac{\partial u_2}{\partial x^3}\right) & \dfrac{\partial u_3}{\partial x^3} \end{bmatrix}. \tag{4}$$

Note that $U = [U_{ij}]$, with $U_{ij} = U_{ji}$.

A rigid body for an 0-x_1-x_2-x_3 coordinate system yields nine fundamental quantities, namely $I_{ij} = \iiint_R x_i x_j dm$, i, $j = 1$, 2, 3, where the integration is performed over the total mass of the body comprising the region R. The inertia matrix (or tensor) is composed of these nine elements, written $I = [I_{ij}]$, with I_{ij} the element in the ith row and jth column of I. Note that

$$I_{11} + I_{22} + I_{33} = \iint_R \int [(x_1)^2 + (x_2)^2 + (x_3)^2] \, dm$$

is the moment of inertia of the body about the origin.

Next consider a small cube inside a deformable body, with the three principal faces normal to the x_1, x_2, x_3 axes. Let p_{ij} be the jth component of the pressure (force per unit area) acting on the face whose normal is in the direction of the x_i axis, $i, j = 1, 2, 3$. The matrix of elements, namely

$$P = \begin{bmatrix} p_{11} & p_{12} & p_{13} \\ p_{21} & p_{22} & p_{23} \\ p_{31} & p_{32} & p_{33} \end{bmatrix}. \tag{5}$$

is called the stress matrix.

Finally, an important square matrix of order n is the Kronecker delta matrix,

$$I = \begin{bmatrix} 1 & 0 & 0 & \cdots & 0 \\ 0 & 1 & 0 & \cdots & 0 \\ & & \vdots & & \\ 0 & 0 & 0 & \cdots & 1 \end{bmatrix} = [\delta_j^i], \qquad i, j = 1, 2, \ldots, n. \tag{6}$$

Do not confuse this matrix with the moment of inertia matrix defined above.

Now we return to the algebra of matrices. Two $m \times n$ matrices, A, B, are said to be equal if, and only if, their corresponding elements are equal, which implies that $a_j^i = b_j^i$ for the complete range of values of i and j. Thus

$$\begin{bmatrix} a_1^1 & a_2^1 & a_3^1 \\ a_1^2 & a_2^2 & a_3^2 \end{bmatrix} = \begin{bmatrix} -1 & 0 & 4 \\ 2 & 7 & -6 \end{bmatrix}$$

implies that

$$a_1^1 = -1,\ a_2^1 = 0,\ a_3^1 = 4,\ a_1^2 = 2,\ a_2^2 = 7,\ a_3^2 = -6.$$

The sum of two $m \times n$ matrices A, B is defined as a new matrix whose elements are obtained by adding the corresponding elements of A and B, so that

$$C = [c_j^i] = A + B = [a_j^i] + [b_j^i] \equiv [a_j^i + b_j^i], \tag{7}$$

with

$$c_j^i = a_j^i + b_j^i$$

for the complete range of values of i and j. Since

$$a_j^i + b_j^i = b_j^i + a_j^i$$

for real or complex numbers, it follows that $A + B = B + A$, the commutative law of addition. It also follows that only matrices of the same order may be added. Let the reader deduce that $(A + B) + C = A + (B + C)$, the associative law of addition, for matrices of like order.

Example 1.

$$\begin{bmatrix} 2 & -1 & 3 \\ 3 & 5 & 0 \end{bmatrix} + \begin{bmatrix} 1 & 3 & -3 \\ -2 & 1 & 4 \end{bmatrix} = \begin{bmatrix} 3 & 2 & 0 \\ 1 & 6 & 4 \end{bmatrix},$$

$$\begin{bmatrix} 2 & -1 \\ 3 & 0 \\ 1 & -2 \end{bmatrix} + \begin{bmatrix} 0 & 0 \\ 0 & 0 \\ 0 & 0 \end{bmatrix} = \begin{bmatrix} 2 & -1 \\ 3 & 0 \\ 1 & -2 \end{bmatrix}.$$

A matrix each of whose elements is the real number zero is called a null matrix, denoted by $N \equiv 0$. Thus if A and N are of the same order, then $A + N = N + A = A$, or $A + 0 = 0 + A = A$. The product of a matrix A by a scalar k (real or complex number) is defined as the matrix whose elements are k times the elements comprising A, so that

$$kA = [ka_j^i] = [a_j^i k] = Ak. \tag{8}$$

It is a simple matter to deduce that $(k + l)A = kA + lA$, $k(A + B) = kA + kB$ provided A and B are of the same order.

The matrix $-A \equiv (-1)A$ is called the negative matrix of A and has the property that $A + (-A) = 0$. Of course the matrix A is the negative matrix of $-A$.

Example 2.

$$3 \begin{bmatrix} 2 & -1 & 4 \\ 0 & 3 & -5 \end{bmatrix} = \begin{bmatrix} 6 & -3 & 12 \\ 0 & 9 & -15 \end{bmatrix},$$

$$\begin{bmatrix} 2 & -3 & 1 \\ 0 & 1 & -2 \end{bmatrix} - \begin{bmatrix} 4 & -5 & 0 \\ -3 & 3 & 1 \end{bmatrix} = \begin{bmatrix} -2 & 2 & 1 \\ 3 & -2 & -3 \end{bmatrix}.$$

To motivate the rule for multiplying two matrices we consider the pair of linear transformations:

$$A: \quad z^i = a^i_\alpha y^\alpha, \quad i = 1, 2, \ldots, m, \quad \alpha = 1, 2, \ldots, p.$$
$$B: \quad y^\alpha = b^\alpha_j x^j, \quad j = 1, 2, \ldots, n.$$

(9)

Since the z's depend linearly on the y's, which in turn depend linearly on the x's, we can solve for the z's in terms of the x's. From Eq. (9) it follows that

$$C: \quad z^i = a^i_\alpha b^\alpha_j x^j$$
$$= c^i_j x^j,$$

with $c^i_j = a^i_\alpha b^\alpha_j$. Thus we define

$$C = AB = [a^i_j] \cdot [b^i_j] \equiv [c^i_j = a^i_\alpha b^\alpha_j]$$

(10)

as the *matrix product* of A and B. In order that the matrix product AB make sense, the matrix A must have the same number of columns as the matrix B has rows, for otherwise the sum on the index α in $a^i_\alpha b^\alpha_j$ could not be performed.

We note that the matrix A above was of order $m \times p$ and that the matrix B was of order $p \times n$. The matrix $C = AB$ is of order $m \times n$. (Note that

$$\frac{m}{p} \cdot \frac{p}{n} = \frac{m}{n},$$

a simple rule for determining the order of the matrix AB.) Moreover, for square matrices A, B of order n, the rule for obtaining the elements of $C = AB$ corresponds to the rule for multiplying determinants of order n, see Eq. (18) of Section A.6. Hence

$$|AB| = |A| \, |B| = |B| \, |A| = |BA|$$

(11)

for square matrices of order n, with $|A|$ the determinant of the elements comprising the square matrix A, etc.

Let the reader deduce that $k(AB) = (kA)B = A(kB)$, with k a scalar, provided AB exists.

Example 3.

$$\begin{bmatrix} 2 & 0 & -1 \\ 3 & 1 & 2 \end{bmatrix} \cdot \begin{bmatrix} 3 \\ 4 \\ -5 \end{bmatrix} = \begin{bmatrix} 2 \cdot 3 + 0 \cdot 4 + (-1)(-5) \\ 3 \cdot 3 + 1 \cdot 4 + 2(-5) \end{bmatrix} = \begin{bmatrix} 11 \\ 3 \end{bmatrix}$$

$$\begin{bmatrix} 2 & -1 \\ 1 & 3 \end{bmatrix} \cdot \begin{bmatrix} 3 & 1 \\ -2 & 0 \end{bmatrix} = \begin{bmatrix} 8 & 2 \\ -3 & 1 \end{bmatrix},$$

with

$$\begin{vmatrix} 2 & -1 \\ 1 & 3 \end{vmatrix} = 7, \quad \begin{vmatrix} 3 & 1 \\ -2 & 0 \end{vmatrix} = 2, \quad \begin{vmatrix} 8 & 2 \\ -3 & 1 \end{vmatrix} = 14.$$

Note that $7 \cdot 2 = 14$.

Example 4. The commutative law does not hold, in general, for multiplication of matrices of the same order. For example,

$$AB = \begin{bmatrix} 1 & 1 \\ 0 & 2 \end{bmatrix} \cdot \begin{bmatrix} 0 & 1 \\ -3 & 2 \end{bmatrix} = \begin{bmatrix} -3 & 3 \\ -6 & 4 \end{bmatrix},$$

$$BA = \begin{bmatrix} 0 & 1 \\ -3 & 2 \end{bmatrix} \cdot \begin{bmatrix} 1 & 1 \\ 0 & 2 \end{bmatrix} = \begin{bmatrix} 0 & 2 \\ -3 & 1 \end{bmatrix} \neq AB.$$

Note, however, that $|AB| = |BA|$. The unit matrix $I = [\delta^i_j]$ of order n does commute with all square matrices of order n, since

$$AI = [a^i_\alpha \delta^\alpha_j] = [a^i_j] = A,$$
$$IA = [\delta^i_\alpha a^\alpha_j] = [a^i_j] = A. \tag{12}$$

Example 5. The product of two matrices A, B can yield the zero matrix with neither A nor B the zero matrix.

$$\begin{bmatrix} 0 & 1 \\ 0 & 0 \end{bmatrix} \cdot \begin{bmatrix} 1 & 0 \\ 0 & 0 \end{bmatrix} = \begin{bmatrix} 0 & 0 \\ 0 & 0 \end{bmatrix}.$$

Thus if $AB = 0$, we cannot conclude that either A or B is a zero matrix.

Example 6. Let **Y** be a 3×1 matrix, A a square matrix of order 3, and **X** a 3×1 matrix, such that

$$\begin{bmatrix} y^1 \\ y^2 \\ y^3 \end{bmatrix} = \begin{bmatrix} a^1_1 & a^1_2 & a^1_3 \\ a^2_1 & a^2_2 & a^2_3 \\ a^3_1 & a^3_2 & a^3_3 \end{bmatrix} \cdot \begin{bmatrix} x^1 \\ x^2 \\ x^3 \end{bmatrix}$$

$$= \begin{bmatrix} a^1_1 x^1 + a^1_2 x^2 + a^1_3 x^3 \\ a^2_1 x^1 + a^2_2 x^2 + a^2_3 x^3 \\ a^3_1 x^1 + a^3_2 x^2 + a^3_3 x^3 \end{bmatrix} = \begin{bmatrix} a^1_\alpha x^\alpha \\ a^2_\alpha x^\alpha \\ a^3_\alpha x^\alpha \end{bmatrix}, \tag{13}$$

and $y^i = a^i_\alpha x^\alpha$, $i = 1, 2, 3$, a set of linear transformations.

In general we note that the set of linear equations $y^i = a^i_\alpha x^\alpha$, $i = 1, 2, \ldots, m$, with α summed from 1 to n, can be represented in matrix form as

$$Y = AX,$$

with **Y** an $n \times 1$ column vector, **X** an $m \times 1$ column vector, and A an $n \times m$ matrix (note that $n/1 = n/m \cdot m/1$).

If the elements comprising a matrix A are differentiable functions of a variable t, we define a new matrix dA/dt from the following considerations:

$$\frac{A(t + \Delta t) - A(t)}{\Delta t} = \frac{1}{\Delta t}[[a_j^i(t + \Delta t)] - [a_j^i(t)]]$$

$$= \left[\frac{a_j^i(t + \Delta t) - a_j^i(t)}{\Delta t}\right], \tag{14}$$

$$\frac{dA(t)}{dt} = \lim_{\Delta t \to 0} \left[\frac{a_j^i(t + \Delta t) - a_j^i(t)}{\Delta t}\right]$$

$$= \left[\lim_{\Delta t \to 0} \frac{a_j^i(t + \Delta t) - a_j^i(t)}{\Delta t}\right] = \left[\frac{da_j^i}{dt}\right]$$

as the definition of dA/dt. Thus to determine the new matrix dA/dt one differentiates every term of the original matrix A. The reader should be aware that this rule is different from the case wherein one differentiates a determinant (a determinant is *not* a matrix except for the case of a scalar matrix when the two are equivalent). For example, if

$$A = \begin{bmatrix} t & \sin t & e^{-t} \\ t^2 & 1 & \cos t \end{bmatrix},$$

then

$$\frac{dA}{dt} = \begin{bmatrix} 1 & \cos t & -e^{-t} \\ 2t & 0 & -\sin t \end{bmatrix}.$$

The *transpose* of a matrix A, written A^T, is a new matrix obtained from A by interchanging the rows and columns of A. Thus, if

$$A = \begin{bmatrix} 2 & 3 & -4 \\ 1 & 2 & 5 \end{bmatrix},$$

then

$$A^T = \begin{bmatrix} 2 & 1 \\ 3 & 2 \\ -4 & 5 \end{bmatrix}.$$

A square matrix A is said to be symmetric if, and only if, $A = A^T$. If $A = -A^T$, we say that the matrix A is skew-symmetric. We now exhibit a symmetric matrix A and a skew-symmetric matrix B.

$$A = A^T = \begin{bmatrix} 2 & -1 & 0 & 3 \\ -1 & 3 & 5 & 0 \\ 0 & 5 & 1 & -3 \\ 3 & 0 & -3 & 6 \end{bmatrix}, \qquad B = -B^T = \begin{bmatrix} 0 & 1 & -2 \\ -1 & 0 & 3 \\ 2 & -3 & 0 \end{bmatrix}.$$

Let the reader quickly deduce for square matrices of order n that

$$(A + B)^T = A^T + B^T,$$
$$(A - B)^T = A^T - B^T,$$
$$(\alpha A)^T = \alpha A^T, \tag{15}$$
$$(A^T)^T = A,$$

from which it immediately follows that $A + A^T$ is a symmetric matrix and $A - A^T$ is a skew-symmetric matrix if A is a square matrix. Since

$$A \equiv \tfrac{1}{2}(A + A^T) + \tfrac{1}{2}(A - A^T),$$

we have verified that any square matrix can be written as a sum of a symmetric and a skew-symmetric matrix. For example,

$$A = \begin{bmatrix} 3 & 0 & 1 \\ 2 & 1 & 3 \\ -7 & 5 & -2 \end{bmatrix} = \begin{bmatrix} 3 & 1 & -3 \\ 1 & 1 & 4 \\ -3 & 4 & -2 \end{bmatrix} + \begin{bmatrix} 0 & -1 & 4 \\ 1 & 0 & -1 \\ -4 & 1 & 0 \end{bmatrix}.$$

Next we prove the important result that if A and B are square matrices of order n, then the transpose of the product AB is the product of the transposes in reverse order:

$$(AB)^T = B^T A^T. \tag{16}$$

Let

$$A = [a^i_j], \quad B = [b^i_j], \quad A^T = [c^i_j = a^j_i], \quad B^T = [d^i_j = b^j_i].$$

Then

$$B^T A^T = [d^i_\alpha c^\alpha_j] = [a^j_\alpha b^\alpha_i], \quad \begin{matrix} i\text{-row} \\ j\text{-column}, \end{matrix}$$
$$(AB)^T = [a^i_\alpha b^\alpha_j]^T = [a^j_\alpha b^\alpha_i],$$

which yields Eq. (16). For example, let

$$A = \begin{bmatrix} 2 & 1 \\ -1 & 3 \end{bmatrix}, \quad B = \begin{bmatrix} -1 & 4 \\ 1 & 8 \end{bmatrix},$$

so that

$$AB = \begin{bmatrix} -1 & 16 \\ 4 & 20 \end{bmatrix}, \quad (AB)^T = \begin{bmatrix} -1 & 4 \\ 16 & 20 \end{bmatrix},$$
$$B^T = \begin{bmatrix} -1 & 16 \\ 4 & 20 \end{bmatrix}, \quad A^T = \begin{bmatrix} 2 & -1 \\ 1 & 3 \end{bmatrix},$$
$$B^T A^T = \begin{bmatrix} -1 & 4 \\ 16 & 20 \end{bmatrix} = (AB)^T.$$

If A is an $m \times p$ matrix, B a $p \times q$ matrix, and C a $q \times n$ matrix, then $A(BC)$ $= (AB)C = ABC$ is an $m \times n$ matrix, by noting that

$$(AB)C = [a^i_\alpha b^\alpha_j] \cdot [c^j_i] = [a^i_\alpha b^\alpha_\beta c^\beta_j],$$
$$A(BC) = [a^i_j] \cdot [b^i_\beta c^\beta_j] = [a^i_\alpha b^\alpha_\beta c^\beta_j]. \tag{17}$$

Hence

$$(ABC)^T = [(AB)C]^T = C^T(AB)^T$$
$$= C^T(B^TA^T) = C^TB^TA^T \tag{18}$$

from Eq. (16). The generalization to the product of any number of matrices is immediately evident.

We conclude this section with a discussion of the *inverse* of a square matrix A. If a matrix A^{-1} exists such that

$$AA^{-1} = I = [\delta^i_j], \qquad i, j = 1, 2, \ldots, n, \tag{19}$$

we call A^{-1} the inverse matrix of A (assumed to be a square matrix of order n). It follows that

$$|AA^{-1}| = |A|\,|A^{-1}| = 1,$$

so of necessity, $|A| \neq 0$.

Conversely, let us assume that the determinant of A does not vanish, i.e., $|A| \neq 0$. From Eq. (8) of Section A.6, it follows that

$$a^i_\alpha \frac{A^\alpha_j}{|A|} = \delta^i_j, \tag{20}$$

with $\{A^i_j\}$ the cofactors of the elements $\{a^i_j\}$ comprising the matrix $A = [a^i_j]$. We see immediately that the elements

$$\frac{A^i_j}{|A|}, \qquad i, j = 1, 2, \ldots, n$$

are precisely the elements of A^{-1}. The elements of A^{-1} are the signed minors of A^T divided by the determinant of the matrix A. It follows from Eq. (8) of Section A.6 that

$$AA^{-1} = A^{-1}A = I. \tag{21}$$

Furthermore if A^{-1} exists we say that A is a nonsingular matrix. Let the reader deduce that if A is nonsingular, then $(A^{-1})^{-1} = A$.

Example 7. Let us find the inverse of the matrix

$$A = \begin{bmatrix} 1 & 3 & -1 \\ -2 & 5 & 3 \\ 2 & -1 & -4 \end{bmatrix},$$

with $|A| = -15$. Now

$$A^T = \begin{bmatrix} 1 & -2 & 2 \\ 3 & 5 & -1 \\ -1 & 3 & -4 \end{bmatrix},$$

so that

$$A_1^1 = \begin{vmatrix} 5 & -1 \\ 3 & -4 \end{vmatrix} = -17, \qquad A_2^1 = - \begin{vmatrix} 3 & -1 \\ -1 & -4 \end{vmatrix} = 13,$$

$$A_1^2 = - \begin{vmatrix} -2 & 2 \\ 3 & -4 \end{vmatrix} = -2, \qquad A_2^2 = \begin{vmatrix} 1 & 2 \\ -1 & -4 \end{vmatrix} = -2,$$

$$A_1^3 = \begin{vmatrix} -2 & 2 \\ 5 & -1 \end{vmatrix} = -8, \qquad A_2^3 = - \begin{vmatrix} 1 & 2 \\ 3 & -1 \end{vmatrix} = 7,$$

$$A_3^1 = \begin{vmatrix} 3 & 5 \\ -1 & 3 \end{vmatrix} = 14,$$

$$A_3^2 = - \begin{vmatrix} 1 & -2 \\ -1 & 3 \end{vmatrix} = -1,$$

$$A_3^3 = \begin{vmatrix} 1 & -2 \\ 3 & 5 \end{vmatrix} = 11,$$

and

$$A^{-1} = - \frac{1}{15} \begin{bmatrix} -17 & 13 & 14 \\ -2 & -2 & -1 \\ -8 & 7 & 11 \end{bmatrix}.$$

Note that

$$AA^{-1} = - \frac{1}{15} \begin{bmatrix} 1 & 3 & -1 \\ -2 & 5 & 3 \\ 2 & -1 & -4 \end{bmatrix} \cdot \begin{bmatrix} -17 & 13 & 14 \\ -2 & -2 & -1 \\ -8 & 7 & 11 \end{bmatrix}$$

$$= - \frac{1}{15} \begin{bmatrix} -15 & 0 & 0 \\ 0 & -15 & 0 \\ 0 & 0 & -15 \end{bmatrix} = \begin{bmatrix} 1 & 0 & 0 \\ 0 & 1 & 0 \\ 0 & 0 & 1 \end{bmatrix} = I.$$

Let A and B be square matrices of order n such that A^{-1} and B^{-1} exist. From the identity

$$ABB^{-1}A^{-1} = I, \tag{22}$$

it follows that $(AB)(B^{-1}A^{-1}) = I$, so that $B^{-1}A^{-1}$ is the inverse of AB, and the inverse of a product of nonsingular matrices of order n is the product of the inverses in reverse order:

$$(AB)^{-1} = B^{-1}A^{-1}. \tag{23}$$

The trace or spur of a square matrix is defined as the sum of the terms along the principal diagonal, i.e., Trace $A = a_\alpha^\alpha$. It follows that if A and B are square matrices of order n, then

$$\text{Trace } (AB) = \text{Trace } [a_\alpha^i b_j^\alpha]$$

$$= a_\alpha^\beta b_\beta^\alpha.$$

Furthermore,

$$\text{Trace } (BA) = \text{Trace } [b_\beta^i a_j^\beta]$$

$$= b_\beta^\alpha a_\alpha^\beta = a_\alpha^\beta b_\beta^\alpha$$

so that

$$\text{Trace } (AB) = \text{Trace } (BA). \tag{24}$$

Before proceeding with a proof of the Hamilton-Cayley theorem let us obtain the extension of Leibniz rule for differentiating a product of two matrices whose elements are functions of a parameter λ. From

$$\frac{d}{d\lambda}(BC) = \frac{d}{d\lambda}[b_\alpha^i c_j^\alpha]$$

$$= \left[\frac{db_\alpha^i}{d\lambda} c_j^\alpha + b_\alpha^i \frac{dc_j^\alpha}{d\lambda}\right]$$

$$= \left[\frac{db_\alpha^i}{d\lambda} c_j^\alpha\right] + \left[b_\alpha^i \frac{dc_j^\alpha}{d\lambda}\right]$$

$$= \frac{dB}{d\lambda}C + B\frac{dC}{d\lambda}, \tag{25}$$

it follows that

$$\frac{d^2}{d\lambda^2}(BC) = \frac{d^2B}{d\lambda^2}C + 2\frac{dB}{d\lambda}\frac{dC}{d\lambda} + B\frac{d^2C}{d\lambda^2},$$

$$\frac{d^3}{d\lambda^3}(BC) = \frac{d^3B}{d\lambda^3}C + 3\frac{d^2B}{d\lambda^2}\frac{dC}{d\lambda} + 3\frac{dB}{d\lambda}\frac{d^2C}{d\lambda^2} + B\frac{d^3C}{d\lambda^3},$$

and, in general

$$\frac{d^k(BC)}{d\lambda^k} = \sum_{r=0}^{k}\binom{k}{r}\frac{d^{k-r}B}{d\lambda^{k-r}}\frac{d^rC}{d\lambda^r}, \tag{26}$$

with $\binom{k}{r}$ the binomial coefficients discussed in Chapter 2. We define $d^0B/d\lambda^0 \equiv B$, etc.

In particular, if the elements of C are linear in λ so that $d^2C/d\lambda^2 = 0$, etc., then

$$\frac{d^k(BC)}{d\lambda^k} = \frac{d^kB}{d\lambda^k}C + k\frac{d^{k-1}B}{d\lambda^{k-1}}\frac{dC}{d\lambda}, \qquad k = 1, 2, 3, \ldots \tag{27}$$

Now consider any square matrix, A, of order n. The matrix A need not be symmetric. The characteristic equation* associated with A is $|a_j^i - \lambda \delta_j^i| = 0$, or

$$p(\lambda) = \alpha_0 + \alpha_1 \lambda + \alpha_2 \lambda^2 + \cdots + \alpha_k \lambda^k + \cdots + \alpha_n \lambda^n = 0.$$

The Hamilton-Cayley theorem states that every square matrix satisfies its characteristic equation, so that

$$p(A) = \alpha_0 I + \alpha_1 A + \alpha_2 A^2 + \cdots + \alpha_n A^n \equiv 0. \tag{28}$$

To verify this result we let $C = A - \lambda I$ and define B as the matrix of the co-factors of C. Thus

$$BC = |C| \, I = (\alpha_0 + \alpha_1 \lambda + \alpha_2 \lambda^2 + \cdots + \alpha_n \lambda^n) I. \tag{29}$$

We note that the elements of C are at most linear in λ, and the elements of B are polynomials in λ of degree at most $(n - 1)$. Furthermore, $C(\lambda = 0) = A$, $dC/d\lambda = -I$.

Let us now differentiate Eq. (29) k times with respect to λ and then set $\lambda = 0$. We obtain

$$\frac{d^k B}{d\lambda^k}\bigg|_{\lambda=0} A - k \frac{d^{k-1} B}{d\lambda^{k-1}}\bigg|_{\lambda=0} = \alpha_k k! \, I. \tag{30}$$

We multiply Eq. (30) by A^k and divide by $k!$, so that

$$\frac{1}{k!} \frac{d^k B}{d\lambda^k}\bigg|_{\lambda=0} A^{k+1} - \frac{1}{(k-1)!} \frac{d^{k-1} B}{d\lambda^{k-1}}\bigg|_{\lambda=0} A^k = \alpha_k A^k. \tag{31}$$

Next a summation on k from 1 to n yields

$$\sum_1^n \alpha_k A^k = -B(\lambda = 0)A, \tag{32}$$

since $d^n B/d\lambda^n = 0$. From Eq. (29) it follows that

$$B(\lambda = 0) \, C(\lambda = 0) = B(\lambda = 0)A = \alpha_0 I,$$

so that

$$p(A) \equiv \sum_{k=0}^n \alpha_k A^k = 0, \tag{33}$$

which concludes the proof of the Hamilton-Cayley theorem. As an example, consider

$$A = \begin{bmatrix} 1 & 0 \\ 2 & 2 \end{bmatrix},$$

whose characteristic equation is

$$\begin{vmatrix} 1 - \lambda & 0 \\ 2 & 2 - \lambda \end{vmatrix} = 0,$$

---

* See Section A.10.

or $p(\lambda) = \lambda^2 - 3\lambda + 2 = 0$. Thus A must satisfy $A^2 - 3A + 2I = 0$. As a check we note that

$$A^2 - 3A + 2I = \begin{bmatrix} 1 & 0 \\ 6 & 4 \end{bmatrix} - 3\begin{bmatrix} 1 & 0 \\ 2 & -2 \end{bmatrix} + 2\begin{bmatrix} 1 & 0 \\ 0 & 1 \end{bmatrix}$$

$$= \begin{bmatrix} 0 & 0 \\ 0 & 0 \end{bmatrix} = 0.$$

Since $p(0) = |A| = 2 \neq 0$ it follows that A^{-1} exists. Multiplying $A^2 - 3A + 2I = 0$ by A^{-1} yields $A - 3I + 2A^{-1} = 0$ so that

$$A^{-1} = -\tfrac{1}{2}(A - 3I)$$

$$= -\frac{1}{2}\begin{bmatrix} 1 & 0 \\ 2 & 2 \end{bmatrix} + \frac{3}{2}\begin{bmatrix} 1 & 0 \\ 0 & 1 \end{bmatrix}$$

$$= \begin{bmatrix} +1 & 0 \\ -1 & +\tfrac{1}{2} \end{bmatrix}.$$

Thus the Hamilton-Cayley theorem affords a method for finding the inverse of a nonsingular square matrix. Numerical methods for inverting square matrices of large order now exist.

PROBLEMS

1. Let

$$A = \begin{bmatrix} 2 & 0 & 1 \\ -1 & 1 & 3 \end{bmatrix}, \qquad B = \begin{bmatrix} 1 & 1 & 2 \\ 0 & -1 & 1 \end{bmatrix}.$$

Determine

a) $3A - 2B$ b) AA^T c) A^TA d) AB^T
e) $|AB^T|$ f) $(AB^T)^{-1}$ g) A^TB h) $|A^TB|$

2. Let A and B be symmetric matrices of order n. Show that AB is a symmetric matrix if A and B commute, i.e., $AB = BA$.

3. Let A be any matrix. Show that AA^T and A^TA are symmetric matrices.

4. Find the inverse of the matrix

$$A = \begin{bmatrix} 1 & 2 & 1 \\ 2 & 5 & 3 \\ 1 & 3 & 4 \end{bmatrix}.$$

5. Write the system of differential equations

$$\frac{dx^i}{dt} = a^i_\alpha x^\alpha, \qquad i, \alpha = 1, 2, \ldots, n,$$

in matrix form.

6. Given $Z = AY$, $Y = BX$, show that $Z = (AB)X$.

7. Show that

$$\begin{bmatrix} 0 & 1 & 0 \\ 1 & 0 & 0 \\ 0 & 0 & 1 \end{bmatrix} \cdot \begin{bmatrix} a_1^1 & a_2^1 & a_3^1 \\ a_1^2 & a_2^2 & a_3^2 \\ a_1^3 & a_2^3 & a_3^3 \end{bmatrix} = \begin{bmatrix} a_1^2 & a_2^2 & a_3^2 \\ a_1^1 & a_2^1 & a_3^1 \\ a_1^3 & a_2^3 & a_3^3 \end{bmatrix}.$$

What theorem concerning determinants can be deduced from this fact? Find a square matrix E_{rs} such that $E_{rs} A$ interchanges the rth and sth rows of A.

8. Show that

$$\frac{d^2}{dt^2} (AB) = \frac{d^2A}{dt^2} B + 2 \frac{dA}{dt} \frac{dB}{dt} + A \frac{d^2B}{dt^2}.$$

9. Show that $(A^{-1})^{-1} = A$ for nonsingular matrices.

10. Show that $|A^{-1}| = |A|^{-1}$ for nonsingular matrices.

11. Show that

$$(A^{-1} BA)^2 \equiv (A^{-1} BA)(A^{-1} BA) = A^{-1} B^2 A,$$

with $B^2 = BB$. What is $(A^{-1} BA)^n$ for any positive integer n?

12. Give an example for which $(\text{Trace } A)(\text{Trace } B) \neq \text{Trace } (AB)$ for square matrices.

13. Show that $\text{Trace } (B^{-1} AB) = \text{Trace } A$.

14. Show that $(ABC)^{-1} = C^{-1} B^{-1} A^{-1}$ for nonsingular matrices A, B, C, of order n.

15. If A is nonsingular show that A has a unique inverse. Hint: assume that $BA = I$ and show that $B = A^{-1}$.

16. If $Y = AX$ with A nonsingular, show that $X = A^{-1} Y$. Is this Cramer's rule?

17. Let A be a skew-symmetric matrix of odd order $A = -A^T$. Show that $|A| = 0$.

18. The scalar identity

$$\frac{1}{a} + \frac{1}{b} = \frac{a+b}{ab} = \frac{1}{a}(a + b)\frac{1}{b},$$

with $ab \neq 0$, suggests that if A and B are nonsingular matrices of order n, then $A^{-1} + B^{-1} = A^{-1} (A + B)B^{-1}$. Verify this trivial identity. Show that $(A + B)^{-1} = B^{-1} (A^{-1} + B^{-1})^{-1} A^{-1}$, provided $A^{-1} + B^{-1}$ is also nonsingular.

19. Let $Y = AX$ and assume that $A^T A$ has an inverse. Show that

$$X = (A^T A)^{-1} A^T Y.$$

20. Assume that B and $A + B$ are nonsingular matrices of order n. From

$$I + AB^{-1} = BB^{-1} + AB^{-1} = (A + B)B^{-1}$$

show that $I + AB^{-1}$ is nonsingular, and that $(I + AB^{-1})^{-1} = B(A + B)^{-1}$.

21. Given that A is of order $m \times n$, $n \leq m$, and $|A^T A| \neq 0$, show that

$$[A(A^T A)^{-1} A^T - I]A = 0.$$

22. Given that A is of order $m \times n, n > m$, show that $|A^TA| = 0$.

23. From the scalar identity

$$\left(\frac{c^2b}{a} + 1\right) \left(\frac{c^2b}{a} + 1\right)^{-1} = 1 \,,$$

show that if A and B are nonsingular matrices of order m and n, respectively, and if C is of order $m \times n$, then

$$C^T(A^{-1}CBC^T + I)(I + A^{-1}CBC^T)^{-1} \equiv C^T \,,$$

provided the indicated inverses exist. Then show that

$$(C^TA^{-1}C + B^{-1})^{-1}C^TA^{-1} = BC^T(A + CBC^T)^{-1} \,,$$

provided the indicated inverses exist.

24. Consider the system of equations:

$$x + 2y = 5 \,,$$
$$2x + 4y = 10 \,,$$
$$3x + 6y = 15 \,.$$

The matrix of the coefficients is

$$\begin{bmatrix} 1 & 2 \\ 2 & 4 \\ 3 & 6 \end{bmatrix} .$$

Show that all 2×2 determinants which can be obtained from this matrix by considering two rows and two columns, vanish. However, there is at least one (actually six) nonzero determinant of order one. We say that the matrix has rank $r = 1$. Show that the rank of the augmented matrix

$$\begin{bmatrix} 1 & 2 & 5 \\ 2 & 4 & 10 \\ 3 & 6 & 15 \end{bmatrix}$$

is also one. Then explain why the system above has at least one solution.

25. Find the inverse of

$$A = \begin{bmatrix} 1 & 0 & 2 \\ -1 & 0 & 1 \\ 1 & 1 & 1 \end{bmatrix}$$

by use of the Hamilton-Cayley theorem.

26. Assume that the eigenvalues of $|A - \lambda I| = 0$ are all different. Show that the corresponding eigenvectors are linearly independent. Since $(A - \lambda_1 I)X_1 = 0, \ldots, (A - \lambda_n I)X_n = 0$, show that

$$(A - \lambda_1 I)(A - \lambda_2 I) \cdots (A - \lambda_n I)(\alpha_1 X_1 + \alpha_2 X_2 + \cdots + \alpha_n X_n) = 0$$

for all $\alpha_1, \alpha_2, \ldots, \alpha_n$. Then deduce that

$$(A - \lambda_1 I)(A - \lambda_2 I) \cdots (A - \lambda_n I) \equiv 0.$$

Since the characteristic equation associated with the square matrix A is of the form

$$(\lambda - \lambda_1)(\lambda - \lambda_2) \cdots (\lambda - \lambda_n) = 0,$$

we see that A satisfies its characteristic equation.

A.9 QUADRATIC FORMS · ORTHOGONAL MATRICES

Let us examine the two-dimensional quadratic form given by

$$Q = [x \ \ y] \cdot \begin{bmatrix} a_{11} & a_{12} \\ a_{21} & a_{22} \end{bmatrix} \cdot \begin{bmatrix} x \\ y \end{bmatrix}$$

$$= [a_{11}x + a_{21}y, \ a_{12}x + a_{22}y] \cdot \begin{bmatrix} x \\ y \end{bmatrix}$$

$$= [a_{11}x^2 + a_{21}yx + a_{12}xy + a_{22}y^2]$$

$$= a_{11}x^2 + a_{12}xy + a_{21}xy + a_{22}y^2. \tag{1}$$

The final result is a scalar, and Q is a quadratic in the variables (x, y) which can be expressed in the form $Q = X^T A X$ with $X = [{}^x_y]$, and

$$A = \begin{bmatrix} a_{11} & a_{12} \\ a_{21} & a_{22} \end{bmatrix}.$$

Since Q is a one-by-one matrix, and hence a scalar, it follows that $Q = Q^T$. However, $Q^T = X^T A^T X$, so that $X^T(A - A^T)X = 0$. Since $A = \frac{1}{2}(A + A^T) + \frac{1}{2}(A - A^T)$, of necessity

$$Q = X^T[\tfrac{1}{2}(A + A^T)]X, \tag{2}$$

so that without loss of generality we may assume that A is a symmetric matrix whenever we deal with quadratic forms.

The n-dimensional quadratic form, $Q = a_{\alpha\beta}x^\alpha x^\beta$, $a_{\alpha\beta} = a_{\beta\alpha}$ for all α, β with $a_{\alpha\beta}$ real for $\alpha, \beta = 1, 2, \ldots, n$, can be expressed in matrix form as

$$Q = X^T A X \tag{3}$$

such that $A = A^T$, $X^T = [x^1 x^2 \cdots x^n]$.

We will return to this quadratic form after a brief discussion of orthogonal matrices. The square of the distance between the origin $O(0, 0, 0)$ and a point $P(x, y, z)$ in a Euclidean space using cartesian coordinations, is

$$L^2 = x^2 + y^2 + z^2 = [x \ y \ z] \cdot \begin{bmatrix} x \\ y \\ z \end{bmatrix} = X^T X. \tag{4}$$

The generalization to a Euclidean n-space is simple. We define

$$L^2 = \mathbf{X}^T\mathbf{X} = [x^1\ x^2 \cdots x^n] \cdot \begin{bmatrix} x^1 \\ x^2 \\ \vdots \\ x^n \end{bmatrix} = \sum_{i=1}^{n} (x^i)^2 \tag{5}$$

as the square of the distance between the origin and a point $P(x^1, x^2, \ldots, x^n)$.

Under the linear transformation $\mathbf{X} = \mathbf{R}\mathbf{Y}$ we obtain $L^2 = (\mathbf{R}\mathbf{Y})^T\ (\mathbf{R}\mathbf{Y}) = \mathbf{Y}^T(\mathbf{R}^T\mathbf{R})\mathbf{Y}$. If the y's are also cartesian coordinates of the point P, then of necessity $L^2 = \mathbf{Y}^T\mathbf{Y} = (y^1)^2 + (y^2)^2 + \cdots + (y^n)^2$, which means that $\mathbf{R}^T\mathbf{R} = \mathbf{I}$, or $\mathbf{R}^T = \mathbf{R}^{-1}$. Any matrix such that

$$\mathbf{R}^T\mathbf{R} = \mathbf{I},$$

$$\mathbf{R}^T = \mathbf{R}^{-1}, \tag{6}$$

is called an orthogonal matrix if the elements of R are real. From Eq. (6) it follows that $|\mathbf{R}^T\mathbf{R}| = |\mathbf{R}^T|\,|\mathbf{R}| = |\mathbf{R}|^2 = 1$, so that $|\mathbf{R}| = \pm 1$. If $|\mathbf{R}| = 1$ and $\mathbf{R}^T\mathbf{R} = \mathbf{I}$, we say that R is a rotation matrix, so that a rotation matrix is always an orthogonal matrix. The matrix of the direction cosines of Example 10 of Section A.5 is a rotation matrix in three dimensions.

It is a simple matter to recognize an orthogonal matrix. From $\mathbf{R}^T\mathbf{R} = \mathbf{I}$ it follows that the sum of the squares of the components of any column (a column vector) must be unity, and the scalar product of any two different column vectors must vanish. Thus if

$$\mathbf{R} = [\mathbf{R}_1\mathbf{R}_2 \cdots \mathbf{R}_n], \tag{7}$$

with $\mathbf{R}_1, \mathbf{R}_2, \ldots, \mathbf{R}_n$ column vectors, then

$$\begin{aligned} \mathbf{R}_i^T\mathbf{R}_i &= 1 \quad \text{for} \quad i = 1, 2, \ldots, n, \\ \mathbf{R}_i^T\mathbf{R}_j &= 0 \quad \text{for} \quad i \neq j, \end{aligned} \tag{8}$$

or simply, $\mathbf{R}_i^T\mathbf{R}_j = \delta_{ij}$ (the Kronecker delta). The most general two-dimensional rotation matrix is

$$\mathbf{R} = \begin{bmatrix} \cos\theta & \sin\theta \\ -\sin\theta & \cos\theta \end{bmatrix}, \tag{9}$$

with θ real. Note that

$$(\cos\theta)^2 + (-\sin\theta)^2 = 1,$$

$$\sin^2\theta + \cos^2\theta = 1,$$

$$\cos\theta \sin\theta + (-\sin\theta)\cos\theta = 0,$$

and

$$|\mathbf{R}| = 1.$$

Let the reader show that

$$R = \begin{bmatrix} \frac{4}{5} & \frac{3}{10}\sqrt{2} & -\frac{3}{10}\sqrt{2} \\ 0 & \frac{1}{2}\sqrt{2} & \frac{1}{2}\sqrt{2} \\ -\frac{3}{5} & \frac{2}{5}\sqrt{2} & -\frac{2}{5}\sqrt{2} \end{bmatrix} \tag{10}$$

is a three-dimensional rotation matrix. It can be shown that the most general three-dimensional rotation matrix involves three arbitrary parameters.

Let us return to the quadratic form of Eq. (3). We ask if it is possible to find an orthogonal transformation $X = RY$ (R is to be an orthogonal matrix) such that the quadratic form can be expressed in the canonical form

$$Q = \sum_{i=1}^{n} \lambda_i (y^i)^2$$

$$= Y^T \cdot \begin{bmatrix} \lambda_1 & 0 & 0 & \cdots & 0 \\ 0 & \lambda_2 & 0 & \cdots & 0 \\ & & \vdots & & \\ 0 & 0 & 0 & \cdots & \lambda_n \end{bmatrix} \cdot Y. \tag{11}$$

The answer will be in the affirmative from the following considerations. For $X = RY$ we obtain

$$\begin{aligned} Q = X^T A X &= (RY)^T A (RY) \\ &= Y^T (R^T A R) Y \\ &= Y^T (R^{-1} A R) Y, \end{aligned} \tag{12}$$

so that Q of Eq. (12) will assume the form of Eq. (11), provided

$$R^{-1} A R = \begin{bmatrix} \lambda_1 & 0 & 0 & \cdots & 0 \\ 0 & \lambda_2 & 0 & \cdots & 0 \\ & & \vdots & & \\ 0 & 0 & 0 & \cdots & \lambda_n \end{bmatrix}, \tag{13}$$

or, equivalently, if an orthogonal matrix R, exists such that

$$AR = R \begin{bmatrix} \lambda_1 & 0 & 0 & \cdots & 0 \\ 0 & \lambda_2 & 0 & \cdots & 0 \\ 0 & 0 & \lambda_3 & \cdots & 0 \\ & & \vdots & & \\ 0 & 0 & 0 & \cdots & \lambda_n \end{bmatrix}. \tag{14}$$

If we write $R = [R_1 R_2 \cdots R_n]$ with R_i, $i = 1, 2, \ldots, n$, column vectors, let the reader show that of necessity

$$\begin{aligned} AR_1 &= \lambda_1 R_1 \\ AR_2 &= \lambda_2 R_2 \\ &\vdots \\ AR_n &= \lambda_n R_n. \end{aligned} \tag{15}$$

Let us examine the equation $\mathbf{AR}_1 = \lambda\mathbf{R}_1$ ($\lambda = \lambda_1$), or

$$(\mathbf{A} - \lambda\mathbf{I})\mathbf{R}_1 = 0. \tag{16}$$

Equation (16) represents a system of n linear homogeneous equations in the n unknowns comprising the column vector $\mathbf{R}_1$. From Section A.7 a necessary and sufficient condition that nontrivial solutions exist is that the determinant of the coefficients vanish, which yields the characteristic equation

$$\begin{vmatrix} (a_{11} - \lambda) & a_{12} & a_{13} & \cdots & a_{1n} \\ a_{21} & (a_{22} - \lambda) & a_{23} & \cdots & a_{2n} \\ & & \vdots & & \\ a_{n1} & a_{n2} & a_{n3} & \cdots & (a_{nn} - \lambda) \end{vmatrix} = 0. \tag{17}$$

The characteristic equation associated with the matrix $\mathbf{A}$ is a polynomial in λ of degree n, so has n roots $\lambda_1, \lambda_2, \ldots, \lambda_n$, which are called the eigenvalues or characteristic roots associated with the matrix $\mathbf{A}$. Let us assume for the moment that the λ_i, $i = 1, 2, \ldots, n$ are real and different from each other.

The root λ_1 guarantees that the equation $\mathbf{AR}_1^* = \lambda_1\mathbf{R}_1^*$ has nontrivial solutions for the components of $\mathbf{R}_1^*$. Since $\alpha\mathbf{AR}_1^* = \alpha\lambda_1\mathbf{R}_1^*$ implies $\mathbf{A}(\alpha\mathbf{R}_1^*) = \lambda_1(\alpha\mathbf{R}_1^*)$, we can find an α such that $\mathbf{R}_1 = \alpha\mathbf{R}_1^*$ is a unit vector. For $\lambda_2, \lambda_3, \ldots, \lambda_n$ one can solve the remaining linear equations of Eq. (15) for the unit vectors (eigenvectors) $\mathbf{R}_2$, $\mathbf{R}_3, \ldots, \mathbf{R}_n$.

We show now that the matrix

$$\mathbf{R} = [\mathbf{R}_1 \ \mathbf{R}_2 \ \mathbf{R}_3 \cdots \mathbf{R}_n]$$

is a rotation matrix. From

$$\mathbf{AR}_1 = \lambda_1\mathbf{R}_1$$
$$\mathbf{AR}_2 = \lambda_2\mathbf{R}_2 \qquad \lambda_1 \neq \lambda_2, \tag{18}$$

it follows that $(\mathbf{AR}_1)^T = \lambda_1\mathbf{R}_1^T$ or $\mathbf{R}_1^T\mathbf{A}^T = \mathbf{R}_1^T\mathbf{A} = \lambda_1\mathbf{R}_1^T$, since $\mathbf{A} = \mathbf{A}^T$. Hence $\mathbf{R}_1^T\mathbf{AR}_2 = \lambda_1\mathbf{R}_1^T\mathbf{R}_2$. From the second equation of (18) we obtain $\mathbf{R}_1^T\mathbf{AR}_2 = \lambda_2\mathbf{R}_1^T\mathbf{R}_2$. Thus, $(\lambda_2 - \lambda_1)\mathbf{R}_1^T\mathbf{R}_2 = 0$, so that $\mathbf{R}_1^T\mathbf{R}_2 = 0$ since $\lambda_1 \neq \lambda_2$. A similar result holds for any two of the eigenvectors, so that the matrix $\mathbf{R}$ is an orthogonal matrix. It is important to note that this result has been derived on the assumption that $\mathbf{A} = \mathbf{A}^T$. It is left as a problem at the end of this section to show that the eigenvalues are real if $\mathbf{A} = \mathbf{A}^T$ with the elements of $\mathbf{A}$ real numbers.

A deeper analysis is required when some of the eigenvalues are equal to each other. In a three-dimensional space, however, at most two of the eigenvalues can be equal to each other (if all three eigenvalues are equal $Q = \mathbf{X}^T\mathbf{AX}$ is already in canonical form). Thus the eigenvectors $\mathbf{R}_1$ and $\mathbf{R}_2$ can be found from the different eigenvalues λ_1, λ_2. The vector product of $\mathbf{R}_1$ and $\mathbf{R}_2$ yields $\mathbf{R}_3$, which completes the orthogonal matrix $\mathbf{R}$.

Example 1. We find an orthogonal transformation which reduces

$$Q = 7x^2 + 7y^2 + 7z^2 + 6xy + 8yz$$

$$= [x \; y \; z] \cdot \begin{bmatrix} 7 & 3 & 0 \\ 3 & 7 & 4 \\ 0 & 4 & 7 \end{bmatrix} \cdot \begin{bmatrix} x \\ y \\ z \end{bmatrix}$$

into a canonical form. The characteristic equation is

$$\begin{vmatrix} 7 - \lambda & 3 & 0 \\ 3 & 7 - \lambda & 4 \\ 0 & 4 & 7 - \lambda \end{vmatrix} = 0,$$

which yields $(\lambda - 7)(\lambda - 12)(\lambda - 2) = 0$, and the eigenvalues are $\lambda_1 = 7, \lambda_2 = 12$, $\lambda_3 = 2$. The equation $(A - \lambda_1 I)R_1 = 0$ becomes

$$\begin{bmatrix} 0 & 3 & 0 \\ 3 & 0 & 4 \\ 0 & 4 & 0 \end{bmatrix} \cdot \begin{bmatrix} r_1 \\ r_2 \\ r_3 \end{bmatrix} = 0,$$

or $3r_2 = 0$, $3r_1 + 4r_3 = 0$, which in turn yields $r_1 = 4, r_2 = 0, r_3 = -3$. Since $r_1^2 + r_2^2 + r_3^2 = 25$, we obtain the unit vector $R_1^T = [\frac{4}{5}, 0, -\frac{3}{5}]$, with R_1 the eigenvector associated with the eigenvalue $\lambda_1 = 7$.

Let the reader show that

$$R_2 = \begin{bmatrix} \frac{3}{10}\sqrt{2} \\ \frac{1}{2}\sqrt{2} \\ \frac{2}{5}\sqrt{2} \end{bmatrix} \qquad R_3 = \begin{bmatrix} -\frac{3}{10}\sqrt{2} \\ \frac{1}{2}\sqrt{2} \\ -\frac{2}{5}\sqrt{2} \end{bmatrix} \qquad (19)$$

are the eigenvectors associated with the eigenvalues $\lambda_2 = 12, \lambda_3 = 2$, respectively. The rotation matrix R is represented in Eq. (10).

The linear (orthogonal) transformation $X = RY$ becomes

$$\begin{bmatrix} x \\ y \\ z \end{bmatrix} = \begin{bmatrix} \frac{4}{5} & \frac{3}{10}\sqrt{2} & -\frac{3}{10}\sqrt{2} \\ 0 & \frac{1}{2}\sqrt{2} & \frac{1}{2}\sqrt{2} \\ -\frac{3}{5} & \frac{2}{5}\sqrt{2} & -\frac{2}{5}\sqrt{2} \end{bmatrix} \cdot \begin{bmatrix} u \\ v \\ w \end{bmatrix},$$

with $Y^T = [u \; v \; w]$, so that

$$x = \tfrac{1}{10}(8u + 3\sqrt{2}v - 3\sqrt{2}w),$$
$$y = \tfrac{1}{2}\sqrt{2}(v + w), \qquad (20)$$
$$z = \tfrac{1}{5}(-3u + 2\sqrt{2}v - 2\sqrt{2}w).$$

Under the linear transformation of Eq. (20) it is a simple matter to show that $Q = 7(x^2 + y^2 + z^2) + 6xy + 8yz$ becomes $Q = 7u^2 + 12v^2 + 2w^2$. The numbers 7, 12, 2 in this canonical form of Q are the eigenvalues associated with the matrix A.

Example 2. *Positive-definite quadratic forms.* Consider $Q = \mathbf{X}^T\mathbf{A}\mathbf{X}$, $\mathbf{A} = \mathbf{A}^T$. If $Q > 0$ for all vectors $\mathbf{X}$ except for the null vector $\mathbf{X} = 0$, we say that Q is a positive-definite quadratic form. Since Q can be reduced to the canonical form

$$Q = \lambda_1(y^1)^2 + \lambda_2(y^2)^2 + \cdots + \lambda_n(y^n)^2,$$

with $\mathbf{X} = \mathbf{R}\mathbf{Y}$, $|\mathbf{R}| \neq 0$, it follows that $\lambda_1 > 0$, $\lambda_2 > 0, \ldots, \lambda_n > 0$, for otherwise Q would be zero or negative for a non-null vector $\mathbf{Y}$, and hence for a non-null vector $\mathbf{X}$. Hence a necessary and sufficient condition that a quadratic form be positive-definite is that the eigenvalues associated with the symmetric matrix $\mathbf{A}$ be greater than zero. We also say, in this case, that $\mathbf{A}$ is a positive-definite matrix.

If $Q = \mathbf{X}^T\mathbf{B}^T\mathbf{B}\mathbf{X} = (\mathbf{B}\mathbf{X})^T(\mathbf{B}\mathbf{X})$, then $Q \geq 0$ for all vectors $\mathbf{X}$, and we say that Q is a positive-semidefinite quadratic form. Hence any matrix of the form $\mathbf{B}^T\mathbf{B}$ is a positive-semidefinite matrix. One can show that an alternative necessary and sufficient condition for the matrix $\mathbf{A} = \mathbf{A}^T$ to be a positive-definite matrix is that

$$|\,a_{11}\,| > 0 \qquad \begin{vmatrix} a_{11} & a_{12} \\ a_{21} & a_{22} \end{vmatrix} > 0 \qquad \begin{vmatrix} a_{11} & a_{12} & a_{13} \\ a_{21} & a_{22} & a_{23} \\ a_{31} & a_{32} & a_{33} \end{vmatrix} > 0 \ldots |\mathbf{A}| > 0. \quad (21)$$

This test is much simpler to apply than the test that the eigenvalues of $\mathbf{A}$ be positive.

Example 3. Consider the system of difference equations

$$p_1(n + 1) = \tfrac{5}{9}p_1(n) + \tfrac{2}{3}p_2(n) + \tfrac{2}{3}p_3(n),$$

$$p_2(n + 1) = \tfrac{2}{9}p_1(n) + \tfrac{1}{3}p_2(n), \qquad\qquad (22)$$

$$p_3(n + 1) = \tfrac{2}{9}p_1(n) \qquad\qquad + \tfrac{1}{3}p_3(n),$$

for $n = 1, 2, 3, \ldots$, which can be written in the matrix form

$$\mathbf{p}(n + 1) = \mathbf{P}\mathbf{p}(n), \qquad n = 1, 2, 3, \ldots, \qquad (23)$$

or

$$\begin{bmatrix} p_1(n + 1) \\ p_2(n + 1) \\ p_3(n + 1) \end{bmatrix} = \begin{bmatrix} \tfrac{5}{9} & \tfrac{2}{3} & \tfrac{2}{3} \\ \tfrac{2}{9} & \tfrac{1}{3} & 0 \\ \tfrac{2}{9} & 0 & \tfrac{1}{3} \end{bmatrix} \cdot \begin{bmatrix} p_1(n) \\ p_2(n) \\ p_3(n) \end{bmatrix}. \qquad (24)$$

To solve Eq. (23) we let $\mathbf{p}(n) = \mathbf{B}\lambda^n$, with $\mathbf{B}$ a column vector, λ a scalar. Then $\mathbf{p}(n + 1) = \mathbf{B}\lambda^{n+1}$ so that $\mathbf{B}\lambda^{n+1} = \mathbf{P}\mathbf{B}\lambda^n$ which yields

$$(\mathbf{P} - \lambda\mathbf{I})\mathbf{B} = 0 \qquad (25)$$

provided $\lambda \neq 0$. We have seen that this system of linear equations (the elements of the column vector $\mathbf{B}$ are the unknowns) will have a nontrivial solution if $|\mathbf{P} - \lambda\mathbf{I}| = 0$, which is the characteristic equation associated with the nonsymmetric matrix $\mathbf{P}$. Equation (25) becomes

$$\begin{vmatrix} \frac{5}{9} - \lambda & \frac{2}{3} & \frac{2}{3} \\ \frac{2}{9} & \frac{1}{3} - \lambda & 0 \\ \frac{2}{9} & 0 & \frac{1}{3} - \lambda \end{vmatrix} = 0, \qquad (26)$$

or

$$(1 - \lambda) \begin{vmatrix} 1 & 1 & 1 \\ \frac{2}{9} & \frac{1}{3} - \lambda & 0 \\ \frac{2}{9} & 0 & \frac{1}{3} - \lambda \end{vmatrix} = 0$$

by adding the second and third row to the first row of the determinant of (26), and removing the common factor $(1 - \lambda)$ from the first row. The eigenvalues are found to be $\lambda_1 = 1$, $\lambda_2 = \frac{1}{3}$, $\lambda_3 = -\frac{1}{9}$.

The eigenvector $\mathbf{B}_1$ associated with $\lambda_1 = 1$ satisfies $(\mathbf{P} - \mathbf{I})\mathbf{B}_1 = 0$, which yields

$$\begin{bmatrix} -\frac{4}{9} & \frac{2}{3} & \frac{2}{3} \\ \frac{2}{9} & -\frac{2}{3} & 0 \\ \frac{2}{9} & 0 & -\frac{2}{3} \end{bmatrix} \cdot \begin{bmatrix} \alpha \\ \beta \\ \gamma \end{bmatrix} = \begin{bmatrix} 0 \\ 0 \\ 0 \end{bmatrix},$$

so that $\alpha = 3\beta = 3\gamma$, and

$$\mathbf{B}_1 = \begin{bmatrix} 3a \\ a \\ a \end{bmatrix}$$

is an eigenvector for arbitrary a. The eigenvector $\mathbf{B}_2$ associated with $\lambda_2 = \frac{1}{3}$ satisfies $(\mathbf{P} - \frac{1}{3}\mathbf{I})\mathbf{B}_2 = 0$, or

$$\begin{bmatrix} \frac{2}{9} & \frac{2}{3} & \frac{2}{3} \\ \frac{2}{9} & 0 & 0 \\ \frac{2}{9} & 0 & 0 \end{bmatrix} \cdot \begin{bmatrix} a_1 \\ b_1 \\ c_1 \end{bmatrix} = \begin{bmatrix} 0 \\ 0 \\ 0 \end{bmatrix},$$

yielding $a_1 = 0$, $b_1 = -c_1$, so that

$$\mathbf{B}_2 = \begin{bmatrix} 0 \\ b \\ -b \end{bmatrix},$$

with b an arbitrary constant. The eigenvector $\mathbf{B}_3$ can be shown to be

$$\mathbf{B}_3 = \begin{bmatrix} -2c \\ c \\ c \end{bmatrix}$$

with c an arbitrary constant.

The general solution of Eq. (23) is

$$\mathbf{p}(n) = \begin{bmatrix} 3a \\ a \\ a \end{bmatrix} + \begin{bmatrix} 0 \\ b \\ -b \end{bmatrix} (\tfrac{1}{3})^n + \begin{bmatrix} -2c \\ c \\ c \end{bmatrix} (-\tfrac{1}{9})^n, \tag{27}$$

so that

$$p_1(n) = 3a - 2c(-\tfrac{1}{9})^n,$$
$$p_2(n) = a + b(\tfrac{1}{3})^n + c(-\tfrac{1}{9})^n, \tag{28}$$
$$p_3(n) = a - b(\tfrac{1}{3})^n + c(-\tfrac{1}{9})^n.$$

If the initial conditions are such that $p_1(1) = 1$, $p_2(1) = 0$, $p_3(1) = 0$, then $a = \tfrac{1}{5}$, $c = \tfrac{9}{5}$, $b = 0$.

PROBLEMS

1. Verify that R of (10) is a rotation matrix by showing that $R^T R = I$.

2. Show that R_2 and R_3 of (19) are the eigenvectors associated with $\lambda_2 = 12$, $\lambda_3 = 2$ of Example (1).

3. Find an orthogonal transformation $\mathbf{X} = R\mathbf{Y}$ which reduces $Q = x^2 + y^2 + z^2 + 2xz + 4\sqrt{2}\,yz$ to canonical form.

4. Show that the eigenvalues of $A\mathbf{X} = \lambda\mathbf{X}$ are real if $A = A^T$ with a_{ij} real, $i, j = 1, 2, \ldots, n$. Hint: assume $\lambda = \lambda_1 + \lambda_2 j$, $\mathbf{X} = \mathbf{X}_1 + \mathbf{X}_2 j$, $j = \sqrt{-1}$, and show that $\lambda_2 = 0$, $\mathbf{X}_2 = 0$.

5. Let $A\mathbf{X}_1 = 0$, $A\mathbf{X}_2 = 0$. Show that $\mathbf{Y} = \alpha\mathbf{X}_1 + \beta\mathbf{X}_2$ satisfies $A\mathbf{Y} = 0$ for arbitrary scalars α, β.

6. If R_1 and R_2 are rotation matrices of order n show that $R_1 R_2$ is a rotation matrix. [Hint: show that $(R_1 R_2)^T = (R_1 R_2)^{-1}$.]

7. If $A\mathbf{X}_1 = \lambda_1 \mathbf{X}_1$, $\lambda_1 \neq 0$, $|A| \neq 0$, show that $A^{-1}\mathbf{X}_1 = 1/\lambda_1 \mathbf{X}_1$.

8. If A and B are positive-definite matrices of order n show that $A + B$ is a positive-definite matrix.

9. Find an example of two matrices A, B of order two which are positive-definite such that AB is not positive-definite.

10. Solve the system of difference equations

$$p_1(n) = \tfrac{1}{2}p_1(n-1) + p_2(n-1) + \tfrac{2}{3}p_3(n-1),$$
$$p_2(n) = \tfrac{1}{6}p_1(n-1), \qquad\qquad\qquad n \geq 1,$$
$$p_3(n) = \tfrac{1}{3}p_1(n-1) \qquad\qquad + \tfrac{1}{3}p_3(n-1),$$

such that $p_1(0) = 0$, $p_2(0) = 1$, $p_3(0) = 0$.

A.10 COORDINATE TRANSFORMATIONS · JACOBIANS

Consider the linear coordinate transformation

$$u = \alpha x + \beta y,$$
$$v = \gamma x + \delta y, \tag{1}$$

with α, β, γ, δ constants. We assume that

$$\Delta = \begin{vmatrix} \alpha & \beta \\ \gamma & \delta \end{vmatrix} > 0, \tag{2}$$

so that one can solve for x and y uniquely in terms of u and v.

We may consider x and y as the coordinates of a point P in a Euclidean space of two dimensions (cartesian coordinates). Every point $P(x, y)$ yields a point $Q(u, v)$ is a new Euclidean space, and conversely (see Fig. 5).

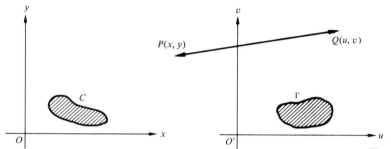

Figure A.5

In particular, the closed curve C will map into the closed curve Γ under the coordinate transformation of (1). We are interested in the relationship between the area enclosed by the curve C and the area enclosed by the curve Γ. It is not difficult to show that straight lines map into straight lines. Note that the straight line $au + bv = c$ becomes

$$a(\alpha x + \beta y) + b(\gamma x + \delta y) = c,$$

or

$$(a\alpha + b\gamma)x + (a\beta + b\delta)y = c,$$

which is a straight line in the xy plane.

Next, consider a rectangle with vertices located at $O(0, 0)$, $B(a, 0)$, $C(a, b)$, $D(0, b)$, which maps into a parallelogram with vertices at O', B', C', D' (see Fig. 6).

From analytic geometry one can show that the area of the parallelogram is $A' = (\alpha\delta - \beta\gamma)A$, with A the area of the rectangle, so that $A' = A\Delta$, with Δ defined in Eq. (2). This result can also be shown to hold for closed polygonal figures. Since any simple closed curve can be approximated by a sequence of polygonal figures, it is not surprising that the area enclosed by the curve Γ is Δ times the area enclosed by the curve C of Fig. 5.

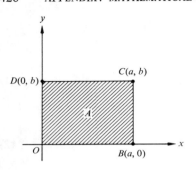
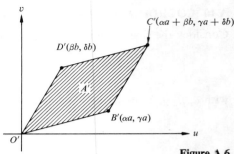

Figure A.6

Let us prove this result by means of the calculus. From Fig. 7 the area enclosed by the simple closed curve C is

$$A = \int_a^b y_2 \, dx - \int_a^b y_1 \, dx$$

$$= - \int_b^a y_2 \, dx - \int_a^b y_1 \, dx$$

$$= - \oint_c y \, dx. \tag{3}$$

The final integral of Eq. (3) is called a line integral, obtained by integrating counterclockwise along the closed curve C.

From Fig. 8 we obtain another representation for the area A, namely

$$A = \int_c^d x_2(y) \, dy - \int_c^d x_1(y) \, dy$$

$$= \int_c^d x_2(y) \, dy + \int_d^c x_1(y) \, dy$$

$$= \oint x \, dy. \tag{4}$$

The line integral, $\oint x \, dy$, is also obtained by integrating counterclockwise along the closed curve C.

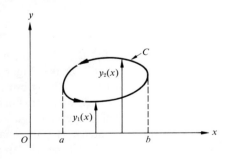

Figure A.7

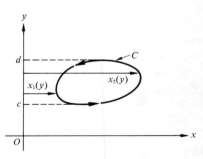

Figure A.8

A simple addition yields the more symmetric result,

$$A = \tfrac{1}{2} \oint (x \, dy - y \, dx). \tag{5}$$

The line integral of (5) is a special case of Green's theorem (vector analysis). It is also the basis for constructing a planimeter, which is a mechanical device used to determine the area enclosed by a simple closed curve.

As an example of Eq. (5), consider an ellipse

$$\frac{x^2}{a^2} + \frac{y^2}{b^2} = 1,$$

which can be written in parametric form as $x = a \cos \theta$, $y = b \sin \theta$, $0 \le \theta \le 2\pi$. Then $dx = -a \sin \theta \, d\theta$, $dy = b \cos \theta \, d\theta$, so that

$$x \, dy - y \, dx = (ab \cos^2 \theta + ab \sin^2 \theta) d\theta$$

$$= abd\theta.$$

Hence the area enclosed by the ellipse is

$$A = \tfrac{1}{2} \int_0^{2\pi} abd\theta = \pi ab.$$

Returning to the linear transformation of (1), the area enclosed by the curve Γ is

$$A' = \tfrac{1}{2} \oint (u \, dv - v \, du). \tag{6}$$

Now, $du = \alpha dx + \beta dy$, $dv = \gamma \, dx + \delta dy$, so that

$$u \, dv - v \, du = (\alpha x + \beta y)(\gamma \, dx + \delta \, dy) - (\gamma x + \delta y)(\alpha \, dx + \beta \, dy)$$

$$= (\alpha\delta - \beta\gamma)(x \, dy - y \, dx), \tag{7}$$

which yields

$$A' = (\alpha\delta - \beta\gamma) \tfrac{1}{2} \oint (x \, dy - y \, dx)$$

$$= (\alpha\delta - \beta\gamma)A = A\Delta, \tag{8}$$

which concludes the proof of our original statement.

Now the Jacobian of the transformation of (1) is defined by the following determinant:

$$J\left(\frac{u, v}{x, y}\right) \equiv \begin{vmatrix} \dfrac{\partial u}{\partial x} & \dfrac{\partial u}{\partial y} \\ \dfrac{\partial v}{\partial x} & \dfrac{\partial v}{\partial y} \end{vmatrix} = \begin{vmatrix} \alpha & \beta \\ \gamma & \delta \end{vmatrix}, \tag{9}$$

so that Eq. (8) becomes

$$A' = \left| J\left(\frac{u, v}{x, y}\right) \right| A. \tag{10}$$

The reason we use the absolute value of the Jacobian is that Δ might be negative, but areas must be non-negative. A negative Jacobian implies that as we move along the curve C in a counterclockwise fashion the corresponding points in the uv plane sweep out the curve Γ in a clockwise fashion, and conversely.

Let us now consider a general transformation

$$
\begin{aligned}
u &= u(x, y), \\
v &= v(x, y).
\end{aligned}
\tag{11}
$$

In advanced calculus texts, it is shown that if the point $P(x_0, y_0)$ maps into the point $Q(u_0, v_0)$, that is, $u_0 = u(x_0, y_0)$, $v_0 = v(x_0, y_0)$, and if the partial derivatives comprising the Jacobian

$$
J\left(\frac{u, v}{x, y}\right) \equiv
\begin{vmatrix}
\dfrac{\partial u}{\partial x} & \dfrac{\partial u}{\partial y} \\[2ex]
\dfrac{\partial v}{\partial x} & \dfrac{\partial v}{\partial y}
\end{vmatrix}
\tag{12}
$$

are continuous, and if, moreover, $J \neq 0$ at $P(x_0, y_0)$, then one can solve for x and y uniquely in terms of u and v, yielding

$$
\begin{aligned}
x &= x(u, v), \\
y &= y(u, v)
\end{aligned}
\tag{13}
$$

for u and v sufficiently close to u_0 and v_0, respectively. Furthermore, $x_0 = x(u_0, v_0)$, $y_0 = y(u_0, v_0)$. This result is known as the implicit function theorem. Let us accept these results. Now in the neighborhood of (x_0, y_0) it follows that

$$
\begin{aligned}
du &= \left(\frac{\partial u}{\partial x}\right)_0 dx + \left(\frac{\partial u}{\partial y}\right)_0 dy, \\[2ex]
dv &= \left(\frac{\partial v}{\partial x}\right)_0 dx + \left(\frac{\partial v}{\partial y}\right)_0 dy,
\end{aligned}
\tag{14}
$$

except for infinitesimals of higher order. The partial derivatives are evaluated at the point $P(x_0, y_0)$.

Now Eq. (14) represents a pair of linear transformations in the differentials. It follows from our previous analysis that any small closed curve, enclosing an area dA in the xy plane containing the point $P(x_0, y_0)$, will map into a small closed curve embracing an area dA' in the uv plane such that

$$
dA' = \left| J\left(\frac{u, v}{x, y}\right)_0 \right| dA,
\tag{15}
$$

except for infinitesimals of higher order.

Equation (15) is a most useful result. It can be extended to three-dimensional transformations involving volumes. Its extension to n dimensions is as follows: Consider the coordinate transformation

$$y^i = y^i(x^1, x^2, \ldots, x^n), \qquad i = 1, 2, \ldots, n, \tag{16}$$

such that all partial derivatives are continuous. If $d\tau = dx^1\,dx^2 \cdots dx^n$ is an element of volume for a Euclidean n-space which maps into an element of volume $d\tau'$, then

$$d\tau' = \left| J\!\left(\frac{y^1, y^2, \ldots, y^n}{x^1, x^2, \ldots, x^n}\right) \right| d\tau, \tag{17}$$

provided $J \neq 0$, with

$$J\!\left(\frac{y}{x}\right) = \begin{vmatrix} \dfrac{\partial y^1}{\partial x^1} & \dfrac{\partial y^1}{\partial x^2} & \cdots & \dfrac{\partial y^1}{\partial x^n} \\[2mm] \dfrac{\partial y^2}{\partial x^1} & \dfrac{\partial y^2}{\partial x^2} & \cdots & \dfrac{\partial y^2}{\partial x^n} \\ \vdots & & & \\ \dfrac{\partial y^n}{\partial x^1} & \dfrac{\partial y^n}{\partial x^2} & \cdots & \dfrac{\partial y^n}{\partial x^n} \end{vmatrix}. \tag{18}$$

From

$$\frac{\partial y^i}{\partial x^\alpha}\frac{\partial x^\alpha}{\partial y^j} = \delta^i_j,$$

it follows that

$$\left| \frac{\partial y^i}{\partial x^\alpha}\frac{\partial x^\alpha}{\partial y^j} \right| = |\delta^i_j| = 1,$$
$$\left| \frac{\partial y^i}{\partial x^j} \right| \cdot \left| \frac{\partial x^i}{\partial y^j} \right| = 1, \tag{19}$$

so that the Jacobian of the y's with respect to the x's is the reciprocal of the Jacobian of the x's with respect to the y's. This, too, is a very useful result.

Example 1. Let $x = r \cos\theta$, $y = r \sin\theta$. Then

$$J\!\left(\frac{x, y}{r, \theta}\right) = \begin{vmatrix} \cos\theta & -r\sin\theta \\ \sin\theta & r\cos\theta \end{vmatrix} = r.$$

Furthermore, $r = (x^2 + y^2)^{1/2}$, $\theta = \tan^{-1} y/x$ except at the origin. Hence

$$J\!\left(\frac{r, \theta}{x, y}\right) = \begin{vmatrix} \dfrac{x}{(x^2 + y^2)^{1/2}} & \dfrac{y}{(x^2 + y^2)^{1/2}} \\[3mm] -\dfrac{y}{x^2 + y^2} & \dfrac{x}{x^2 + y^2} \end{vmatrix}$$

$$= (x^2 + y^2)^{-1/2} = \frac{1}{r}, \qquad r \neq 0,$$

which yields

$$J\left(\frac{x, y}{r, \theta}\right) \cdot J\left(\frac{r, \theta}{x, y}\right) = 1.$$

The element of area, using polar coordinates, is

$$dA = J\left(\frac{x, y}{r, \theta}\right) dr \, d\theta = r \, dr \, d\theta.$$

PROBLEMS

1. Let $x = r \sin \theta \cos \phi$, $y = r \sin \theta \sin \phi$, $z = r \cos \theta$, with (r, θ, ϕ) spherical coordinates. Show that

$$J\left(\frac{x, y, z}{r, \theta, \phi}\right) = r^2 \sin \theta \, .$$

What is the element of volume dV in spherical coordinates?

2. Let $u = x/y$, $v = y$ be a coordinate transformation. What region of the u-v plane will the first quadrant of the x-y plane map into under this transformation. Show that

$$J\left(\frac{u, v}{x, y}\right) = \frac{1}{v} \qquad \text{for} \qquad v \neq 0 \, .$$

3. Let

$$u = \frac{x}{x^2 + y^2}, \qquad v = \frac{-y}{x^2 + y^2}$$

be a coordinate transformation. Show that the circle $x^2 + y^2 = a^2$ maps into the circle $u^2 + v^2 = 1/a^2$. Show that

$$J\left(\frac{u, v}{x, y}\right) = u^2 + v^2 \, .$$

4. Let $u = ln(x + y)$, $v = y^2 - x^2$. Show that

$$J\left(\frac{u, v}{x, y}\right) = 2 \, .$$

5. Let $u = x^2 - y^2$, $v = 2xy$. Show that

$$J\left(\frac{u, v}{x, y}\right) = 4\sqrt{u^2 + v^2} \, .$$

Solve for x^2 and y^2 in terms of u, v. Into what curves do the hyperbolas $x^2 - y^2 = a$ and $2xy = b$ map?

A.11 THE DIRAC DELTA FUNCTION ·
ELEMENTARY DIFFERENTIAL EQUATIONS

Consider the family of curves defined by

$$f_a(t) = \frac{1}{a^2}[a - |t|], \qquad -a \le t \le a, \quad a > 0$$

$$= 0 \qquad\qquad \text{otherwise.} \tag{1}$$

A typical member of this family of curves is shown in Fig. 9. We note that for all $a > 0$,

$$\int_{-\infty}^{\infty} f_a(t)\, dt = 1, \tag{2}$$

so that

$$\lim_{a \to 0} \int_{-\infty}^{\infty} f_a(t)\, dt = 1, \tag{3}$$

since the limit of a sequence of ones is unity.

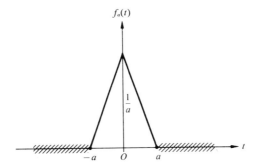

Figure A.9

Now for $t \ne 0$, we note that $\lim_{a \to 0} f_a(t) = 0$, since the bases of the triangles tend to zero. Moreover,

$$\lim_{a \to 0} f_a(0) = \lim_{\substack{a \to 0 \\ a > 0}} 1/a = \infty,$$

so that

$$\lim_{a \to 0} f_a(t) = 0 \qquad \text{for} \qquad t \ne 0,$$

$$\lim_{a \to 0} f_a(0) = \infty. \tag{4}$$

From a mathematical point of view, a function which vanishes everywhere except at $t = 0$ and is infinite at $t = 0$, cannot be integrated in the usual sense. This did not deter the famous English quantum physicist, P. A. M. Dirac, from defining a function, $\delta(t)$, called the Dirac δ (delta) function,* with the property that $\delta(t) = 0$

---

* Do not confuse the Dirac δ-function with the Kronecker δ_j^i.

for $t \neq 0$ such that

$$\int_{-\infty}^{\infty} \delta(t) \, dt = 1. \tag{5}$$

In a more general sense, the function $\delta(t - \tau)$ possesses the property that $\delta(t - \tau) = 0$ for $t \neq \tau$, such that

$$\int_{-\infty}^{\infty} \delta(t - \tau) \, dt = 1. \tag{6}$$

We may imagine that at $t = \tau$ a spike occurs as regards the function $\delta(t - \tau)$, and the area underneath this spike is unity. We also choose $\delta(t - \tau) = \delta(\tau - t)$, so that δ is an even function in the neighborhood of $t = \tau$. Let us examine the following integral:

$$\int_{-\infty}^{\infty} f(\tau) \, \delta(t - \tau) \, d\tau, \tag{7}$$

with $f(\tau)$ continuous at $\tau = t$ (a fixed parameter for the moment). Whenever the variable of integration τ is less than t, the value of $\delta(t - \tau)$ is zero, so that there is no contribution to the value of the integral. However, in the neighborhood of the spike ($\tau = t$) we have $f(\tau) \approx f(t)$ since $f(\tau)$ is assumed to be continuous at $\tau = t$. As we integrate over the τ-interval containing the spike, $f(\tau)$ essentially remains constant, and from Eq. (6) we obtain the value $f(t)$ as a contribution to the integral. For $\tau > t$ we have $\delta(t - \tau) = 0$, so again there is no contribution to the value of the integral. Thus we obtain

$$\int_{-\infty}^{\infty} f(\tau) \, \delta(t - \tau) \, d\tau = f(t) \tag{8}$$

whenever $f(\tau)$ is continuous at $\tau = t$. It can be shown (L. Schwarz) that one may safely apply the Dirac δ function when used in its proper context given by Eq. (8).

The graph of the unit step function $U(t - t_0)$ defined by

$$U(t - t_0) = \int_{-\infty}^{t} \delta(t_0 - \tau) \, d\tau \tag{9}$$

is shown in Fig. 10. Thus,

$$U(t - t_0) = 0 \qquad \text{for} \qquad t < t_0,$$
$$ = 1 \qquad \text{for} \qquad t \geq t_0. \tag{10}$$

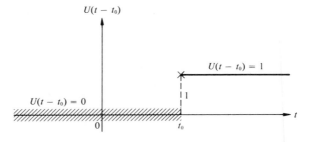

Figure A.10

One may consider the delta function, $\delta(t - t_0)$, as the derivative of the unit step function, $U(t - t_0)$. Note that $U'(t - t_0) = 0$ for $t \neq t_0$. Of course, in the strict sense, $U(t - t_0)$ is not differentiable at $t = t_0$.

The derivative of the δ function possesses the property that $\delta'(t) = -\delta'(-t)$, and has meaning only when an integration is carried out over its argument. Thus, quite formally, we have, on integrating by parts,

$$\int_{-\infty}^{\infty} f(\tau)\, \delta'(\tau - t)\, d\tau = f(\tau)\, \delta(\tau - t)\Big|_{-\infty}^{\infty} - \int f'(\tau)\, \delta(\tau - t)\, d\tau$$
$$= -f'(t), \tag{11}$$

whenever $f'(\tau)$ is continuous at $\tau = t$.

Example 1.

$$\int_{-\infty}^{\infty} \sin \tau\, \delta(\tau - \pi/2)\, d\tau = \sin \pi/2 = 1,$$

$$\int_{-\infty}^{\infty} \sin \tau\, \delta'(\tau - \pi)\, d\tau = -\cos \pi = 1,$$

$$\int_{-\infty}^{\infty} e^\tau\, \delta(2\tau)\, d\tau = \int_{-\infty}^{\infty} e^{w/2}\, \delta(w)\, (dw/2) = \tfrac{1}{2}.$$

To evaluate

$$\int_{-\infty}^{\infty} f(t)\, \delta(t^2 - 4)\, dt,$$

we note that an impulse occurs at $t = \pm 2$. In the neighborhood of $t = -2$ we have $t^2 - 4 = (t - 2)(t + 2) \approx -4(t + 2)$. Let $w = -4(t + 2)$, $dt = -dw/4$, so that the contribution to the integral at $t = -2$ is

$$\int_{\infty}^{-\infty} f\left(-\frac{w}{4} - 2\right) \delta(w) \left(-\frac{dw}{4}\right) = \frac{1}{4} f(-2).$$

Similarly, the contribution of the impulse at $t = +2$ to the integral is $\tfrac{1}{4} f(2)$. Thus, in general,

$$\int_{-\infty}^{\infty} f(t)\, \delta(t^2 - a^2)\, dt = \frac{1}{2|a|} [f(a) + f(-a)], \tag{12}$$

and $\delta(t^2 - a^2)$ may be represented by

$$\delta(t^2 - a^2) = \frac{1}{2|a|} [\delta(t - a) + \delta(t + a)].$$

The Gaussian function of Chapter 4, namely

$$p(x - y) = \frac{1}{\sqrt{2\pi}\sigma} \exp\left[-\frac{1}{2\sigma^2}(x - y)^2\right], \qquad \sigma > 0, \tag{14}$$

has the property that

$$\int_{-\infty}^{\infty} p(x)\, dx = 1$$

for $\sigma > 0$ and arbitrary y. We observe that for $x \neq y$, $\lim_{\sigma \to 0} p(x - y) = 0$, whereas $\lim_{\sigma \to 0} p(0) = \infty$.

Let the reader show that

$$\int_{-\infty}^{\infty} \exp(ax)\, p(x - y)\, dx$$

$$= \exp\left[a(y + \sigma^2/2)\right] \frac{1}{\sqrt{2\pi}\sigma} \int_{-\infty}^{\infty} \exp\left[-\frac{1}{2\sigma^2}(x - y + a\sigma^2)^2\right] dx$$

$$= \exp\left[a(y + \sigma^2/2)\right]. \tag{15}$$

As $\sigma \to 0$ ($\sigma > 0$), we obtain

$$\lim_{\sigma \to 0} \int_{-\infty}^{\infty} e^{ax}\, p(x - y)\, dx = e^{ay} = \int_{-\infty}^{\infty} e^{ax}\, \delta(x - y)\, dx, \tag{15}$$

so that $\lim_{\sigma \to 0} p(x - y)$ behaves like $\delta(x - y)$ in connection with the integral of (16).

Let us now consider the differential equation

$$\frac{d^2x}{dt^2} + \omega^2 x = 0, \tag{17}$$

with ω a positive constant. We assume a solution in the form $x = Ae^{\lambda t}$, with A and λ constants. Thus $\ddot{x} = A\lambda^2 e^{\lambda t}$, which yields

$$Ae^{\lambda t}(\lambda^2 + \omega^2) = 0, \tag{18}$$

if $x = Ae^{\lambda t}$ is to be a solution of $\ddot{x} + \omega^2 x = 0$.

A nontrivial solution ($x(t) \not\equiv 0$) occurs if

$$\lambda^2 + \omega^2 = 0, \tag{19}$$

called the characteristic equation. The eigenvalues are $\lambda = \pm \omega j$, which yields the two solutions $x_1(t) = A_1 e^{\omega j t}$ and $x_2(t) = A_2 e^{-\omega j t}$. Since $\ddot{x} + \omega^2 x = 0$ is linear in x, it follows that

$$x(t) = A_1 e^{\omega j t} + A_2 e^{-\omega j t} \tag{20}$$

is a general solution of $\ddot{x} + \omega^2 x = 0$, with A_1 and A_2 arbitrary constants of integration. Since

$$e^{\omega j t} = \cos(\omega t) + j \sin(\omega t),$$

$$e^{-\omega j t} = \cos(\omega t) - j \sin(\omega t),$$

it follows that

$$x(t) = (A_1 + A_2) \cos \omega t + j(A_1 - A_2) \sin \omega t$$

$$= A \cos \omega t + B \sin \omega t \tag{21}$$

is the general solution of $\ddot{x} + \omega^2 x = 0$, with A and B arbitrary constants of integration.

Of more general interest is the inhomogeneous equation

$$\frac{d^2x}{dt^2} + \omega^2 x = f(t), \tag{22}$$

with $f(t) = 0$ for $t < 0$, $x(t) = 0$ for $t < 0$. We call $f(t)$ the forcing or driving function. We will assume that $f(t)$ is continuous for $t > 0$. Now

$$f(t) = \int_{-\infty}^{\infty} \delta(t - \tau) f(\tau)\, d\tau, \tag{23}$$

so that

$$\frac{d^2 x}{dt^2} + \omega^2 x = \int_{-\infty}^{\infty} \delta(t - \tau) f(\tau)\, d\tau. \tag{24}$$

Equation (24) suggests that we look for a solution of the form

$$x(t) = \int_{-\infty}^{\infty} h(t - \tau) f(\tau)\, d\tau, \tag{25}$$

with $h(t)$ unknown at present. Quite formally we have

$$\frac{dx}{dt} = \int_{-\infty}^{\infty} h'(t - \tau) f(\tau)\, d\tau,$$

$$\frac{d^2 x}{dt^2} = \int_{-\infty}^{\infty} h''(t - \tau) f(\tau)\, d\tau, \tag{26}$$

where the differentiation is with respect to the argument $t - \tau$. Substituting into (24) yields

$$\int_{-\infty}^{\infty} [h''(t - \tau) + \omega^2 h(t - \tau)]\, f(\tau)\, d\tau = \int_{-\infty}^{\infty} \delta(t - \tau) f(\tau)\, d\tau, \tag{27}$$

which suggests that

$$h''(t) + \omega^2 h(t) = \delta(t), \tag{28}$$

with $h(t) = 0$ for $t < 0$. Now Eq. (28) is exactly of the same form as Eq. (22). The driving function is the unit impulse, $\delta(t)$, which occurs at $t = 0$.

Integrating Eq. (28) from $t = 0-$ to $t = 0+$, yields

$$\int_{0-}^{0+} h''(t)\, dt + \omega^2 \int_{0-}^{0+} h(t)\, dt = \int_{0-}^{0+} \delta(t)\, dt = 1,$$

$$h'(0+) - h'(0-) + \omega^2 \int_{0-}^{0+} h(t)\, dt = 1. \tag{29}$$

Now $h'(0-) = 0$ since $h(t) = 0$ for $t < 0$. The value of

$$\int_{0-}^{0+} h(t)\, dt$$

must be negligible, so that $h'(0+) = 1$. Immediately after the impulse, we have $\delta(t) = 0$, so we need only solve

$$h''(t) + \omega^2 h(t) = 0$$

with the new initial conditions $h(0) = 0$, $h'(0) = 1$. From Eq. (21) we have

$$h(t) = A \cos \omega t + B \sin \omega t,$$

$$h'(t) = -A\omega \sin \omega t + B\omega \cos \omega t. \tag{30}$$

From the initial conditions we obtain $A = 0$, $B\omega = 1$, so that

$$h(t) = 1/\omega \sin \omega t, \qquad t \geq 0$$
$$= 0, \qquad\qquad t < 0. \tag{31}$$

We call $h(t)$ the *response* of the system to a unit impulse (at $t = 0$). The graphs of $h(t)$ versus t and $h(t - \tau)$ versus τ are shown in Fig. 11.

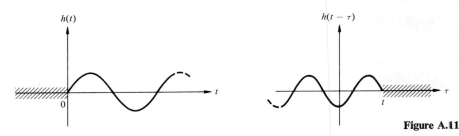

Figure A.11

Since $h(t - \tau) = 0$ for $\tau > t$ and $f(\tau) = 0$ for $\tau < 0$, it follows from Eq. (25) that

$$x(t) = \int_0^t h(t - \tau) f(\tau) \, d\tau. \tag{32}$$

Hence we hope that

$$x(t) = \frac{1}{\omega} \int_0^t \sin [\omega(t - \tau)] f(\tau) \, d\tau \tag{33}$$

is a solution of our original equation $\ddot{x} + \omega^2 x = f(t)$.

It is known from the calculus that if

$$x(t) = \int_0^t h(t, \tau) f(\tau) \, d\tau, \tag{34}$$

then

$$\frac{dx}{dt} = h(t, t) f(t) + \int_0^t \frac{\partial h(t, \tau)}{\partial t} f(\tau) \, d\tau. \tag{35}$$

Applying this result to $x(t)$ of Eq. (33) yields

$$\frac{dx}{dt} = \int_0^t \cos [\omega(t - \tau)] f(\tau) \, d\tau,$$

$$\frac{d^2 x}{dt^2} = f(t) - \omega \int_0^t \sin [\omega(t - \tau)] f(\tau) \, d\tau$$

$$= f(t) - \omega^2 x, \tag{36}$$

so that $\ddot{x} + \omega^2 x = f(t)$. The general solution of $\ddot{x} + \omega^2 x = f(t)$, $t \geq 0$, is

$$x(t) = A \cos \omega t + B \sin \omega t + \frac{1}{\omega} \int_0^t \sin [\omega(t - \tau)] f(\tau) \, d\tau, \tag{37}$$

with A and B constants which can be determined from the initial conditions $x(0) = x_0$, $\dot{x}(0) = \dot{x}_0$.

Consider the general linear nth order differential equation with constant coefficients,

$$\frac{d^n x}{dt^n} + a_1 \frac{d^{n-1} x}{dt^{n-1}} + \cdots + a_n x = f(t), \tag{38}$$

with $f(t) = 0$ for $t < 0$.

The response of the system to a unit impulse is obtained by solving the homogeneous equation

$$\frac{d^n h(t)}{dt^n} + a_1 \frac{d^{n-1} h(t)}{dt^{n-1}} + \cdots + a_n h(t) = 0,$$

subject to the initial conditions

$$
\begin{aligned}
h(0) &= 0, \\
\dot{h}(0) &= 0, \\
\ddot{h}(0) &= 0, \\
&\;\;\vdots \\
h^{(n-2)}(0) &= 0, \\
h^{(n-1)}(0) &= \left. \frac{d^{n-1} h(t)}{dt^{n-1}} \right|_{t=0} = 1,
\end{aligned}
\tag{39}
$$

with $h(t) = 0$ for $t < 0$. A particular solution of Eq. (38) is

$$x(t) = \int_0^t h(t - \tau) f(\tau) \, d\tau. \tag{40}$$

The general solution of Eq. (38) is the sum of the homogeneous solution ($f(t) = 0$) of Eq. (38), involving n arbitrary constants of integration and the particular solution given by Eq. (40).

Example 2. Let us determine the most general solution of $\dddot{x} - \dot{x} = f(t)$, $f(t) = 0$ for $t < 0$. The general solution of the homogeneous equation $\dddot{h} - \dot{h} = 0$ is $h(t) = a + be^t + ce^{-t}$, obtained by setting $h(t) = e^{\lambda t}$, which yields $\lambda^3 - \lambda = 0$, or $\lambda = 0, 1, -1$. To determine the response function we set $h(0) = 0$, $\dot{h}(0) = 0$, $\ddot{h}(0) = 1$. This yields

$$
\begin{aligned}
a + b + c &= 0 & b &= \tfrac{1}{2}, \\
b - c &= 0 \Rightarrow c = \tfrac{1}{2}, \\
b + c &= 1 & a &= -1,
\end{aligned}
$$

so that

$$h(t) = -1 + \tfrac{1}{2}e^t + \tfrac{1}{2}e^{-t} = -1 + \cosh t.$$

Thus

$$x(t) = A + Be^t + Ce^{-t} + \int_0^t f(\tau)\,[-1 + \cosh(t - \tau)]\,d\tau \tag{41}$$

is the most general solution of $\dddot{x} - \dot{x} = f(t)$ for $t \geq 0$.

Example 3. Let us first solve the equation $\ddot{h} - 2\dot{h} + h = 0$ subject to the initial conditions $h(0) = 0$, $\dot{h}(0) = 1$. Setting $h(t) = e^{\lambda t}$ yields $\lambda^2 - 2\lambda + 1 = 0$, or $\lambda = 1, 1$. Thus $h(t) = ae^t + be^t = ce^t$ is a solution of $\ddot{h} - 2\dot{h} + h = 0$, and $h(t)$ involves only one constant of integration. Let us now apply the variation of parameter method. Consider $h(t) = c(t)e^t$, so that $\dot{h} = e^t(\dot{c} + c)$, $\ddot{h} = e^t(\ddot{c} + 2\dot{c} + c)$, which yields

$$e^t[\ddot{c} + 2\dot{c} + c - 2\dot{c} - 2c + c] = e^t\ddot{c} = 0,$$

in order that $\ddot{h} - 2\dot{h} + h = 0$. Hence $\ddot{c} = 0$, and $c = \alpha + \beta t$. Thus $h(t) = (\alpha + \beta t)e^t$ involves two arbitrary constants α, β. The condition $h(0) = 0$ yields $\alpha = 0$, and the condition $\dot{h}(0) = 1$ yields $\beta = 1$, so that $h(t) = te^t$ is the response of the system to a unit impulse.

The general solution of $\ddot{x} - 2\dot{x} + x = f(t)$ is

$$x(t) = (A + Bt)\,e^t + \int_0^t f(\tau)\,(t - \tau)\,e^{t-\tau}\,d\tau \qquad (42)$$

for $t \geq 0$. In particular, for $f(t) = 2e^t$, we obtain

$$x(t) = (A + Bt)\,e^t + \int_0^t 2e^\tau (t - \tau)\,e^{t-\tau}\,d\tau$$

$$= (A + Bt)\,e^t + 2e^t \int_0^t (t - \tau)\,d\tau$$

$$= (A + Bt)\,e^t + t^2\,e^t$$

for $t \geq 0$.

If the characteristic equation associated with the differential equation ($a_i =$ constant, $i = 1, 2, \ldots, n$)

$$\frac{d^n x}{dt^n} + a_1 \frac{d^{n-1}x}{dt^{n-1}} + a^2 \frac{d^{n-2}x}{dt^{n-1}} + \cdots + a_n x = 0, \qquad (43)$$

namely

$$\lambda^n + a_1 \lambda^{n-1} + a_2 \lambda^{n-2} + \cdots + a_n = 0, \qquad (44)$$

has n different roots $\lambda_1, \lambda_2, \ldots, \lambda_n$, then

$$x(t) = A_1 \exp(\lambda_1 t) + A_2 \exp(\lambda_2 t) + \cdots + A_n \exp(\lambda_n t) \qquad (45)$$

is the general solution of the differential equation of (43).

A special solution is

$$x(t) = \frac{\exp(\lambda_1 t) - \exp(\lambda_2 t)}{\lambda_1 - \lambda_2}, \qquad \lambda_1 \neq \lambda_2. \qquad (46)$$

If $\lambda_2 \to \lambda_1$, then

$$x_1(t) \to t \exp(\lambda_1 t) = \frac{\partial}{\partial \lambda_1}[\exp(\lambda_1 t)],$$

so from heuristic reasoning we may expect that $t \exp(\lambda_1 t)$ is a solution of (43) if λ_1

is a double root of (44). It can be shown that if λ_1 is a multiple root of order k of Eq. (44), then

$$\exp(\lambda_1 t), \ t \exp(\lambda_1 t), \ t^2 \exp(\lambda_1 t), \ \ldots, \ t^{k-1} \exp(\lambda_1 t)$$

are solutions of (43).

For example, the characteristic polynomial associated with

$$\frac{d^5 x}{dt^5} + \frac{d^4 x}{dt^4} - 2\frac{d^3 x}{dt^3} - 2\frac{d^2 x}{dt^2} + \frac{dx}{dt} + x = 0 \tag{47}$$

is

$$\lambda^5 + \lambda^4 - 2\lambda^3 - 2\lambda^2 + \lambda + 1 = (\lambda + 1)^3 (\lambda - 1)^2 = 0,$$

so that $\lambda = 1$ is a double root and $\lambda = -1$ is a triple root. The general solution of (47) is

$$x(t) = (a + bt) e^t + (c + dt + et^2) e^{-t}. \tag{48}$$

PROBLEMS

1. Evaluate

$$\int_{-\infty}^{\infty} \delta(x - 1)e^x \, dx, \qquad \int_{-\infty}^{\infty} \delta(y + 2) (y^3 - y) \, dy,$$

$$\int_{-\infty}^{\infty} \delta'(t - 1) \sin(\pi t) \, dt, \qquad \int_{-\infty}^{\infty} e^{itx} \delta(t) \, dt.$$

2. Show that

$$\int_{-\infty}^{\infty} \delta''(t - \tau) f(t) \, dt = f''(\tau),$$

provided $f''(t)$ is continuous at $t = \tau$.

3. Show that

$$\int_{-\infty}^{\infty} \int_{-\infty}^{\infty} \delta(x - y) \, \delta(y - z) f(x, y) \, dy \, dx = f(z, z),$$

provided $f(x, y)$ is continuous.

4. For $a \neq b$ show that

$$\int_{-\infty}^{\infty} \delta[(t - a) (t - b)] f(t) \, dt = \frac{1}{|b - a|} [f(a) + f(b)],$$

if $f(t)$ is continuous at $t = a, b$.

5. Let $f_a(x) = ae^{-ax}$ for $x \geq 0$, $f_a(x) = 0$ for $x < 0$, with $a > 0$. Show that

$$\int_{-\infty}^{\infty} f_a(x) \, dx = 1, \qquad \lim_{a \to \infty} f_a(x) = 0 \qquad \text{for} \qquad x \neq 0,$$

$$\lim_{a \to \infty} f_a(0) = \infty.$$

Next, show that

$$\lim_{a \to \infty} \int_{-\infty}^{\infty} f_a(x - y) e^{bx} \, dx = e^{by}.$$

6. Graph the unit step functions $U(t - 3)$, $U(t + 2)$, versus t.

7. Graph

$$f_1(t) = U(t) + U(t - 1),$$
$$f_2(t) = U(t - a) - U(t - b), \quad b > a,$$
$$f_3(t) = U(t) + U(t - 1),$$
$$f_4(t) = U(t) - 2U(t - 1) + U(t - 2).$$

8. Show by means of the response function that a solution of $\ddot{x} + x = 1$ is $x(t) = 1 - \cos t$, $t \geq 0$.

9. Find the general solution of $\ddot{x} + x = \sin t$, $t \geq 0$.

10. Find the general solution of $\dddot{x} - 3\ddot{x} + 3\dot{x} - x = 6e^t$, $t \geq 0$.

11. Consider the linear system of differential equations $dX/dt + AX = F(t)$, $A = A^T$. Let $X = RY$, R a constant matrix, $|R| \neq 0$. Show that

$$\frac{dY}{dt} + R^{-1} ARY = R^{-1} F(t).$$

Next, consider the system

$$\frac{d}{dt} \begin{bmatrix} x \\ y \end{bmatrix} + \begin{bmatrix} 1 & -1 \\ -1 & 1 \end{bmatrix} \cdot \begin{bmatrix} x \\ y \end{bmatrix} = \begin{bmatrix} 1 \\ t \end{bmatrix}.$$

Find an orthogonal matrix such that $R^{-1} AR$ is a diagonal matrix. Then set

$$\begin{bmatrix} x \\ y \end{bmatrix} = R \cdot \begin{bmatrix} u \\ v \end{bmatrix}$$

and solve for $u(t)$, $v(t)$, and $x(t)$, $y(t)$.

A.12 TAYLOR SERIES · EXTREMA · LAGRANGE MULTIPLIERS

Let us consider a real valued function $f(x)$ which has a continuous second derivative for all x in a neighborhood of $x = a$, that is, for all x such that $|x - a| \leq K$. For this region we have

$$\int_a^x f''(x) \, dx = f'(x) - f'(a),$$

$$\int_a^x dx \int_a^x f''(x) \, dx = \int_a^x f'(x) \, dx - f'(a) \int_a^x dx \tag{1}$$

$$= f(x) - f(a) - f'(a) (x - a),$$

so that

$$f(x) = f(a) + f'(a) (x - a) + \int_a^x dx \int_a^x f''(x) \, dx. \tag{2}$$

The same result applies if $f''(x)$ is Riemann-integrable for the region $|x - a| \leq K$. Next let us assume that $f'''(x)$ is continuous for $|x - a| \leq K$. Then

$$\int_a^x f'''(x) \, dx = f''(x) - f''(a),$$

$$\int_a^x dx \int_a^x dx \int_a^x f'''(x) \, dx = f(x) - f(a) - f'(a) (x - a) - \frac{f''(a) (x - a)^2}{2!} \tag{3}$$

by applying the result of (1). If the nth derivative of $f(x)$ is Riemann-integrable it is a simple matter to show that

$$f(x) = f(a) + f'(a)(x - a) + \frac{f''(a)}{2!}(x - a)^2 + \cdots + \frac{f^{(n-1)}(a)(x - a)^{n-1}}{(n - 1)!} + R_n,$$

(4)

with

$$R_n = \int_a^x dx \int_a^x \cdots \int_a^x f^{(n)}(x)\, dx.$$

(5)

The integral involving R_n is an nth fold integral, and we call R_n the remainder after n terms.

Now suppose that a constant M exists such that

$$|f^{(n)}(x)| < M$$

(6)

for $|x - a| \leq K$, and for all integers n. Then

$$|R_n| \leq \left| \int_a^x dx \int_a^x \cdots \int_a^x M\, dx \right| = \frac{M|x - a|^n}{n!} \leq \frac{MK^n}{n!}$$

(7)

for all n. From elementary calculus it is known that the series

$$\sum_0^\infty \frac{K^n}{n!}$$

converges for any fixed constant K (ratio test), so that

$$\lim_{n \to \infty} \frac{K^n}{n!} = 0.$$

The reader is urged to derive this result from elementary principles. Thus, as $n \to \infty$, we conclude that $R_n \to 0$, and the infinite series obtained from Eq. (4) by letting $n \to \infty$ must converge to $f(x)$.

Under the conditions specified above we obtain the important Taylor series expansion of $f(x)$, given by

$$f(x) = f(a) + f'(a)(x - a) + \frac{f''(a)}{2!}(x - a)^2 + \cdots$$

$$+ \frac{f^{(n)}(a)}{n!}(x - a)^n + \cdots = \sum_{n=0}^\infty \frac{f^{(n)}(a)}{n!}(x - a)^n.$$

(8)

This is the Taylor series expansion of $f(x)$ about the point $x = a$. The special case $a = 0$ yields the Maclaurin series.

$$f(x) = \sum_{n=0}^\infty \frac{f^{(n)}(0)}{n!} x^n.$$

(9)

It must be emphasized that the series' expansions above can only be applied when $f(x)$ has derivatives of all orders and the remainder R_n can be shown to approach zero as $n \to \infty$.

Example 1. Let $f(x) = \sin x$, so that $f'(x) = \cos x$, $f''(x) = -\sin x$, $f'''(x) = -\cos x$, $f^{(iv)}(x) = \sin x$, etc. Thus $|f^{(n)}(x)| \le 1$ for all n and all values of x. From $f(0) = 0$, $f'(0) = 1$, $f''(0) = 0$, $f'''(0) = -1$, $f^{(iv)}(0) = 0$, etc., the Maclaurin expansion of Eq. (9) yields

$$\sin x = x - \frac{x^3}{3!} + \frac{x^5}{5!} - \frac{x^7}{7!} + \cdots = \sum_{n=0}^{\infty} (-1)^n \frac{x^{2n+1}}{(2n+1)!}, \tag{10}$$

which converges to $\sin x$ for all real values of x.

Let the reader deduce that

$$\cos x = 1 - \frac{x^2}{2!} + \frac{x^4}{4!} - \frac{x^6}{6!} + \cdots = \sum_{n=0}^{\infty} (-1)^n \frac{x^{2n}}{(2n)!}, \tag{11}$$

and that

$$e^x = \sum_{n=0}^{\infty} \frac{x^n}{n!},$$

$$\frac{1}{1-x} = \sum_{n=0}^{\infty} x^n, \qquad |x| < 1, \tag{12}$$

$$ln(1-x) = -\sum_{n=0}^{\infty} \frac{x^{n+1}}{n+1}, \qquad |x| < 1.$$

We choose

$$e^z \equiv \sum_{n=0}^{\infty} \frac{z^n}{n!}$$

as the definition of the exponential function for complex z. Let the reader deduce that

$$e^{j\theta} = \cos \theta + j \sin \theta, \tag{13}$$

with $j = \sqrt{-1}$. From Euler's formula we have

$$e^{-j\theta} = \cos \theta - j \sin \theta,$$

so that

$$\cos \theta = \frac{e^{j\theta} + e^{-j\theta}}{2},$$

$$\sin \theta = \frac{e^{j\theta} - e^{-j\theta}}{2j}. \tag{14}$$

Furthermore,

$$(e^{j\theta})^n = e^{j(n\theta)} = \cos n\theta + j \sin n\theta,$$

$$(\cos \theta + j \sin \theta)^n = \cos n\theta + j \sin n\theta \tag{15}$$

for all integers n. Equation (15) is DeMoivre's formula. Thus for $n = 2$ we obtain

$$(\cos \theta + j \sin \theta)^2 = \cos^2 \theta - \sin^2 \theta + 2j \sin \theta \cos \theta$$

$$= \cos 2\theta + j \sin 2\theta,$$

so that

$$\cos 2\theta = \cos^2 \theta - \sin^2 \theta,$$

$$\sin 2\theta = 2 \sin \theta \cos \theta.$$

There are several alternative forms of the Taylor series expansion of Eq. (8). If we replace x by $a + h$ we obtain

$$f(a + h) = f(a) + f'(a)h + f''(a)\frac{h^2}{2!} + f'''(a)\frac{h^3}{3!} + \cdots \tag{16}$$

Now set $a = x$, so that

$$f(x + h) = f(x) + f'(x)h + f''(x)\frac{h^2}{2!} + f'''(x)\frac{h^3}{3!} + \cdots \tag{17}$$

Next consider a function of two variables, say $f(x, y)$. Let $\phi(t) = f(x + ht, y + kt)$, with x, y, h, k fixed for the moment, t a variable. Let us assume that $\phi(t)$ has a Maclaurin series expansion about $t = 0$ which converges for $|t| \le 1$. Then $\phi(0) = f(x, y)$,

$$\left(\frac{d\phi}{dt}\right)_{t=0} = \frac{\partial f}{\partial x} h + \frac{\partial f}{\partial y} k,$$

$$\left(\frac{d^2\phi}{dt^2}\right)_{t=0} = \frac{\partial^2 f}{\partial x^2} h^2 + 2 \frac{\partial^2 f}{\partial x \partial y} hk + \frac{\partial^2 f}{\partial y^2} k^2, \tag{18}$$

$$\vdots$$

so that

$$\phi(t) = \phi(0) + \phi'(0)t + \phi''(0)\frac{t^2}{2!} + \cdots, \tag{19}$$

$$\phi(1) = \phi(0) + \phi'(0) + \frac{\phi''(0)}{2!} + \cdots,$$

which yields

$$f(x + h, y + k) = f(x, y) + \left(\frac{\partial f}{\partial x} h + \frac{\partial f}{\partial y} k\right)$$

$$+ \frac{1}{2!}\left(\frac{\partial^2 f}{\partial x^2} h^2 + 2 \frac{\partial^2 f}{\partial x \partial y} hk + \frac{\partial^2 f}{\partial y^2} k^2\right)$$

$$+ \cdots \tag{20}$$

as the extension of (17) to a function of two variables.

Let us now turn to the problem of determining at what points a function $f(x)$ has a minimum or a maximum (extremal), locally. One says that $f(x)$ has an extremum at the point $x = c$ if an $\eta > 0$ exists such that $f(c + h) - f(c)$ has the same sign for $|h| < \eta$. If $f(c + h) \geq f(c)$ for $|h| < \eta$, we say that $f(x)$ has a local minimum at $x = c$, and if $f(d + h) \leq f(d)$ for $|h| < \eta$, we say that $f(x)$ has a local maximum at $x = d$ (see Fig. 12).

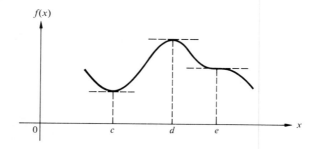

Figure A.12

If $f(c)$ is a local minimum and if $f'(c)$ exists, then

$$f'(c) = \lim_{\substack{h \to 0 \\ h > 0}} \frac{f(c + h) - f(c)}{h} \geq 0$$

$$= \lim_{\substack{h \to 0 \\ h > 0}} \frac{f(c) - f(c - h)}{h} \leq 0, \tag{21}$$

so of necessity, $f'(c) = 0$. A similar remark applies if $f(d)$ is a local maximum. Hence, a necessary condition that $f(x)$ be an extremal for $x = c$ is that $f'(c) = 0$. In Fig. 12, $f'(e) = 0$, but $f(x)$ is not an extremal at $x = e$.

Now assume that $f'(c) = 0$, and apply Eq. (2) with a replaced by c, assuming also that $f''(x)$ is continuous in a neighborhood of $x = c$. Thus

$$f(x) = f(c) + \int_c^x \int_c^x f''(x)\, dx. \tag{22}$$

If $f''(c) > 0$, then for x sufficiently close to c, the double integral of (22) will be nonnegative, and $f(x) \geq f(c)$ for all x close to c. Hence $f(x)$ has a local minimum at $x = c$. Similarly, if $f''(c) < 0$, then $f(x)$ has a local maximum at $x = c$. These are familiar results of the elementary calculus.

If $f'(c) = f''(c) = 0$ one must investigate the higher derivatives of $f(x)$. It can be shown that a necessary and sufficient condition for $f(x)$ to have an extremal value at $x = c$ is that $f'(c) = 0$ and that the first nonvanishing derivative of $f(x)$ at $x = c$ be of even order. Furthermore, if $f^{(2n)}(c) > 0$, a minimum occurs, and if $f^{(2n)}(c) < 0$, a maximum occurs.

From Eq. (20) it follows that if $x = a$, $y = b$ makes $f(x, y)$ an extremal, then

$f(a + h, b + k) - f(a, b)$ will be one-signed, provided $\partial f/\partial x = 0$, $\partial f/\partial y = 0$, when evaluated at $x = a$, $y = b$, and if

$$\frac{\partial^2 f}{\partial x^2} h^2 + 2 \frac{\partial^2 f}{\partial x \partial y} hk + \frac{\partial^2 f}{\partial y^2} k^2 \tag{23}$$

is one-signed for all h and k sufficiently small; the partial derivatives are evaluated at $x = a$, $y = b$. Let $\alpha = f_{xx}$, $\beta = f_{xy}$, $\gamma = f_{yy}$, $h/k = \xi$, so that

$$z = \alpha \xi^2 + 2 \beta \xi + \gamma \tag{24}$$

must be one-signed. Since (24) represents a parabola in the ξz plane we cannot have two distinct real roots of $z = 0$, for otherwise z would be both positive and negative for real values of $\xi = h/k$. Now the roots of $z = 0$ are

$$z_{1, 2} = -\beta \pm \sqrt{\beta^2 - \alpha \gamma}, \tag{25}$$

so, of necessity, $\beta^2 \le \alpha \gamma$. Thus an extremal of $f(x, y)$ will occur at $x = a$, $y = b$, if

$$\frac{\partial f}{\partial x} = 0$$
$$\frac{\partial f}{\partial y} = 0 \tag{26}$$

and

$$\left(\frac{\partial^2 f}{\partial x \partial y} \right)^2 - \frac{\partial^2 f}{\partial x^2} \frac{\partial^2 f}{\partial y^2} < 0. \tag{27}$$

If $f_{xx} > 0$ or $f_{yy} > 0$, a minimum occurs, and if $f_{xx} < 0$ or $f_{yy} < 0$, a maximum occurs.

Example 2. Let us find the values of x, y for which $f(x, y) = xy - x^2 y - xy^2$ is an extremal. From

$$\frac{\partial f}{\partial x} = y - 2xy - y^2 = y(1 - 2x - y) = 0,$$

$$\frac{\partial f}{\partial y} = x - x^2 - 2xy = x(1 - x - 2y) = 0,$$

we note that $(x = 0, y = 0)$, $(x = 1, \ y = 0)$, $(x = 0, y = 1)$, $(x = \frac{1}{3}, y = \frac{1}{3})$, yield $f_x = f_y = 0$, for which $f(x, y) = 0, 0, 0, \frac{1}{27}$, respectively. Now $f_{xy} = 1 - 2x - 2y$, $f_{xx} = -2y$, $f_{yy} = -2x$. The inequality of (27) is satisfied only for $x = y = \frac{1}{3}$. Since $f_{xx} < 0$ at $x = y = \frac{1}{3}$, it follows that $f(x, y)$ has a local maximum. It should be clear that $f(x, y) = xy - x^2 y - xy^2$ can be made as large as you please by considering large negative values of x and y.

The Method of Lagrange Multipliers. Suppose we wish to find x, y such that $z = f(x, y)$ is an extremal subject to the constraint $\phi(x, y) = \text{constant} = a$. If we can solve for y in terms of x, say $y = \psi(x)$, from the constraint equation $\phi(x, y) = a$, then $z = f(x, \psi(x)) = g(x)$. Thus we need only set $dz/dx = dg/dx = 0$, solve for $x = x_0$, and determine $y_0 = \psi(x_0)$. In many cases, however, it is difficult to obtain y explicitly in terms of x. The constraint equation yields

$$\frac{\partial \phi}{\partial x} + \frac{\partial \phi}{\partial y} \frac{dy}{dx} = 0, \tag{28}$$

and

$$\frac{dz}{dx} = \frac{\partial f}{\partial x} + \frac{\partial f}{\partial y} \frac{dy}{dx} \overset{\text{set}}{=} 0 \tag{29}$$

for an extremal.

Eliminating dy/dx, provided $\partial \phi / \partial y \neq 0$, yields

$$\frac{\partial f}{\partial x} + \frac{\partial f}{\partial y} \left(-\frac{\dfrac{\partial \phi}{\partial x}}{\dfrac{\partial \phi}{\partial y}} \right) = 0. \tag{30}$$

If we define $\lambda = - (f_y/\phi_y)$, we obtain the pair of equations

$$\frac{\partial f}{\partial x} + \lambda \frac{\partial \phi}{\partial x} = 0,$$

$$\frac{\partial f}{\partial y} + \lambda \frac{\partial \phi}{\partial y} = 0, \tag{31}$$

subject to the constraint $\phi(x, y) = a$. In principle we can solve these equations for $x = x_0, y = y_0, \lambda = \lambda_0$.

Lagrange noted that (31) could be obtained by considering the new function $W = f(x, y) + \lambda \phi(x, y)$, with λ an arbitrary parameter. We now treat x and y as if they are independent variables. To find an extremal of W we set $W_x = 0$, $W_y = 0$, which yields the pair of equations of (31). The parameter λ is called a Lagrange multiplier.

The parameter λ has a geometric significance. Let us suppose that $\phi(x, y) = a$ is a simple closed curve with a continuous varying slope. Although $z = f(x, y)$ is a surface in the x-y-z space, for any fixed value of z, say $z = z_0$, $f(x, y) = z_0$ is a curve in the x-y space. As z_0 varies, we obtain a family of curves. It is evident from Fig. 13 that $z = f(x, y)$ will be an extremal subject to the constraint $\phi(x, y) = a$ when the curve $f(x, y) = z_0$ is tangent to the curve $\phi(x, y) = a$.

At the point P, the vectors normal to the curves are parallel. From vector analysis this implies that the gradient of f, namely ∇f, is parallel to the gradient of ϕ, say $\nabla \phi$. Thus $\nabla f = - \lambda \nabla \phi$, or

$$\frac{\partial f}{\partial x} \mathbf{i} + \frac{\partial f}{\partial y} \mathbf{j} = - \lambda \left[\frac{\partial \phi}{\partial x} \mathbf{i} + \frac{\partial \phi}{\partial y} \mathbf{j} \right],$$

which is equivalent to the pair of equations of (31).

More generally, if $y = f(x_1, x_2, \ldots, x_n)$ is to be extremalized subject to the conditions $\phi_i(x_1, x_2, \ldots, x_n) = c_i$, $i = 1, 2, \ldots, m$, $m < n$, we form

$$W = f(x_1, x_2, \ldots, x_n) + \sum_{i=1}^{m} \lambda_i \phi_i(x_1, x_2, \ldots, x_n) \tag{32}$$

and set

$$\frac{\partial W}{\partial x_j} = \frac{\partial f}{\partial x_j} + \sum_{i=1}^{m} \lambda_i \frac{\partial \phi_i}{\partial x_j} = 0, \qquad j = 1, 2, \ldots, n. \tag{33}$$

The introduction of the Lagrange multipliers, $\lambda_1, \lambda_2, \ldots, \lambda_m$ enables one to consider $x_1, x_2, \ldots, x_n$ as independent variables. Equation (33) along with the constraints $\phi_i(x_1, x_2, \ldots, x_n) = c_i$ yield $(n + m)$ equations for $x_1, x_2, \ldots, x_n$, $\lambda_1, \lambda_2, \ldots, \lambda_m$. It is hoped that these values yield an extremal for $y = f(x_1, x_2, \ldots, x_n)$. The actual test that y is a local minimum or maximum is a matter for advanced calculus texts.

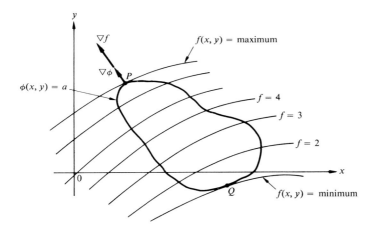

Figure A.13

Example 3. We wish to find the ratio of altitude to radius of a cylindrical glass (open top) having a maximum volume for a fixed surface area. We have

$$V = \pi x^2 y, \qquad S = 2\pi xy + \pi x^2 = \text{constant}.$$

Set $W = \pi x^2 y + \lambda(2\pi xy + \pi x^2)$, so that

$$\frac{\partial W}{\partial x} = 2\pi[xy + \lambda(y + x)] = 0,$$

$$\frac{\partial W}{\partial y} = \pi[x^2 + 2x\lambda] = 0.$$

Eliminating λ yields

$$\frac{xy}{x^2} = \frac{y + x}{2x}, \qquad \text{or} \qquad \frac{y}{x} = 1,$$

since $x \neq 0$.

It should be clear that had we desired to minimize the surface area for a fixed volume we would have considered

$$U = 2\pi xy + \pi x^2 + \lambda \pi x^2 y,$$

and $U_x = U_y = 0$ would have yielded

$$\frac{y}{x} = 1 \qquad (\lambda \to 1/\lambda).$$

PROBLEMS

1. Derive the result of Eq. (11).
2. Derive the results of Eq. (12).
3. Derive Euler's formula of Eq. (13).
4. From DeMoivre's formula show that

$$\cos 3\theta = \cos^3 \theta - 3 \cos \theta \sin^2 \theta,$$

$$\sin 3\theta = 3 \cos^2 \theta \sin \theta - \sin^3 \theta,$$

$$\cos 4\theta = \cos^4 \theta - 6 \cos^2 \theta \sin^2 \theta + \sin^4 \theta,$$

$$\sin 4\theta = 4 \cos^3 \theta \sin \theta - 4 \cos \theta \sin^3 \theta.$$

5. From

$$\frac{1}{x(x - 1)} = \frac{1}{x} + \frac{1}{1 - x},$$

show that

$$\frac{1}{x(x - 1)} = \frac{1}{x} + \sum_{n=0}^{\infty} x^n \qquad \text{for} \qquad 0 < |x| < 1.$$

6. Show that the ratio of altitude to diameter is unity for a cylindrical can having maximum volume for a fixed surface area.

7. Consider a cylindrical buoy with two conical ends. Let x be the radius of the cylinder, y the altitude of the cylinder, and z the altitude of the cones. Show that $x:y:z = \sqrt{5}/2 : 1 : 1$ yields a maximum volume for a fixed surface area.

8. Find the maximum distance from the origin to the curve $x^3 + y^3 - 3xy = 0$.

9. We wish to maximize

$$H = -\sum_{i=1}^{n} p_i \ln p_i$$

subject to the constraint

$$\sum_{i=1}^{n} p_i = 1, \qquad p_i \geq 0, i = 1, 2, \ldots, n.$$

By the method of Lagrange multipliers show that $p_1 = p_2 = \ldots = p_n = 1/n$.

10. For Problem 9 an additional constraint is imposed, namely

$$\sum_{i=1}^{n} p_i t_i = T = \text{constant},$$

with $t_1, t_2, \ldots, t_n$ fixed positive constants. Show that

$$p_j = Ae^{-\mu t_j}, \qquad j = 1, 2, \ldots, n$$

yields an extremal value for H, with A and μ constants which can be obtained from the two constraints.

APPENDIX B

Normal distribution:
values of $F(x)$ for the indicated values of x.

$$F(x) = \int_{-\infty}^{x} \frac{1}{\sqrt{2\pi}} e^{-t^2/2} \, dt$$

x	.00	.01	.02	.03	.04	.05	.06	.07	.08	.09
.0	.5000	.5040	.5080	.5120	.5160	.5199	.5239	.5279	.5319	.5359
.1	.5398	.5438	.5478	.5517	.5557	.5596	.5636	.5675	.5714	.5753
.2	.5793	.5832	.5871	.5910	.5948	.5987	.6026	.6064	.6103	.6141
.3	.6179	.6217	.6255	.6293	.6331	.6368	.6406	.6443	.6480	.6517
.4	.6554	.6591	.6628	.6664	.6700	.6736	.6772	.6808	.6844	.6879
.5	.6915	.6950	.6985	.7019	.7054	.7088	.7123	.7157	.7190	.7224
.6	.7257	.7291	.7324	.7357	.7389	.7422	.7454	.7486	.7517	.7549
.7	.7580	.7611	.7642	.7673	.7704	.7734	.7764	.7794	.7823	.7852
.8	.7881	.7910	.7939	.7967	.7995	.8023	.8051	.8078	.8106	.8133
.9	.8159	.8186	.8212	.8238	.8264	.8289	.8315	.8340	.8365	.8389
1.0	.8413	.8438	.8461	.8485	.8508	.8531	.8554	.8577	.8599	.8621
1.1	.8643	.8665	.8686	.8708	.8729	.8749	.8770	.8790	.8810	.8830
1.2	.8849	.8869	.8888	.8907	.8925	.8944	.8962	.8980	.8997	.9015
1.3	.9032	.9049	.9066	.9082	.9099	.9115	.9131	.9147	.9162	.9177
1.4	.9192	.9207	.9222	.9236	.9251	.9265	.9279	.9292	.9306	.9319
1.5	.9332	.9345	.9357	.9370	.9382	.9394	.9406	.9418	.9429	.9441
1.6	.9452	.9463	.9474	.9484	.9495	.9505	.9515	.9525	.9535	.9545
1.7	.9554	.9564	.9573	.9582	.9591	.9599	.9608	.9616	.9625	.9633
1.8	.9641	.9649	.9656	.9664	.9671	.9678	.9686	.9693	.9699	.9706
1.9	.9713	.9719	.9726	.9732	.9738	.9744	.9750	.9756	.9761	.9767
2.0	.9772	.9778	.9783	.9788	.9793	.9798	.9803	.9808	.9812	.9817
2.1	.9821	.9826	.9830	.9834	.9838	.9842	.9846	.9850	.9854	.9857
2.2	.9861	.9864	.9868	.9871	.9875	.9878	.9881	.9884	.9887	.9890
2.3	.9893	.9896	.9898	.9901	.9904	.9906	.9909	.9911	.9913	.9916
2.4	.9918	.9920	.9922	.9925	.9927	.9929	.9931	.9932	.9934	.9936
2.5	.9938	.9940	.9941	.9943	.9945	.9946	.9948	.9949	.9951	.9952
2.6	.9953	.9955	.9956	.9957	.9959	.9960	.9961	.9962	.9963	.9964
2.7	.9965	.9966	.9967	.9968	.9969	.9970	.9971	.9972	.9973	.9974
2.8	.9974	.9975	.9976	.9977	.9977	.9978	.9979	.9979	.9980	.9981
2.9	.9981	.9982	.9982	.9983	.9984	.9984	.9985	.9985	.9986	.9986

From Introduction to *Theory of Statistics* by Mood and Graybill. Copyright © 1956 by McGraw-Hill, Inc. Used with permission of McGraw-Hill Book Company.

For larger values of x it is more convenient to use $1 - F(x)$. The following tabulation of $1 - F(x)$ is given to four significant figures followed by the power of 10.

	.0	.2	.4	.6	.8
3.0	.1350–2	.6871–3	.3369–3	.1591–3	.7235–4
4.0	.3167–4	.1335–4	.5413–5	.2112–5	.7933–6
5.0	.2867–6	.9964–7	.3332–7	.1072–7	.3316–8

Chi-square distribution: values of *u* for indicated C_n and *n*.

$$C_n(u) = \int_0^u \frac{x^{(n-2)/2}e^{-x/2}}{2^{n/2}\Gamma(n/2)}\,dx$$

C_n → n ↓	.995	.990	.975	.950	.900	.750	.500	.250	.100	.050	.025	.010	.005
1	7.88	6.63	5.02	3.84	2.71	1.32	.455	.102	.0158	$.0^2393$	$.0^3982$	$.0^3157$	$.0^4393$
2	10.6	9.21	7.38	5.99	4.61	2.77	1.39	.575	.211	.103	.0506	.0201	.0100
3	12.8	11.3	9.35	7.81	6.25	4.11	2.37	1.21	.584	.352	.216	.115	.0717
4	14.9	13.3	11.1	9.49	7.78	5.39	3.36	1.92	1.06	.711	.484	.297	.207
5	16.7	15.1	12.8	11.1	9.24	6.63	4.35	2.67	1.61	1.15	.831	.554	.412
6	18.5	16.8	14.4	12.6	10.6	7.84	5.35	3.45	2.20	1.64	1.24	.872	.676
7	20.3	18.5	16.0	14.1	12.0	9.04	6.35	4.25	2.83	2.17	1.69	1.24	.989
8	22.0	20.1	17.5	15.5	13.4	10.2	7.34	5.07	3.49	2.73	2.18	1.65	1.34
9	23.6	21.7	19.0	16.9	14.7	11.4	8.34	5.90	4.17	3.33	2.70	2.09	1.73
10	25.2	23.2	20.5	18.3	16.0	12.5	9.34	6.74	4.87	3.94	3.25	2.56	2.16
11	26.8	24.7	21.9	19.7	17.3	13.7	10.3	7.58	5.58	4.57	3.82	3.05	2.60
12	28.3	26.2	23.3	21.0	18.5	14.8	11.3	8.44	6.30	5.23	4.40	3.57	3.07
13	29.8	27.7	24.7	22.4	19.8	16.0	12.3	9.30	7.04	5.89	5.01	4.11	3.57
14	31.3	29.1	26.1	23.7	21.1	17.1	13.3	10.2	7.79	6.57	5.63	4.66	4.07
15	32.8	30.6	27.5	25.0	22.3	18.2	14.3	11.0	8.55	7.26	6.26	5.23	4.60
16	34.3	32.0	28.8	26.3	23.5	19.4	15.3	11.9	9.31	7.96	6.91	5.81	5.14
17	35.7	33.4	30.2	27.6	24.8	20.5	16.3	12.8	10.1	8.67	7.56	6.41	5.70
18	37.2	34.8	31.5	28.9	26.0	21.6	17.3	13.7	10.9	9.39	8.23	7.01	6.26
19	38.6	36.2	32.9	30.1	27.2	22.7	18.3	14.6	11.7	10.1	8.91	7.63	6.84
20	40.0	37.6	34.2	31.4	28.4	23.8	19.3	15.5	12.4	10.9	9.59	8.26	7.43
21	41.4	38.9	35.5	32.7	29.6	24.9	20.3	16.3	13.2	11.6	10.3	8.90	8.03
22	42.8	40.3	36.8	33.9	30.8	26.0	21.3	17.2	14.0	12.3	11.0	9.54	8.64
23	44.2	41.6	38.1	35.2	32.0	27.1	22.3	18.1	14.8	13.1	11.7	10.2	9.26
24	45.6	43.0	39.4	36.4	33.2	28.2	23.3	19.0	15.7	13.8	12.4	10.9	9.89
25	46.9	44.3	40.6	37.7	34.4	29.3	24.3	19.9	16.5	14.6	13.1	11.5	10.5
26	48.3	45.6	41.9	38.9	35.6	30.4	25.3	20.8	17.3	15.4	13.8	12.2	11.2
27	49.6	47.0	43.2	40.1	36.7	31.5	26.3	21.7	18.1	16.2	14.6	12.9	11.8
28	51.0	48.3	44.5	41.3	37.9	32.6	27.3	22.7	18.9	16.9	15.3	13.6	12.5
29	52.3	49.6	45.7	42.6	39.1	33.7	28.3	23.6	19.8	17.7	16.0	14.3	13.1
30	53.7	50.9	47.0	43.8	40.3	34.8	29.3	24.5	20.6	18.5	16.8	15.0	13.8

"Student's" distribution: values of u for indicated values of G_n and n.

$$G_n(u) = \int_{-\infty}^{t} \frac{\Gamma\left(\dfrac{n+1}{2}\right)}{\sqrt{\pi n}\ \Gamma(n/2)\left(1 + \dfrac{x^2}{n}\right)^{(n+1)/2}}\, dx$$

n \\ G_n	.75	.90	.95	.975	.99	.995	.9995
1	1.000	3.078	6.314	12.706	31.821	63.657	636.619
2	.816	1.886	2.920	4.303	6.965	9.925	31.598
3	.765	1.638	2.353	3.182	4.541	5.841	12.941
4	.741	1.533	2.132	2.776	3.747	4.604	8.610
5	.727	1.476	2.015	2.571	3.365	4.032	6.859
6	.718	1.440	1.943	2.447	3.143	3.707	5.959
7	.711	1.415	1.895	2.365	2.998	3.499	5.405
8	.706	1.397	1.860	2.306	2.896	3.355	5.041
9	.703	1.383	1.833	2.262	2.821	3.250	4.781
10	.700	1.372	1.812	2.228	2.764	3.169	4.587
11	.697	1.363	1.796	2.201	2.718	3.106	4.437
12	.695	1.356	1.782	2.179	2.681	3.055	4.318
13	.694	1.350	1.771	2.160	2.650	3.012	4.221
14	.692	1.345	1.761	2.145	2.624	2.977	4.140
15	.691	1.341	1.753	2.131	2.602	2.947	4.073
16	.690	1.337	1.746	2.120	2.583	2.921	4.015
17	.689	1.333	1.740	2.110	2.567	2.898	3.965
18	.688	1.330	1.734	2.101	2.552	2.878	3.922
19	.688	1.328	1.729	2.093	2.539	2.861	3.883
20	.687	1.325	1.725	2.086	2.528	2.845	3.850
21	.686	1.323	1.721	2.080	2.518	2.831	3.819
22	.686	1.321	1.717	2.074	2.508	2.819	3.792
23	.685	1.319	1.714	2.069	2.500	2.807	3.767
24	.685	1.318	1.711	2.064	2.492	2.797	3.745
25	.684	1.316	1.708	2.060	2.485	2.787	3.725
26	.684	1.315	1.706	2.056	2.479	2.779	3.707
27	.684	1.314	1.703	2.052	2.473	2.771	3.690
28	.683	1.313	1.701	2.048	2.467	2.763	3.674
29	.683	1.311	1.699	2.045	2.462	2.756	3.659
30	.683	1.310	1.697	2.042	2.457	2.750	3.646
40	.681	1.303	1.684	2.021	2.423	2.704	3.551
60	.679	1.296	1.671	2.000	2.390	2.660	3.460
120	.677	1.289	1.658	1.980	2.358	2.617	3.373
∞	.674	1.282	1.645	1.960	2.326	2.576	3.291

From *Statistical Tables for Biological, Agricultural, and Medical Research* by Fisher and Yates, published by Oliver & Boyd, Edinburgh, by permission of the authors and publishers.

F distribution: values of F for indicated values of $\mathcal{F}_{m,n}$ and m,n.

m degrees of freedom in numerator; n in denominator

$$\mathcal{F}_{m,n}(F) = \int_0^F \frac{\Gamma[(m+n)/2]m^{m/2}n^{n/2}x^{(m-2)/2}(n+mx)^{-(m+n)/2}}{\Gamma(m/2)\Gamma(n/2)}\,dx$$

n	$\mathcal{F}$	1	2	3	4	5	6	7	8	9	10	12	15	20	30	60	120	∞
1	.90	39.9	49.5	53.6	55.8	57.2	58.2	58.9	59.4	59.9	60.2	60.7	61.2	61.7	62.3	62.8	63.1	63.3
	.95	161	200	216	225	230	234	237	239	241	242	244	246	248	250	252	253	254
	.975	648	800	864	900	922	937	948	957	963	969	977	985	993	1000	1010	1010	1020
	.99	4,050	5,000	5,400	5,620	5,760	5,860	5,930	5,980	6,020	6,060	6,110	6,160	6,210	6,260	6,310	6,340	6,370
	.995	16,200	20,000	21,600	22,500	23,100	23,400	23,700	23,900	24,100	24,200	24,400	24,600	24,800	25,000	25,200	25,400	25,500
2	.90	8.53	9.00	9.16	9.24	9.29	9.33	9.35	9.37	9.38	9.39	9.41	9.42	9.44	9.46	9.47	9.48	9.49
	.95	18.5	19.0	19.2	19.2	19.3	19.3	19.4	19.4	19.4	19.4	19.4	19.4	19.5	19.5	19.5	19.5	19.5
	.975	38.5	39.0	39.2	39.2	39.3	39.3	39.4	39.4	39.4	39.4	39.4	39.4	39.4	39.5	39.5	39.5	39.5
	.99	98.5	99.0	99.2	99.2	99.3	99.3	99.4	99.4	99.4	99.4	99.4	99.4	99.4	99.5	99.5	99.5	99.5
	.995	199	199	199	199	199	199	199	199	199	199	199	199	199	199	199	199	199
3	.90	5.54	5.46	5.39	5.34	5.31	5.28	5.27	5.25	5.24	5.23	5.22	5.20	5.18	5.17	5.15	5.14	5.13
	.95	10.1	9.55	9.28	9.12	9.01	8.94	8.89	8.85	8.81	8.79	8.74	8.70	8.66	8.62	8.57	8.55	8.53
	.975	17.4	16.0	15.4	15.1	14.9	14.7	14.6	14.5	14.5	14.4	14.3	14.3	14.2	14.1	14.0	13.9	13.9
	.99	34.1	30.8	29.5	28.7	28.2	27.9	27.7	27.5	27.3	27.2	27.1	26.9	26.7	26.5	26.3	26.2	26.1
	.995	55.6	49.8	47.5	46.2	45.4	44.8	44.4	44.1	43.9	43.7	43.4	43.1	42.8	42.5	42.1	42.0	41.8
4	.90	4.54	4.32	4.19	4.11	4.05	4.01	3.98	3.95	3.93	3.92	3.90	3.87	3.84	3.82	3.79	3.78	3.76
	.95	7.71	6.94	6.59	6.39	6.26	6.16	6.09	6.04	6.00	5.96	5.91	5.86	5.80	5.75	5.69	5.66	5.63
	.975	12.2	10.6	9.98	9.60	9.36	9.20	9.07	8.98	8.90	8.84	8.75	8.66	8.56	8.46	8.36	8.31	8.26
	.99	21.2	18.0	16.7	16.0	15.5	15.2	15.0	14.8	14.7	14.5	14.4	14.2	14.0	13.8	13.7	13.6	13.5
	.995	31.3	26.3	24.3	23.2	22.5	22.0	21.6	21.4	21.1	21.0	20.7	20.4	20.2	19.9	19.6	19.5	19.3
5	.90	4.06	3.78	3.62	3.52	3.45	3.40	3.37	3.34	3.32	3.30	3.27	3.24	3.21	3.17	3.14	3.12	3.11
	.95	6.61	5.79	5.41	5.19	5.05	4.95	4.88	4.82	4.77	4.74	4.68	4.62	4.56	4.50	4.43	4.40	4.37
	.975	10.0	8.43	7.76	7.39	7.15	6.98	6.85	6.76	6.68	6.62	6.52	6.43	6.33	6.23	6.12	6.07	6.02
	.99	16.3	13.3	12.1	11.4	11.0	10.7	10.5	10.3	10.2	10.1	9.89	9.72	9.55	9.38	9.20	9.11	9.02
	.995	22.8	18.3	16.5	15.6	14.9	14.5	14.2	14.0	13.8	13.6	13.4	13.1	12.9	12.7	12.4	12.3	12.1
	.90	3.78	3.46	3.29	3.18	3.11	3.05	3.01	2.98	2.96	2.94	2.90	2.87	2.84	2.80	2.76	2.74	2.72
	.95	5.99	5.14	4.76	4.53	4.39	4.28	4.21	4.15	4.10	4.06	4.00	3.94	3.87	3.81	3.74	3.70	3.67

6	.975	4.85	4.90	4.96	5.07	5.17	5.27	5.37	5.46	5.52	5.60	5.70	5.82	5.99	6.23	6.60	7.26	8.81
	.99	6.88	6.97	7.06	7.23	7.40	7.56	7.72	7.87	7.98	8.10	8.26	8.47	8.75	9.15	9.78	10.9	13.7
	.995	8.88	9.00	9.12	9.36	9.59	9.81	10.0	10.2	10.4	10.6	10.8	11.1	11.5	12.0	12.9	14.5	18.6
7	.90	2.47	2.49	2.51	2.56	2.59	2.63	2.67	2.70	2.72	2.75	2.78	2.83	2.88	2.96	3.07	3.26	3.59
	.95	3.23	3.27	3.30	3.38	3.44	3.51	3.57	3.64	3.68	3.73	3.79	3.87	3.97	4.12	4.35	4.74	5.59
	.975	4.14	4.20	4.25	4.36	4.47	4.57	4.67	4.76	4.82	4.90	4.99	5.12	5.29	5.52	5.89	6.54	8.07
	.99	5.65	5.74	5.82	5.99	6.16	6.31	6.47	6.62	6.72	6.84	6.99	7.19	7.46	7.85	8.45	9.55	12.2
	.995	7.08	7.19	7.31	7.53	7.75	7.97	8.18	8.38	8.51	8.68	8.89	9.16	9.52	10.1	10.9	12.4	16.2
8	.90	2.29	2.31	2.34	2.38	2.42	2.46	2.50	2.54	2.56	2.59	2.62	2.67	2.73	2.81	2.92	3.11	3.46
	.95	2.93	2.97	3.01	3.08	3.15	3.22	3.28	3.35	3.39	3.44	3.50	3.58	3.69	3.84	4.07	4.46	5.32
	.975	3.67	3.73	3.78	3.89	4.00	4.10	4.20	4.30	4.36	4.43	4.53	4.65	4.82	5.05	5.42	6.06	7.57
	.99	4.86	4.95	5.03	5.20	5.36	5.52	5.67	5.81	5.91	6.03	6.18	6.37	6.63	7.01	7.59	8.65	11.3
	.995	5.95	6.06	6.18	6.40	6.61	6.81	7.01	7.21	7.34	7.50	7.69	7.95	8.30	8.81	9.60	11.0	14.7
9	.90	2.16	2.18	2.21	2.25	2.30	2.34	2.38	2.42	2.44	2.47	2.51	2.55	2.61	2.69	2.81	3.01	3.36
	.95	2.71	2.75	2.79	2.86	2.94	3.01	3.07	3.14	3.18	3.23	3.29	3.37	3.48	3.63	3.86	4.26	5.12
	.975	3.33	3.39	3.45	3.56	3.67	3.77	3.87	3.96	4.03	4.10	4.20	4.32	4.48	4.72	5.08	5.71	7.21
	.99	4.31	4.40	4.48	4.65	4.81	4.96	5.11	5.26	5.35	5.47	5.61	5.80	6.06	6.42	6.99	8.02	10.6
	.995	5.19	5.30	5.41	5.62	5.83	6.03	6.23	6.42	6.54	6.69	6.88	7.13	7.47	7.96	8.72	10.1	13.6
10	.90	2.06	2.08	2.11	2.15	2.20	2.24	2.28	2.32	2.35	2.38	2.41	2.46	2.52	2.61	2.73	2.92	3.29
	.95	2.54	2.58	2.62	2.70	2.77	2.84	2.91	2.98	3.02	3.07	3.14	3.22	3.33	3.48	3.71	4.10	4.96
	.975	3.08	3.14	3.20	3.31	3.42	3.52	3.62	3.72	3.78	3.85	3.95	4.07	4.24	4.47	4.83	5.46	6.94
	.99	3.91	4.00	4.08	4.25	4.41	4.56	4.71	4.85	4.94	5.06	5.20	5.39	5.64	5.99	6.55	7.56	10.0
	.995	4.64	4.75	4.86	5.07	5.27	5.47	5.66	5.85	5.97	6.12	6.30	6.54	6.87	7.34	8.08	9.43	12.8
12	.90	1.90	1.93	1.96	2.01	2.06	2.10	2.15	2.19	2.21	2.24	2.28	2.33	2.39	2.48	2.61	2.81	3.18
	.95	2.30	2.34	2.38	2.47	2.54	2.62	2.69	2.75	2.80	2.85	2.91	3.00	3.11	3.26	3.49	3.89	4.75
	.975	2.72	2.79	2.85	2.96	3.07	3.18	3.28	3.37	3.44	3.51	3.61	3.73	3.89	4.12	4.47	5.10	6.55
	.99	3.36	3.45	3.54	3.70	3.86	4.01	4.16	4.30	4.39	4.50	4.64	4.82	5.06	5.41	5.95	6.93	9.33
	.995	3.90	4.01	4.12	4.33	4.53	4.72	4.91	5.09	5.20	5.35	5.52	5.76	6.07	6.52	7.23	8.51	11.8
15	.90	1.76	1.79	1.82	1.87	1.92	1.97	2.02	2.06	2.09	2.12	2.16	2.21	2.27	2.36	2.49	2.70	3.07
	.95	2.07	2.11	2.16	2.25	2.33	2.40	2.48	2.54	2.59	2.64	2.71	2.79	2.90	3.06	3.29	3.68	4.54
	.975	2.40	2.46	2.52	2.64	2.76	2.86	2.96	3.06	3.12	3.20	3.29	3.41	3.58	3.80	4.15	4.77	6.20
	.99	2.87	2.96	3.05	3.21	3.37	3.52	3.67	3.80	3.89	4.00	4.14	4.32	4.56	4.89	5.42	6.36	8.68
	.995	3.26	3.37	3.48	3.69	3.88	4.07	4.25	4.42	4.54	4.67	4.85	5.07	5.37	5.80	6.48	7.70	10.8

F distribution: values of F for indicated values of $\mathscr{F}_{m,n}$ and m,n.

m degrees of freedom in numerator: n in denominator

$$\mathscr{F}_{m,n}(F) = \int_0^F \frac{\Gamma[(m+n)/2]m^{m/2}n^{n/2}x^{(m-2)/2}(n+mx)^{-(m+n)/2}}{\Gamma(m/2)\Gamma(n/2)}\,dx$$

n	$\mathscr{F}$	1	2	3	4	5	6	7	8	9	10	12	15	20	30	60	120	∞
20	.90	2.97	2.59	2.38	2.25	2.16	2.09	2.04	2.00	1.96	1.94	1.89	1.84	1.79	1.74	1.68	1.64	1.61
	.95	4.35	3.49	3.10	2.87	2.71	2.60	2.51	2.45	2.39	2.35	2.28	2.20	2.12	2.04	1.95	1.90	1.84
	.975	5.87	4.46	3.86	3.51	3.29	3.13	3.01	2.91	2.84	2.77	2.68	2.57	2.46	2.35	2.22	2.16	2.09
	.99	8.10	5.85	4.94	4.43	4.10	3.87	3.70	3.56	3.46	3.37	3.23	3.09	2.94	2.78	2.61	2.52	2.42
	.995	9.94	6.99	5.82	5.17	4.76	4.47	4.26	4.09	3.96	3.85	3.68	3.50	3.32	3.12	2.92	2.81	2.69
30	.90	2.88	2.49	2.28	2.14	2.05	1.98	1.93	1.88	1.85	1.82	1.77	1.72	1.67	1.61	1.54	1.50	1.46
	.95	4.17	3.32	2.92	2.69	2.53	2.42	2.33	2.27	2.21	2.16	2.09	2.01	1.93	1.84	1.74	1.68	1.62
	.975	5.57	4.18	3.59	3.25	3.03	2.87	2.75	2.65	2.57	2.51	2.41	2.31	2.20	2.07	1.94	1.87	1.79
	.99	7.56	5.39	4.51	4.02	3.70	3.47	3.30	3.17	3.07	2.98	2.84	2.70	2.55	2.39	2.21	2.11	2.01
	.995	9.18	6.35	5.24	4.62	4.23	3.95	3.74	3.58	3.45	3.34	3.18	3.01	2.82	2.63	2.42	2.30	2.18
60	.90	2.79	2.39	2.18	2.04	1.95	1.87	1.82	1.77	1.74	1.71	1.66	1.60	1.54	1.48	1.40	1.35	1.29
	.95	4.00	3.15	2.76	2.53	2.37	2.25	2.17	2.10	2.04	1.99	1.92	1.84	1.75	1.65	1.53	1.47	1.39
	.975	5.29	3.93	3.34	3.01	2.79	2.63	2.51	2.41	2.33	2.27	2.17	2.06	1.94	1.82	1.67	1.58	1.48
	.99	7.08	4.98	4.13	3.65	3.34	3.12	2.95	2.82	2.72	2.63	2.50	2.35	2.20	2.03	1.84	1.73	1.60
	.995	8.49	5.80	4.73	4.14	3.76	3.49	3.29	3.13	3.01	2.90	2.74	2.57	2.39	2.19	1.96	1.83	1.69
120	.90	2.75	2.35	2.13	1.99	1.90	1.82	1.77	1.72	1.68	1.65	1.60	1.54	1.48	1.41	1.32	1.26	1.19
	.95	3.92	3.07	2.68	2.45	2.29	2.18	2.09	2.02	1.96	1.91	1.83	1.75	1.66	1.55	1.43	1.35	1.25
	.975	5.15	3.80	3.23	2.89	2.67	2.52	2.39	2.30	2.22	2.16	2.05	1.94	1.82	1.69	1.53	1.43	1.31
	.99	6.85	4.79	3.95	3.48	3.17	2.96	2.79	2.66	2.56	2.47	2.34	2.19	2.03	1.86	1.66	1.53	1.38
	.995	8.18	5.54	4.50	3.92	3.55	3.28	3.09	2.93	2.81	2.71	2.54	2.37	2.19	1.98	1.75	1.61	1.43
∞	.90	2.71	2.30	2.08	1.94	1.85	1.77	1.72	1.67	1.63	1.60	1.55	1.49	1.42	1.34	1.24	1.17	1.00
	.95	3.84	3.00	2.60	2.37	2.21	2.10	2.01	1.94	1.88	1.83	1.75	1.67	1.57	1.46	1.32	1.22	1.00
	.975	5.02	3.69	3.12	2.79	2.57	2.41	2.29	2.19	2.11	2.05	1.94	1.83	1.71	1.57	1.39	1.27	1.00
	.99	6.63	4.61	3.78	3.32	3.02	2.80	2.64	2.51	2.41	2.32	2.18	2.04	1.88	1.70	1.47	1.32	1.00
	.995	7.88	5.30	4.28	3.72	3.35	3.09	2.90	2.74	2.62	2.52	2.36	2.19	2.00	1.79	1.53	1.36	1.00

ANSWERS TO SELECTED PROBLEMS

Chapter 1

Pages 9–11

2. a) $AB' + A'B$ b) A c) $AC + BC$

3. a) True   b) False unless $C \supset AB$ c) True
   d) False unless $B' \supset A$ e) True   f) True
   g) True   h) True

6. a) ABC' b) ABC c) $A + B + C$
   d) $AB + BC + CA$ e) $A'B' + B'C' + C'A'$ f) $AB'C' + BA'C' + CA'B'$
   g) $A'B'C'$ h) $ABC' + ACB' + BCA'$ i) $A' + B' + C'$

9. a) C b) $A'B$ c) S

14. No

Chapter 2

Pages 17–18

1. 216   2. 32   3. 24   4. 40,320

5. 720   6. 1152   7. 15,120   8. 7^{10}

9. 720   10. 30   11. $(n-1)$

12. $f(n) = f(n-1) + f(n-2) + f(n-3)$, $n > 3$, and $f(1) = f(2) = 0$, $f(3) = 1$

13. $N(T) = \dfrac{5+\sqrt{5}}{10}\left(\dfrac{1+\sqrt{5}}{2}\right)^{T} + \dfrac{5-\sqrt{5}}{10}\left(\dfrac{1-\sqrt{5}}{2}\right)^{T}$

14. $n!/(n-k)!$ 15. n^k 16. $M^k - (M-1)^k$

Page 22

2. a) 90   b) 30   c) 60   d) 35   e) 24

4. a) 35   b) 20   c) 53

5. $2(k!)\,(n-k-1)!$

Pages 34–36

1. a) 35   b) 56   2. 120   3. 900

4. 1260   10. $\binom{2n}{n}^2$ 11. $\binom{n-k-1}{k-1}$

456

12. $\binom{n+1}{m}$ 13. $\binom{k+l-1}{l}\binom{m+-k-l}{m-l}$ 14. $\binom{m+1}{2}\binom{n+1}{2}$

19. $\binom{n+k-1}{k-1}$ 23. $\binom{m+n}{m}$. Yes.   24. $1+\binom{n}{2}+\binom{n}{4}$

Pages 38–40

3. $\dfrac{1}{2n-1}\dbinom{2n-1}{n}$ 4. $\binom{n}{k}(m-1)^{n-k}$ 5. $\binom{n-k}{m-k}$ 6. 651

Chapter 3

Pages 48–50

1. $\frac{175}{396}$, $\binom{5}{3}7^3 5^2/12^5$ 2. 35/128   3. 15/64

4. 13/25   5. 1/2   6. $\binom{8}{3}14^5/15^8$

7. $\dfrac{2r!(n-r-1)!}{n!}$ 8. 1/32, 1/64, 5/16   9. $\binom{4}{2}\binom{3\,5}{1\,1}/\binom{3\,9}{1\,3}$

10. $2\binom{2\,3}{1\,0}/\binom{2\,6}{1\,3}$ 11. 3/8, $\binom{2n}{n}/2^{2n}$ 12. $\binom{4}{3}\binom{4\,8}{3}/\binom{5\,2}{6}$

13. 10/63, 44/63   14. 35/63   15. 31/66

16. 17/60   17. a) 1/35   b) 1/35   c) 2/7
                  d) 3/7   e) 1/2   f) 1/6
                  g) 1/7

18. 12/25   19. 1/6   20. 255/4096

21. 37/216   22. $125/6^4$ 23. $\dfrac{2}{2n-1}\dbinom{2n-1}{n}2^{-2n}$

24. $\dfrac{a}{a+b}$ 25. $\binom{k-1}{m-1}/\binom{n}{m}$

Pages 61–62

4. 5/11   5. 1/7   6. 75/159   7. $\dfrac{\frac{135}{512}}{\frac{135}{512}+\frac{36}{125}}$

8. 8/17   9. 1/3   10. 2/3   11. 4/7

12. a) False   b) True   c) False

14. 3/4

Pages 70–72

1. $1-\frac{13}{4}\left(\frac{3}{4}\right)^9$ 2. 100/243

3. 7/16   5. $p_n=\frac{1}{3}+\frac{8}{3}\left(\frac{1}{4}\right)^n$

6. $P=\dfrac{p_1}{1-(1-p_1)(1-p_2)}$ 7. $p(A)=\dfrac{p_1}{1-(1-p_1)(1-p_2)(1-p_3)}$

$p(B)=\dfrac{(1-p_1)p_2}{1-(1-p_1)(1-p_2)(1-p_3)}$

8. $\frac{1}{2}$, $\binom{2n+1}{n} 2^{-(2n+1)}$ 9. $(n-1)(\frac{1}{2})^n$

10. 3/11   11. $\frac{1}{2}[1-(1-2p)^n]$

12. $f_{2n} = \frac{3}{5} - \frac{4}{15}(\frac{1}{16})^n$ 16. $F_0 = 1$; yes

Pages 85–87

5. $m(n+1)/2$ 6. $p_k = \sqrt{r}$, $k = 1, 2, \dots, n$ 8. $\dfrac{n}{m+1}$

12. $\mu = n+1-n(1-p)^n$ 21. $\mu_k = \frac{5}{2} - \frac{1}{2}(\frac{2}{3})^k$

23. a) 4/7   b) 2/7   c) $\mu = 3$

Page 100

12. a) 8/11   b) $\frac{1}{2}(\frac{5}{16})^{n-1}$ c) $E(X) = 16/11$, $V(X) = 80/121$

13. $\sigma^2 = \dfrac{k(n+1)(n-k)}{(k+2)(k+1)^2}$

Chapter 4

Page 126

1. 1/10   6. $x = \mu$, $x = \mu \pm \dfrac{b}{\sqrt{3}}$ 7. $t = \alpha$

Pages 136–138

5. $A = \frac{3}{4} e$,
    $P(x) = 0$ for $x < 0$
    $\quad = \frac{1}{4} x^3$ for $0 \leq x \leq 1$
    $\quad = 1 - \frac{3}{4} e^{-(x-1)}$ for $x \geq 1$

6. $a = \alpha^2$,
    $F(x) = 0$ for $x < 0$
    $\quad = 1 - (1 + \alpha x) e^{-\alpha x}$ for $x \geq 0$

7. $0 \leq Y \leq 1$ 10. $p(y) = \dfrac{1}{2\sqrt{y}}$, $0 < y \leq 1$

11. $p(y) = \dfrac{1}{2\sqrt{y}}$, $0 < y \leq 1$

Pages 144–146

1. $\mu = 1$, $\nu_2 = 5/3$, $\sigma^2 = 2/3$ 2. $M(\theta) = \dfrac{1}{\beta - \alpha} \dfrac{\sinh \beta\theta - \sinh \alpha\theta}{\theta}$,

$\mu = 0$,

$\sigma^2 = \frac{1}{3}(\beta^3 - \alpha^3)$

4. $M(\theta) = \left(1 - \dfrac{\theta}{\alpha}\right)^{-2}, \ \theta < \alpha,$ 8. $\mu = \alpha\sqrt{\pi/2}$ 17. $F_1(x) = \max\,[x, E(x)]$

$\mu = 2/\alpha,$

$\sigma^2 = 2/\alpha^2$

Pages 166–167

2. $f(x|y) = \dfrac{3(x^2 + y^2)}{1 + 3y^2}$

$E(X|y) = \dfrac{3}{4}\dfrac{1 + 2y^2}{1 + 3y^2}$

5. $p(x, y) = \dfrac{1}{\alpha\beta}e^{-x/\alpha}\,e^{y((1/\alpha)-(1/\beta))}U(x)U(y)U(x-y),$

$g(y|x) = \dfrac{\beta - \alpha}{\alpha\beta}\dfrac{e^{y((1/\alpha)-(1/\beta))}}{e^{x((1/\alpha)-(1/\beta))} - 1}, \ \text{for } 0 \leqq y \leqq x, \beta \neq \alpha,$

$f(x) = \dfrac{e^{-x/\beta} - e^{-x/\alpha}}{\beta - \alpha}\,U(x) \ \text{for } \beta \neq \alpha$

6. $E(X|y > 0) = y^{-1}, E(Y|x) = \dfrac{2}{1 + x}$

7. $E(Y|x) = \dfrac{1}{\gamma}\dfrac{1 - e^{\gamma x} + \gamma x\,e^{\gamma x}}{e^{\gamma x} - 1}, \gamma = \dfrac{\beta - \alpha}{\alpha\beta} \neq 0$

$\lim_{\beta \to \alpha} E(Y|x) = \tfrac{1}{2}x$

Pages 173–174

1. $y = x + 1$ 2. $y = \tfrac{1}{2}x, \ x = y + \alpha$ 3. $y = -\tfrac{2}{33}x + \tfrac{7}{11}, y = \tfrac{1}{3}\tfrac{5x + 2}{3x + 1}$

Pages 177–179

3. $h(u) = \tfrac{1}{4}[2 - |u|]$ for $|u| \leqq 2$

    $= 0$ otherwise

Same form for $k(v)$.

5. $h(u) = \tfrac{1}{8}u$ for $0 \leqq u \leqq 2$

    $= \tfrac{1}{4}$ for $2 \leqq u \leqq 4$

    $= \tfrac{1}{8}(6 - u)$ for $4 \leqq u \leqq 6$

    $= 0$ otherwise

$k(v) = \tfrac{1}{4}$ for $0 \leqq v \leqq 4$

    $= 0$ otherwise

7. $h(u) = \dfrac{u}{\sigma^2}e^{-u^2/2\sigma^2}\,U(u)$

$k(v) = \dfrac{1}{\pi}\dfrac{1}{1 + v^2}, \ -\infty < v < \infty$

8. $h(s) = \dfrac{\beta}{\alpha+\beta}\,\delta(s) + \dfrac{1}{\alpha+\beta}\,e^{-s/\alpha}\,U(s)$

9. $h(v) = \dfrac{1}{\alpha-\beta}\,[e^{-v/\alpha} - e^{-v/\beta}]\,U(v),\ \alpha \neq \beta$

$\qquad = \dfrac{v}{\alpha^2}\,e^{-v/\alpha}\,U(v),\ \alpha = \beta$

$\quad k(w) = \dfrac{1}{\alpha\beta}\left(\dfrac{w}{\alpha} + \dfrac{1-w}{\beta}\right)^{-2},\ 0 \leqq w \leqq 1,\ \alpha \neq \beta$

$\qquad = \text{o otherwise}$

For $\alpha = \beta$, W is uniform, $U(0, 1)$.

Page 190

7. $A^{-1} = \frac{1}{11}\begin{bmatrix} 14 & -1 & 3 \\ -1 & 4 & -1 \\ 3 & -1 & 3 \end{bmatrix}$

Page 195

3. 96

Page 199

3. $P = \frac{1}{2}$

Chapter 5

Page 207

1. a) 10   b) .369
2. a) .4   b) 2.4/9
3. a) $p^4(1-p)^6$ b) $\binom{10}{4}p^4(1-p)^6$
4. a) 6   b) .4   c) .68
5. a) 3   b) 3

Page 211

1. $\frac{1}{2}$ 2. 5

Page 214

1. a) $5/t^2$, $10/t^2$ b) $1/t^2$, $15/t^2$
2. a) 5/9   b) 80/1296

Page 218

  2. 5.3×10^5, 42

Page 223

  2. a) a^2 b) ∞

Chapter 6

Page 233

  1. $\frac{1}{2}$ for both urns
  2. .3, .6, .1 for urns I, II, III, respectively

Page 244

  6. $\hat{x} = (z\sigma_0^2 + \mu\sigma_1^2)/(\sigma_0^2 + \sigma_1^2)$

Page 257

  3. a) $X = .778\,Y - 1.62$ b) $X = 1.19\,Y - 1.53$

Page 268

  2. $\begin{bmatrix} .839 & -.193 \\ -.193 & .049 \end{bmatrix}$

  3. a) $952\frac{1}{3}$, 10.9, 13.4   b) 20.8, 1.37, .52

Chapter 7

Pages 273–274

  1. a).683   b) 3.29   c) $-.56$ d) 4.56
  2. a) .477   b) 4.6   c) -2.56 d) 2.56
  3. a) .683   b) 2.29   c) $-.56$ d) 2.56

Page 277

  1. 10.04 to 13.96
  2. 10.355 to 13.645
  3. 9.424 to 14.576
  4. a) 4.08 to 11.92   b) 2.848 to 13.152   c) 1.418 to 14.582

Page 283

1. 1.0 to 5.1 (both *a* and *b*)
2. .72 to 9.8 (both *a* and *b*)

Page 286

1. a) 3.1 to 4.7   b) 6.2 to 7.9
2. a) 1.7 to 6.1   b) 4.9 to 9.3

Page 292

1. 2.4 to 3.8   2. .31 to 3.2   3. .15 to 6.5

Page 297

1. b) 2, 2/9   c) $(9, -\sqrt{7})/\sqrt{88}$

Chapter 8
Page 309

6. a) $k(k+1)/n(n+1)$ b) $k(n-k+1)/(n+1)(n+2)$
7. a) $\theta_1 - \theta_2/2 + k\theta_2/(n+1)$ b) $k(n-k+1)\theta_2^2/(n+1)^2(n+2)$
8. a) $\lambda_1 + \lambda_2/n$ b) λ_2^2/n^2

Page 317

1. a) 76   b) .018
2. a) .62/n   b) ∞
4. a) Y_{46} b) $.693/\lambda$ c) $2/91\lambda^2$

Page 319

1. 2/5

Pages 325–326

1. $n = 8$ 4. .34   5. .59   6. $n = 78$

Page 327

1. .875   2. $n = 6$ 4. $n = 8$ 6. Y_{37} to Y_{65}

Chapter 9

Page 333

1. a) 2.41   b) .912
2. a) $(\xi_1 + .78\xi_0)/1.78$ b) $8.5/(\xi_1 - \xi_0)^2$
3. a) $(2.56\xi_0 + 1.65\xi_1)/4.21$ b) $18/(\xi_1 - \xi_0)^2$
4. a) .241   b) .62

Page 337

2. a) .0139   b) .0278   3. a) 53   b) 45 or 55

Page 339

1. Between .01 and .002

Pages 341–342

1. Slightly greater than .10   2. Between .025 and .05

Pages 346–347

2. a) .4   b) 2.8   c) Between 50% and 75%
3. a) $p = .9$ b) .001   c) .64   d) Between 75% and 90%

Page 351

2. .09   3. .0006

Page 353

1. .012

Page 356

1. .00008

Appendix A

Page 366

4. $u_n = 2^{n-1}$ 5. $u_n = a^{(-1)^{n+1}}$

Page 369

1. $u_n = 3 \cdot 2^{n-1} - 3^n$
2. $u_n = \left(\dfrac{3 - \sqrt{5}}{2}\right)^n$

3. $u_n = (a + bn)2^n + c(-3)^n$

5. $u_n = 1 - \dfrac{n}{z}$

6. $u_n = \frac{1}{2}[1 + (-1)^n]$, $v_n = \frac{1}{2}[1 - (-1)^n]$

Page 372

1. $u_n = \dfrac{5}{48}(-3)^n + \dfrac{9}{16} - \dfrac{n}{4}$

2. $u_n = \left(\dfrac{1}{2} + \dfrac{n}{4}\right)(-1)^{n+1} - \dfrac{1}{2} + \dfrac{3}{4}n$

3. $u_n = -\frac{26}{45}(-2)^n - \frac{2}{9} + \frac{2}{3}n - \frac{1}{5}\cdot 3^n$

4. $u_n = \frac{1}{2}(1-n)(-4)^n$

5. $u_n = 2 - \frac{13}{6}n + \frac{3}{2}n^2 - \frac{1}{3}n^3$

6. $u_n = 25\cdot 2^n - 25 - 19n - 6n^2$

Pages 395–396

1. 29   6. $(-1, 2, 3, -2)$ 10. 320

Pages 401–402

1. $\dfrac{x}{1} = \dfrac{y}{-3} = \dfrac{z}{-9} = \dfrac{u}{-4} = \lambda$

2. $x = -(a+b)$
$y = 2a + 3b$, $-\infty < a < \infty$
$u = a$, $-\infty < b < \infty$
$z = 5b$

3. $x = y = 0$, $z = u = \lambda$, $-\infty < \lambda < \infty$

4. For $\lambda = 2$, $x = a$, $y = -2a$, $-\infty < a < \infty$, For $\lambda = 3$, $x = b$, $y = -b$,
$-\infty < b < \infty$

Page 414

1. a) $3A - 2B = \begin{bmatrix} 4 & -2 & -1 \\ -3 & 5 & 7 \end{bmatrix}$

b) $AA^T = \begin{bmatrix} 5 & 1 \\ 1 & 11 \end{bmatrix}$

c) $A^TA = \begin{bmatrix} 5 & -1 & -1 \\ -1 & 1 & 3 \\ -1 & 3 & 10 \end{bmatrix}$

4. $\frac{1}{2}\begin{bmatrix} 11 & -5 & 1 \\ -5 & 3 & -1 \\ 1 & -1 & 1 \end{bmatrix}$

Page 424

3. $R = \begin{bmatrix} \frac{2}{3}\sqrt{2} & \frac{1}{6}\sqrt{2} & -\frac{1}{6}\sqrt{2} \\ -\frac{1}{3} & \frac{2}{3} & -\frac{2}{3} \\ 0 & \frac{1}{2}\sqrt{2} & \frac{1}{2}\sqrt{2} \end{bmatrix}$

10. $\mathbf{p}(n) = \frac{1}{10}\begin{pmatrix} 6 \\ 1 \\ 3 \end{pmatrix} + \frac{2}{5}\begin{pmatrix} 1 \\ 1 \\ -2 \end{pmatrix}(\frac{1}{6})^n + \frac{1}{2}\begin{pmatrix} -2 \\ 1 \\ 1 \end{pmatrix}(-\frac{1}{3})^n$

Page 440

9. $x(t) = a \sin t + b \cos t - \frac{1}{2} t \cos t$

10. $x(t) = (a + bt + ct^2)e^t + t^3 e^t$

11. $R = \begin{bmatrix} \dfrac{1}{\sqrt{2}} & -\dfrac{1}{\sqrt{2}} \\ \dfrac{1}{\sqrt{2}} & \dfrac{1}{\sqrt{2}} \end{bmatrix}$

$u(t) = \dfrac{a + (1+t)^2}{2\sqrt{2}}$

$v(t) = \dfrac{be^{-2t} + 2t - 3}{4\sqrt{2}}$

Page 448

8. $L = \frac{3}{2}\sqrt{2}$

INDEX